# SERVOMECHANISMS AND REGULATING SYSTEM DESIGN

# General Electric Series

### WRITTEN FOR THE ADVANCEMENT OF
### ENGINEERING PRACTICE

PHYSICAL LAWS AND EFFECTS
by C. F. Hix, Jr. and R. P. Alley

ECONOMIC OPERATION OF POWER SYSTEMS
by Leon K. Kirchmayer

DIGITAL COMPUTER PROGRAMMING
by D. D. McCracken

THE ART AND SCIENCE OF PROTECTIVE RELAYING
by C. Russell Mason

APPLIED ELECTRICAL MEASUREMENT
by Isaac F. Kinnard

AIRCRAFT GAS TURBINES
by C. W. Smith

AN INTRODUCTION TO POWER SYSTEM ANALYSIS
by Frederick S. Rothe

D-C POWER SYSTEMS FOR AIRCRAFT
by R. H. Kaufmann and H. J. Finison

TRANSIENTS IN POWER SYSTEMS
by Harold A. Peterson

SERVOMECHANISMS AND REGULATING SYSTEM DESIGN, TWO VOLUMES
Volume I, Second Edition
by Harold Chestnut and Robert W. Mayer

TRANSFORMER ENGINEERING
by the late L. F. Blume, A. Boyajian, G. Camilli, T. C. Lennox, S. Minneci,
and V. M. Montsinger, Second Edition

CIRCUIT ANALYSIS OF A-C POWER SYSTEMS, TWO VOLUMES
by Edith Clarke

CAPACITORS FOR INDUSTRY
by W. C. Bloomquist, C. R. Craig, R. M. Partington, and R. C. Wilson

PROTECTION OF TRANSMISSION SYSTEMS AGAINST LIGHTNING
by W. W. Lewis

MAGNETIC CONTROL OF INDUSTRIAL MOTORS
by Gerhart W. Heumann, Second Edition

POWER SYSTEM STABILITY
Volume I—Steady State Stability; II—Transient Stability;
by Selden B. Crary

MATERIALS AND PROCESSES
by J. F. Young, Second Edition

ELECTRIC MOTORS IN INDUSTRY
by D. R. Shoults and C. J. Rife; edited by T. C. Johnson

# SERVOMECHANISMS AND
# REGULATING SYSTEM DESIGN

## VOLUME I

### HAROLD CHESTNUT and ROBERT W. MAYER

*Both of the General Electric Company*

### SECOND EDITION

*One of a series written by General Electric authors
for the advancement of engineering practice*

JOHN WILEY & SONS, INC., NEW YORK

CHAPMAN & HALL, LTD., LONDON

# PREFACE

The material in this book has its origin in our experience and the experience of other General Electric Company engineers in designing control systems and regulators for the armed services and for industry. Although we have worked most intimately with position and steering controls, we have also profited greatly from our associates who have worked on voltage, speed, and other regulating systems. The association that we have had with the Servomechanisms Laboratory at the Massachusetts Institute of Technology, directed by Dr. Gordon S. Brown, and the Massachusetts Institute of Technology Radiation Laboratory Servomechanism group under N. B. Nichols has also been beneficial in providing us with a broader understanding of the subject of servomechanism control systems.

For some years now the material contained in this and its companion volume has been presented to General Electric engineers of the Aeronautic and Ordnance System Divisions and of the Technical Education Programs. This material has also been presented to both undergraduate and graduate students at a number of universities in the United States as well as abroad. These students have had widely differing backgrounds of practical experience and previous training. The experience of teaching these students and of working with some of them on advanced design problems has guided us in developing the material in Volumes I and II. The comments and feedback from both students and professors have been most helpful to the authors in improving the accuracy of the material and in clarifying the presentation.

This book, Volume I, is adapted to the needs of engineers and engineering students who have not had previous training or experience in the field of closed-loop control systems. Because the solution of linear differential equations during both transient and steady-state operation is important to an understanding of control system performance, this subject is presented briefly from the operational and Laplace transform points of view.   Circuit theory and system stability are also presented because of their importance as background material.   Chapters 7 through 9 describe closed-loop control system elements, operation, performance, and methods of analysis.   The nomenclature and symbols recommended by the ASA C-85 are used throughout the book.   Chapters 10 through 12 present the complex plane and attenuation-frequency methods of analyzing and synthesizing some simpler forms of servomechanisms and regulators.   Chapter 13 is new with this edition and describes the root-locus approach to the analysis and synthesis of feedback control systems.   Chapter 14 extends the design procedure to the more complex multi-loop systems with multiple inputs frequently encountered in present-day practice.   The comparison of steady-state and transient performance of servomechanisms in Chapter 15 presents information useful for system synthesis.   Because of the extensive use of computers to the solution of feedback control problems, Chapter 16 has been added in this edition to describe some of the principles involved in the use of analog computers to solve control systems problems.   To extend its usefulness to undergraduate and graduate students, we have given in this volume numerous problems illustrating and extending the material presented in the text.

Volume II, published in 1955, is devoted to the needs of the practicing designer and of the advanced graduate student.   It deals with such problems as the means for establishing design specifications as well as for reducing the effects of extraneous unwanted signal inputs.   Factors influencing the selection of control elements for the power and stabilizing portions of control systems are discussed.   The effects of non-linear operation as caused by saturation as well as deliberate gain changes are described.   Amplifier design factors to minimize gain changes, drift, and changes in tubes and other components are presented.   Chapters are also devoted to all a-c servomechanism design and to the very important subject of measurement techniques.

We wish to acknowledge the assistance we have received from our colleagues A. P. Adamson and P. Cushman.   We wish also to acknowledge the assistance of our former associates, F. H. Andrix, J. L. Bower, Sidney Godet, and J. R. Moore.   Mrs. Cecile Lester's calculations and Miss Anna Kosinski's typing have aided greatly in the preparation of this book.   The help of Mr. W. E. Sollecito, who has prepared Chapter 16 on the use of analog computers as well as provided additional advice and counsel for this edition, is gratefully acknowledged.   The comments and suggestions of Professor Thomas J. Higgins for modifying this edition are also appreciated.   We are also grateful to many of the students and the staff of the Technical Education Divisions who have contributed to the make-up of this book.   Dr. C. F. Greene, Mr. W. B. Jordan, Mr. R. O. Dunham, and Mr. P. L. Alger deserve particular mention for their interest in this undertaking.

The understanding and patience of our families throughout this endeavor have been greatly appreciated and have provided material assistance to its successful completion.

HAROLD CHESTNUT<br>ROBERT W. MAYER

*April, 1959*

# CONTENTS

            Systems . . . . . . . . . . 447

    14.0 INTRODUCTION    447
    14.1 DESIGN OF MORE COMPLEX SYSTEMS    448
         Series Modification of Transfer Function
         Inclusion of a Servomechanism in a More Comprehensive
            Control System
    14.2 MULTIPLE INPUTS AND LOAD DISTURBANCES    452
         General Case of Multiple Inputs
         Multiple-Position Inputs
         Response to Input Signal and Load Disturbance
         A Regulator-Type Problem
    14.3 EQUIVALENT BLOCK DIAGRAM REPRESENTATION    462
         Equivalent Block Diagram of Stabilizing
            Transformer
         Simplifying Interconnected Multiple-Loop Systems
    14.4 POSITION CONTROL SYSTEM WITH LOAD DISTURBANCE    466
         Determination of $C/R$
         Determination of $C/T_L$
    14.5 VOLTAGE REGULATOR WITH LOAD DISTURBANCE    477
         Determination of $C/R = (E_T/V)$
         Determination of $C/Q = (E_T/E_L)$

Chapter 15 Comparison of Steady-State and Transient Performance
            of Servomechanisms . . . . . . . . 487

    15.0 INTRODUCTION    487
    15.1 ESTIMATION OF CLOSED-LOOP POLES FROM OPEN-LOOP
         ATTENUATION CHARACTERISTICS    489
         Description of the Method
         Closed-Loop Poles for Low Gain
         Closed-Loop Poles at High Gain
         Closed-Loop Poles at Intermediate Values of Gain
    15.2 DESCRIPTION OF SERVOMECHANISM BEING
         CONSIDERED    498
         Definition of Terms Used to Describe System Performance
            Characteristics
         Open-Loop Attenuation-Frequency Characteristics
    15.3 EFFECT OF VALUE OF $\omega_c$ ON FREQUENCY RESPONSE AND
         TRANSIENT RESPONSE    503
    15.4 COMPARISON OF STEADY-STATE AND TRANSIENT
         PERFORMANCE CHARTS    504
         Effect of Using Parameter $\omega_1/\omega_c$ for Abscissa
         Comparison of Maximum Steady-State Value $[C/R|_m]$ and
            Peak Transient Value $[C/R|_p]$ of Output-Input
            Ratio

# 1

# THE AUTOMATIC CONTROL PROBLEM

## 1.0  Introduction

Recent trends in the development of modern civilization have been in the direction of greater control.  With the advent of the steam engine and the material improvements brought about by the industrial revolution, man has had available greater quantities of power for his use.  To utilize this power effectively, he has been required to learn how to control and how to regulate it.  The increased interdependence of individuals and groups of individuals upon one another during this period has made it necessary for a greater measure of regulation to be exerted in the field of social activity as well.

As part of the control process, whether it be of persons or of things, certain standards are established.  The performance of the equipment or of the individual is compared to these standards, and according to the difference, appropriate action is taken to bring about a closer correspondence between the desired objectives and the actual performance.  Examples of this type of regulating action are common in the operation of production or accounting groups in business as well as in the operation of mechanical, electrical, thermal, and other engineering equipment.[112]*  In some of these regulated systems a long interval of time occurs before the performance being controlled is compared to the desired objectives.  An annual manufacturing inventory or a quarterly financial statement illustrates this point.  For the automatically controlled engineering equipment, the comparison may be made many times per second.  The point of interest is that the need for good control is present in many phases of our existence.  The problem is to determine the desired objectives and the best ways of producing these objectives.  Although the material of this book is limited to a study of problems pertaining to the field of engineering applications of automatic control, there is the possibility that some of the philosophy of feedback control set forth here might be employed to advantage for other forms of control problems.

---

* Superior reference numbers refer to Bibliography at end of book.

Fortunately for engineers, the desired objectives for their equipment are fairly well defined and the means for measuring the performance of this equipment are relatively simple and accurate. For example, it is desired that the voltage and frequency of a power system be maintained within certain tolerances,[18, 22] that the speed or position of a motor shaft should obey certain prescribed conditions,[25] or that the motion of one instrument or shaft should faithfully duplicate the motion of another.[24, 104] All these are problems in which the nature of the control requirements and references for describing these requirements can be established fairly well in advance. The meters, oscillographs, or error-sensing elements for determining the quality of performance are generally available.[113, 114]

The advances of the technical arts have made available, in form suitable for control, amounts of power with high speeds of response such that man is unable to compete with machines for the power portion of the control. Furthermore, in the measuring or error-sensing portion of the control, instruments are in many cases more accurate, more rapid, more reliable, and cheaper than a human being who might be called upon to do a similar job manually. Thus man has found means for having some of his mental labor as well as much of his physical work done by machines. With these power and sensing means available, the field of automatic control is opened to relieve man of many of the monotonous and disagreeable aspects of many routine tasks and to make possible the accomplishment of labors that are humanly impossible. It is these features that make automatic control so attractive. Not only is it possible to reduce the amount of manual labor required but it may also be possible to achieve a higher degree of performance than would otherwise be possible.

In this chapter the general form of the feedback control problem is presented. The factors of stability and accuracy associated with such a control are indicated. Next the means that have been developed for solving these engineering problems are described. To emphasize the various phases of the actual solution to the design problem, the general steps in solving a typical control problem are outlined. A brief review is presented of the development of the regulator and servomechanism arts up to the present time, when they are being merged to form the more unified science of feedback control systems. An attempt is made to indicate the direction that will be taken by future developments in the field of automatic control.

## 1.1   Description of Feedback Control System

The terms servomechanism and regulator have been described and defined many times in the literature. As used in this book, they refer to a feedback control system in which the difference between the *reference input* and some function of the *controlled variable* is used to supply an *actuating signal* to the control elements and the controlled system.[110] The amplified actuating signal endeavors to reduce to zero the difference between reference input and the controlled variable.   A supplemental source of power is available in such systems to provide amplification at one or more points in the feedback control system so that the possibility exists for self-excited oscillations or instability.

Figure 1.1–1 is a block diagram representation of a simplified feedback control system.   In addition to the principal variables described

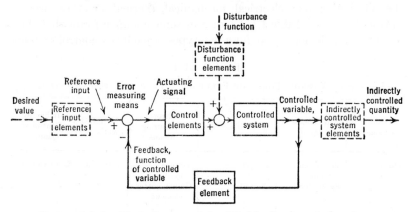

FIGURE 1.1–1.   Block diagram of simplified feedback control system.

above and shown by the solid-line portions of the diagram, the *desired value*, the *indirectly controlled quantity*, and the *disturbance function* are shown.   The desired value represents the value it is desired that the control system reproduce, and it differs from the actual reference input by the characteristics of the reference input elements.   The indirectly controlled quantity represents the quantity that is the actual system output.   It differs from the controlled variable by the characteristics of the indirectly controlled system elements.   The disturbance function represents an unwanted input to the system that tends to cause the controlled variable to differ from the reference input.   Disturbances may occur at one or more points in a control system and the position shown is merely a common one for many controls.   The disturbance function elements shown by dotted lines are intermediate between the disturbance function and the controlled system itself.   The dotted lines associated with the reference input and indirectly controlled system elements serve to indicate that these elements, when equal to unity, have a limited effect on the feedback control problem.

In many feedback control systems, the operation of all parts of the control system is continuous and automatic.  By means of the continued use of the actuating error, such a feedback control system can be made accurate without requiring high accuracy or constant performance characteristics for all the control elements.  Although the principles described in this book are slanted particularly toward continuous control systems, the general ideas are useful for intermittently controlled or even open loop control systems for which feedback is not present.

The principles of feedback control operation may be used effectively for any one of a number of different physical kinds of control problems whether they employ electrical, mechanical, thermal, or other forms of control elements.  Table 1.1–1 indicates some common forms that these variables and elements take for a few types of feedback control systems.

TABLE 1.1–1

LISTING OF VARIOUS FORMS OF FEEDBACK CONTROL SYSTEM QUANTITIES

| Desired Value | Reference Input | Feedback | Error-Measuring Means | Controlled Variable | Indirectly Controlled Quantity |
|---|---|---|---|---|---|
| Voltage | Potentiometer voltage | Voltage | Voltage detector | Terminal voltage | Load voltage |
|  | Spring tension | Current | Galvanometer element |  |  |
| Position | Angular shaft position | Angular shaft position | Differential gears | Machine tool position | Dimensions of metal being cut |
|  | Electric field | Angular shaft position | Selsyn control transformer |  |  |
| Temperature | Thermostat contact setting | Bimetal position | Bimetal thermostat | Oven temperature | Process temperature |
|  | Potentiometer voltage | Thermoelectric voltage | Thermocouple |  |  |
| Speed | Standard voltage | Voltage | Voltage detector | Governor speed | Alternator speed |
|  | Calibrated spring position | Governor position | Linkage position |  |  |

**Requirements of Stability and Accuracy.**  The basic principle of feedback control or closed-loop operation tends to make for accurate performance since the control system endeavors continually to correct any error that exists.  However, this corrective action can give rise to a dangerous condition of unstable operation when used with control elements having a large amount of amplification and significant delays in their time of response.[6] An unstable control system is one in which any temporary disturbance can cause the control to be unable to maintain a constant value after the removal of such a disturbance. Such an unstable control system is one that is no longer effective in maintaining the controlled variable very nearly equal to the desired value. Instead, large sustained oscillations or erratic control of the controlled variable may take place, rendering the control useless.

If stable feedback control system performance is like that of a manually controlled system with a capable and well-trained operator, unstable feedback control system performance may be compared to that of the manually controlled system with an untrained and irresponsible operator. Rapid and destructive response of the system may result in which adequate control is impossible, and destructive action of the controlled variable may occur.

If in an effort to increase the accuracy of the control system, one increases the amplification of the control without taking adequate steps to insure stable operation, the advantages of the feedback control principle prove illusory. Furthermore, it is necessary to do more than have a system that is stable; one must have a system that has an adequate margin of stability and can recover rapidly and smoothly from the shocks of irregular inputs or of severe disturbances.

The requirements of stability and accuracy are mutually incompatible. The higher the desired accuracy, the smaller is the actuating error that can be tolerated for proper corrective action, and the sooner must full corrective action be initiated. Thus, to be accurate, a system requires high amplification. However, with high amplification more corrective action of the controlled variable can take place for a given error, and the time during which the corrective action is required is decreased.

Time delays in the various control elements and the controlled system that were not significant in a low gain system may become appreciable for the system with high amplification. After the corrective action is started and the need for correction has ceased, the inherent time delay of the system elements may prevent stopping the action of the control elements in time to prevent an overshoot by the controlled variable. The overshoot may be greater than that which initiated the control motion, and the process of continued corrective action, building up to violent oscillations, is thus started.

Following the above line of reasoning, one sees that the time delays present in the control elements cause the instability. By appropriate use of "anticipation" means to compensate for the inherent time "delays" in the control elements, it is possible to obtain a high gain system with satisfactory stability. Although improved accuracy and adequate stability can be obtained, they are achieved only at the expense of additional equipment or complexity.

**Mathematical Basis for Stability.** Essential and valuable as is the physical picture of stability, mathematical definitions provide more useful and exact means of describing system performance. The principal mathematical means for determining stability of linear control systems are the following:

1. Locating by analytical or graphical means the actual position on the complex plane of each of the roots of the characteristic equation of the system.

2. Applying Routh's stability criterion [2] to the coefficients of the system's characteristic equation.

3. Applying Nyquist's criterion [6] to a graphical plot of the open-loop response of the system as a function of frequency for a sinusoidal driving function.

4. Plotting the root locus [120] of the open-loop transfer function to show the location of the closed-loop poles for all possible values of system gain.

The labor involved in locating the exact position of the roots of the characteristic equation or in calculating their values is such as to limit the use of this method. The Routh criterion involves the use of a brief, simple algebraic process and permits the ready determination of the system stability. However, the graphical data necessary for applying Nyquist's criterion provide quantitative information on the accuracy of the system, the degree of system stability, as well as the system stability itself. Hence the Nyquist stability criterion in one or more of its modified forms is used extensively to determine system stability. The importance of the transient response of control systems and the greater ease with which this may be obtained from the root locus plot of a system has caused increasing use of this method of indicating system stability and performance.

The Nyquist stability criterion places on a firm mathematical basis the well-known physical fact that, when the fed-back signal to a control element is equal in magnitude and in phase with the actuating signal producing it, instability will result. Thus the Nyquist criterion establishes the necessary conditions for stability in terms of the ratio between the sinusoidal actuating signal and the feedback signal. The ratio is expressed by an amplitude and a phase relationship as a function of frequency. This ratio can be determined with the feedback not connected to the error-measuring element; thus the system need not be a closed-loop one under the conditions during which the stability as a feedback control system is evaluated. As such, the analysis of the problem is reduced somewhat in complexity, although the results are valid for the more complicated feedback control condition of system operation.

The root locus is a graphical method for representing the mathematical relationships between the characteristics of the control system with the control loop open and those with the control loop closed. Primary emphasis is placed on determining the possible location of the closed loop roots for which the characteristic equation is equal to zero. The value of the system gain is allowed to vary from 0 to ∞ and the effect on the location of closed-loop roots is noted. Although the root-locus method is inherently a "cut and try" procedure, the general form of these loci have been worked out for many of the systems commonly encountered. Also, a number of general rules for locating the root locus have been set forth which greatly facilitate establishing the locus for systems for which the general forms are not worked out. In addition, a mathematical method has been worked out by Donahue [134] that gives good and rapid answers for obtaining the root locus of a number of systems without resorting to graphical means. The root-locus method is well adapted for use with control systems having complex roots in their series elements. The direct indication of the individual roots of the closed-loop system provides more transient response information than is obtained by the frequency response method of Nyquist. Further, the way is available for working out the complete transient response to the more common types of transient inputs.

**Features of Feedback Control System Performance.** The two principal advantages of feedback control over control without feedback are that lower tolerances and greater time delays can be permitted for the control elements. To appreciate some of the advantages of the feedback control system, a comparison will be made between the open-loop and closed-loop (feedback) control systems. Figures 1.1–2 and 1.1–3

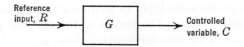

Reference input, $R$ → $G$ → Controlled variable, $C$

FIGURE 1.1–2.   Open-loop control system.

are block diagrams showing how the controlled variable $C$ is related to the reference input $R$ for each of these two systems. The ratios of the controlled variable to the reference input for the open-loop and feedback control systems are, respectively,

$$\frac{C}{R} = G \qquad\qquad (1.1\text{--}1)$$

and

$$\frac{C}{R} = \frac{G_1}{1 + G_1} \qquad\qquad (1.1\text{--}2)$$

where $C/E = G_1$ and $E$ is the actuating signal.

The terms $G$ and $G_1$ represent the transfer functions of the control elements. In addition to gain or constant terms, the transfer functions

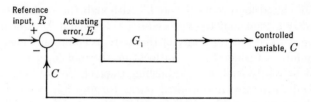

FIGURE 1.1–3. Feedback control system with direct feedback.

may contain time functional relationships having a wide range of values from 0 to ∞ under varying input conditions.

In contrast with the feedback control system in which the controlled variable is compared directly to the reference input to provide the error signal that actuates the control system elements, the open-loop control system makes no direct comparison of these two variables. Thus it is assumed that the transfer function $G$ is known and fixed so that the value of the controlled variable is known for each and every value of the reference input and its time variation. An example of this is a meter element; the deflection of the meter pointer is calibrated against a standard input, for example, a voltage. Subsequently it is assumed that the meter response is identical with its calibration figure and that the same input voltage will produce the same pointer deflection. However, a change in the characteristics of the transfer function $G$ of the meter element may cause the same input to produce a value of output different from the calibrated value. The change in the value of the output, in terms of a change of the transfer function alone, is

$$\left.\begin{matrix}\text{Change in}\\\text{controlled}\\\text{variable}\end{matrix}\right\} = \frac{\text{Change in } G}{\text{Proper value of } G} \times \left\{\begin{matrix}\text{Proper value}\\\text{of controlled}\\\text{variable}\end{matrix}\right. \qquad (1.1\text{--}3)$$

From a knowledge of the value of the controlled variable alone, it is impossible to distinguish between a change in the reference input and a

change in the transfer function. Thus very close tolerances in manufacture and constancy of controller characteristics with time are required
to obtain high performance of an open-loop system.

For the closed-loop system there is less need for maintaining the
transfer function constant, provided that the value of the transfer function $G_1$ is large. This may be seen from Equation 1.1–4, where the expression for the change in the value of the controlled variable in terms
of its proper value and the transfer function $G_1$ of a feedback control
system are shown.

$$\left.\begin{array}{l}\text{Change in}\\ \text{controlled}\\ \text{variable}\end{array}\right\} = \left(\frac{1}{1 + G_1}\right)\frac{\text{Change in } G_1}{\text{Proper value of } G_1} \times \left\{\begin{array}{l}\text{Proper value}\\ \text{of controlled}\\ \text{variable}\end{array}\right.$$

$$(1.1\text{--}4)$$

Although the change in the controlled variable is proportional to the
change in the transfer function $G_1$, there is a greatly reduced multiplying
factor of $1/1 + G_1$ that decreases the size of the actual change in the
controlled variable caused by changes in $G_1$. If $G_1$ has a value of the
order of 10 or more, the advantages of feedback control operation in this
respect are at once evident. Thus even with the use of lower precision
components or ones subject to wider variation under use, it is still possible to maintain high-precision feedback control performance.

Two additional items are worthy of note in this brief comparison of
open-loop and feedback control systems. First, it is not always physically possible to perform a direct comparison of the controlled variable to
the reference input as shown in Figure 1.1–3. For example, the reference input may contain *present* input data for a computer that has as its
controlled variable some functional relationship of the reference input
such as the *future* value of the controlled variable after some period of
time, for instance, $T_f$. Only by performing a duplicate calculation or
by allowing the time $T_f$ to transpire is it possible to know if the performance of the system $T_f$ seconds ago was correct. Thus it is clear that
for certain control problems it is difficult to provide an error-sensing
device that can compare the value of the controlled variable to the
reference input to modify the controlled variable properly.

Second, a feedback control system may be designed to have the controlled variable very nearly equal to the reference input for only certain
types of input signals. For other signals the feedback control system
may purposely be designed to make the controlled variable reproduce
little or none of the input.[66] As an example of this, position servomechanisms are frequently designed to possess low band-pass characteristics. By this it is meant that reference input signals having low fre-

quency or constant values are transmitted without appreciable error. The system transmission for higher frequency signals, which generally represent extraneous inputs, is purposely designed to be small, and the controlled variable has a high error for this type of input.

## 1.2   Feedback Control System Design

As already pointed out, it is difficult to achieve both a high accuracy and a high degree of stability in a feedback control system without increasing its complexity and cost.  The design engineer continually balances these factors in his effort to arrive at the system that will satisfy the job requirements.  For this reason it is important that the design engineer have available methods of synthesis and analysis that make his process of arriving close to the optimum design a simple one.

Present-day methods of synthesis and analysis have already gone far in satisfying this need.  The work of both Nyquist [6] and Bode [14] has been developed and extended.  There are now available methods of synthesis and analysis that remove much of the drudgery from the problem of servomechanism system design.  These methods now make possible the synthesis of more complex multiloop systems that hitherto have presented an overwhelming analytical problem when only the more classical differential equation methods were available.  With these design methods, the designer is less burdened with laborious mathematical studies and is able to devote more of his time to understanding the physical principles involved in his problem.  As a result the control of more complex physical processes is made possible.

A satisfactory feedback control system may now be designed many times faster than was possible only a few years ago.  Complete systems need not always be set up to arrive at optimum conditions by the "cut-and-try" process.[66]  If it is necessary to determine some of the parameters in this fashion, the number of permutations and combinations is rapidly reduced by using present-day methods of analysis as a guide. The design engineer need no longer struggle with the solution of a high-order differential equation to determine the system characteristics. More important still, he need no longer attempt to synthesize a servomechanism system by determining the effects of various parameter changes in the coefficients of the differential equation and then the effects of the changes of these coefficients on the over-all system characteristics.  It is truly a field, today, in which a practicing engineer can confidently engage without being a highly trained mathematician or an experienced cut-and-try experimenter.

**Recommended Design Procedure.**  In order for the practicing engineer to arrive at a feedback control system design that best meets the requirements of a particular application, it is desirable that a general design procedure be available. Such a procedure has grown up in the last few years. By using the recommended procedure as a reminder of points to check, the engineer will arrive at a good common-sense design that best meets the requirements of the job. Such a design should be *reliable* in performance, *economical* in cost and operation, *capable* of ready manufacture, *light* and *durable*, and easily *serviced*.

A suggested procedure in designing a feedback control system is outlined below.

1. Obtain a complete understanding of the job requirements.

2. Interpret these requirements in terms of such closed-loop design characteristics as frequency response and transient response.

3. Establish the approximate open-loop characteristic that will satisfy the closed-loop requirements.

4. Determine the characteristics of the existing components that are a part of the job.

5. Select components, design amplifier and stabilizing circuits, and perform such other design requirements as to satisfy the necessary open-loop characteristics.

6. Refine the open-loop characteristics to gain circuit simplicity and facilitate manufacture.

7. Check the design experimentally if possible.

It is of interest to examine each of these points in more detail.

The importance of completely understanding the requirements of the job is often overlooked in the haste to proceed with the more material aspects of the design. It should be realized, however, that without proper information regarding the job that the feedback control system must perform, the final design may be over- or underdesigned. Complete information should always be obtained on such important characteristics as the required speed of response, smoothness of operation, duty cycle, power supply stability, operating temperatures, allowable errors, and types of input motion or load disturbances.

Having acquired this information from the customer, the designer must, as a first step, interpret it in terms of the customary performance characteristics of the servomechanism system. If the customer has not already given definite information on the frequency response or transient response, these requirements must be interpreted from the data that the customer does have available.[56] The designer should know as a function of frequency the *allowable* characteristics for $\dfrac{\text{error}}{\text{reference}}$,

$\dfrac{\text{controlled variable}}{\text{reference}}$ , and $\dfrac{\text{controlled variable}}{\text{load disturbance}}$ if he is to make a good design. After having made this interpretation of the customer's problem, the designer should have a clear conception of the closed-loop characteristics that the system must exhibit, and he should be in a position to proceed with the determination of the open-loop characteristics.

The most direct path in design is to decide what is required and then to proceed to design the device directly from these requirements. This often has not been possible in servomechanism design because there was no path to establish the system parameters directly from the closed-loop characteristics. Instead, extremely time-consuming "cut-and-try" methods were used. In more recent years the complex plane plots and attenuation-phase diagrams [62, 86] have greatly reduced use of the cut-and-try process but have not completely eliminated it. Where requirements of the control systems have been formulated in terms of transient response needs or where non-linear elements are a dominant part of the control characteristic, the use of an analog computer can greatly facilitate the control system design.

In an effort to reduce further the use of the cut-and-try process, a series of charts has been made available [97] that makes it possible for the servomechanism design engineer to go directly from the desired closed-loop frequency or transient response to the open-loop attenuation diagram. In this way the gap between the closed-loop and open-loop characteristics is considerably shortened. Later in the design it may be necessary to refine the open-loop characteristic to fit the requirements of the problem more exactly.

For a new system in which the motors or other control elements are not yet established, the next logical step is to choose devices such as generators, motors, or other power elements that have the proper dynamic characteristics to satisfy the open-loop characteristic without the need of additional feedback to improve their dynamic response.[93] However, many times the requirements are such that additional feedback about the output devices will be required to improve their speed of response. Frequently, because of economic considerations, the servomechanism designer will find that he has the problem of using a control element whose dynamic properties are somewhat inadequate for the job. It is then the task of the designer to modify the dynamic properties of this element as best he can and to make the best compromises in the open-loop response so as to meet most nearly the closed-loop response.

Before the designer can modify the dynamic response of these already existent components, he must, of course, know their dynamic properties. Thus, if such components already exist in the system, the designer should proceed to obtain the characteristics of these components before attempting to synthesize the open-loop characteristic. It is here that, many times, certain measurement techniques prove to be very useful in saving time in determining the characteristics of the devices.[63]

Having the characteristics of the output devices and the desired open-loop response, the designer is then in a position to select the circuit components and design the amplifiers and other elements required to meet the open-loop characteristic. Charts have been compiled that make it possible to select the desired network configuration after its transfer function has been determined from the open-loop characteristic.[84] Both a-c and d-c amplifier design are well treated in the current literature.[5, 33] However, there are certain aspects of amplifier design such as "drift" and change of "stage gain" as a result of tube aging, power supply variations, and other factors that are of great importance to the servomechanism design engineer. A portion of Volume II is devoted to a development of the equations governing drift and changes in gain due to the causes outlined above.

In many cases before the design is frozen it may be necessary to make further refinements. From a practical design standpoint it may be found that considerable circuit simplification may be achieved by slight modifications of the network transfer functions. If this is done, it may be necessary to refine the open-loop characteristics to include the change. One example of this is the use of feedback circuits to achieve transfer functions similar to simple series circuit elements but using smaller components. At this stage where the design is essentially complete, it may be desirable to use an analog computer or other analytical means to establish the effects on system performance of the variation in the tolerances of the various components making up the system. If necessary on the basis of these checks, further changes in the design may be required.

After the design is completed, it is important that it be checked experimentally if possible. Such a check is valuable for two reasons. First, it guarantees the customer receipt of a system that meets his specifications; second, it provides the engineer with valuable experience for use in his future designs if the check should reveal errors. Many experimental techniques have been devised to measure the closed-loop characteristics of the final system as a check on design. Some of these are described in Volume II.

## 1.3   Development of the Field of Feedback Control Systems

Regulator and servomechanism are terms that have been applied to feedback control systems. Although equipments of the two types may be similar if not identical in their physical appearance, the difference in name arises primarily from the different nature of the types of inputs and disturbances to which the control is subjected and from the number of integrating elements in the control.   The close functional similarity of these two types of control systems has resulted in their recently being given the common title of feedback control systems.

The regulator is a type of device long used in many different forms in the central station and industrial control fields to regulate such quantities as power system voltages, paper drive speeds, or roll tension in winding applications.[74, 104]   Regulators are designed primarily to maintain the controlled variable or system output very nearly equal to a desired value at which it is to be regulated despite fluctuations of the load on the output.   Although occasionally it is necessary to maintain control of the output as the desired value is varied over a range of values, this is not the principal feature of regulator operation.   Generally a regulator does not contain any integrating elements.

The term servomechanism is more recent, apparently being first used in an outstanding paper by H. L. Hazen [8] in which in 1934 he set forth a detailed analysis of on-off and continuous-control servomechanisms for position control.   The major emphasis in that paper, and in many other servomechanism applications after that time, [9, 26, 31] was on the design of a control capable of producing a controlled output position very nearly equal to a reference input position, which in general is a simple function of time.   The effect of load fluctuations and other disturbances was generally not of major importance in this type of system and was given less emphasis in the servomechanism design.   Generally one or more integrating elements are contained in the forward transfer function of a servomechanism system.

Many of the military applications required during the first World War indicated the desirability of having rapid, accurate, and automatic control of position for such applications as remote indicators and power drives for moving heavy loads.   Early developments of considerable importance in this field of servomechanisms during the 1920's were automatic controls for steering ships and for positioning naval guns on shipboard.   Minorsky's work in providing automatically controlled ship steering is a classic in the development of servomechanisms. [1, 3]

Because of the understandable necessity for military secrecy in much of the development in the field of position controls, and because of the somewhat different design emphasis on regulator and servomechanism applications, it is not surprising that the similarity of these two phases of the control problem was not emphasized and exploited more fully. Although during the second World War there was little exchange of information between the servomechanism and regulator design engineers, since 1945 there has been a healthy exchange of ideas.

Early designers in the field of feedback control systems made almost exclusive use of the differential equation method of problem analysis for it aided their intuition and gave them a physical picture of the requirements of the control system.   The work of Minorsky and Hazen makes use of the differential equation approach.   Later this differential equation or *transient* approach was greatly extended by Brown, Hall, [52] and others to provide general non-dimensionalized information [49, 59] concerning servomechanism response and design methods for the simpler control systems.   The use of the Laplace transform was found to be advantageous for this work.   Although still used extensively, the transient method of analysis has been generally supplanted by the *steady-state* sinusoidal analysis and synthesis methods.

In the early 1930's work in the seemingly unrelated field of feedback amplifier design by Nyquist [6] and Black [7] brought about the development of the theory of the stability of closed-loop systems on the basis of the system open-loop response to steady-state sinusoidal excitation. This basic concept provided data upon which later developments were made to provide the modern techniques of feedback control design, which are based upon steady-state response characteristics.   Bode in 1938 [14] showed the intimate relationship between the attenuation frequency and phase characteristics of minimum-phase electrical networks, a relationship later used for the more general control problems.

The impetus of military demands for automatic controls in the second World War permitted concentration of a large amount of effort in the field of servomechanisms.   Tremendous strides were made during this period in extending the design and analysis techniques as well as in the construction and operation of vastly improved feedback control systems.

Harris in 1941 [26] and Hall in 1943 [31] illustrated how the complex plane approach of Nyquist could be used for purposes of servomechanism design and analysis.   In addition, these men provided a most useful interpretation of the various vectors on the complex plane in terms of their physical significance as part of the servomechanism problem.   During the years 1941 to 1945 Bomberger and Weber,[28] MacColl,[41] Nichols,[62] Bode,[43] and others [46] indicated how Bode's attenuation phase concepts could be applied to the servomechanism design problem to provide a more direct method of servo system analysis and synthesis.   The effects of the extraneous inputs (noise) on servomechanism performance and design were considered by Weiner, Phillips,[62] Hall, and others during this same period.   An effort was made to establish criteria for the "optimum" servomechanism performance under the condition of combined signal and noise inputs to a servomechanism.

Of comparable importance to the development of analytical tools for solving feedback control analysis and synthesis problems was the development of improved power sources, error indicators, and other components for supplying the practical needs of the servomechanism designer. Typical of these are such devices as the amplidyne for obtaining a high-gain rapid-response d-c generator,[20, 21] the selsyn generator-control transformer for supplying an electrical signal proportional to rotational error,[47] and a number of hydraulic pumps, motors, and amplifier units for sources of power and control.

Since the end of the second World War a great deal of the control system information developed during the war has been published in books,[41, 42, 60, 61, 62, 85, 86, 115, 131] and articles that have materially aided the widespread development and use of servomechanism design methods. At present general servomechanism concepts are being used in many applications previously considered to be regulator problems. Gradually, under the leadership of such men as Brown, Herwald, Crever, and Ahrendt, an effort has been made to draw the fields of regulator and servomechanism design together under the more inclusive heading, feedback control systems. Under the stimulus of the postwar demand for goods, faster and more accurate industrial controls are being designed and built utilizing components developed in wartime. Steel and paper mill drives and machine tool controls are representative of such applications.[74, 104] Simple position-control servomechanisms are being used in more complicated control systems for guided missile and other intricate applications.

Recent progress in a number of fields of technological endeavor has served to expand and modify servomechanisms, regulators, and other feedback control systems. Developments in control components have resulted in greatly miniaturized tubes, motors, synchros, and other devices.[135] In addition, power elements at vastly greater power levels have been employed as part of control loops. The discovery and rapid exploitation of transistors and other solid state devices have revolutionized the hardware making up error-detectors, amplifiers, and other low power-level circuits in control systems. The vastly improved understanding of magnetic amplifiers and correspondingly rapid strides in materials and techniques of construction have resulted in widespread use of these reliable and long-lived control elements. The different impedance levels of these components have served to modify some of the control hardware used to stabilize systems using these newer components.

The rapid strides in the computer arts have markedly influenced control systems thinking and practice. The widespread availability of relatively inexpensive analog computers has caused a great deal of control system design to be performed and checked by computer.[127] Analog computer components are frequently incorporated with actual servomechanism or regulator hardware to simulate more complex control systems. Finally, analog computer elements are more frequently being designed into control systems to provide the computation function as an inherent portion of the control system. It is apparent that the concept of what constitutes the system being controlled is expanding appreciably.

Although digital computers have not served so extensively as a means of determinining control system performance, they have influenced control system development by expanding the use of "logic" circuitry and by directing the trend toward sampled-data techniques.[134] The size of digital computers has been so reduced that in a number of instances they have been incorporated into control systems as a part of the real-time control loop. This coupled with their ability to perform many involved computations with speed and accuracy points to their more widespread use as an integral part of the control system itself.

In addition to the components developments in recent times, analytical and systems progress has kept pace. The describing function concept set forth by Kochenburger[106] and others has made possible the more extensive analysis of non-linear systems in general. A large number of non-linearities such as backlash, friction, and saturation have been handled in this fashion. Although some non-linearities such as multiplication have not yielded to this treatment, a greater freedom for handling non-linear compensation and stabilizing means have resulted from the use of the describing function. In Volume II a number of these ideas is set forth.

Although in many cases the error and other signals that supplied a control system were not continuous, the analysis of systems until comparatively recent times had been based primarily on the assumption that the data were continuous. The work of Linvill, Ragazzini, and others has served to establish and clarify methods of analyzing systems with periodically sampled data. Essentially two separate approaches have been used. One, the approximate frequency response method of Linvill includes the effect of sampling as an amplitude and phase change on the remainder of the system that is handled in the customary frequency response basis. The second, the z-transform method of Ragazzini and others is a transient method in which the effect of each sample of data is superposed on top of the effect of the sum of all the other samples. The results of this method are exact only at the instants of sampling. Each of these methods has the inherent advantages and disadvantages of the frequency response or transient response information that they provide. Where possible analog computer studies of such sampled data systems can be employed to advantage.

Great as has been the progress in control system applications, large segments of engineering activity remain available for future development. Without question, automatic feedback controls have become an important and integral part of the modern manufacturing and industrial processes. Automatic flight control and military applications of automatic control are being further extended.[87, 92] Already somewhat automatically controlled, the chemical process-control industries will become more completely automatic in the future. The nuclear power field by its very nature and importance is one where automatic control of the power generation process as well as the instrumentation and alarms will employ control devices to an increasing extent.

More widespread use of simple computers for providing means of completing the feedback control loop will permit more fully automatic operation of comprehensive control problems.[112] Automatic approach and landing of airplanes is a current example of use of such computers in control. Air traffic control will doubtless be another area of a similar nature. The control of the process industries in like fashion will use computers and on-line analyzers to improve the product yield and quality.[132, 133]

In addition to the more automatic direct control of a process will be the more automatic control of the information portion of the system associated with that process. By means of data-logging of the use of the raw materials, of the completion of finished parts, and of the inventory of raw and finished stocks, improved production control of the manufacture process can be realized. Using information about such supplemental quantities as bearing temperatures in a steam turbine, efficiencies of the boiler units, as well as heat rises in the generator, alarm or signal systems may be initiated that will perform the appropriate preplanned action. Better insight of the control processes is leading to increased work in the field of control of economic systems on a fairly broad basis.

In the field of analytical development, the future will doubtless see greater understanding and use of non-linear control elements and systems. Methods of handling multiple non-linearities will be sought as well as means for handling various mathematical operations such as arise in the use of computers with control systems. Increasing use will be made of computers themselves, both analog and/or digital, to solve many design problems. Problems associated with the use of sampled-data systems with increasingly complex control will continue to receive attention. More emphasis will be given the area of "quantized" controls in which the signal is changed in discrete steps, as by a ratchet or stair-stepped fashion depending only on the magnitude of its change from its previous change point. This is another form of sampling in which the sampling is done on an amplitude rather than time base. The problems associated with "optimizing" systems on a broad basis will receive increasing effort. Complex controls with minimum-time, greatest efficiency, minimum cost, maximum output per dollar spent will be studied and built.

In addition there doubtless will be improvements in the components and equipment that make up the feedback control system.[119] Smaller, more accurate, and reliable error- and rate-measuring devices as well as greater power and lighter, faster control elements are representative of the component advances that should be made in the future. More emphasis will be placed on obtaining components that incorporate the control and information-handling portion of the system's problem. The area of sensors, transducers, and analyzers will receive increasing attention as controls of newer processes are devised. As in the past, improvements in components will continue to make possible greater improvements in systems in the future.

# 2

## MANIPULATION OF COMPLEX NUMBERS

### 2.0 Introduction

In the study of feedback control problems the magnitude and time relationships between such quantities as position, speed, voltage, current, force, and torque must be determined. For a given system a knowledge of the behavior of certain of these quantities under the influence of various external conditions constitutes a knowledge of the performance characteristics of the system.

The quantities of interest are real physical quantities, all of which are produced by physical devices and all behave according to the physical laws of nature. Therefore they are independent of any mathematical notation or process that might be used in their analysis.

It is frequently convenient, however, to represent such physical quantities by complex mathematical symbols that indicate more than the information describing the real quantities themselves.[19, 32] This use of complex variables to represent real physical quantities has the advantage of simplifying the mathematical processes necessary to solve the problem. On the other hand, it has the disadvantage of obscuring the values of true physical quantities through the introduction of mathematical quantities having vague physical meaning.

It is the purpose of this chapter to introduce some of the notations and definitions of complex variables that are used in later chapters. By acquiring a facility in the manipulation of the complex variables, one is able to take advantage of the mathematical simplicity without suffering appreciably from a decrease in the physical interpretation of the phenomenon involved.

Because of the similarity between servomechanisms and electrical networks, the methods employed in network analysis are also used extensively in the study of servomechanisms. Representation of sinusoidally varying physical quantities as complex quantities having real and imaginary parts independent of each other is the basis of a well-known method of analyzing networks under steady-state conditions. The manner by which quantities are expressed in complex form, algebraically and graphically, is emphasized in this chapter, whereas the reason for using complex variables will be made apparent in later chapters.

## 2.1   Three Forms of Complex Quantities

Complex quantities are usually expressed on one of three forms: [32] (1) rectangular or Cartesian; (2) polar; (3) exponential.   Any complex quantity can be expressed in any one of the three forms, the choice of form depending largely upon the algebraic operation to be performed.

**Rectangular Form.**   The complex quantity $\bar{P}$ is drawn on the complex plane in Figure 2.1–1.   The real part of the complex quantity is measured

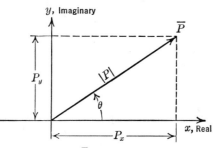

FIGURE 2.1–1.   $\bar{P}$ shown on complex plane.

along the horizontal or real axis and the imaginary part along the vertical or imaginary axis.   The axes are labeled $x$ and $y$ for convenience in designation of the parts.   The significance attributed to the terms real and imaginary can be considered merely that of definition, that is, the projection of the complex quantity on the $x$-axis is said to be its real component, and its projection on the $y$-axis is said to be its imaginary component.

The point $P$ might be regarded as a point in the complex plane displaced from the origin a distance $P_x$ along the real axis and a distance $P_y$ along the imaginary axis.   The angle $\theta$ between the $x$-axis and the line to $P$, and the length of the arrow, denoted by $|P|$, are two other quantities that, when specified, completely determine the location of point $P$.   The quantities $|P|$ and $\theta$ are the polar coordinates of point $P$ and are the basis of the polar and exponential forms discussed in the following sections.

The algebraic expression for $\bar{P}$ is

$$\bar{P} = P_x + jP_y \qquad (2.1\text{–}1)$$

where
$$P_x = P \cos \theta,$$
$$P_y = P \sin \theta,$$
$$j = \sqrt{-1}, \text{ an imaginary number.}$$

The magnitude $|P|$ of $\bar{P}$ may be expressed as

$$|P| = \sqrt{P_x{}^2 + P_y{}^2} \qquad (2.1\text{--}2)$$

Also, by trigonometry,

$$\tan \theta = \frac{P_y}{P_x} \qquad (2.1\text{--}3)$$

and

$$\theta = \tan^{-1} \frac{P_y}{P_x}$$

The property of the imaginary number $j$ is such that when $j$ is multiplied by a positive real number, $A$, the product $jA$ is a complex quantity having a zero real part and a positive imaginary part of magnitude $A$. Similarly, multiplication of $jA$ by $j$ yields $j^2A = -A$, a complex quantity having a zero imaginary part and a negative real part of magnitude $A$. Two additional multiplications by $j$ yield $-jA$ and $+A$, respectively. These quantities are shown in Figure 2.1–2.

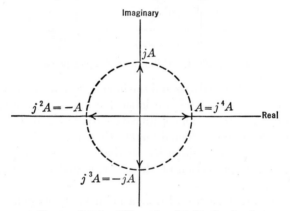

FIGURE 2.1–2.   Effect of multiplication by $j$.

The effect of multiplication by $j$ is thus seen to be a rotation of 90° in the counterclockwise direction. The fact that 90° counterclockwise rotation is also obtained when $j$ multiplies an original quantity that is neither wholly real nor wholly imaginary is easily verified by operating on the real and imaginary parts separately and adding the results by the method illustrated later in this chapter.

**Polar Form.**   In polar form, the complex quantity of Figure 2.1–1 is expressed as follows:

$$\bar{P} = |P|\underline{/\theta} \qquad (2.1\text{--}4)$$

where $|P|$ denotes the magnitude of the complex quantity, and $\underline{/\theta}$ means "at the angle $\theta$" with respect to the positive real axis.

**Exponential Form.** In exponential form the same complex quantity is given by the expression,

$$\bar{P} = |P|e^{j\theta} \tag{2.1-5}$$

where $|P|$ denotes the magnitude as previously stated, $e = 2.718$, the base of natural logarithms, and $\theta$ is the angle in radians measured from the positive real axis.

The similarity between the polar and exponential forms is immediately apparent. The polar form is merely another way of writing the exponential form, and knowledge of how to manipulate the exponential form constitutes a knowledge of how to manipulate the polar form. Therefore, the rules governing manipulation will be given for the rectangular and the exponential forms only.

## 2.2 Equivalence of Different Forms of Complex Numbers

From Equation 2.1–1 and the geometry of Figure 2.1–1,

$$\bar{P} = |P|\cos\theta + j|P|\sin\theta$$
$$= |P|(\cos\theta + j\sin\theta) \tag{2.2-1}$$

The functions $\cos\theta$ and $\sin\theta$ may be expanded in a Taylor series; the resulting series are

$$\cos\theta = 1 - \frac{\theta^2}{2!} + \frac{\theta^4}{4!} - \frac{\theta^6}{6!} + \cdots, \text{ etc.} \tag{2.2-2}$$

$$\sin\theta = \frac{\theta}{1!} - \frac{\theta^3}{3!} + \frac{\theta^5}{5!} - \frac{\theta^7}{7!} + \cdots, \text{ etc.} \tag{2.2-3}$$

where ! is the factorial sign and $\theta$ is measured in radians. Recalling that $j^2 = -1$, Equations 2.2–2 and 2.2–3 may be written in rearranged forms:

$$\cos\theta = 1 + \frac{(j\theta)^2}{2!} + \frac{(j\theta)^4}{4!} + \frac{(j\theta)^6}{6!} + \cdots, \text{ etc.} \tag{2.2-4}$$

$$j\sin\theta = \frac{j\theta}{1!} + \frac{(j\theta)^3}{3!} + \frac{(j\theta)^5}{5!} + \frac{(j\theta)^7}{7!} + \cdots, \text{ etc.} \tag{2.2-5}$$

Adding Equations 2.2–4 and 2.2–5 gives

$$\cos\theta + j\sin\theta = 1 + \frac{(j\theta)}{1!} + \frac{(j\theta)^2}{2!} + \frac{(j\theta)^3}{3!} + \cdots, \text{ etc.} \tag{2.2-6}$$

The right-hand member of Equation 2.2–6 is equal to the series expansion of the exponential function, $e^{j\theta}$, namely,

$$e^{j\theta} = 1 + \frac{j\theta}{1!} + \frac{(j\theta)^2}{2!} + \frac{(j\theta)^3}{3!} + \cdots$$

$$e^{j\theta} = \cos\theta + j\sin\theta \qquad (2.2\text{–}7)$$

Similarly, it may be shown that

$$e^{-j\theta} = \cos\theta - j\sin\theta \qquad (2.2\text{–}8)$$

Equations 2.2–7 and 2.2–8 are identities, that is, they are satisfied for all values of $\theta$. Two other important identities can be obtained, one by adding Equations 2.2–7 and 2.2–8 and the other by subtracting Equation 2.2–8 from Equation 2.2–7. They are

$$\cos\theta = \frac{e^{j\theta} + e^{-j\theta}}{2} \qquad (2.2\text{–}9)$$

$$\sin\theta = \frac{e^{j\theta} - e^{-j\theta}}{2j} \qquad (2.2\text{–}10)$$

Substitution of Equation 2.2–7 in Equation 2.2–1, which was obtained from Equation 2.1–1, shows that the right-hand members of Equations 2.1–1 and 2.1–5 are equivalent. This constitutes proof that the rectangular and the exponential forms are equivalent. The polar form, being merely a symbolic representation of the exponential form, is also equivalent to the rectangular form. A general expression of the equivalence of the three forms is

$$\underbrace{P(\cos\theta \pm j\sin\theta)}_{\text{rectangular}} = \underbrace{P/\!\pm\theta}_{\text{polar}} = \underbrace{Pe^{\pm j\theta}}_{\text{exponential}}$$

The unit of the angle $\theta$ is the radian. However, since tables of trigonometric functions are usually in terms of degrees instead of radians, it is customary to express $\theta$ in degrees in the rectangular and polar forms. It is permissible to use degrees instead of radians *only in the numerical* evaluation of trigonometric functions. When angles occur in exponential functions or by themselves in the final result, they must be expressed in radians.

Since the magnitude of the complex quantity is generally a number, the sign $|\ |$ indicating magnitude has not been retained; the symbol $P$, therefore, represents the magnitude of the complex quantity $\bar{P}$.

By means of the general expression of equivalence stated above, it is possible to transform complex quantities from one form to another readily. A number of transformations are shown in Table 2.2–1 below.

TABLE 2.2–1

| $P$ | $\theta°$ | $\theta$ radian | Rectangular | Polar | Exponential |
|-----|-----------|-----------------|-------------|-------|-------------|
| 5 | 53.1° | 0.927 | $3 + j4$ | $5\underline{/53.1°}$ | $5e^{j0.927}$ |
| 10 | −45° | $-\pi/4$ | $7.07 - j7.07$ | $10\underline{/-45°}$ | $10e^{-j\pi/4}$ |
| 10 | 120° | $2\pi/3$ | $-5 + j8.66$ | $10\underline{/120°}$ | $10e^{j2\pi/3}$ |
| 1 | 270° | $3\pi/2$ | $0 - j1$ | $1\underline{/270°}$ | $e^{j3\pi/2}$ |

## 2.3   Manipulation of Complex Quantities

It was stated in Section 2.1 that the form in which a complex quantity is expressed depends to a large extent upon what algebraic operation is to be performed. In addition and subtraction complex quantities must be expressed in rectangular form if a single resultant complex quantity is to be obtained. In multiplication, division, raising to a power, or extracting a root the exponential and polar forms are usually more convenient than the rectangular form. Multiplication and division are, however, frequently carried out in rectangular form. In this section the methods of performing these algebraic processes with complex numbers are described.

**Addition and Subtraction.** The rule for addition or subtraction of two complex quantities is as follows: *According to the rules of ordinary algebra, obtain the algebraic sum of the real parts and the algebraic sum of the imaginary parts. The resultant complex quantity is then the algebraic sum of the real parts plus j times the algebraic sum of the imaginary parts.* The rule is illustrated by the equations and figures that follow.

$$\bar{P} = P_x + jP_y \tag{2.3–1}$$

$$\bar{Q} = Q_x + jQ_y \tag{2.3–2}$$

Adding Equations 2.3–1 and 2.3–2 to obtain the resultant gives

$$\bar{R} = \bar{P} + \bar{Q} = (P_x + Q_x) + j(P_y + Q_y) \tag{2.3–3}$$

Graphical representations of addition and subtraction are shown in Figures 2.3–1 and 2.3–2, respectively.

Comparison of Figures 2.3–1 and 2.3–2 reveals that subtraction is performed graphically by rotating through 180° the complex quantity that is to be subtracted, and then performing graphical addition. This rule *for graphical subtraction* corresponds to the rule for subtraction of ordinary algebraic expressions; namely, *change the sign of the subtrahend and*

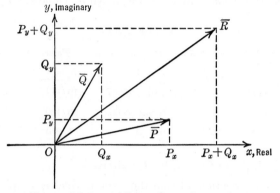

FIGURE 2.3–1.   Addition of complex numbers
$$\overline{R} = \overline{P} + \overline{Q}.$$

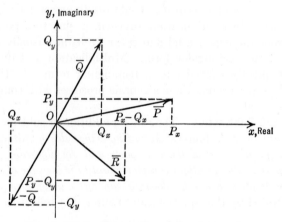

FIGURE 2.3–2.   Subtraction of complex numbers
$$\overline{R} = \overline{P} - \overline{Q}.$$

*add to the minuend.* Numerical examples illustrating the rules for addition and subtraction of complex quantities are given below.

Given:
$$\overline{P} = 5.0 + j1.0 = 5.1 \underline{/11.3°}$$
$$\overline{Q} = 2.0 + j3.46 = 4 \underline{/60°}$$

Adding $\overline{P}$ and $\overline{Q}$ gives
$$\overline{P} + \overline{Q} = (5.0 + 2.0) + j(1.0 + 3.46)$$
$$= 7 + j4.46$$

Subtracting $\bar{Q}$ from $\bar{P}$ gives

$$\bar{P} - \bar{Q} = \bar{P} + (-\bar{Q})$$
$$= (5.0 + j1.0) - (2.0 + j3.46)$$
$$= (5.0 - 2.0) + j(1.0 - 3.46)$$
$$\bar{P} - \bar{Q} = 3.0 - j2.46$$

**Multiplication and Division.** Multiplication and division of complex quantities expressed in exponential form are performed according to the ordinary algebraic rules governing multiplication and division of exponentials. *In multiplication the magnitudes are multiplied and the exponents are added.*

$$\bar{P} = Pe^{j\theta_1} \tag{2.3–4}$$

$$\bar{Q} = Qe^{j\theta_2} \tag{2.3–5}$$

$$\bar{P} \cdot \bar{Q} = Pe^{j\theta_1} \cdot Qe^{j\theta_2}$$
$$= PQe^{j(\theta_1 + \theta_2)} \tag{2.3–6}$$

*In division, the magnitude of the dividend is divided by the magnitude of the divisor, and the exponent of the divisor is subtracted from the exponent of the dividend.*

$$\frac{\bar{P}}{\bar{Q}} = \frac{Pe^{j\theta_1}}{Qe^{j\theta_2}} = \frac{P}{Q}e^{j(\theta_1 - \theta_2)} \tag{2.3–7}$$

The procedure applied to polar forms is similar.

$$\bar{P} = P\underline{/\theta_1} \tag{2.3–8}$$

$$\bar{Q} = Q\underline{/\theta_2} \tag{2.3–9}$$

$$\bar{P} \cdot \bar{Q} = PQ\underline{/\theta_1 + \theta_2} \tag{2.3–10}$$

$$\frac{\bar{P}}{\bar{Q}} = \frac{P}{Q}\underline{/\theta_1 - \theta_2} \tag{2.3–11}$$

The numerical examples in Table 2.3–1 illustrate the use of these rules.

TABLE 2.3–1

EXAMPLE OF MULTIPLICATION AND DIVISION OF COMPLEX NUMBERS

|  | *Exponential* | *Polar* |
|---|---|---|
| $\bar{P}$ | $5.1e^{j0.197}$ | $5.1\underline{/11.3°}$ |
| $\bar{Q}$ | $4.0e^{j\pi/3}$ | $4.0\underline{/60°}$ |
| $\bar{P} \cdot \bar{Q}$ | $20.4e^{j1.244}$ | $20.4\underline{/71.3°}$ |
| $\dfrac{\bar{P}}{\bar{Q}}$ | $1.275e^{-j0.850}$ | $1.275\underline{/-48.7°}$ |

The product and the quotient of two complex quantities are represented graphically in Figures 2.3–3 and 2.3–4, respectively.

Multiplication and division of complex quantities expressed in rectangular form are somewhat longer than the same operations for polar

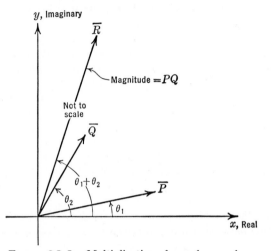

FIGURE 2.3–3.   Multiplication of complex numbers

$$\bar{R} = \bar{P} \cdot \bar{Q}.$$

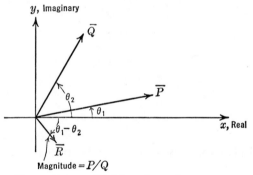

FIGURE 2.3–4.   Division of complex numbers

$$\bar{R} = \frac{\bar{P}}{\bar{Q}}.$$

and exponential form. Since the use of the rectangular form of the complex numbers may lead to needlessly laborious calculations and to frequent errors, it is recommended that the polar or exponential form of the complex numbers be used for multiplication and division whenever possible.

**Forming the Conjugate.**  During certain manipulations of complex numbers, it is convenient to obtain the conjugate of a complex number. *The conjugate of a complex number is another complex number having a real part equal to the real part of the first and having an imaginary part equal to the negative of the imaginary part of the first.*  Thus, if

$$\bar{P}_1 = P_x + jP_y = P\underline{/\theta}$$

$$\bar{P}_2 = P_x - jP_y = P\underline{/-\theta}$$

(2.3–12)

then $\bar{P}_2$ is the conjugate of $\bar{P}_1$ and $\bar{P}_1$ is the conjugate of $\bar{P}_2$.  Figure 2.3–5 illustrates this conjugate relationship.

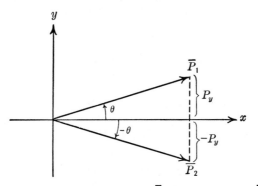

FIGURE 2.3–5.  Complex number $\bar{P}_1$ and its conjugate $\bar{P}_2$.

The property of conjugate complex numbers is particularly convenient for the processes of addition and multiplication.  When two conjugate numbers are added, the resultant sum is a real number with a magnitude equal to twice the real part of either of the conjugates.  Thus

$$\bar{P}_1 + \bar{P}_2 = 2P_x$$

(2.3–13)

When two conjugate numbers are multiplied, the resultant product is a real number with a resultant magnitude equal to the square of the magnitude of either of the numbers.  Thus

$$\bar{P}_1 \cdot \bar{P}_2 = P\underline{/\theta} \cdot P\underline{/-\theta} = P^2$$

(2.3–14)

Expressions for a few conjugate complex quantities in rectangular, polar, and exponential form are given in Table 2.3–2.

TABLE 2.3-2

TWO COMPLEX QUANTITIES AND THEIR CONJUGATES EXPRESSED IN
ALTERNATE FORMS

| Rectangular | Polar | Exponential |
|---|---|---|
| $P_x + jP_y$ | $P\underline{/\theta}$ | $Pe^{j\theta}$ |
| $P_x - jP_y$ | $P\underline{/-\theta}$ | $Pe^{-j\theta}$ |
| $10 - j10$ | $14.1\underline{/-45°}$ | $14.1e^{-j\pi/4}$ |
| $10 + j10$ | $14.1\underline{/45°}$ | $14.1e^{+j\pi/4}$ |

**Raising to a Power; Extracting a Root.** The operations of raising a complex quantity to a power and of extracting a root of a complex quantity are governed by the same rule; hence the explanation of one operation explains the other. The procedure is illustrated in the following example.

*Given:* The complex quantity $\overline{P} = P_x + jP_y$

*Required:* To find $\overline{R} = (\overline{P})^n$, where $n$ is any real number, integral or fractional.

First, express $\overline{P}$ in exponential form:

$$\overline{P} = Pe^{j\theta} \tag{2.3-15}$$

where

$$P = \sqrt{P_x{}^2 + P_y{}^2}$$

$$\theta = \tan^{-1}\frac{P_y}{P_x}$$

Second, raise both factors, $P$ and $e^{j\theta}$, to the power $n$.

$$(\overline{P})^n = (Pe^{j\theta})^n$$

$$= P^n e^{jn\theta} \tag{2.3-16}$$

Finally, convert to rectangular form, using Equation 2.2-7:

$$\overline{R} = (\overline{P})^n = P^n (\cos n\theta + j \sin n\theta) \tag{2.3-17}$$

The example may be clarified by assigning numerical values to $P_x$, $P_y$, and $n$. Let $P_x = 3$, $P_y = 4$, and $n = -\frac{1}{2}$. Then

$$P = \sqrt{3^2 + 4^2} = 5$$

$$\theta° = \tan^{-1}\tfrac{4}{3} = 53.1°$$

Using Equation 2.3–16,

$$(\bar{P})^{-\frac{1}{2}} = (5)^{-\frac{1}{2}} e^{-j\theta/2}$$

$$= \frac{1}{\sqrt{5}} \left( \cos \frac{\theta}{2} - j \sin \frac{\theta}{2} \right)$$

$$= \frac{1}{\sqrt{5}} [\cos 26.6° - j \sin 26.6°]$$

$$(\bar{P})^{-\frac{1}{2}} = 0.400 - j0.200$$

**Logarithm of a Complex Quantity.** Occasionally in performing mathematical operations on complex quantities it is necessary to obtain the logarithm of the quantity. This is done most easily when the complex number is expressed in its exponential form, where the number is considered to be the product of its magnitude times the exponential. The logarithm is then obtained by taking the logarithm of the magnitude and adding to it the logarithm of the exponential. Thus taking the logarithm to the base $e$ of $Pe^{j\theta}$ gives

$$\ln Pe^{j\theta} = \ln P + \ln e^{j\theta} \qquad (2.3\text{–}18)$$

$$\ln Pe^{j\theta} = \ln P + j\theta \qquad (2.3\text{–}19)$$

From this it can be seen that the logarithm of a complex number is itself a complex number having its real part equal to the logarithm of the magnitude of the original number and its imaginary part equal to the angle in radians of the original number.

## 2.4   Example from Servomechanism Application

Many of the mathematical operations involved in servomechanism design are performed with the aid of complex numbers. As an illustration, consider the case where it is desired to determine magnitude and angle of the resultant complex number represented by

$$\frac{C}{R} = \frac{\dfrac{C}{E}}{1 + \dfrac{C}{E}}$$

where

$$\frac{C}{E}(j\omega) = \frac{200(1 + j0.4\omega)^2}{j\omega(1 + j1.8\omega)^2(1 + j0.025\omega)}$$

and

$$\omega = 2$$

First determine the value of $C/E$ in its polar form.

$$1 + j0.4(2) = 1.28\underline{/38.7}$$

$$(1 + j0.8)^2 = 1.64\underline{/77.3}$$

$$j\omega = 2\underline{/90°}$$

$$1 + j1.8(2) = 3.74\underline{/74.5}$$

$$(1 + j3.6)^2 = 13.96\underline{/149.0}$$

$$1 + j0.025(2) = 1.00\underline{/2.9}$$

Combining these values gives

$$\frac{C}{E} = 11.74\underline{/-164.5}$$

To determine the value of $1 + C/E$ in the denominator, it is necessary to express $C/E$ in rectangular form,

$$\frac{C}{E} = -11.31 - j3.14$$

Performing the addition, then expressing the denominator in polar form, gives

$$1 + \frac{C}{E} = 1 - 11.31 - j3.14 = 10.78\underline{/-163.1}$$

Finally,

$$\frac{C}{R} = \frac{11.74\underline{/-164.50}}{10.78\underline{/-163.1}} = 1.09\underline{/-1.4}$$

# 3

# SOLUTION OF LINEAR DIFFERENTIAL EQUATIONS

## 3.0 Introduction

In describing the operation of feedback control systems, one may generally write differential equations that indicate in mathematical form the performance of the equipment. Frequently these differential equations are quite complex and contain functional relationships between the variables that are not constant over the entire region of operation. However, by judicious approximation and subject to the limitation of the region for which the results are valid, it is in many cases possible to describe the operation of the system by a linear differential equation with constant coefficients.[8, 9, 62, 86]

The solution of the linear differential equation yields the complete expression for the performance of the feedback control system for the given input conditions. The advantage of this method is that both the transient and the steady-state components are obtained. The excellence of performance of a feedback control system is frequently based to a large extent upon the speed and smoothness with which the system responds to a transient input. The differential equations of the system alone give the complete transient solution directly.[19] Therefore, it is necessary to be able to obtain the solution of linear differential equations. Although the response of a system initially at rest to a sudden impulse will not represent the general transient condition, the stability or instability of a system to this input is the same as for any other transient condition for the same system parameters.

In addition to the transient conditions, the mathematical solution gives the steady-state portion of the system response. The steady-state form of response to a sinusoidal input has been found to be of great help in developing useful criteria of system synthesis. It is worthwhile, therefore, to understand the mathematical methods of solution of linear differential equations before proceeding further in the study of feedback controls.

It is well to keep in mind that the process of obtaining the solution of a linear differential equation is frequently long and arduous for any but the most simplified of systems. Also the effects upon the performance made by various modifications of the system elements are not readily apparent. The usefulness of this method for synthesis of feedback control systems is therefore limited.

The purpose of this chapter is threefold: (1) to show how differential equations are obtained and how they may be solved mathematically, (2) to introduce the concept of time constants, and (3) to show that physical quantities can be represented by the complex quantities described in the preceding chapter.

Since the operation of ordinary electrical circuits is frequently determined on the basis of their differential equations, the material in this chapter is developed around electrical circuits. The reader should realize, however, that a servomechanism is seldom purely electrical; it may contain mechanical, hydraulic, thermal, or other elements. Nonetheless the same methods of solution described herein are applicable to equations for the other forms of elements.[57]

The differential equations of these other forms of elements are basically similar to the differential equations of the electrical circuits. The major differences appear in the literal coefficients used and in the physical significance of the terms. To illustrate the similarity in form and method of handling the equations for these other types of elements, a number of examples are worked out at the conclusion of this chapter for the solution of the differential equations of performance for typical servomechanism elements.

### 3.1   Series Resistance-Inductance Network

A common means of obtaining power amplification in servomechanism elements is to establish a magnetic field proportional to some control quantity. A voltage is established proportional to the control quantity, and the current produced by this voltage establishes a magnetic field in an inductance. For accurate control and response, it is desirable for the current at all times to be proportional to the applied voltage. Schematically, this control can be represented as a series resistance-inductance network, an analysis of which follows.

Figure 3.1–1 shows a simple electrical circuit consisting of a resistance element $R$ and an inductance element $L$ in series. These elements, constant in value, are considered to have no non-linearities. A source of d-c voltage, the battery $E$ is assumed to have negligible internal resistance. The circuit is completed by closing the switch $S$ at the time $t = 0$.

The applied voltage is equal to the sum of the voltage drops around the circuit.

$$L\frac{di}{dt} + Ri = E \qquad (3.1\text{--}1)$$

It is desired to determine the value of the current $i$ as a function of time to establish the correlation between the applied voltage and current necessary for evaluating the effectiveness of this element in a control system.

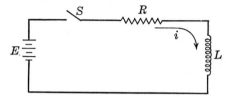

FIGURE 3.1–1.    Series $RL$ circuit with d-c voltage impressed.

The answer can be obtained by a number of different methods. The classical mathematical method will be considered first.

**Classical Solution.**  By separating variables, Equation 3.1–1 may be rewritten as follows:

$$L \int \frac{di}{E - Ri} = \int dt \qquad (3.1–2)$$

Integrating Equation 3.1–2 gives

$$-\frac{L}{R} \ln (E - Ri) = t + C_1 \qquad (3.1–3)$$

where $C_1$ is a constant of integration and ln denotes "logarithm to the base $e$."

From the definitions of logarithms, Equation 3.1–3 may be rewritten as follows:

$$E - Ri = e^{-Rt/L + C_2} \qquad (3.1–4)$$

or

$$i = \frac{E}{R} + C_3 e^{-Rt/L} \qquad (3.1–5)$$

To evaluate $C_3$, which arises from the constants of integration, the initial conditions at $t = 0$ must be examined. The current through $L$ before the switch is closed is zero. Since there cannot be an instantaneous change in energy and, therefore, no change in current through an inductive element, it follows that at $t = 0$, $i = 0$.

Substituting $t = 0$ and $i = 0$ in Equation 3.1–5 gives

$$C_3 = -\frac{E}{R} \qquad (3.1–6)$$

Substituting Equation 3.1–6 in Equation 3.1–5 gives the complete expression for current as a function of time, as

$$i = \frac{E}{R} - \frac{E}{R} e^{-Rt/L} \qquad (3.1\text{–}7)$$

a plot of which is shown as a function of time in Figure 3.1–2.

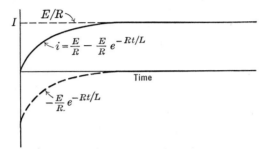

FIGURE 3.1–2. Current through series $RL$ circuit as a function of time after closing switch for constant d-c voltage impressed.

**Transient and Steady-State Form of Solution.**   Another method of determining the current in the $RL$ circuit is suggested by the results of the classical solution.[19]   Examination of Equation 3.1–7 and the corresponding plot, Figure 3.1–2, shows the current at any time to be a function of two types of components: (1) $E/R$, which has the same form as the applied voltage and contains no terms that are exponentially decaying, and (2) $-E/Re^{-Rt/L}$, which decays exponentially after the instant of switching to a value that is negligible in comparison with the constant value.

These two components have been described by mathematicians as the particular and the complementary portions of the solution, respectively. The particular solution, having the same form as the applied driving function, is also referred to by engineers as the steady-state solution since it indicates the nature of the response that remains after all switching transients have decayed to a negligible value.

The complementary solution, corresponding to the portion of the solution that complements the particular solution by enabling it to describe correctly the initial values of the quantity being determined, is called by engineers the transient solution.   The term transient is an apt one since it refers to the exponentially decaying portion of the solution that subsides to zero when the transient effects have subsided.

The suggested alternate method of solution for the current is to assume from the outset that the current $i$ is composed of these two types of components: $i_s$, a steady-state current, and $i_t$, a transient current.

Thus
$$i = i_s + i_t \tag{3.1-8}$$

Substituting Equation 3.1–8 in Equation 3.1–1 gives

$$\left(L\frac{di_s}{dt} + Ri_s\right) + \left(L\frac{di_t}{dt} + Ri_t\right) = E \tag{3.1-9}$$

The steady-state current $i_s$ is dependent only upon the applied voltage $E$ and has the same form as $E$. Since $E$ is constant, $i_s$ does not change with time. Hence

$$\frac{di_s}{dt} = 0, \qquad i_s = \frac{E}{R} \tag{3.1-10}$$

The transient current $i_t$ must be determined from that part of Equation 3.1–9 remaining after Equation 3.1–10 is substituted in it:

$$L\frac{di_t}{dt} + Ri_t = 0 \tag{3.1-11}$$

The definition of the transient term indicates it to be exponential in form. One can assign a magnitude $I_T$ for the transient component and use the constant $p$ for the coefficient of the power of the exponential. Thus $i_t$ is of the form,

$$i_t = I_T e^{pt} \tag{3.1-12}$$

Substituting Equation 3.1–12 in Equation 3.1–11 and performing the differentiation indicated gives

$$(Lp + R)I_T e^{pt} = 0 \tag{3.1-13}$$

Since $I_T$ may well have any value and since $e^{pt}$ will take on different values as a function of time, Equation 3.1–13 for the transient solution is valid for all values of time only if

$$Lp_1 + R = 0 \tag{3.1-14}$$

The particular value of $p$ in Equation 3.1–12 for which Equation 3.1–13 is true is $p_1$. From Equation 3.1–14, $p_1$ is found to be,

$$p_1 = -\frac{R}{L} \tag{3.1-15}$$

It will be noted that the value of the coefficient $p_1$ is independent of the voltage applied and is dependent only on $L$ and $R$, i.e., the circuit arrangement. Substituting Equation 3.1–15 in Equation 3.1–12 gives

$$i_t = I_T e^{-Rt/L} \tag{3.1-16}$$

To evaluate the magnitude of $I_T$, it is necessary to return to a consideration of the physics of the problem as was done in the classical method of solution. The total current $i$ is expressed for all values of time by substituting the values of $i_s$ and $i_t$ from Equations 3.1–10 and 3.1–16 in Equation 3.1–8. Thus

$$i = \frac{E}{R} + I_T e^{-Rt/L} \qquad (3.1\text{--}17)$$

If the fact that $i = 0$ at $t = 0$ is applied,

$$I_T = -\frac{E}{R} \qquad (3.1\text{--}18)$$

If the value of $I_T$ from Equation 3.1–18 is placed in Equation 3.1–17, the resulting expression for the current $i$ is

$$i = \frac{E}{R} - \frac{E}{R} e^{-Rt/L} \qquad (3.1\text{--}19)$$

Thus the same expression for current is obtained but with the aid of a clearer physical interpretation of the components of the solution.

**Summary of the Solution of Differential Equations.** The method of solution using steady-state and transient components as described above is general and may be used for more complicated networks. A brief summary of the process is outlined below.

1. Write the differential equation for the desired quantity in terms of its steady-state and transient components as well as the applied voltage.

2. Evaluate the steady-state component of the desired quantity from the value(s) of the applied voltage.

3. Choose the transient component or components of the form $I_n e^{p_n t}$ and substitute in the equation for the desired quantity with the applied forces or voltage set equal to zero.

4. Determine the values of $p_n$ in such a way that they make the coefficient of $I_n e^{p_n t}$ zero. Note that the number of values of $p_n$ that can be evaluated in this way is equal to the order of the original differential equation. When two roots are equal, for instance, $p_1 = p_2$, the two transient components are $I_1 e^{p_1 t} + I_2 t e^{p_1 t}$, thus permitting two coefficients $I_1$ and $I_2$ to be evaluated corresponding to the two $p_1$ roots.

5. Determine the values of the magnitudes of the transient components $I_n$ from the steady-state and transient solutions with the aid of

the initial conditions present in the circuit. These are established from such physical considerations as the energy in an inductance or a capacitance remaining constant during the switching.

These principles are illustrated in Section 3.8. A more thorough presentation of a method of solution of differential equations utilizing an approach somewhat similar to the one outlined above is described in Chapter 4, where the Laplace transform method of solution is presented.

## 3.2  Characteristic Equation

Referring to the above discussion of the transient component of the solution, the reader will notice that the choice of the exponential form of the solution was based on the fact that the exponential form had been obtained by the classical method of solution. This same choice may also be made if it is realized that *the derivative or integral of an exponential has the same form as the original exponential.* Thus, if

$$i = Ie^{pt} \qquad (3.2\text{-}1)$$

then

$$\frac{di}{dt} = Ipe^{pt} \qquad (3.2\text{-}2)$$

and

$$\frac{d^2i}{dt^2} = Ip^2e^{pt} \qquad (3.2\text{-}3)$$

In similar fashion,

$$\int i\,dt = \frac{I}{p}e^{pt} \qquad (3.2\text{-}4)$$

Hence, if the substitution $i = Ie^{pt}$ is made, the original differential equation for the transient component is modified in form so that the derivative symbols $d^n(\ )/dt^n$ are replaced by $p^n$ and the integrals $\int^n (\ )\,dt$ are replaced by $1/p^n$.

Thus, if the differential equation is

$$a_0\frac{d^ni}{dt^n} + a_1\frac{d^{n-1}i}{dt^{n-1}} + \cdots + a_{n-1}\frac{di}{dt} + a_ni + a_{n+1}\int i\,dt$$

$$+ \cdots + a_{n+q}\int^q i\,dt^q = f(t) \quad (3.2\text{-}5)$$

then, with $i = Ie^{pt}$,

$$\left(a_0p^n + a_1p^{n-1} + \cdots + a_{n-1}p + a_n + \frac{a_{n+1}}{p} + \cdots + \frac{a_{n+q}}{p^q}\right)i = f(t)$$

$$(3.2\text{-}6)$$

The original equation rewritten with the derivatives and integrals replaced by the appropriate $p$ and $1/p$ form is said to be in operational form with the operator $p(\ )$ representing $d(\ )/dt$.

It will be noted that *the substitution of the operator $p(\ )$ for $d(\ )/dt$ is* not the result of an arbitrary selection of this definition for $p$.  Rather it is a *logical outgrowth of the choice of the exponential form of solution $e^{pt}$ for the general linear differential Equation 3.2–5*.

Since the form of the transient response is independent of the applied voltage, $f(t)$ in Equation 3.2–6 may be set equal to zero without affecting the *form of the transient*.  In this form the equation is said to be in its *reduced form*.  The reduced form of Equation 3.2–6 is

$$\left( a_0 p^n + a_1 p^{n-1} + \cdots + a_{n-1}p + a_n + \frac{a_{n+1}}{p} + \cdots + \frac{a_{n+q}}{p^q} \right) I e^{pt} = 0$$

$$(3.2\text{–}7)$$

Of equal or greater interest than the reduced equation is the *characteristic equation*, which is obtained by dividing by $Ie^{pt}$ and multiplying the resultant polynomial in $p$ by such a power of $p$ as to remove all values of $p$ from the denominators and to leave one constant term, this term corresponding to the $p^0$ coefficient.  The characteristic equation corresponding to the reduced form of Equation 3.2–7 is

$$a_0 p^{n+q} + a_1 p^{n+q-1} + \cdots + a_{n-1}p^{1+q} + a_n p^q + a_{n+1}p^{q-1} + \cdots + a_{n+q}$$

$$= 0 \quad (3.2\text{–}8)$$

Those particular values of $p$ that make Equation 3.2–8 valid, that is, make the polynomial in $p$ equal to zero, are the defining values of the $p_n$ and are the roots of the characteristic equation.  It is these roots that appear in the $i = I_n e^{p_n t}$ equations and that determine the form of the transient response.  The characteristic equation and its use in determining system stability are discussed further in Chapter 6.

### 3.3   Series Resistance-Capacitance Network

Figure 3.3–1 shows a simple electrical circuit consisting of a resistance element $R$ and a capacitance element $C$ connected in series.  The d-c voltage $E$ is placed in series with $R$ and $C$ by the closing of switch $S$ at time $t = 0$.  The condenser is originally uncharged.

The voltage equation for the circuit with the switch closed is

$$Ri + \frac{1}{C} \int i \, dt = E \qquad (3.3\text{–}1)$$

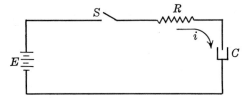

FIGURE 3.3–1.   Series $RC$ circuit with d-c voltage impressed.

Expressing $i$ in terms of steady-state and transient components

$$i = i_s + i_t \qquad (3.3\text{–}2)$$

When the switch is closed, the current charges the capacitor until

$$\frac{1}{C} \int i \, dt = E \qquad (3.3\text{–}3)$$

At this time, that is, at the steady-state condition,

$$Ri = E - \frac{1}{C} \int i \, dt = 0 \qquad (3.3\text{–}4)$$

Therefore,

$$Ri_s = 0 \text{ and } i_s = 0 \qquad (3.3\text{–}5)$$

For the transient current, let

$$i_t = I_T e^{pt} \qquad (3.3\text{–}6)$$

and

$$\left(R + \frac{1}{Cp}\right) I_T e^{pt} = 0 \qquad (3.3\text{–}7)$$

For Equation 3.3–7 to be valid at any time, $p$ must have the value $p_1$.

$$p_1 = -\frac{1}{RC} \qquad (3.3\text{–}8)$$

Using Equations 3.3–5, 3.3–6, and 3.3–8 in Equation 3.3–2 yields

$$i = i_s + i_t = 0 + I_T e^{-t/RC} \qquad (3.3\text{–}9)$$

At $t = 0$, Equation 3.3–1 becomes

$$Ri = E \qquad (3.3\text{–}10)$$

Substituting Equation 3.3–10 in Equation 3.3–9 at $t = 0$ gives

$$I_T = \frac{E}{R} \qquad (3.3\text{–}11)$$

The resultant expression for the total current as a function of time is

$$i = \frac{E}{R} e^{-t/RC} \qquad (3.3\text{–}12)$$

which is illustrated in Figure 3.3–2.

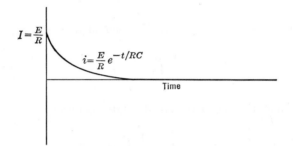

FIGURE 3.3–2.  Current through series $RC$ circuit as a function of time after closing switch for constant d-c voltage impressed.

## 3.4  Time Constants

Of particular importance in transient solutions is the exponential portion $e^{pt}$, since this reveals the decay of the transient component. It will be noticed that $p$ is a measure of the rate of decay. Use is generally made of the reciprocal form, $1/p$, which has the dimensions of time (seconds), to define a *time constant* for the circuit.

The time constant, $T$, is defined as the *time in seconds for a transient exponential term to be reduced to $e^{-1} = 0.368$ of its initial value*. This means that

$$+pT = -1 \qquad (3.4\text{–}1)$$

or

$$T = -\frac{1}{p} \text{ seconds} \qquad (3.4\text{–}2)$$

In the $RL$ series circuit in Section 3.1, $T = L/R$; in the $RC$ series circuit of Section 3.3, $T = RC$.

From the above it appears that the time constant is a characteristic of the system and is independent of the voltage applied. As a matter of fact, the time constants are determined directly from the characteristic equation.

Another useful interpretation of the time constant is shown in Figure 3.4–1, where the current through an $RC$ circuit such as was determined in the previous section is shown. *The time constant is the time that would*

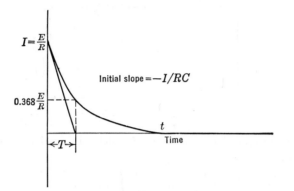

FIGURE 3.4–1. *T*, illustrating two definitions of the time constant, for the case of the current in a series $RC$ circuit.

*be required for the transient to disappear completely if its rate continued at its initial value.* Thus, determining the initial rate of the transient from Equation 3.3–12,

$$\frac{d}{dt}(Ie^{-t/RC}) = -\frac{I}{RC} \qquad (3.4\text{–}3)$$

From Equation 3.4–3 and Figure 3.4–1,

$$-\frac{I}{RC}(T) = -I \qquad (3.4\text{–}4)$$

and

$$T = RC \qquad (3.4\text{–}5)$$

This second interpretation is most useful in obtaining time constants experimentally.

### 3.5   Series Resistance-Inductance-Capacitance Network

A series resistance-inductance-capacitance network has two separate elements in which energy may be stored, and it has, therefore, a second-order differential equation. This means that there are two values of $p$ that will make the characteristic equation equal to zero. Therefore an oscillatory solution is possible. An oscillatory solution is evidenced by the values of $p$ being complex, as is illustrated in the following example.

Figure 3.5–1 shows a series $RLC$ network connected to a d-c voltage source $E$ by switch $S$ at time $t = 0$.

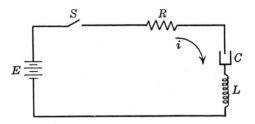

FIGURE 3.5–1.   Series $RLC$ circuit with d-c voltage impressed.

The voltage equation when $S$ is closed is obtained by summing the voltage drops.   Thus

$$L\frac{di}{dt} + Ri + \frac{1}{C}\int i\,dt = E \tag{3.5-1}$$

As in the case of a series $RC$ network, the steady-state current is zero because the capacitor is charged to the full supply voltage $E$.   Hence

$$i_s = 0 \tag{3.5-2}$$

The transient current is found by setting the left-hand side of Equation 3.5–1 equal to zero, giving the reduced equation

$$\left(Lp + R + \frac{1}{Cp}\right)i = 0 \tag{3.5-3}$$

in which $i$ is of the form

$$i = I_n e^{p_n t} \tag{3.5-4}$$

Multiplying Equation 3.5–3 by $Cp$ gives

$$(LCp^2 + RCp + 1)i = 0 \tag{3.5-5}$$

Dividing through Equation 3.5–5 by $i$ gives the characteristic equation

$$LCp^2 + RCp + 1 = 0 \tag{3.5-6}$$

Solving Equation 3.5–6 for $p$ yields two values for $p$:

$$p_1 = -\frac{R}{2L} + \frac{1}{2}\sqrt{\left(\frac{R}{L}\right)^2 - \frac{4}{LC}} \tag{3.5-7}$$

and

$$p_2 = -\frac{R}{2L} - \frac{1}{2}\sqrt{\left(\frac{R}{L}\right)^2 - \frac{4}{LC}} \tag{3.5-8}$$

It should again be noted that, corresponding to the second-order differential equation (Equation 3.5–1), there are two values of $p$ to be determined from the characteristic equation, Equation 3.5–6.

Depending on the values of the circuit parameters, the quantity under the square root sign, $(R/L)^2 - 4/LC$, may be positive, negative, or zero. Figure 3.5–2 shows how the values of the roots, $p_1$ and $p_2$, vary as $(R/L)^2 - 4/LC$ has a value that may be positive, zero, or negative.

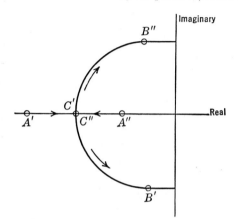

FIGURE 3.5–2. Location on complex plane for roots of characteristic equation of second-order differential equation, with response

> Overdamped $(A', A'')$,
> Oscillatory $(B', B'')$,
> Critically damped $(C', C'')$.

For a positive value of $(R/L)^2 - 4/LC$, that is, $(R/L)^2 > 4/LC$, the values of $p_1$ and $p_2$ are real, unequal and negative corresponding to points $A'$ and $A''$ on the real axis of Figure 3.5–2. For negative values of $(R/L)^2 - 4/LC$, that is, $(R/L)^2 < 4/LC$, the two values of $p$ are complex conjugates corresponding to points $B'$ and $B''$ on Figure 3.5–2. For $(R/L)^2 = 4/LC$, the values of $p_1$ and $p_2$ are real, equal, and negative as shown by points $C'$ and $C''$ on Figure 3.5–2. Corresponding to these three conditions for the value of $(R/L)^2 - 4/LC$ as cited above, the form of response of the current will be highly damped, oscillatory, or critically damped, respectively. These three forms of response are shown in Figure 3.5–3, where the value of the $R/L$ ratio alone has been changed to obtain these three conditions.

To determine the response for the current of this $RLC$ circuit, the expression for the transient current is

$$i_t = I_1 e^{p_1 t} + I_2 e^{p_2 t} \qquad (3.5\text{–}9)$$

corresponding to the two values of $p$. Note that the presence of the series capacitance causes the steady-state current to be zero so that $i_t$ is the complete solution for the current.

Since the system is being started from rest, there is no current flowing initially, and the initial value of the voltage on the condenser is zero.

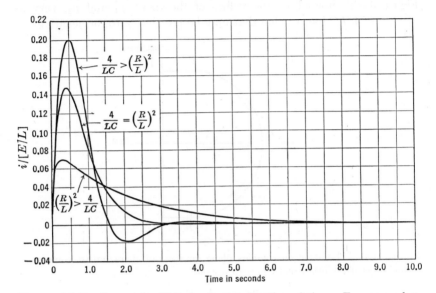

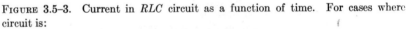

FIGURE 3.5-3. Current in $RLC$ circuit as a function of time. For cases where circuit is:

$$\text{Overdamped} \left(\frac{R}{L}\right)^2 > \frac{4}{LC}$$

$$\text{Oscillatory} \frac{4}{LC} > \left(\frac{R}{L}\right)^2$$

$$\text{Critically damped} \frac{4}{LC} = \left(\frac{R}{L}\right)^2$$

$$\text{where } i = \frac{E}{L}\left[\frac{e^{p_1 t} - e^{p_2 t}}{p_1 - p_2}\right].$$

Hence the values of current and rate of change of current at $t = 0$ are, from Equation 3.5-1,

$$i_t = 0 \qquad\qquad (3.5\text{--}10)$$

$$\frac{di_t}{dt} = \frac{E}{L} \qquad\qquad (3.5\text{--}11)$$

Placing Equations 3.5–10 and 3.5–11 in 3.5–9 permits the following values of $I_1$ and $I_2$ to be determined:

$$I_1 = -I_2 \tag{3.5-12}$$

and

$$I_1 = \frac{(E)}{(L)}\left[\frac{1}{p_1 - p_2}\right] \tag{3.5-13}$$

Substituting these values back in Equation 3.5–9 yields the following expression for current:

$$i = \frac{E}{L}\left[\frac{e^{p_1 t} - e^{p_2 t}}{p_1 - p_2}\right] \tag{3.5-14}$$

Since high-accuracy servomechanisms tend to be oscillatory in nature, the case where $p_1$ and $p_2$ are complex will be considered in more detail. Let

$$\frac{R}{2L} = \alpha = \text{decrement factor in seconds}^{-1} \tag{3.5-15}$$

and

$$\frac{1}{2}\sqrt{\frac{4}{LC} - \left(\frac{R}{L}\right)^2} = \beta = \begin{array}{l}\text{natural frequency of} \\ \text{the system in} \\ \text{radians per second}\end{array} \tag{3.5-16}$$

Then

$$p_1 = -\alpha + j\beta \tag{3.5-17}$$

$$p_2 = -\alpha - j\beta \tag{3.5-18}$$

When these values of $p_1$ and $p_2$ are substituted in Equation 3.5–14,

$$i = \frac{E}{L}e^{-\alpha t}\left[\frac{e^{j\beta t} - e^{-j\beta t}}{2j\beta}\right] \tag{3.5-19}$$

Applying the definition for $\sin \beta t$ in terms of its exponential components, Equation 3.5–19 may be written as

$$i = \frac{E\,e^{-\alpha t}}{L\ \beta}\sin \beta t \tag{3.5-20}$$

Thus it can be seen that the current is oscillatory with a frequency $\beta$ radians per second and, at the same time, is exponentially damped with a decrement factor, $\alpha$. Although $p_1$ and $p_2$, the two roots of the characteristic equation, are complex conjugates, the resultant current is real. A form that an oscillatory current response can have is shown by the curve in Figure 3.5–3 for $4/LC > (R/L)^2$.

### 3.6 Steady-State Response to a Sinusoidally Impressed Voltage

In the preceding examples the networks have had impressed d-c voltages for which the steady values of current were not time varying after the transients had decayed. As has been shown, the *form of the transient response is independent of the type of voltage applied* and is determined entirely from the circuit elements and the initial conditions. *The initial magnitude of the transient response*, however, *is affected by the initial conditions.* The use of a sinusoidally impressed voltage serves to modify the steady-state component of current. In this section only the steady-state response will be considered. The transient part of the response can be evaluated by the methods previously outlined, its initial magnitude alone being affected by the initial value of sinusoidal voltage and the energy stored in the system.

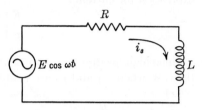

FIGURE 3.6–1. Series $RL$ circuit with sinusoidal voltage impressed.

In Figure 3.6–1 is shown a series $RL$ circuit excited by a voltage $E$ cos $\omega t$. The voltage equation is then

$$L\frac{di_s}{dt} + Ri_s = \frac{E}{2}(e^{+j\omega t} + e^{-j\omega t}) \tag{3.6-1}$$

It appears that $i_s$ may be thought of as being composed of two components, one $i_{s+}$ caused by $(E/2)e^{+j\omega t}$, the other $i_{s-}$ caused by $(E/2)e^{-j\omega t}$. It further appears that for an equality to be obtained $i_{s+}$ must be exponentially varying as $e^{+j\omega t}$ and $i_{s-}$ as $e^{-j\omega t}$. Thus let

$$i_s = i_{s+} + i_{s-} \tag{3.6-2}$$

and

$$i_{s+} = I_+e^{+j\omega t} \tag{3.6-3}$$

$$i_{s-} = I_-e^{-j\omega t} \tag{3.6-4}$$

where $I_+$ is the complex magnitude of $i_{s+}$ and $I_-$ is the complex magnitude of $i_{s-}$.

If the equation for $(E/2)e^{+j\omega t}$ is considered,

$$L\frac{d}{dt}[I_+e^{+j\omega t}] + RI_+e^{+j\omega t} = \frac{E}{2}e^{+j\omega t} \tag{3.6-5}$$

$$LI_+j\omega e^{+j\omega t} + RI_+e^{+j\omega t} = \frac{E}{2}e^{+j\omega t}$$

and dividing through by $e^{j\omega t}$ gives

$$LI_{+}j\omega + RI_{+} = \frac{E}{2} \qquad (3.6\text{–}6)$$

Therefore,

$$I_{+} = \frac{E}{2(R + j\omega L)} \qquad (3.6\text{–}7)$$

Apply the following definition:

$$\bar{Z} = Z\underline{/\theta_Z} \qquad (3.6\text{–}8)$$

where

$$Z = \sqrt{R^2 + (\omega L)^2}$$

$$\theta_Z = \tan^{-1} \frac{\omega L}{R}$$

Equation 3.6–7 may be written as

$$I_{+} = \frac{E}{2Z} e^{-j\theta_Z} \qquad (3.6\text{–}9)$$

In similar fashion, from the $e^{-j\omega t}$ components,

$$I_{-} = \frac{E}{2Z} e^{+j\theta_Z} \qquad (3.6\text{–}10)$$

Substitute Equations 3.6–9 and 3.6–10 in Equation 3.6–2 to obtain

$$i_s = \frac{E}{Z} \left( \frac{e^{j(\omega t - \theta_Z)} + e^{-j(\omega t - \theta_Z)}}{2} \right) \qquad (3.6\text{–}11)$$

which reduces to

$$i_s = \frac{E}{Z} \cos (\omega t - \theta_Z) \qquad (3.6\text{–}12)$$

The term $Z$ is called the *impedance* of the network and indicates the ratio of voltage to current for alternating current flow. As such, it is similar to resistance for direct current, but it differs in the sense that it is not directly proportional to the power loss. The impedance angle $\theta_Z$ represents the angle in radians by which the current lags the applied voltage. This angle corresponds to the time $t = \theta_Z/\omega$, in seconds, as shown in Figure 3.6–2.

A convenient form for indicating current and voltage may be obtained by analyzing the complex plane plot of the various components. As il-

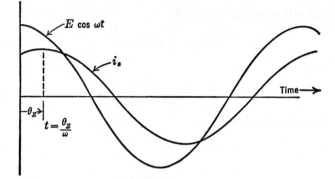

FIGURE 3.6–2.    Steady-state sinusoidal impressed voltage and current in $RL$ circuit as a function of time.

lustrated in Figure 3.6–3, both the current and the voltage may be represented by two complex quantities. As time increases, the quantities having the factor $e^{+j\omega t}$ change angular position in a counterclockwise direction at a rate determined by $\omega$, whereas the quantities having the factor $e^{-j\omega t}$ rotate clockwise at the same speed. At any time $t$,

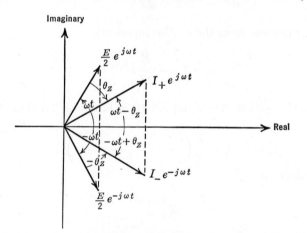

FIGURE 3.6–3.    Complex plane diagram of sinusoidal components of voltage and current in series $RL$ circuit.

$(E/2)e^{+j\omega t}$ and $(E/2)e^{-j\omega t}$ are conjugates, and $I_{+}e^{j\omega t}$ and $I_{-}e^{-j\omega t}$ are conjugates. The resultant of the voltages is real and equal to $E \cos \omega t$. The resultant of the currents is real and equal to $i_s$.    Thus

$$\frac{E}{2} e^{j\omega t} + \frac{E}{2} e^{-j\omega t} = E \cos \omega t \tag{3.6–13}$$

But

$$E \cos \omega t = Re(Ee^{j\omega t}) \tag{3.6-14}$$

where $Re$ indicates the "real part of" the quantity in question. It follows that

$$\frac{E}{2} e^{j\omega t} + \frac{E}{2} e^{-j\omega t} = Re(Ee^{j\omega t}) \tag{3.6-15}$$

In like manner,

$$i_s = i_{s+} + i_{s-} \tag{3.6-16}$$

$$i_s = I_+ e^{j\omega t} + I_- e^{-j\omega t}$$

$$i_s = \left( \frac{Ie^{-j\theta z}}{2} \right) e^{j\omega t} + \left( \frac{Ie^{j\theta z}}{2} \right) e^{-j\omega t}$$

$$i_s = \frac{Ie^{j(\omega t - \theta z)}}{2} + \frac{Ie^{-j(\omega t - \theta z)}}{2}$$

$$i_s = I \cos (\omega t - \theta_Z) \tag{3.6-17}$$

$$i_s = Re(Ie^{j(\omega t - \theta z)}) \tag{3.6-18}$$

where $I/2$ equals the scalar magnitude of $I_+$ or $I_-$.

Thus it is possible to represent the current and voltage, both of which are real physical quantities, by a complex quantity for each one. This statement applies provided one realizes that it is only the "real" part of the complex vectors that represent the actual values of the quantities being considered. This complex plane representation is illustrated in Figure 3.6–4.

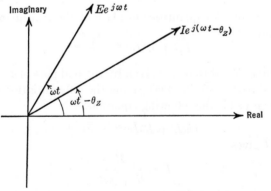

FIGURE 3.6–4.   Twice the positively rotating sinusoidal components of current and voltage in series $RL$ circuit.

Since the speed of rotation is the same for both complex quantities in Figure 3.6–4, $\theta_Z$, the angle between the quantities, remains constant;

therefore it is not necessary to plot voltage and current at all instants of time but only at one instant, such as $\omega t = 0$. This is illustrated in Figure 3.6–5, which shows the phase relationship between current and voltage. If the instantaneous value of voltage or current is desired at any time $t$, Equation 3.6–14 or 3.6–18 can be used.

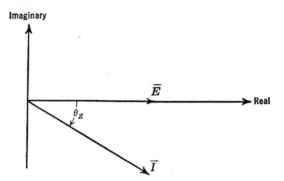

FIGURE 3.6–5.  Sinusoidal components of current and voltage in series $RL$ circuit at time $t = 0$.

**Replacing $p$ by $j\omega$ for Steady-State Sinusoidal Calculations.**  It can now be shown that for steady-state operation with sinusoidal applied voltage, the impedance can be found by letting $p = j\omega$ in the polynomial function of $p$ of the original voltage expression, Equation 3.6–1, which is restated below in operational form:

$$(Lp + R)i_s = E \cos \omega t \qquad (3.6\text{–}19)$$

Introducing complex quantities in place of the real quantities $i_s$ and $E \cos \omega t$ gives

$$(Lp + R)\bar{I}e^{j\omega t} = \bar{E}e^{j\omega t} \qquad (3.6\text{–}20)$$

where it is understood that $i_s$ is given by the real part of $\bar{I}e^{j\omega t}$ and $E \cos \omega t$ by the real part of $\bar{E}e^{j\omega t}$.  Performing the differentiation indicated by the operator $p$ yields the following equation:

$$(j\omega L + R)\bar{I}e^{j\omega t} = \bar{E}e^{j\omega t} \qquad (3.6\text{–}21)$$

Solving for $\bar{I}$ gives

$$\bar{I} = \frac{\bar{E}}{R + j\omega L} \qquad (3.6\text{–}22)$$

By the definition of impedance,

$$\bar{I} = \frac{\bar{E}}{\bar{Z}} \qquad (3.6\text{–}23)$$

Therefore,

$$\bar{Z} = R + j\omega L \qquad (3.6\text{–}24)$$

Thus it has been shown for the $RL$ network that the impedance can be obtained by replacing $d(\ )/dt$ by $p$ and $p$ by $j\omega$ in the original voltage equation. Since the polynomial function of $p$ obtained when the differential equation is rewritten in its operational form contains all the terms that appear in the resulting expression for impedance, it is obviously possible to obtain the impedance from the original differential equation.

This rule is general for all types of circuits. Hence to obtain the steady-state solution for current with sinusoidal voltages impressed, the steps outlined below should be taken.

**Summary of Method of Obtaining Steady-State Solution for Sinusoidally Impressed Voltages**

1. Write differential equation of network.
2. Rewrite differential equation in the reduced operational form.
3. Replace $p$ by $j\omega$ in the polynomial expression of the reduced operational form to obtain the magnitude and phase angle of impedance $\bar{Z}$ from the modified polynomial.
4. Choose impressed voltage as a reference of time $t = 0$, and determine the magnitude and angular position of the current from

$$\bar{I} = \frac{E/0°}{Z/\theta_Z} = \frac{E}{Z/\theta_Z}$$

The solution of a series $RLC$ network shown in Figure 3.6–6 is illustrated below as an example:

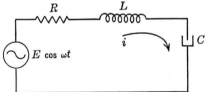

FIGURE 3.6–6.   Series $RLC$ circuit with sinusoidal voltage impressed.

$E = 115/0°$

$R = 40$ ohms

$L = 0.1856$ henry

$C = 66.2$ microfarads

$\omega = 377$

The differential equation is

$$L\frac{di}{dt} + Ri + \frac{1}{C}\int i\,dt = E\cos\omega t$$

The operational form of the differential equation with the voltage set equal to zero is

$$\left(Lp + R + \frac{1}{Cp}\right)i = 0$$

The impedance is

$$\bar{Z} = R + j\left(\omega L - \frac{1}{\omega C}\right)$$

Using the foregoing values gives

$$|Z| = |40 + j(70 - 40)| = 50$$

$$\theta_Z = \tan^{-1}\frac{\omega L - \dfrac{1}{\omega C}}{R} = 36.85°$$

$$\bar{I} = \frac{115\underline{/0°}}{50\underline{/36.85°}} = 2.3\underline{/-36.85°}$$

Figure 3.6–7 illustrates on the complex plane the relationships existing between the current, voltage, and impedance.

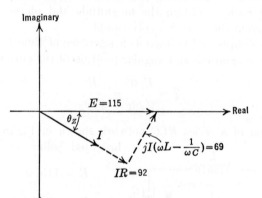

FIGURE 3.6–7.   Sinusoidal components of current and voltages in series $RLC$ circuit
with sinusoidal voltage impressed.

## 3.7   Steady-State Response to a Time Power Series Input

Another important type of input function for which the steady-state
response of a network is frequently sought is that of a power series in
time.   For example, the applied voltage may be represented as

$$e = E_1 t + E_2 t^2 + E_3 t^3 \tag{3.7–1}$$

With $E_2$ and $E_3$ each equal to zero, the input function has a constant
rate of change with time, namely, $E_1$ volts per second.   With $E_1$ and
$E_3$ each equal to zero, the input has a constant acceleration although its
rate of change will have a varying magnitude depending on the value
of $t$.

As in the case of the steady-state response for a sinusoidally impressed voltage treated in Section 3.6, the transient portion of the solution will not be developed as its method of solution has been described previously. However, the steady-state output voltage response $e_o$ of the $RC$ network shown in Figure 3.7–1 will be determined for an input voltage,

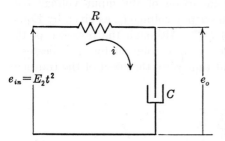

$$e_{in} = E_2 t^2 \qquad (3.7\text{--}2)$$

The voltage equation for this network is

FIGURE 3.7–1. *RC* network having input $E_2 t^2$.

$$Ri + \frac{1}{C} \int i\, dt = E_2 t^2 \qquad (3.7\text{--}3)$$

A descending power series in time is the form of steady-state solution for $i$ that is chosen, with the highest power of $t$ being equal to the highest power of $t$ in the input. Thus

$$i = I_2 t^2 + I_1 t + I_0 \qquad (3.7\text{--}4)$$

Integrating Equation 3.7–4 gives

$$\int i\, dt = \frac{I_2 t^3}{3} + \frac{I_1 t^2}{2} + I_0 t + C_1 \qquad (3.7\text{--}5)$$

Substituting these values of $i$ and $\int i\, dt$ in Equation 3.7–3 and grouping terms of like powers of $t$ gives

$$\frac{I_2 t^3}{3C} + \left[\frac{I_1}{2C} + RI_2\right] t^2 + \left[\frac{I_0}{C} + RI_1\right] t + RI_0 + \frac{C_1}{C} = E_2 t^2 \qquad (3.7\text{--}6)$$

By equating the coefficients for each of the powers of $t$, the following values are obtained for the various constants:

$$I_2 = 0$$
$$I_1 = 2CE_2$$
$$I_0 = -RCI_1 = -2RC^2 E_2 \qquad (3.7\text{--}7)$$
$$C_1 = -RCI_0 = +2R^2 C^3 E_2$$

Since the equation for the output voltage $e_o$ is

$$e_o = \frac{1}{C} \int i\, dt \qquad (3.7\text{--}8)$$

from Equations 3.7–5 and 3.7–7 the output voltage is found to be

$$e_o = E_2t^2 - 2RCE_2t + 2R^2C^2E_2 \qquad (3.7-9)$$

Shown on Figure 3.7–2 is a comparison of the input voltage $E_2t^2$ and the steady-state component of output voltage $e_o$, as given by Equation 3.7–9, both as a function of $t/T$. Although the presence of the positive constant term in the steady-state solution for $e_o$ indicates a more positive output than input at time zero, the effect of the transient

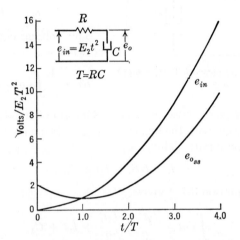

FIGURE 3.7–2.  Comparison of actual input voltage, $e_{in}$, and steady-state component of output voltage, $e_{o_{ss}}$, as a function of $t$.

term will be to reduce the actual value of the output voltage to zero at this time.  It is apparent that, for greater values of $t$ than $T$, the steady-state component of output voltage continues to lag the input voltage by an ever-increasing amount.

The steady-state solution for networks having inputs that are power series in time is handled fairly simply by means of the classical method of solution as described above.  Use of the operator $p$ is not required for this portion of the solution.

## 3.8  Solutions of Linear Differential Equations for Other Types of Systems

The same methods of solution of differential equations for their transient and steady-state portions that have been illustrated for electrical networks apply equally well to mechanical and other systems.  To illustrate this method for these different cases, the following examples are worked out in detail.

**Motor Synchronizing on a Fixed Signal.**   Frequently in servomechanism operation a motor initially at rest is required to come to correspondence at another fixed position.   Figure 3.8–1 shows the motor coupled directly to the load.   The input to the motor produces a torque that is proportional to the difference between the controlled load position and the reference input position.

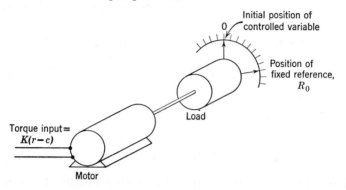

FIGURE 3.8–1.   Motor driving load from an initial position 0 to correspondence at position $R_0$.

$$\text{Combined inertia} = J \text{ slug-ft}^2$$
$$\text{Damping} = D \text{ lb-ft/radian/second}$$
$$\text{Stiffness} = K \text{ lb-ft/radian}$$

Thus, the motor torque $= K(r - c)$, and the position of the reference is $r (= R_0)$.

There are present, in the load and the motor, mechanical friction and electrical damping torques both of which are proportional to the motor speed; friction and damping torque $= D(dc/dt)$. Static friction forces are negligible.

The complete torque equation can now be written as

$$J \frac{d^2c}{dt^2} + D \frac{dc}{dt} + Kc = Kr \qquad (3.8\text{–}1)$$

The steady state displacement is $R_0$, so

$$c(t) = R_0 + C_1 e^{+p_1 t} + C_2 e^{+p_2 t} \qquad (3.8\text{–}2)$$

where $C_1$ and $C_2$ are the coefficients for the transient terms corresponding to the roots $p_1$ and $p_2$.

From Equation 3.8–1, the characteristic equation can be written as

$$p^2 + \frac{D}{J} p + \frac{K}{J} = 0 \qquad (3.8\text{–}3)$$

In the interest of obtaining a more general form for the solution, let

$$\sqrt{\frac{K}{J}} = \omega_0 = \text{undamped natural frequency} \qquad (3.8\text{–}4)$$

and

$$\frac{D}{2\sqrt{KJ}} = \zeta = \text{damping factor} \qquad (3.8\text{–}5)$$

If these substitutions are made, the characteristic equation may now be written as

$$p^2 + 2\zeta\omega_0 p + \omega_0{}^2 = 0 \qquad (3.8\text{–}6)$$

from which the two roots are

$$p_1 = -[\zeta - \sqrt{\zeta^2 - 1}\,]\omega_0 \qquad (3.8\text{–}7)$$

$$p_2 = -[\zeta + \sqrt{\zeta^2 - 1}\,]\omega_0 \qquad (3.8\text{–}8)$$

For the condition of the controlled variable $c$ initially at rest at position zero and the reference held constant at $R_0$, there are three different forms for the solution for $c(t)$ depending on whether $\zeta$ is greater than 1, less than 1, or equal to 1.

When $\zeta > 1$,

$$c(t) = R_0 - \frac{R_0}{2\sqrt{\zeta^2 - 1}}[(\zeta + \sqrt{\zeta^2 - 1}\,)e^{-(\zeta - \sqrt{\zeta^2 - 1})\omega_0 t}$$
$$- (\zeta - \sqrt{\zeta^2 - 1}\,)e^{-(\zeta + \sqrt{\zeta^2 - 1})\omega_0 t}] \quad (3.8\text{–}9)$$

When $\zeta < 1$, the system has complex roots and the oscillatory response is given by the equation

$$c(t) = R_0 - \frac{R_0}{\sqrt{1 - \zeta^2}}\,e^{-\zeta\omega_0 t}\sin[\sqrt{1 - \zeta^2}\,\omega_0 t + \phi] \quad (3.8\text{–}10)$$

where $\phi = \tan^{-1}\sqrt{1 - \zeta^2}/\zeta$.

For the limiting case where $\zeta = 1$, critical damping occurs and the response is

$$c(t) = R_0 - R_0(1 + \omega_0 t)e^{-\omega_0 t} \qquad (3.8\text{–}11)$$

Figure 3.8–2 shows various forms that $c(t)$, the controlled load position, can have as a function of $\omega_0 t$ for the values of the damping factor $\zeta$ indicated.

These curves, developed by Gordon S. Brown of the Massachusetts Institute of Technology, are most useful in that they permit one to evaluate rapidly the form of the response of a motor synchronizing, or other similar problems involving a quadratic characteristic equation, by a determination of $\zeta$ alone. The amount of overshoot and the time to reach any desired fraction of the initial displacement can be read from these curves and transferred into actual time of response by knowledge of the value of $\omega_0$, the undamped natural frequency.

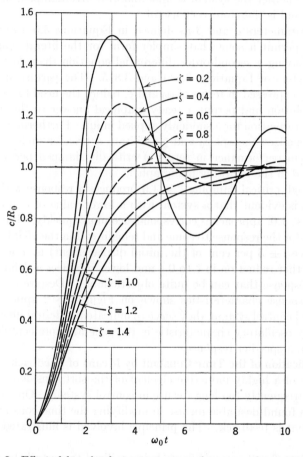

FIGURE 3.8–2.  Effect of damping factor $\zeta$ on nature of response of controlled variable when synchronizing on a step function of position input, $R_0$.

$$\zeta = \frac{D}{2\sqrt{KJ}}$$

$$\omega_0 = \sqrt{K/J}$$

$$p^2 + 2\zeta\omega_0 p + \omega_0^2 = 0$$

Equations 3.8–9, 3.8–10, and 3.8–11 show reasons for the selection of the parameters $\zeta$ and $\omega_0$ in defining the system performance.[86]   For systems in which the damping ratio $\zeta$ is small, the response is oscillatory; and, as indicated by Equation 3.8–10, the frequency of the oscillation is $\sqrt{1 - \zeta^2}\,\omega_0$.   Hence, for low values of $\zeta$, $\omega_0$ gives a measure of the oscillation frequency of the system.   The damping factor $\zeta$ serves to indicate directly whether the system is underdamped, overdamped, or critically damped and is therefore very useful.

The parameters $\alpha$ and $\beta$ as defined in Equations 3.5–15 and 3.5–16 seem to permit a somewhat simpler form for the literal solution of a system having a second-order differential equation than do the $\omega_0$ and $\zeta$ parameters of Equations 3.8–4 and 3.8–5.   The performance charts, however, expressed in terms of $\omega_0$ and $\zeta$, reduce the need for obtaining a literal solution and permit a ready graphical answer to the desired response information for a suddenly applied input.   Furthermore, the non-dimensionalized factors $\omega_0$ and $\zeta$ facilitate a broader understanding of the system performance in terms of critically damped performance as illustrated in the following paragraph.

Although critical damping $\zeta = 1.0$ produces a response with no overshoot, it is evident that a system with a lower value of $\zeta$, for instance, $0.6 < \zeta < 1.0$, approaches correspondence more quickly.   Furthermore, the time for the response to come and remain within the vicinity of correspondence ($\pm$ 5 per cent of the initial displacement) is shorter.   However, further reduction in $\zeta$ to 0.4 and lower produces a definitely oscillatory response that can be quite objectionable.   Despite the fact that these response characteristics shown on Figure 3.8–2 apply only to a simplified control system, they serve to indicate the desirability of having a slightly oscillatory characteristic in the general, more complex system to obtain a speedier response.

**Modification of the Time Constant by Means of Feedback.**   The time constant of a highly inductive element of the sort considered in Figure 3.1–1 is frequently too long for use in control systems.   One means that has been found desirable for use in modifying the time constant of such an element is feedback.   The principle involved is illustrated in Figure 3.8–3.

In Figure 3.8–3 an amplifier is being utilized to control the current in a highly inductive circuit in its output.   The total resistance limiting the steady-state current in the output is $R$, and the inductance is $L$.   In order to reduce the effective magnitude of the time constant $T = L/R$ of the output circuit, a feedback voltage proportional to the output current is obtained from the voltage drop across a portion, $H$, of the total resistance $R$.   The feedback scheme is such that instead of the input

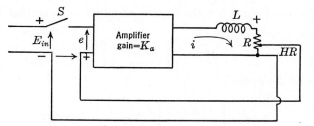

FIGURE 3.8–3.  Series $RL$ circuit, using amplifier and feedback to reduce effective time constant of circuit.

voltage $E_{in}$ being used directly to control the amplifier and its output, the voltage difference $E_{in} - HRi$ is used.  Thus

$$E_{in} - HRi = e \qquad (3.8\text{–}12)$$

and

$$K_a e = L\frac{di}{dt} + Ri \qquad (3.8\text{–}13)$$

Combining Equations 3.8–12 and 3.8–13, eliminating $e$, and writing the resultant equation in operational form gives

$$[Lp + R(1 + K_a H)]i = K_a E_{in} \qquad (3.8\text{–}14)$$

Divided by $(1 + K_a H)$, this becomes

$$\left[\frac{L}{1 + K_a H}p + R\right]i = \frac{K_a}{1 + K_a H}E_{in} \qquad (3.8\text{–}15)$$

By letting

$$L' = \frac{L}{1 + K_a H}$$

Equation 3.8–15 can be written as

$$(L'p + R)i = \frac{K_a}{1 + K_a H}E_{in} \qquad (3.8\text{–}16)$$

Using for the solution of this equation, the method outlined in Section 3.1, one can write the equation for current $i$ as

$$i = i_s + i_t \qquad (3.8\text{–}17)$$

where

$$i_s = \left[\frac{K_a}{1 + K_a H}\right]\frac{E_{in}}{R} \qquad (3.8\text{–}18)$$

and

$$i_t = I_t e^{-t/(L'/R)} \qquad (3.8\text{–}19)$$

For the condition when the system initially has no current flowing at $t = 0$,

$$I_t = - \left[ \frac{K_a}{1 + K_a H} \right] \frac{E_{in}}{R} \qquad (3.8\text{--}20)$$

and the total current is

$$i = \left[ \frac{K_a}{1 + K_a H} \right] \frac{E_{in}}{R} [1 - e^{-t/(L'/R)}] \qquad (3.8\text{--}21)$$

If $L'$ is replaced by its equivalent and $T = L/R$ is defined as the time constant of the $RL$ output circuit, Equation 3.8–21 becomes

$$i = \left[ \frac{K_a}{1 + K_a H} \right] \frac{E_{in}}{R} [1 - e^{-t/T(1/1 + K_a H)}] \qquad (3.8\text{--}22)$$

If the current of Equation 3.8–22 is compared with that of Equation 3.1–19, which is the case for a $R$ and $L$ network without any amplifier or feedback present, it appears that the time constant and the magnitude of the current have been reduced by a factor of $1/1 + K_a H$. One should appreciate that the amplifier gain is not being used effectively to produce a response of increased current magnitude; rather it is being used to "force" a faster time of response for the current.

Consider as an example the case where it is desired to maintain the same magnitude of current for a given voltage $E_{in}$, with feedback as would be obtained without feedback and without an amplifier. Then

$$\frac{K_a}{1 + K_a H} \frac{E_{in}}{R} = \frac{E_{in}}{R} \qquad (3.8\text{--}23)$$

from which

$$H = \frac{K_a - 1}{K_a} \qquad (3.8\text{--}24)$$

As an illustration let

$$K_a = 10$$

$$H = \tfrac{9}{10}$$

$$\frac{L}{R} = T$$

Figure 3.8–4 shows the current through the inductance $L$ as a function of $t/T$ for the three conditions:

(a) Normal gain and no feedback, $i = \dfrac{E_{in}}{R}(1 - e^{-t/T})$

(b) Increased gain and no feedback, $i = \dfrac{10E_{in}}{R}(1 - e^{-t/T})$

(c) Increased gain and feedback, $i = \dfrac{E_{in}}{R}(1 - e^{-10t/T})$

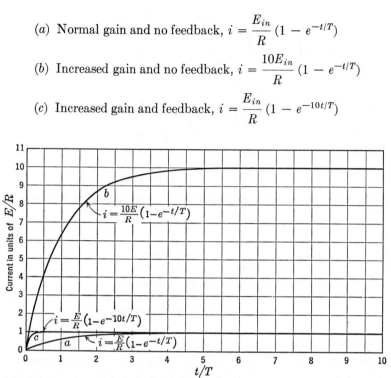

FIGURE 3.8–4.   Comparison of current flowing in inductance of Figure 3.8–3 for:

(a) Normal gain, no feedback.
(b) Increased gain, no feedback ($K_a = 10$).
(c) Increased gain and feedback ($K_a = 10$, $H = \frac{9}{10}$).

From curves $a$ and $b$ one can see that, by increasing the gain alone, the time constant is unchanged although the magnitude of the current is increased proportional to the gain.  From $b$ and $c$, one can see that with feedback the rate of change of current is lower for $c$ than $b$ after the initial instant.   In terms of its steady-state value, however, the current approaches this value in a much shorter time when feedback is employed.

**Mechanical Spring-Mass System.**  In Figure 3.8–5, a mass $M$ is connected by a spring to a platform $P$.  Attached to the mass is a viscous damper that exerts a force proportional to the velocity of the mass. This arrangement might represent schematically a system in which the effect of the vibration of a measuring means located on the mass $M$ is to be determined.

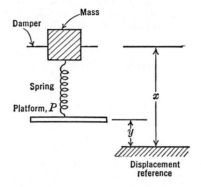

FIGURE 3.8–5.  Spring-mass system fastened to platform moving with sinusoidal motion.

Constants

$$\text{Mass} = M, \text{ slugs}$$
$$\text{Damping coefficient} = D, \text{ lb/ft/sec}$$
$$\text{Spring constant} = K, \text{ lb/ft}$$
$$x = \text{position of mass, ft}$$
$$X_0 = \text{unstressed length of spring, ft}$$
$$y = \text{position of platform, ft}$$

Consider the case where the platform is initially at rest having no velocity but having a displacement $Y_0$.  At time $t = 0$ the platform position is started in a cosine motion of displacement given by the equation

$$y = Y_0 \cos \omega t$$

Determine the motion of the mass as a function of time following the start of this motion.

The forces acting on the mass tending to accelerate it are

$$\text{Spring force} = -K(x - X_0 - y)$$

$$\text{Damping force} = -D \frac{dx}{dt}$$

$$\text{Gravitational force} = -Mg$$

where the symbols are as shown in Figure 3.8–5.

The sum of these forces produces an acceleration of the mass.   Thus

$$M \frac{d^2 x}{dt^2} = -K(x - X_0 - y) - D \frac{dx}{dt} - Mg \qquad (3.8\text{–}25)$$

Separate variables and place $y = Y_0 \cos \omega t$ to obtain the differential equation of motion:

$$M \frac{d^2 x}{dt^2} + D \frac{dx}{dt} + Kx = KY_0 \cos \omega t + KX_0 - Mg \quad (3.8\text{–}26)$$

The displacement $x$ is evidently the sum of three components:

$X_c =$ a steady-state component that is constant in value and is dependent on $KX_0 - Mg$ for its magnitude

$X_s =$ a steady-state component that is sinusoidally varying in amplitude and is determined from $KY_0 \cos \omega t$

$X_t =$ a transient component that decays in time, the form of the decay being determined by the characteristics of $Mp^2 + Dp + K = 0$

Thus

$$x = X_c + X_s + X_t \quad (3.8\text{–}27)$$

*Evaluation of Constant Steady-State Component, $X_c$.* By placing the value for $x$ from Equation 3.8–27 in the differential equation of motion and equating like terms, the value of $X_c$ can be obtained from the equation

$$KX_c = KX_0 - Mg$$

or

$$X_c = X_0 - \frac{M}{K} g \quad (3.8\text{–}28)$$

*Evaluation of Steady-State Sinusoidal Component, $X_s$.* To evaluate the steady-state sinusoidal term $X_s$, the polynomial in $p$ of the reduced form of the system equation, namely,

$$Mp^2 + Dp + K \quad (3.8\text{–}29)$$

has $p$ replaced by $j\omega$, and the impedance is

$$\bar{Z} = Z(j\omega) = |Z| \underline{/\theta_Z} \quad (3.8\text{–}30)$$

where

$$|Z| = |Z(j\omega)| = \sqrt{[K - \omega^2 M]^2 + [\omega D]^2} \quad (3.8\text{–}31)$$

and

$$\theta_Z = \tan^{-1} \frac{\omega D}{K - \omega^2 M} \quad (3.8\text{–}32)$$

The term impedance, applied originally in the case of electrical networks, is now used to describe the characteristics of mechanical systems when being subjected to sinusoidally varying driving forces.

Dividing the sinusoidal driving force $KY_0/\underline{0^\circ}$ by the impedance $\bar{Z}$ of Equation 3.8–30 gives the value $X_s$ in a polar form as

$$X_s = \frac{KY_0/\underline{0^\circ}}{|Z|/\underline{\theta_Z}} \tag{3.8–33}$$

In the form of a sinusoidally varying quantity, this is

$$X_s = \frac{KY_0}{|Z|} \cos(\omega t - \theta_Z) \tag{3.8–34}$$

*Evaluation of the Transient Component, $X_t$.* The form of the transient component $X_t$ is

$$X_t = X_1 e^{p_1 t} + X_2 e^{p_2 t} \tag{3.8–35}$$

where $p_1$ and $p_2$ are the roots of the characteristic equation

$$Mp^2 + Dp + K = 0 \tag{3.8–36}$$

Hence

$$p_1 = -\frac{D}{2M} + \frac{1}{2M}\sqrt{D^2 - 4KM}$$

and

$$\tag{3.8–37}$$

$$p_2 = -\frac{D}{2M} - \frac{1}{2M}\sqrt{D^2 - 4KM}$$

To evaluate the coefficients $X_1$ and $X_2$ in Equation 3.8–25, it is necessary to know the position and velocity of the mass $M$ at time $t = 0$.

From the problem statement, the initial displacement of $y$ is $Y_0$ and the mass is at rest. Hence, from Equation 3.8–26,

$$x\big|_{t=0} = Y_0 + X_0 - \frac{M}{K}g \tag{3.8–38}$$

and, since the initial velocity is zero,

$$\frac{dx}{dt}\bigg|_{t=0} = 0 \tag{3.8–39}$$

By putting into Equation 3.8–38 the values of the $X_c$, $X_s$, and $X_t$ components of $x$ at time $t = 0$, these equations are obtained:

$$X_0 - \frac{M}{K} g + \frac{KY_0}{\sqrt{[K - \omega^2 M]^2 + [\omega D]^2}} \cos(-\theta_Z) + X_1 + X_2$$

$$= Y_0 + X_0 - \frac{M}{K} g$$

or

$$X_1 + X_2 = Y_0 \left( 1 - \frac{K \cos(-\theta_Z)}{\sqrt{[K - \omega^2 M]^2 + [\omega D]^2}} \right) \qquad (3.8\text{--}40)$$

By substituting in Equation 3.8–39 the first derivatives of $X_c$, $X_s$, and $X_t$ at $t = 0$, these equations are obtained:

$$-\frac{\omega K Y_0 \sin(-\theta_Z)}{\sqrt{[K - \omega^2 M]^2 + [\omega D]^2}} + p_1 X_1 + p_2 X_2 = 0$$

or

$$p_1 X_1 + p_2 X_2 = \frac{-\omega K Y_0 \sin \theta_Z}{\sqrt{[K - \omega^2 M]^2 + [\omega D]^2}} \qquad (3.8\text{--}41)$$

From these two equations the values for $X_1$ and $X_2$, the magnitudes of the transient terms, can be evaluated. With these, the solution for $x$, including both steady-state and transient terms, is complete.

The numerical solution below is based upon the following constants:

$$M = 0.1 \text{ slug}$$
$$D = 5 \text{ lb-sec per ft}$$
$$K = 40 \text{ lb per ft}$$
$$Y_0 = 0.1 \text{ ft}$$
$$\omega = 80 \text{ sec}^{-1}$$
$$X_0 = 0.5 \text{ ft}$$

Equation 3.8–27 indicates the literal form of the solution with Equations 3.8–28, 3.8–34, and 3.8–35 defining the three components of position. Use the above numerical values and Equation 3.8–28 to obtain

$$X_c = 0.5 - \frac{(0.1)(32.2)}{40} = 0.4195$$

To evaluate $X_s$ it is first necessary to determine $|Z|$ and $\theta_Z$ as given by Equations 3.8–31 and 3.8–32.

$$|Z| = \sqrt{[40 - 80^2(0.1)]^2 + [80(5)]^2} = 721.1$$

$$\theta_Z = \tan^{-1} \frac{80(5)}{40 - 640} = +146.3°$$

With these values, $X_s$ is equal to

$$X_s = \frac{(40)(0.1)}{721.1} \cos (80t - 146.3°)$$

Before $X_t$ of Equation 3.8–35 is evaluated, $p_1$ and $p_2$ must be obtained from $M$, $D$, $K$, and Equations 3.8–37.

$$p_1 = -\frac{5}{2(0.1)} + \frac{1}{2(0.1)} \sqrt{5^2 - 4(40)(0.1)} = -10$$

$$p_2 = -25 - 15 = -40$$

By substituting these values of $p_1$ and $p_2$ in Equations 3.8–40 and 3.8–41, $X_1$ and $X_2$ may be evaluated from equations

$$X_1 + X_2 = 0.1 \left[ 1 - \frac{40 \cos 146.3°}{721.1} \right]$$

and

$$-10X_1 - 40X_2 = -\frac{80(40)(0.1 \sin 146.3°)}{721.1}$$

from which

$$X_1 = +0.1313$$

$$X_2 = -0.0267$$

and

$$X_t = 0.1313e^{-10t} - 0.0267e^{-40t}$$

Totaling the three components of position, the resultant expression for the position of the mass is

$$x = 0.4195 + 0.0055 \cos (80t - 146.3°) + 0.1313e^{-10t} - 0.0267e^{-40t}$$

A check on the accuracy of the numerical work is provided by noting that this equation for $x$ at $t = 0$ is equal to 0.5195, that is, $(X_c + Y_0)$. Also note $\dfrac{dx}{dt}\Big|_{t=0} = 0$, as originally premised.

Figure 3.8–6 shows the desired information concerning the displacement of the center of mass as a function of time following the start of the driving motion. The transient motion of the mass is initially superimposed on the sinusoidal motion corresponding to the steady-state response. Within a half second the transient has subsided and a steady-state sinusoidal motion of the mass has been established with a much smaller amplitude than the displacement of the platform.

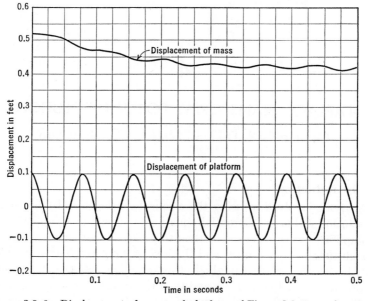

FIGURE 3.8–6.  Displacement of mass and platform of Figure 3.8–5 as a function of time.

The preceding examples of two electrical and one mechanical systems have illustrated the ways in which the solution of linear differential equations can be used to produce useful results when applied to systems of interest to control systems designers.  Although in many instances designers tend to concern themselves principally with steady-state performance, frequently some of the more challenging control problems are concerned with the response to transient conditions that can be most directly understood with the application of the solution of linear differential equations.  Further, by dividing up the solution of certain non-linear problems into pieces, each of which is itself linear, the same methods of solution may be employed effectively for some systems which are non-linear.

# 4

# LAPLACE TRANSFORMS FOR THE SOLUTION
# OF LINEAR DIFFERENTIAL EQUATIONS

## 4.0 Introduction

The work involved in using the classical mathematical approach to the solution of linear differential equations outlined in Chapter 3 may be simplified by reducing the method to a routine mathematical process through the use of the direct and the inverse Laplace transform. Contrasted with the classical method of determining first the steady-state solution from the driving force and then the transient solution from the initial conditions, the Laplace transformation uses the same approach for both the steady-state and the transient forms of solution. In addition, the method of evaluating the response for systems having discontinuous inputs or initial values of energy storage is handled directly by the Laplace transform. Through use of the Laplace transform one is able to present a clearer physical representation of the problem during its formulation. Once the physics of the problem has been set up and the transform of the response determined, the solution for the response itself can be obtained in a routine fashion.

Although a knowledge of the mathematical manipulation of vectors in the complex plane is essential for the development of the Laplace transformation, this transformation can be readily and easily used without this mathematical background, just as one may use trigonometric tables without the ability to derive and compute them. Because of the advantages that the Laplace transform method possesses, the Laplace transform will be described in some detail so that the solution of such a transient problem as the response of a system to a step function of input may be handled in a straightforward fashion. In addition, an understanding of the Laplace transform is an important asset in the understanding of many worth-while papers and textbooks on servomechanisms. For a complete presentation of this method, however, more specialized textbooks on this subject are recommended,[38] such as *Transients in Linear Systems* by Gardner and Barnes.[29] The material that follows draws heavily from this reference.

## 4.1  Nature of the Laplace Transform

The Laplace transformation is a functional transformation in that it changes the expression for a given quantity from a function of time, $f(t)$, to a function of the complex operator, $F(s)$, where $s$ is the complex operator. For physical systems, such as are considered in servomechanisms, the complex operator $s = (a + jb)$ is obtained in a fashion similar to the way the quantity $p_n$ was determined in the solution for the roots of the characteristic equation as described in Chapter 3. By means of the Laplace transformation not only can such mathematical operations in time as differentiation and integration be transformed into their $s$ equivalents, but also driving functions that are functions of time can be expressed in transform ($s$) form.

The criterion by which a function of time may be judged transformable or not is given here. A real function $f(t)$ has a Laplace transform if it is defined and single-valued almost everywhere for $0 \leq t$, with $t$ a real variable, and if $f(t)$ is such that

$$\int_0^\infty f(t)e^{-\sigma t}\, dt < \infty \qquad (4.1–1)$$

for some real number $\sigma$. Hence $f(t)$ is said to be $\mathcal{L}$ transformable.

From this definition of $\mathcal{L}$ transformable, it seems evident that the functions of time that describe the performance of actual control systems, would be in this category for they are real and generally continuous, hence single-valued. For satisfactory system operation these functions when multiplied by $e^{-\sigma t}$ have a value that approaches zero as $t$ approaches infinity. Their integral with respect to time is therefore less than infinity.

For a time function $f(t)$ that is $\mathcal{L}$ transformable, the direct Laplace ($\mathcal{L}$) transformation is defined as

$$\int_0^\infty f(t)e^{-st}\, dt = \mathcal{L}[f(t)] = F(s) \qquad (4.1–2)$$

where $s$ is a complex variable such that its real part is greater than $\sigma$, the number described in the definition for $\mathcal{L}$ transformability. The limits of integration of the integral are approached by a limit process. For example, the lower limit corresponds to the value of the integral at $t = 0+$, that is, just after time equals zero.

Since the integration of the time expression $f(t)e^{-st}$ is quite straightforward for many of the time functions encountered in the solution of linear differential equations such as are used to describe servomechanism systems, it is possible to determine readily the value of $F(s)$ corresponding to these time functions. When in a solution of a differential equation the transformation into $s$ functions of all the time operations indicated is completed, the inverse Laplace transformation is utilized. The inverse transformation is generally defined implicitly by the definition

$$f(t) = \mathcal{L}^{-1}[F(s)], \quad 0 \leq t \qquad (4.1\text{-}3)$$

where originally $F(s)$ is defined by Equation 4.1-2.

The limitation on the time for which $f(t)$ is valid is a consequence of the limits of integration in Equation 4.1-2 from 0 to $\infty$. One may choose $t = 0$ as the moment at which the action starts. Then, this restriction does not impose any real limitation for the solution of most servomechanism problems.

The implicit expression of Equation 4.1-3 is a valid method of performing the inverse transformation because of the uniqueness property of the $\mathcal{L}$ transform. That is, there is only one value of $F(s)$ for the Laplace transform of $f(t)$, $\mathcal{L}[f(t)]$. Conversely, if $f(t)$ is an $\mathcal{L}^{-1}$ transform of $F(s)$, then $f(t)$ is unique, and any other $\mathcal{L}^{-1}$ transform of $F(s)$ is equal to $f(t)$ almost everywhere for $0 \leq t$.

Therefore, common practice consists of using a table of transform pairs in which the time function $f(t)$ and the corresponding $F(s)$ are grouped. These are used for the direct and inverse Laplace transformation, that is, to obtain $F(s)$ or $f(t)$. Such a table of transform pairs for a number of commonly used time functions is given later in Table 4.2-1.

An explicit expression for $f(t)$ in terms of $F(s)$, the $\mathcal{L}$ transform of $f(t)$, is the following:

$$\frac{1}{2\pi j} \int_{c-j\infty}^{c+j\infty} F(s)e^{ts}\, ds = f(t), \quad 0 \leq t \qquad (4.1\text{-}4)$$

in which $c > \sigma$, the value given in Equation 4.1-1, for which $f(t)$ is $\mathcal{L}$ transformable. Equation 4.1-4, although generally not used in analytical solutions for $\mathcal{L}^{-1}[F(s)]$, nevertheless provides a useful relationship upon which a method of graphically performing the transformation from the $s$ to the time domain has been developed.

## 4.2  Development of a Table of Transform Pairs

Since a great deal of the value of the Laplace transform method of solution lies in its ability to represent driving functions in transform ($s$) form, the method of obtaining $F(s)$ corresponding to a number of the more common functions of time will be described in detail. In so doing a table of transform pairs showing both $f(t)$ and $F(s)$ will be developed that can be used in practical problems as required.

**Constant Input of Magnitude _A_.** If the criterion of Equation 4.1–1 is applied, it is evident that a constant signal is a function of time that is $\mathcal{L}$ transformable, any value of $\sigma > 0$ providing an integral of less than infinite value. Substituting $A$ for $f(t)$ in Equation 4.1–2 then yields

$$\mathcal{L}[A] = \int_0^\infty A e^{-st}\, dt \qquad (4.2\text{–}1)$$

Performing the integration indicated gives

$$\mathcal{L}[A] = -\frac{A}{s} e^{-st} \Big|_0^\infty \qquad (4.2\text{–}2)$$

and, finally,

$$\mathcal{L}[A] = +\frac{A}{s} \qquad (4.2\text{–}3)$$

**Step Function _u(t)_.** The term step function, $u(t)$, is used to describe the instantaneous application of a constant signal of unit magnitude at time $t = 0$. Figure 4.2–1 shows the plot of a step function versus time.

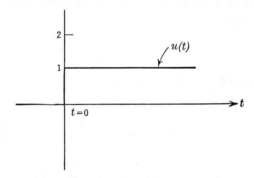

FIGURE 4.2–1.   Step function of time occurring at $t = 0$.

Since the step function is $\mathcal{L}$ transformable, Equation 4.1–2 may be employed. The value of $f(t)$ for the step function is unity almost everywhere; hence Equation 4.1–2 becomes

$$\mathcal{L}[u(t)] = \int_0^\infty 1 e^{-st}\, dt \qquad (4.2\text{–}4)$$

Integrating, and applying the limits indicated, gives

$$\mathcal{L}[u(t)] = -1 \frac{e^{-st}}{s} \Big|_0^\infty = \frac{1}{s} \qquad (4.2\text{–}5)$$

It will be noted that, with the exception of the constant $A$, Equations 4.2–3 and 4.2–5 are the same $s$ function, corresponding to a constant and a step function of time, respectively. Further consideration reveals, however, that "almost everywhere" for values of time from 0+ to ∞, the two time functions are identical, both being constants. Hence the $\mathcal{L}$ transform for both time functions should be the same.

**A Damped Exponential, $e^{-\alpha t}$.** Equation 4.1–2 may be employed since $e^{-\alpha t}$ for negative values of $-\alpha$ is $\mathcal{L}$ transformable. Hence

$$\mathcal{L}[e^{-\alpha t}] = \int_0^\infty e^{-\alpha t} e^{-st}\, dt \qquad (4.2\text{–}6)$$

Performing the integration indicated gives

$$\mathcal{L}[e^{-\alpha t}] = -\left. \frac{e^{-(s+\alpha)t}}{s+\alpha} \right|_0^\infty = \frac{1}{s+\alpha} \qquad (4.2\text{–}7)$$

Thus the transform of an exponential in time is a rational algebraic fraction of $s$.

**A Time-Varying Sinusoid, $\sin \beta t$.** Utilizing the identity described in Equation 2.2–10 gives

$$\sin \beta t = \frac{e^{j\beta t} - e^{-j\beta t}}{2j} \qquad (4.2\text{–}8)$$

With this equation substituted in Equation 4.1–2, the $\mathcal{L}$ transform of $\sin \beta t$ may be written as

$$\mathcal{L}[\sin \beta t] = \frac{1}{2j}\left[ \int_0^\infty e^{j\beta t} e^{-st}\, dt - \int_0^\infty e^{-j\beta t} e^{-st}\, dt \right] \qquad (4.2\text{–}9)$$

$$\mathcal{L}[\sin \beta t] = \frac{1}{2j}\left[ \frac{e^{(j\beta-s)t}}{j\beta - s} - \frac{e^{-(j\beta+s)t}}{-j\beta - s} \right]_0^\infty \qquad (4.2\text{–}10)$$

from which

$$\mathcal{L}[\sin \beta t] = \frac{\beta}{s^2 + \beta^2} \qquad (4.2\text{–}11)$$

**A Time-Varying Cosinusoid with a Phase Angle, $\cos(\beta t + \psi)$.** From trigonometry,

$$\cos(\beta t + \psi) = \cos \psi \cos \beta t - \sin \psi \sin \beta t \qquad (4.2\text{–}12)$$

Also, from Equation 2.2–9,

$$\cos \beta t = \frac{e^{j\beta t} + e^{-j\beta t}}{2} \qquad (4.2\text{–}13)$$

Hence

$$\mathcal{L}[\cos(\beta t + \psi)] = \frac{\cos\psi}{2}\int_0^\infty (e^{j\beta t - st} + e^{-j\beta t - st})\, dt$$
$$- \frac{\sin\psi}{2j}\int_0^\infty (e^{j\beta t - st} - e^{-j\beta t - st})\, dt \quad (4.2\text{–}14)$$

In similar fashion to the method utilized in obtaining the transform for Equation 4.2–11 above,

$$\mathcal{L}[\cos(\beta t + \psi)] = \frac{\cos\psi}{2}\left[\frac{e^{+j\beta t - st}}{(j\beta - s)} + \frac{e^{-j\beta t - st}}{-(j\beta + s)}\right]_0^\infty - \frac{\beta\sin\psi}{s^2 + \beta^2} \quad (4.2\text{–}15)$$

Finally,

$$\mathcal{L}[\cos(\beta t + \psi)] = \frac{s\cos\psi - \beta\sin\psi}{s^2 + \beta^2} = \frac{a_1 s + a_0}{s^2 + \beta^2} \quad (4.2\text{–}16)$$

where

$$a_1 = \cos\psi$$

$$a_0 = -\beta\sin\psi$$

**A Damped Sinusoid,** $e^{-\alpha t}\sin\beta t$. Grouping the product of the two time functions as a product of exponentials gives

$$\mathcal{L}[e^{-\alpha t}\sin\beta t] = \frac{1}{2j}\int_0^\infty (e^{-\alpha t}e^{(-s + j\beta)t} - e^{-\alpha t}e^{-(s + j\beta)t})\, dt \quad (4.2\text{–}17)$$

$$\mathcal{L}[e^{-\alpha t}\sin\beta t] = \frac{1}{2j}\left(\frac{1}{s + \alpha - j\beta} - \frac{1}{s + \alpha + j\beta}\right) \quad (4.2\text{–}18)$$

$$\mathcal{L}[e^{-\alpha t}\sin\beta t] = \frac{\beta}{(s + \alpha)^2 + \beta^2} \quad (4.2\text{–}19)$$

**A Quantity That Increases Linearly with Time,** $t$.

$$\mathcal{L}[t] = \int_0^\infty te^{-st}\, dt \quad (4.2\text{–}20)$$

This integration can be performed by integrating by parts, that is,

$$\int u\, dv = uv - \int v\, du$$

Letting $u = t$ and $v = \dfrac{e^{-st}}{-s}$,

$$\int_0^\infty te^{-st}\, dt = -\frac{te^{-st}}{s}\bigg|_0^\infty + \int_0^\infty \frac{e^{-st}}{s}\, dt = 0 + \frac{1}{s^2} \quad (4.2\text{–}21)$$

and therefore

$$\mathcal{L}[t] = \frac{1}{s^2} \quad (4.2\text{–}22)$$

**A Function Translated in Time,** $f(t - a)$.

$$\mathcal{L}[f(t - a)] = e^{-as}F(s) \qquad (4.2\text{--}23)$$

The physical significance of $f(t - a)$ is illustrated in Figure 4.2–2, where it is shown that $f(t - a)$ has the same form as $f(t)$ but is shifted in time by $a$ seconds. Note that, during the interval $0 < t < a, f(t - a)$ is equal to zero.

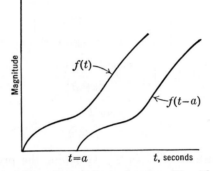

FIGURE 4.2–2.   Comparison of an arbitrary function, $f(t)$, with this function translated $a$ seconds in time, $f(t - a)$.

Equation 4.1–2 expressed in terms of the variable $\tau = (t - a)$ instead of $t$ is

$$\mathcal{L}[f(\tau)] = \int_0^\infty f(\tau)e^{-s\tau} \, d\tau = F(s) \qquad (4.2\text{--}24)$$

but

$$\int_0^\infty f(\tau)e^{-s\tau} \, d\tau = \int_a^\infty f(t - a)e^{-st}e^{+as} \, dt \qquad (4.2\text{--}25)$$

Since the integration of Equation 4.2–25 is with respect to $t$, one may write

$$\int_0^\infty f(\tau)e^{-s\tau} \, d\tau = e^{+as}\int_a^\infty f(t - a)e^{-st} \, dt \qquad (4.2\text{--}26)$$

With $f(t - a) = 0 < t < a$, the lower limit of integration can be made zero without changing the value of the integral.

From Equations 4.2–24 and 4.2–26,

$$\mathcal{L}[f(t - a)] = \int_0^\infty f(t - a)e^{-st} \, dt = e^{-as}F(s) \qquad (4.2\text{--}27)$$

The condition represented by a time function translated by a constant time interval does not occur in truly linear control systems. However, some systems do have nearly fixed time delays associated with the time of measurement.  For these systems the transform of Equation 4.2–23 is valid and useful.

These time functions above represent some of the more common driving functions encountered in the study of servomechanisms.  The corresponding operation $F(s)$ and time $f(t)$ expressions listed below are a summary of the transform pairs derived above as well as another found useful.  More comprehensive tables of transform pairs can be found in Gardner and Barnes' *Transients in Linear Systems* and other textbooks on the Laplace transform.

TABLE 4.2–1

SUMMARY OF LAPLACE TRANSFORM PAIRS

| $F(s)$ | $f(t)$ |
|---|---|
| 1. $\dfrac{1}{s}$ | A constant value of unity; or the unit step function, $u(t)$. |
| 2. $\dfrac{1}{s + \alpha}$ | $e^{-\alpha t}$ |
| 3. $\dfrac{1}{s^2 + \beta^2}$ | $\dfrac{1}{\beta} \sin \beta t$ |
| 4. $\dfrac{a_1 s + a_0}{s^2 + \beta^2}$ | $\cos (\beta t + \psi)$, where $a_1 = \cos \psi$ $a_0 = -\beta \sin \psi$ |
| 5. $\dfrac{1}{(s + \alpha)^2 + \beta^2}$ | $\dfrac{1}{\beta} e^{-\alpha t} \sin \beta t$ |
| 6. $\dfrac{1}{s^2}$ | $t$ |
| 7. $\dfrac{1}{s^n}$ | $\dfrac{1}{(n - 1)!} t^{n-1}$ |
| 8. $\dfrac{1}{(s + \alpha)^n}$ | $\dfrac{1}{(n - 1)!} t^{n-1} e^{-\alpha t}$ |
| 9. $e^{-as} F(s)$ | $f(t - a)$ |

## 4.3  Transformation of Differentiation and Integration Operations

The transformation of the operations of differentiation and integration from functions of time to functions of $s$ compares in importance with the transformation of the driving functions of time to their Laplace counterparts.  These transformations are found to be similar in form to the substitution of $p$ for $d(\ )/dt$ and $1/p$ for $\int (\ ) \, dt$ employed in Chapter 3.  In addition, the values of initial conditions are included specifically in the transformed quantities.

**Theorem for Differentiation.** If the function $f(t)$ and its derivative are $\mathcal{L}$ transformable, and if $f(t)$ has the $\mathcal{L}$ transform $F(s)$, then

$$\mathcal{L}\left[\frac{df(t)}{dt}\right] = sF(s) - f(0+) \qquad (4.3\text{–}1)$$

Since functions with finite discontinuities arise in such problems where step functions are impressed, the additive term $f(0+)$ in the above equation is the value of the function $f(t)$ as the origin is approached from the right-hand side, that is, the positive value of time. Although the $+$ in $0+$ is frequently omitted, its presence is implied, and the value of the constant $f(0)$ that is sometimes used corresponds to the value of the function $f(t)$ just after the switching interval has occurred.

Proof of this theorem follows from the definition of $\mathcal{L}[f(t)]$. Thus, from Equation 4.1–2,

$$\int_0^\infty f(t)e^{-st}\,dt = F(s) \qquad (4.3\text{–}2)$$

Let $u = f(t)$ and $dv = e^{-st}\,dt$. Then the integration by parts, namely,

$$\int u\,dv = uv - \int v\,du$$

yields

$$\int_0^\infty f(t)e^{-st}\,dt = \frac{f(t)e^{-st}}{-s}\bigg|_0^\infty - \int_0^\infty \frac{e^{-st}}{-s}\left(\frac{df(t)}{dt}\right)dt \qquad (4.3\text{–}3)$$

and

$$\int_0^\infty f(t)e^{-st}\,dt = \frac{f(0+)}{s} + \frac{1}{s}\int_0^\infty \frac{df(t)}{dt}e^{-st}\,dt \qquad (4.3\text{–}4)$$

The term on the left of the equal sign is $F(s)$ as in Equation 4.3–2, and, by the definition of the $\mathcal{L}$ transform,

$$\int_0^\infty \frac{df(t)}{dt}e^{-st}\,dt = \mathcal{L}\left[\frac{df(t)}{dt}\right] \qquad (4.3\text{–}5)$$

Hence

$$\mathcal{L}\left[\frac{df(t)}{dt}\right] = sF(s) - f(0+) \qquad (4.3\text{–}6)$$

This theorem may be extended to higher order derivatives readily. The case of the $\mathcal{L}$ transform of $d^2f(t)/dt^2$ will be illustrated in the following example, and further differentiation may be handled in similar fashion.

With $\mathcal{L}\left[\dfrac{df(t)}{dt}\right] = sF(s) - f(0+)$,

$$\mathcal{L}\left[\frac{d^2f(t)}{dt^2}\right] = s[sF(s) - f(0+)] - \frac{df(t)}{dt}(0+)$$

$$\mathcal{L}\left[\frac{d^2f(t)}{dt^2}\right] = s^2F(s) - sf(0+) - \frac{df(t)}{dt}(0+)$$

(4.3–7)

Thus the $\mathcal{L}$ transform of the second derivative of $f(t)$ is $s^2F(s)$, which is similar to the result previously obtained by representing $d^2f(t)/dt^2$ by $p^2$. However, in addition to the more orderly method of arriving at the resultant operational expression by means of the $\mathcal{L}$ transform, the effect of the initial values of $f(t)$ and $df(t)/dt$ is included. It will be recalled that these initial conditions were required in the classical solution, but their introduction was handled separately as required to evaluate certain undetermined coefficients of the solution.

**Theorem for Integration.** If the function $f(t)$ is $\mathcal{L}$ transformable and has the transform $F(s)$, its integral

$$f^{(-1)}(t) = \int f(t)\, dt = \int_0^t f(t)\, dt + f^{(-1)}(0+)$$

is likewise $\mathcal{L}$ transformable, and

$$\mathcal{L}\left[\int f(t)\, dt\right] = \frac{F(s)}{s} + \frac{f^{(-1)}(0+)}{s} \qquad (4.3–8)$$

As in the preceding theorem for differentiation, the possibility of discontinuities at the origin is considered and provision is made for including the value for the integral of the function $f^{(-1)}(0+)$ at the time $t = 0+$, that is, just after switching.

Proof of this theorem is handled by integration of the defining equation for the $\mathcal{L}$ transformation, Equation 4.1–2,

$$\int_0^\infty f(t)e^{-st}\, dt = F(s) \qquad (4.3–9)$$

Substituting $u = e^{-st}$ and $dv = f(t)\, dt$ into the integration-by-parts equation

$$\int u\, dv = uv - \int v\, du$$

gives

$$\int_0^\infty f(t)e^{-st}\, dt = e^{-st}\int f(t)\, dt \,\Big|_0^\infty + s\int_0^\infty \left[\int f(t)\, dt\right]e^{-st}\, dt \quad (4.3–10)$$

$$\int_0^\infty f(t)e^{-st}\, dt = -f^{(-1)}(0+) + s\int_0^\infty \left[\int f(t)\, dt\right]e^{-st}\, dt \quad (4.3–11)$$

By utilizing the definition for the $\mathcal{L}$ transform, Equation 4.3–11 may be written as

$$\mathcal{L}\left[\int f(t)\,dt\right] = \frac{F(s)}{s} + \frac{f^{(-1)}(0+)}{s} \qquad (4.3\text{–}8)$$

In a similar fashion repeated integrations may be handled readily. For example,

$$\mathcal{L}\left\{\int\left[\int f(t)\,dt\right]dt\right\} = \frac{1}{s}\left[\frac{F(s)}{s} + \frac{f^{(-1)}}{s}(0+)\right] + \frac{f^{(-2)}(0+)}{s}$$

$$\mathcal{L}\left\{\int\left[\int f(t)\,dt\right]dt\right\} = \frac{F(s)}{s^2} + \frac{f^{(-1)}}{s^2}(0+) + \frac{f^{(-2)}(0+)}{s} \qquad (4.3\text{–}12)$$

where $f^{(-2)}(0+)$ is the value of the double integral of $f(t)$ immediately after switching.

A summary of the transformation pairs for the operations of differentiation and integration described above is presented in Table 4.3–1.

TABLE 4.3–1

TABLE OF LAPLACE TRANSFORM PAIRS FOR DIFFERENTIATION AND INTEGRATION

| $F(s)$ | $f(t)$ |
|---|---|
| 1. $sF(s) - f(0+)$ | $\dfrac{df(t)}{dt}$ |
| 2. $s^2F(s) - sf(0+) - \dfrac{df(t)}{dt}(0+)$ | $\dfrac{d^2f(t)}{dt^2}$ |
| 3. $\dfrac{F(s)}{s} + \dfrac{f^{(-1)}(0+)}{s}$ | $\int f(t)\,dt$ |
| 4. $\dfrac{F(s)}{s^2} + \dfrac{f^{(-1)}(0+)}{s^2} + \dfrac{f^{(-2)}(0+)}{s}$ | $\int\left[\int f(t)\,dt\right]dt$ |

**Linearity Theorem.** The linearity theorem supplements the differentiation and integration theorems and provides a basis for the transformation of a sum of time terms to the sum of the corresponding operational terms and vice versa. The linearity theorem may be stated as follows.

If the functions $f(t)$, $f_1(t)$, and $f_2(t)$ are $\mathcal{L}$ transformable and have $\mathcal{L}$ transforms $F(s)$, $F_1(s)$, and $F_2(s)$, respectively, and $a$ is a constant or a variable that is independent of $t$ and $s$, then

$$\mathcal{L}[af(t)] = aF(s)$$

and

$$\mathcal{L}[f_1(t) \pm f_2(t)] = F_1(s) \pm F_2(s)$$

$$(4.3\text{–}13)$$

If the functions $F(s)$, $F_1(s)$, and $F_2(s)$ are $\mathcal{L}$ transforms of functions $f(t), f_1(t)$, and $f_2(t)$, respectively, and $a$ is a constant or a variable that is independent of $t$ or $s$, then

$$\mathcal{L}^{-1}[aF(s)] = af(t), \quad 0 \leq t$$

and    (4.3-14)

$$\mathcal{L}^{-1}[F_1(s) \pm F_2(s)] = f_1(t) \pm f_2(t), \quad 0 \leq t$$

The relationships of Equations 4.3–13 and 4.3–14 may be obtained from the linear property of the integral defining the $\mathcal{L}$ transform, Equation 4.1–2, and from the definition of the inverse transform, $\mathcal{L}^{-1}$, Equation 4.1–3.

**Final Value and Initial Value Theorems.** The final value and initial value theorems express the value of a function of time as $t$ approaches $\infty$ and $t$ approaches $0+$ in terms of the corresponding values of the transform of the function as $s$ approaches 0 and $s$ approaches $\infty$, respectively. These theorems may be stated as follows.

*Final Value.* If the function $f(t)$ and its first derivative are $\mathcal{L}$ transformable and the transform of $f(t)$ is $F(s)$, and there are no singularities of $sF(s)$ on the axis of imaginaries or in the right half-plane, then

$$\lim_{s \to 0} sF(s) = \lim_{t \to \infty} f(t) \qquad (4.3\text{–}15)$$

This equation indicates that the value that the function $f(t)$ has as $t \to \infty$, that is, during the steady state, can be determined from the limiting value of $s$ times its transform, with $s$ allowed to approach zero. This theorem is useful in determining from $F(s)$ the steady-state behavior of $f(t)$ without performing the entire $\mathcal{L}^{-1}$ transformation of $F(s)$. It should be noted that this theorem does not apply to the determination of time functions having sinusoidal excitation since the roots of $sF(s)$ lie along the axis of imaginaries for this case.

*Initial Value.* If the function $f(t)$ and its first derivative are $\mathcal{L}$ transformable and $f(t)$ has the $\mathcal{L}$ transform $F(s)$, and the lim $sF(s)$ exists, then

$$\lim_{s \to \infty} sF(s) = \lim_{t = 0+} f(t) \qquad (4.3\text{–}16)$$

This equation indicates that the value that the function $f(t)$ has just after the time equals zero can be determined from the limiting value of $s$ times its transform, with $s$ allowed to approach infinity. This theorem is particularly useful in establishing the initial value of $f(t)$ at $t = 0+$ without actually carrying out the $\mathcal{L}^{-1}$ transformation of $F(s)$. This equation permits one to evaluate the initial conditions of $f(t)$ that have been used in arriving at $F(s)$; it does not establish the physical conditions of the problem that the initial values represent. Since this theorem describes the value of the function initially, there is no restriction on the presence of singularities of $F(s)$.

### 4.4  Application of $\mathcal{L}$ Transform to Simple Control Problems

To illustrate the method by which the Laplace transformation is applied to actual problems, two cases will be described in some detail. The first case is a simple position control problem; the second case is the problem of an elementary network such as is used as a portion of a more complicated control system.

**Position Control.** A simple position control system is shown in block form in Figure 4.4–1. The position control system is one that is identical

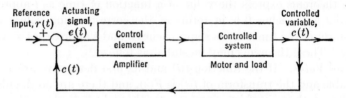

FIGURE 4.4–1.   Position control servomechanism described in Section 3.8.

to that solved by means of the differential equation approach in Section 3.8. $r(t)$ represents the reference input and is a function of time. $c(t)$ is the position of the controlled variable, load, and is likewise a function of time. The amplifier has as its input a signal proportional to the difference in position between $r(t)$ and $c(t)$. The amplifier output is a current proportional to the amplifier input. This same current passes through the motor and produces a torque on the motor and its connected load that is proportional to the amplifier output. The motor and load have rotational inertia as well as a damping torque that is proportional to the motor speed. The torques acting on the motor load are, therefore,

Electromagnetic torque-damping torque =

$$\text{torque available for acceleration}\quad(4.4\text{–}1)$$

By expressing all constants in terms of motor quantities, Equation 4.4–1 may be written as the following differential equation:

$$K[r(t) - c(t)] - D\frac{dc(t)}{dt} = J\frac{d^2c(t)}{dt^2}\qquad(4.4\text{–}2)$$

where $K$ = torque in pound-feet per radian of actuating error, $r(t) - c(t)$,

$D$ = torque in pound-feet per radian per second motion of the motor,

$J$ = inertia in slug square feet of motor and load referred to the motor.

By grouping the terms in $c(t)$ together, Equation 4.4–2 can be expressed as

$$J \frac{d^2c(t)}{dt^2} + D \frac{dc(t)}{dt} + Kc(t) = Kr(t) \qquad (4.4\text{–}3)$$

In Equation 4.4–3 the controlled variable $c(t)$ represents the response of the motor and load as a function of time and is therefore referred to as the *response function*.

The reference input $r(t)$ in Equation 4.4–3 is likewise a function of time and represents the *driving function* applied to the system.

Let the initial values of $c(t)$ and its first derivative be $c(0)$ and $c'(0)$, respectively.

If the Laplace transformation is applied to Equation 4.4–3, this equation becomes

$$\mathcal{L}\left[ J \frac{d^2c(t)}{dt^2} + D \frac{dc(t)}{dt} + Kc(t) \right] = \mathcal{L}[Kr(t)] \qquad (4.4\text{–}4)$$

It is important to note that *the actual differential equations* of the control elements *should be used to obtain the Laplace transform* when initial conditions are to be considered. Since the initial conditions of the control elements themselves can be determined in terms of their stored energy, it is desirable to express the values of the initial conditions in the Laplace transform in terms of these stored energies. Although the use of operational expressions may be satisfactory for obtaining only the sinusoidal steady-state response of the system, as was indicated in Section 3.6, the differential equations must be used for determining the transient response of a system in which the initial conditions are of importance.

For any reference input $r(t)$, such as those considered in Section 4.2, the $\mathcal{L}$ transform can be determined with the aid of a table of transform pairs such as are listed in Table 4.2–1 or one similar. The transform $R(s)$ thus obtained from the driving function $r(t)$ as

$$\mathcal{L}[r(t)] = R(s) \qquad (4.4\text{–}5)$$

is called the *driving transform*.

The response function $c(t)$ and its derivatives are unknown; hence it is not definitely known whether they are $\mathcal{L}$ transformable. However, as was indicated in connection with the condition for being $\mathcal{L}$ transformable, if the system is stable and has a finite response for a finite input, these functions may be transformed as implied by Equation 4.4–4. Proceeding on this basis, and using Equations 4.3–1 and 4.3–7 for obtaining the transform of the differentiation, one obtains

$$\mathcal{L}\left[c(t)\right] = C(s) \tag{4.4–6}$$

$$\mathcal{L}\left[\frac{dc(t)}{dt}\right] = sC(s) - c(0) \tag{4.4–7}$$

$$\mathcal{L}\left[\frac{d^2c(t)}{dt^2}\right] = s^2C(s) - sc(0) - c'(0) \tag{4.4–8}$$

where $C(s)$ is the *response transform*.

Substituting Equations 4.4–5 through 4.4–8 into Equation 4.4–4 gives

$$Js^2C(s) - Jsc(0) - Jc'(0) + DsC(s) - Dc(0) + KC(s) = KR(s) \tag{4.4–9}$$

When the $C(s)$ terms are grouped together,

$$(Js^2 + Ds + K)C(s) = KR(s) + (Js + D)c(0) + Jc'(0) \tag{4.4–10}$$

Solving for $C(s)$ gives

$$C(s) = \frac{KR(s) + (Js + D)c(0) + Jc'(0)}{Js^2 + Ds + K} \tag{4.4–11}$$

It will be noted that the expression of Equation 4.4–10 is somewhat similar to the operational form of solution obtained by use of the classical solution as illustrated by Equation 3.8–19. However, the $p$ has been replaced by $s$, the initial values of $c$, namely $c(0)$ and $c'(0)$ appear explicitly, and the driving function $R(s)$ is present.

Equation 4.4–11 may be written in a more general form, namely:

$$C(s) = \left[\frac{1}{Js^2 + Ds + K}\right][KR(s) + (Js + D)c(0) + Jc'(0)] \tag{4.4–12}$$

which has a form typical of all transform solutions.

*Response function* = [*System function*] [*Excitation function*]

The *system function* will be a fraction, generally with polynomials in $s$ in both numerator and denominator. *The denominator of the system function when set equal to zero is the same characteristic equation described in Section 3.2 with p replaced by s.* The factors of this characteristic equation provide information as to the characteristic response of the system and indicate the nature of the rate of decay and frequency of oscillation of transient terms. The system function incorporates all the essential information regarding the physical system but is independent of any boundary conditions that are included in the excitation function.

The *excitation function* includes the driving transform and excitation signal contributed by the initial conditions, the latter in the form of an *initial excitation function*. The excitation function contains the transform of all the information pertaining to the excitations applied to the system either from external forces, the reference input function, or from internal conditions of energy storage, the initial excitation function.

To obtain the expression for $c(t)$ from $C(s)$ of Equation 4.4–11, it is necessary to determine $\mathcal{L}^{-1}[C(s)]$. In literal form, from Equation 4.1–3,

$$c(t) = \mathcal{L}^{-1}\left[\frac{KR(s) + (Js + D)c(0) + Jc'(0)}{Js^2 + Ds + K}\right] \qquad (4.4\text{–}13)$$

For a specific value of the reference input $r(t)$, the corresponding reference input transform $R(s)$ could be determined with the aid of the table of transform pairs. Rationalizing the bracketed expression for $\mathcal{L}^{-1}$, one would obtain an expression in $s$ for the response transform. This response transform may be evaluated in one of two ways:

1. By use of the table of transforms to obtain the time function corresponding to the response transform.

2. Modifying the response transform, breaking it down into a sum of simpler transforms, and evaluating the time functions for each of these with the aid of the transform pair tables.

The first of these methods is straightforward and requires no amplification. However, for physical systems of general interest, it is seldom that this can be done directly from most sets of transform tables. The second method is more general; it will be discussed in detail in Section 4.5.

**Elementary Resistance-Capacitance Network.** To illustrate the application of the Laplace transformation to electrical networks, the expression for the $\mathcal{L}$ transform of the output voltage of the network shown in Figure 4.4–2 will be determined. The input voltage to the network $e_{in}(t)$ and the output voltage $e_o(t)$ are functions of

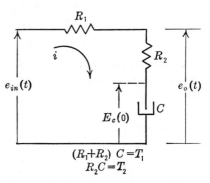

FIGURE 4.4–2. Network for which $\mathcal{L}$ transform of output voltage, $e_o(t)$, is desired.

time.   Let $E_c(0)$ be the initial value of the voltage on the capacitor $C$ at the start of the problem.

The differential equation for the network is

$$e_{in}(t) = (R_1 + R_2)i(t) + \frac{1}{C}\int i(t)\, dt \qquad (4.4\text{--}14)$$

whereas the differential equation for the output voltage $e_o(t)$ is

$$e_o(t) = R_2 i(t) + \frac{1}{C}\int i(t)\, dt \qquad (4.4\text{--}15)$$

Applying the Laplace transformation to all the terms of Equations 4.4–14 and 4.4–15 gives

$$E_{in}(s) = (R_1 + R_2)I(s) + \frac{I(s)}{Cs} + \frac{E_c(0)}{s} \qquad (4.4\text{--}16)$$

and

$$E_o(s) = R_2 I(s) + \frac{I(s)}{Cs} + \frac{E_c(0)}{s} \qquad (4.4\text{--}17)$$

where

$$E_{in}(s) = \mathcal{L}[e_{in}(t)]$$

$$E_o(s) = \mathcal{L}[e_o(t)]$$

$$I(s) = \mathcal{L}[i(t)]$$

and

$$E_c(0) = \frac{i^{(-1)}(0)}{C}$$

Eliminating $I(s)$ from Equations 4.4–16 and 4.4–17 gives

$$E_o(s) = \frac{(T_2 s + 1)}{(T_1 s + 1)} E_{in}(s) + \frac{(T_1 - T_2)}{(T_1 s + 1)} E_c(0) \qquad (4.4\text{--}18)$$

where $T_2 = R_2 C$ and $T_1 = (R_1 + R_2)C$.

Although Equation 4.4–18 is not separated into the form of a product of system and excitation functions shown in Equation 4.4–12, nevertheless the inverse transformation for $E_o(s)$ may be readily indicated as

$$\mathcal{L}^{-1}[E_o(s)] = e_o(t) = \mathcal{L}^{-1}\left[\frac{(T_2 s + 1)}{(T_1 s + 1)} E_{in}(s) + \frac{(T_1 - T_2)}{(T_1 s + 1)} E_c(0)\right]$$

$$(4.4\text{--}19)$$

Again, as in the previous example, the value of the response time function is influenced by the driving function, that is, the nature of the input function, and the value of the initial energy present in the system.

Although the bracketed term in Equation 4.4–19 might be one for which the inverse transform could be performed directly from a table of transforms, frequently the expression for $E_{in}(s)$ is sufficiently complicated so that it is necessary to use the more general method for obtaining the inverse transform as described in the following section.

## 4.5 Performing the Inverse Laplace Transformation

As indicated in the preceding sections, the process for obtaining the inverse transformation, $\mathcal{L}^{-1}[F(s)]$, is seldom one that can be satisfactorily handled solely by direct reference to transform tables. The more general method is to express $F(s)$ as a sum of partial fractions with constant coefficients. The inverse transformation of each of these simple partial fractions can readily be obtained from the table of transforms, and the complete expression of $\mathcal{L}^{-1}[F(s)]$ is merely the sum of the results from all the inverse transformations. This process is explained in this section, which is a summary of the methods outlined by Gardner and Barnes in their *Transients in Linear Systems*.[29]

In general the response transform $F(s)$ is a rational algebraic fraction that can be represented as

$$F(s) = \frac{A(s)}{B(s)} = \frac{a_m s^m + a_{m-1} s^{m-1} + \cdots + a_1 s + a_0}{s^n + b_{n-1} s^{n-1} + \cdots + b_1 s + b_0} \qquad (4.5\text{--}1)$$

The $a$'s and $b$'s are real constants, and $m$ and $n$ are real positive integers. Note it is essential that the coefficient of $s^n$, the highest power of $s$ in the denominator, be made equal to unity. Because of the nature of the system and excitation functions that will in general be encountered in studies of transients in servomechanisms, the order of the highest power of $s$ in the denominator, that is, $s^n$, is equal to or greater than the highest power of $s$ in the numerator, that is, $s^m$.

To express $F(s)$ as a sum of partial fractions, it is necessary first to determine the factors of the denominator $B(s)$. A number of methods of determining these factors are outlined in Section 6.2. For the present purpose it will suffice to indicate these factors in literal form so that Equation 4.5–1 may be written as

$$\frac{A(s)}{B(s)} = \frac{A(s)}{(s - s_1)(s - s_2) \cdots (s - s_k) \cdots (s - s_n)} \qquad (4.5\text{--}2)$$

where $s_1, s_2, \cdots, s_k$, and $s_n$ are the factors of the denominator and may be real or complex. At present, all the factors are considered to be different, although in Section 4.7 the cases where there are repeated factors are discussed. The factor $s_k$ may be considered to be representative.

The fraction $A(s)/B(s)$ can now be written as a sum of partial fractions, each partial fraction having for its denominator a factor of $B(s)$. There will be $n$ of these partial fractions corresponding to the $n$th power of $s$ in the denominator of Equation 4.5–1. Letting the coefficients of these partial fractions be the $C$'s, Equation 4.5–2 may be rewritten as

$$\frac{A(s)}{B(s)} = \frac{C_1}{(s - s_1)} + \frac{C_2}{(s - s_2)} + \cdots \frac{C_k}{(s - s_k)} + \cdots \frac{C_n}{(s - s_n)} \qquad (4.5\text{–}3)$$

To evaluate the typical coefficients $C_k$, multiply both sides of Equation 4.5–3 by the denominator of the $C_k$ term, namely, $(s - s_k)$. The resulting equation is

$$(s - s_k)\frac{A(s)}{B(s)} = C_1\frac{(s - s_k)}{(s - s_1)} + C_2\frac{(s - s_k)}{(s - s_2)} + \cdots + C_k + \cdots \frac{C_n(s - s_k)}{(s - s_n)}$$

$$(4.5\text{–}4)$$

Since $B(s)$ contains the factor $(s - s_k)$, the left term contains $(s - s_k)$ in both numerator and denominator; hence the $(s - s_k)$ factor of this term has been removed by the process of multiplying by $(s - s_k)$.

If now $s$ is replaced by $s_k$, all the terms that contain $(s - s_k)$ on the right of the equal sign in Equation 4.5–4 become zero; the only term that remains is the coefficient $C_k$, which is to be evaluated. The equation defining $C_k$ is then

$$C_k = \left[ (s - s_k)\frac{A(s)}{B(s)} \right]_{s = s_k} \qquad (4.5\text{–}5)$$

When Equation 4.5–5 is written with the denominator in its expanded form, it is evident that the substitution $s - s_k$ permits $C_k$ to be evaluated as a constant coefficient,

$$C_k = \frac{A(s_k)}{(s_k - s_1)(s_k - s_2) \cdots (s_k - s_{k-1})(s_k - s_{k+1}) \cdots (s_k - s_n)}$$

$$(4.5\text{–}6)$$

Equation 4.5–5 or its expanded form, Equation 4.5–6, permits the evaluation of all the $C$ coefficients from $C_1$ to $C_n$ as $k$ is set equal to all values from 1 to $n$. Hence the literal coefficients arbitrarily assigned in Equation 4.5–3 have been explicitly defined and can be readily evaluated.

Referring to Equation 4.5–3, one sees that the expression $F(s) = A(s)/B(s)$ has been reduced to a sum of partial fractions in which the constant coefficients are now defined. The actual operation of inverse transformation is now a simple one in which the transformation pair for each term can readily be obtained from such a table as Table 4.2–1.  For a typical form,

$$\mathcal{L}^{-1}\left[\frac{C_k}{s - s_k}\right] = C_k e^{s_k t}, \quad 0 \le t \tag{4.5-7}$$

The complete inverse transform is then the sum of the inverse transforms from each term:

$$\mathcal{L}^{-1}[F(s)] = C_1 e^{s_1 t} + C_2 e^{s_2 t} + \cdots C_k e^{s_k t} + \cdots C_n e^{s_n t} \tag{4.5-8}$$

## 4.6  Examples of the Inverse Transformation

The process of obtaining the inverse Laplace transformation outlined in Section 4.5 can be employed directly when the $s_k$ quantity in the $(s - s_k)$ factor of the denominator is real or complex and when each factor is different.  The process will be illustrated in a number of examples of typical factors.

**Factors Having Real Roots.**  Determine

$$\mathcal{L}^{-1}\left[\frac{a_1 s + a_0}{(s + \alpha)(s + \gamma)(s + \delta)}\right]$$

in which $\alpha$, $\gamma$, and $\delta$ are real numbers and are all different.

As indicated by Equation 4.5–8, the inverse transform is a series of exponentials.  Thus

$$\mathcal{L}^{-1}\left[\frac{a_1 s + a_0}{(s + \alpha)(s + \gamma)(s + \delta)}\right] = C_1 e^{-\alpha t} + C_2 e^{-\gamma t} + C_3 e^{-\delta t}, \quad 0 \le t$$

$$\tag{4.6-1}$$

where

$$C_1 = \frac{a_1 s + a_0}{(s + \gamma)(s + \delta)}\bigg|_{s=-\alpha} = \frac{-a_1\alpha + a_0}{(-\alpha + \gamma)(-\alpha + \delta)}$$

$$C_2 = \frac{a_1 s + a_0}{(s + \alpha)(s + \delta)}\bigg|_{s=-\gamma} = \frac{-a_1\gamma + a_0}{(-\gamma + \alpha)(-\gamma + \delta)}$$

$$C_3 = \frac{a_1 s + a_0}{(s + \alpha)(s + \gamma)}\bigg|_{s=-\delta} = \frac{-a_1\delta + a_0}{(-\delta + \alpha)(-\delta + \gamma)}$$

**One Factor Having a Root at Zero.**  Determine

$$\mathcal{L}^{-1}\left[\frac{a_1 s + a_0}{s(s + \gamma)(s + \delta)}\right]$$

where $\gamma$ and $\delta$ are real and different.  Recalling that $\mathcal{L}^{-1}\left[1/s\right] = 1$, one may write the inverse transform as a constant plus a series of exponentials.

$$\mathcal{L}^{-1}\left[\frac{a_1 s + a_0}{s(s + \gamma)(s + \delta)}\right] = C_1 + C_2 e^{-\gamma t} + C_3 e^{-\delta t}, \quad 0 \le t \quad (4.6\text{-}2)$$

where

$$C_1 = \left.\frac{a_1 s + a_0}{(s + \gamma)(s + \delta)}\right|_{s=0} = \frac{a_0}{\gamma \delta}$$

$$C_2 = \left.\frac{a_1 s + a_0}{s(s + \delta)}\right|_{s=-\gamma} = \frac{-a_1\gamma + a_0}{-\gamma(-\gamma + \delta)}$$

$$C_3 = \left.\frac{a_1 s + a_0}{s(s + \gamma)}\right|_{s=-\delta} = \frac{-a_1\delta + a_0}{-\delta(-\delta + \gamma)}$$

It will be noted that the factor $s$ could be considered as a special case of $(s + \alpha)$, where $\alpha \to 0$. Comparing this solution with that for the preceding example will serve to verify this statement.

**Factors Having Complex Conjugate Roots.** Determine

$$\mathcal{L}^{-1}\left[\frac{a_1 s + a_0}{s(s + \alpha + j\beta)(s + \alpha - j\beta)}\right]$$

where $\alpha$ and $\beta$ are real numbers.

Considering complex roots to be no different from any other kind of roots, one has

$$\mathcal{L}^{-1}\left[\frac{a_1 s + a_0}{s[(s + \alpha)^2 + \beta^2]}\right] = C_1 + C_2 e^{(-\alpha + j\beta)t} + C_3 e^{(-\alpha - j\beta)t}$$

where

$$C_1 = \frac{a_0}{\alpha^2 + \beta^2}$$

$C_2$ and $C_3$ are somewhat more difficult to obtain and are determined as follows:

$$C_2 = \left[\frac{a_1 s + a_0}{s(s + \alpha + j\beta)}\right]_{s=-\alpha+j\beta} = \frac{a_1(-\alpha + j\beta) + a_0}{(-\alpha + j\beta)(2j\beta)}$$

Expressing $C_2$ as a magnitude and an angle gives

$$C_2 = \frac{[(a_0 - a_1\alpha)^2 + (a_1\beta)^2]^{\frac{1}{2}}e^{j\psi_1}}{2j\beta[\alpha^2 + \beta^2]^{\frac{1}{2}}e^{j\psi_2}} = \frac{[(a_0 - a_1\alpha)^2 + (a_1\beta)^2]^{\frac{1}{2}}}{2\beta\beta_0}e^{j(\psi - \pi/2)}$$

where

$$\psi_1 = \tan^{-1} \frac{a_1\beta}{a_0 - a_1\alpha}$$

$$\psi_2 = \tan^{-1} \frac{\beta}{-\alpha}$$

Note that it is essential to associate the minus sign properly with the numerator or denominator since this is necessary to determine in what trigonometric quadrant the angle of the inverse tangent is located.

$$\psi = \psi_1 - \psi_2$$

and

$$\beta_0 = [\alpha^2 + \beta^2]^{\frac{1}{2}}$$

$$C_3 = \left[\frac{a_1s + a_0}{s(s + \alpha - j\beta)}\right]_{s=-\alpha-j\beta} = \frac{a_1(-\alpha - j\beta) + a_0}{(-\alpha - j\beta)(-2j\beta)}$$

Coefficients $C_2$ and $C_3$ are conjugate complex numbers since $-j$ appears in $C_3$ wherever $+j$ appears in $C_2$. The final result can be written as

$$\mathcal{L}^{-1}\left[\frac{a_1s + a_0}{s[(s + \alpha)^2 + \beta^2]}\right]$$

$$= \frac{a_0}{\beta_0^2} + \frac{[(a_0 - a_1\alpha)^2 + (a_1\beta)^2]^{\frac{1}{2}}}{\beta\beta_0} e^{-\alpha t} \frac{[e^{j(\psi - \pi/2)}e^{j\beta t} + e^{-j(\psi - \pi/2)}e^{-j\beta t}]}{2}$$

$$= \frac{a_0}{\beta_0^2} + \frac{[(a_0 - a_1\alpha)^2 + (a_1\beta)^2]^{\frac{1}{2}}}{\beta\beta_0} e^{-\alpha t} \sin(\beta t + \psi), \quad 0 \le t \qquad (4.6\text{-}3)$$

Thus the solution is in the form of a constant and an exponentially decaying sinusoid with an initial phase angle.

Since $C_2e^{(-\alpha+j\beta)t}$ and $C_3e^{(-\alpha-j\beta)t}$ are conjugate complex functions, the sum of their imaginary parts is zero, and the sum of their real parts is twice the real part of either. Consequently, these two terms combine into a single sinusoidal function. Hence, for purposes of calculation, it is necessary only to determine the magnitude and phase angle of one term, usually $C_2e^{(-\alpha+j\beta)t}$, and take two times the real part of it to obtain the combined sinusoidal portion of the inverse transform.

*This method of evaluating only one complex coefficient from which are obtained the magnitude and the phase angle of the sinuosidal function can be used with any set of conjugate factors.*

Thus, considering the example above and using the value of $C_2$, one obtains the combined value of the sinusoidal terms as

$$2Re\left[\frac{[(a_0 - a_1\alpha)^2 + (a_1\beta)^2]^{1/2}}{2\beta\beta_0} e^{j(\psi - \pi/2)}e^{(-\alpha+j\beta)t}\right]$$

where $Re$ means "take the real part of the bracketed expression." This expression can then be simplified to obtain the final form of the sinusoidal term. The presence of $\pi/2$ in combination with $\psi$, however, often proves to be cumbersome in the mathematical manipulations. This factor $(\pi/2)$ is a result of the $2j\beta$ term in the denominator of the original expression for $C_2$,

$$\frac{a_1(-\alpha + j\beta) + a_0}{(-\alpha + j\beta)(2j\beta)}$$

It is desirable then to obtain a means for determining the sinusoidal term without including the $j$ term in the denominator. This may be done as follows.

Using $I_m$ to indicate "take the imaginary part of the bracketed expression," one can show that

$$Re\left[\frac{Ne^{j\gamma}}{j} e^{j\omega t}\right] = I_m[Ne^{j\gamma}e^{j\omega t}] \qquad (4.6-4)$$

where $Ne^{j\gamma}$ is any complex number.

In this equation,

$$Re\left[\frac{Ne^{j\gamma}}{j} e^{j\omega t}\right] = Re\left[N\frac{\{\cos(\omega t + \gamma) + j\sin(\omega t + \gamma)\}}{j}\right]$$

$$= N\sin(\omega t + \gamma)$$

Also,

$$I_m[Ne^{j\gamma}e^{j\omega t}] = I_m[N\{\cos(\omega t + \gamma) + j\sin(\omega t + \gamma)\}]$$

$$= N\sin(\omega t + \gamma)$$

Thus the identity is verified.

The expression for the sinusoidal term of the inverse transform in the original example may now be written by taking twice the imaginary part of $C_2$ and omitting $j$ in the denominator. The 2 factor in the denominator may also be eliminated if only the imaginary part is taken rather than two times it.  Thus the sinusoidal term corresponding to $C_2$ and $C_3$ is

$$I_m \left[ \frac{a_1(-\alpha + j\beta) + a_0}{\beta(-\alpha + j\beta)} e^{(-\alpha + j\beta)t} \right]$$

$$= I_m \left[ \frac{[(a_0 - a_1\alpha)^2 + (a_1\beta)^2]^{\frac{1}{2}} e^{j\psi_1}}{\beta(\alpha^2 + \beta^2)^{\frac{1}{2}} e^{j\psi_2}} e^{-\alpha t} e^{j\beta t} \right]$$

$$= I_m \left[ \frac{[(a_0 - a_1\alpha)^2 + (a_1\beta)^2]^{\frac{1}{2}}}{\beta(\alpha^2 + \beta^2)^{\frac{1}{2}}} e^{-\alpha t} e^{j(\beta t + \psi)} \right]$$

$$= \frac{[(a_0 - a_1\alpha)^2 + (a_1\beta)^2]^{\frac{1}{2}}}{\beta \beta_0} e^{-\alpha t} \sin(\beta t + \psi), \quad 0 \le t \quad (4.6\text{-}5)$$

where $\psi_1$, $\psi_2$, $\psi$, and $\beta_0$ have the same values as before.

**Factors Having Imaginary Roots.**  Determine

$$\mathcal{L}^{-1} \left[ \frac{a_1 s + a_0}{(s + \alpha)(s^2 + \omega^2)} \right]$$

where $\alpha$ and $\omega$ are real numbers.

This inverse transform is a special case of the general one illustrated for complex roots.  Because *any system subject to sinusoidal excitation has present in the denominator of its response transform a factor of the form* $s^2 + \omega^2$ (see Equations 4.2–11 or 4.2–16), it is worth while to repeat this type of inverse transformation for the sake of emphasis.

$$\mathcal{L}^{-1} \left[ \frac{a_1 s + a_0}{(s + \alpha)(s - j\omega)(s + j\omega)} \right] = C_1 e^{-\alpha t} + C_2 e^{+j\omega t} + C_3 e^{-j\omega t}$$

where

$$C_1 = \frac{a_1 s + a_0}{s^2 + \omega^2} \bigg|_{s = -\alpha} = \frac{-a_1\alpha + a_0}{+\alpha^2 + \omega^2}$$

$$C_2 = \frac{a_1 s + a_0}{(s + \alpha)(s + j\omega)} \bigg|_{s = +j\omega} = \frac{j\omega a_1 + a_0}{(j\omega + \alpha)2j\omega}$$

$$C_3 = \frac{a_1 s + a_0}{(s + \alpha)(s - j\omega)} \bigg|_{s = -j\omega} = \frac{-j\omega a_1 + a_0}{(-j\omega + \alpha)(-2j\omega)}$$

It is important to note that in evaluating the coefficients $C_2$ and $C_3$ of the $1/(s^2 + \omega^2)$ term, $s$ is replaced by $+j\omega$ and $-j\omega$.  Rather than calculate both $C_2$ and $C_3$ in determining the inverse transform, use the method for conjugate factors as given above. Thus the inverse transform is

$$\mathcal{L}^{-1}\left[\frac{a_1 s + a_0}{(s + \alpha)(s^2 + \omega^2)}\right] = \frac{-a_1\alpha + a_0}{\alpha^2 + \omega^2} e^{-\alpha t} + I_m\left[\frac{a_0 + j\omega a_1}{\omega(\alpha + j\omega)} e^{j\omega t}\right]$$

(4.6-6)

Expanding the coefficient of $e^{j\omega t}$ gives

$$\frac{a_0 + j\omega a_1}{\omega(\alpha + j\omega)} = \frac{[a_0^2 + (\omega a_1)^2]^{1/2} e^{j\psi_1}}{\omega[\alpha^2 + \omega^2]^{1/2} e^{j\psi_2}}$$

$$= \frac{1}{\omega}\left[\frac{a_0^2 + (\omega a_1)^2}{\alpha^2 + \omega^2}\right]^{1/2} e^{j\psi}$$

where

$$\psi_1 = \tan^{-1}\frac{\omega a_1}{a_0}$$

$$\psi_2 = \tan^{-1}\frac{\omega}{\alpha}$$

and

$$\psi = \psi_1 - \psi_2$$

Hence

$$I_m\left[\frac{a_0 + j\omega a_1}{\omega(\alpha + j\omega)} e^{j\omega t}\right] = \frac{1}{\omega}\left[\frac{a_0^2 + (\omega a_1)^2}{\alpha^2 + \omega^2}\right]^{1/2} \sin(\omega t + \psi) \quad (4.6-7)$$

## 4.7 Inverse Transformation for Repeated Factors

The process for evaluating the coefficients of the partial fractions as well as the form of the inverse transformation itself is modified when there are a number of equal roots, corresponding to the condition where there are repeated factors in the $B(s)$ term. Although the method of obtaining the coefficient of the partial fractions outlined in Equations 4.5–3 through 4.5–6 gives a clue to a method that may be employed, it is not complete in itself.

Consider the following case where there are three repeated factors $(s - s_1)$ in the denominator of the $A(s)/B(s)$ expression.

$$\frac{A(s)}{B(s)} = \frac{A_s}{(s - s_1)^3(s - s_4) \cdots (s - s_k) \cdots (s - s_n)} \quad (4.7-1)$$

where there are three factors $(s - s_1)$, and the other factors, $(s - s_4)$ to $(s - s_n)$, are all different. Since there are $n$ factors there must be $n$

coefficients, one for each of the factors, including one for each of the $(s - s_1)$ factors.  Writing equation 4.7–1 as a sum of partial fractions in which the $(s - s_1)$ factor is represented by the $(s - s_1)^3$, $(s - s_1)^2$, and $(s - s_1)$ terms gives

$$\frac{A(s)}{B(s)} = \frac{C_{11}}{(s - s_1)^3} + \frac{C_{12}}{(s - s_1)^2}$$

$$+ \frac{C_{13}}{(s - s_1)} + \frac{C_4}{(s - s_4)} + \cdots + \frac{C_k}{(s - s_k)} + \cdots + \frac{C_n}{(s - s_n)} \quad (4.7\text{–}2)$$

where the $C$ coefficients are yet to be determined.

To evaluate the $C_1$ coefficients, Equation 4.7–2 must be multiplied by $(s - s_1)^3$.

Thus

$$(s - s_1)^3 \frac{A(s)}{B(s)} = C_{11} + C_{12}(s - s_1) + C_{13}(s - s_1)^2$$

$$+ \frac{C_4(s - s_1)^3}{(s - s_4)} + \cdots + \frac{C_k(s - s_1)^3}{(s - s_k)} + \cdots + \frac{C_n(s - s_1)^3}{s - s_n} \quad (4.7\text{–}3)$$

In the quantity on the left, $(s - s_1)^3$ is a factor of $B(s)$ also, so it may be divided out of both numerator and denominator.  Now, by letting $s = s_1$, the left term becomes a number while all the terms on the right except $C_{11}$ become zero.

Although this procedure can be used to evaluate $C_{11}$, it alone is insufficient to evaluate any of the remaining $C_1$ coefficients in Equation 4.7–3, since each of them is multiplied by a $(s - s_1)$ factor.  If the term $C_{11}$ on the right side of Equation 4.7–3 could be eliminated and also the factor $(s - s_1)$ that multiplies $C_{12}$, a repetition of the process of letting $s = s_1$ would evaluate $C_{12}$.  These eliminations can be accomplished by differentiating Equation 4.7–3 once with respect to $s$.  Thus

$$\frac{d}{ds}\left[ (s - s_1)^3 \frac{A(s)}{B(s)} \right] = C_{12} + 2C_{13}(s - s_1) + \cdots \quad (4.7\text{–}4)$$

Now, by letting $s = s_1$, the value of $C_{12}$ is determined as

$$C_{12} = \frac{d}{ds}\left[ (s - s_1)^3 \frac{A(s)}{B(s)} \right]_{s=s_1} \quad (4.7\text{–}5)$$

The procedure of differentiating Equation 4.7–4 again and then placing $s = s_1$ may be performed again to evaluate $C_{13}$. From this process

$$C_{13} = \frac{1}{2}\frac{d^2}{ds^2}\left[(s - s_1)^3\frac{A(s)}{B(s)}\right]_{s=s_1} \tag{4.7-6}$$

The general procedure described above when there are three equal factors in the denominator can be modified to be used for any number of repeated roots.

To evaluate the other coefficients $C_4$ to $C_n$, the same method that has been employed previously can be used. Thus for the general term, as for Equation 4.5–5,

$$C_k = \left[(s - s_k)\frac{A(s)}{B(s)}\right]_{s=s_k} \tag{4.7-7}$$

To find the inverse transform of the $C_1$ terms, corresponding to the repeated factors, reference should be made to item 8 of the table of transformation pairs, Table 4.2–1, where it is shown that

$$\mathcal{L}^{-1}\left[\frac{1}{(s + a)^n}\right] = \frac{1}{(n - 1)!}t^{n-1}e^{-at} \tag{4.7-8}$$

As previously for Equation 4.5–7, the inverse transform of the $C_k/(s - s_k)$ term is

$$\mathcal{L}^{-1}\left[\frac{C_k}{s - s_k}\right] = C_k e^{s_k t} \quad 0 \leq t \tag{4.7-9}$$

The following example will serve to illustrate the above principles. Find

$$\mathcal{L}^{-1}\left[\frac{a_2 s^2 + a_1 s + a_0}{(s + a)^3 s^2}\right]$$

in which $\alpha$ is a real, positive number and $a_0$, $a_1$, and $a_2$ are real numbers.

$$\mathcal{L}^{-1}\left[\frac{a_2 s^2 + a_1 s + a_0}{(s + a)^3 s^2}\right]$$

$$= \mathcal{L}^{-1}\left[\frac{C_{11}}{(s + a)^3} + \frac{C_{12}}{(s + a)^2} + \frac{C_{13}}{(s + a)} + \frac{C_{41}}{s^2} + \frac{C_{42}}{s}\right]$$

$$= C_{11}\frac{t^2}{2}e^{-at} + C_{12}te^{-at} + C_{13}e^{-at} + C_{41}t + C_{42}, \quad 0 \leq t$$

where

$$C_{11} = \left[\frac{a_2 s^2 + a_1 s + a_0}{s^2}\right]_{s=-\alpha} = \frac{a_2 \alpha^2 - a_1 \alpha + a_0}{\alpha^2}$$

$$C_{12} = \left[\frac{d}{ds}\left(\frac{a_2 s^2 + a_1 s + a_0}{s^2}\right)\right]_{s=-\alpha} = \frac{-a_1 \alpha + 2a_0}{\alpha^3}$$

$$C_{13} = \frac{1}{2!}\left[\frac{d}{ds}\left(\frac{-a_1 s - 2a_0}{s^3}\right)\right]_{s=-\alpha} = \frac{-a_1 \alpha + 3a_0}{\alpha^4}$$

$$C_{41} = \left[\frac{a_2 s^2 + a_1 s + a_0}{(s+\alpha)^3}\right]_{s=0} = \frac{a_0}{\alpha^3}$$

$$C_{42} = \left[\frac{d}{ds}\left(\frac{a_2 s^2 + a_1 s + a_0}{(s+\alpha)^3}\right)\right]_{s=0} = \frac{a_1 \alpha - 3a_0}{\alpha^4}$$

With this treatment of the case of the inverse transformation for repeated factors of the denominator, the methods necessary for the determination of the response as a function of time for servomechanisms
problems with constant coefficients are complete. Although the methods
for performing the inverse transformation as described in Section 4.5
have been illustrated by means of only literal examples in Sections 4.6
and 4.7, the examples chosen should provide adequate assistance for any
specific numerical problem. For purposes of clarity, however, two numerical problems are worked in detail in the following section.

## 4.8  Applications of $\mathcal{L}^{-1}$ Transform to Problems of Section 4.4

**Position Control Problem.**  Suppose in the simple control problem of
Section 4.4, the reference input motion $r$ is to vary in a cosine fashion so
that

$$r = R_0 \cos 2t$$

Furthermore, consider the system to have no initial velocity (that is,
be at rest) with the controlled variable displacement $c = R_0$ at $t = 0$.
The system parameters are the following:

$$J = 0.05 \text{ slug feet}^2$$
$$D = 1.6 \text{ lb-ft per radian per second}$$
$$K = 20 \text{ lb-ft per radian}$$

from which $\zeta$ of Section 3.8 is 0.8, and the system is slightly oscillatory.

Using these constants and initial conditions, one can evaluate the response of the system by substitution in the response transform given in
Equation 4.4–11.

First, from transform pair 4 given in Table 4.2–1,

$$\mathcal{L}[R_0 \cos 2t] = \frac{R_0 s}{s^2 + 2^2} \tag{4.8–1}$$

From the condition that the initial controlled variable displacement is $R_0$, $r(0) = R_0$. Since the initial velocity is zero $r'(0) = 0$, using these values in Equation 4.4–11 gives

$$C(s) = \frac{\dfrac{20R_0 s}{s^2 + 2^2} + (0.05s + 1.6)R_0}{0.05s^2 + 1.6s + 20} \tag{4.8–2}$$

which, when placed over a common denominator, becomes

$$C(s) = \frac{20R_0 s + (s^2 + 2^2)(0.05s + 1.6)R_0}{0.05(s + j2)(s - j2)(s + 16 - j12)(s + 16 + j12)} \tag{4.8–3}$$

Note that the coefficient of $s$ in all the factors of the denominator is unity as required by Equation 4.5–1. The factors of the denominator are characterized as having complex roots, one pair having no real part corresponding to the cosine driving force, the other having a negative real part corresponding to the damped oscillatory response of the system. By dividing the expression for $C(s)$ by the magnitude $R_0$, and by taking the inverse transform, the time response is obtained:

$$\frac{c(t)}{R_0} = \mathcal{L}^{-1}\left[\frac{400s + (s^2 + 2^2)(s + 32)}{(s - j2)(s + j2)(s + 16 - j12)(s + 16 + j12)}\right] \tag{4.8–4}$$

If the form of this inverse transform is compared with those illustrated in Section 4.6, the form of the desired time function may be written as

$$\frac{c(t)}{R_0} = I_m\left[\frac{400(j2)e^{j2t}}{2(16 - j10)(16 + j14)}\right]$$

$$+ I_m\left[\left\{\frac{400(-16 + j12) + [(-16 + j12)^2 + 2^2][+16 + j12]}{12[(-16 + j12)^2 + 2^2]}\right\}e^{(-16 + j12)t}\right]$$

$$\tag{4.8–5}$$

Simplified, these expressions are

$$\frac{c(t)}{R_0} = I_m\left[\frac{400j}{396 + j64}e^{j2t}\right]$$

$$+ I_m\left[\left\{\frac{400}{12}\frac{(-16 + j12)}{(116 - j384)} + \frac{(16 + j12)}{12}\right\}e^{(-16 + j12)t}\right] \tag{4.8–6}$$

Performing the operations indicated gives

$$c(t) = 0.997R_0 \cos(2t - 9.2°) + 0.017R_0 e^{-16t}\sin(12t + 110.1°) \tag{4.8–7}$$

When the magnitude of the coefficients of the steady-state ($\cos 2t$) and transient ($e^{-16t} \sin 12t$) terms of Equation 4.8–7 are compared it is apparent that the transient effect is very small for the initial conditions considered. It will be noted that the transient response term is derived from the system function, whereas the steady-state response term is derived from the excitation function. From the steady-state term it appears that the output is shifted in phase by some 9.2° from the input, although the maximum amplitude of the output is less than 0.5 per cent different from the maximum value of the input.

**Elementary Resistance-Capacitance Network.** A problem of considerable importance in the field of servomechanisms is the determination of the steady-state response of a system to an input that is a power series in time. To illustrate this problem, the expression for the output voltage $e_o(t)$ for Figure 4.4–2, which has been set forth in Equation 4.4–19, will be determined with

$$e_{in}(t) = E_1 t \qquad (4.8\text{–}8)$$

$$\mathcal{L}[E_1 t] = E_{in}(s) = \frac{E_1}{s^2} \qquad (4.8\text{–}9)$$

Since only the steady-state solution is required, the initial condenser voltage $E_c(0)$ in Equation 4.4–19 can be set equal zero. Under this condition and with the value of $E_{in}(s)$ from Equation 4.8–9, Equation 4.4–19 can be written as

$$e_o(t) = \mathcal{L}^{-1}\left[ \frac{(T_2 s + 1)}{(T_1 s + 1)} \frac{E_1}{s^2} \right] \qquad (4.8\text{–}10)$$

The stipulation that the steady state alone is of interest means that only those terms in the inverse transform need be determined that are derived from the driving function $E_1/s^2$. Thus

$$e_o(t)\Big|_{\text{steady state}} = \mathcal{L}^{-1}\left[ \frac{C_1}{s^2} + \frac{C_2}{s} \right] \qquad (4.8\text{–}11)$$

where

$$C_1 = E_1\left( \frac{T_2 s + 1}{T_1 s + 1} \right)\Big|_{s=0} = E_1 \qquad (4.8\text{–}12)$$

and

$$C_2 = \frac{d}{ds}\left[ \frac{E_1(T_2 s + 1)}{T_1 s + 1} \right]\Big|_{s=0} = -(T_1 - T_2)E_1 \qquad (4.8\text{–}13)$$

With these values of $C_1$ and $C_2$, one may refer to Table 4.2–1 and determine that

$$e_o(t)\Big|_{\text{steady state}} = E_1 t - (T_1 - T_2)E_1 \qquad (4.8\text{–}14)$$

Figure 4.8–1 presents a comparison of the input voltage and the volt-age output given by Equation 4.8–14. These curves show the steady-state component of output voltage to be of the same slope as the driving input voltage, with a constant voltage difference of $(T_1 - T_2)E_1$ volts.

The preceding example points out the ease with which one can evaluate the steady-state system response for an input that is a power series in

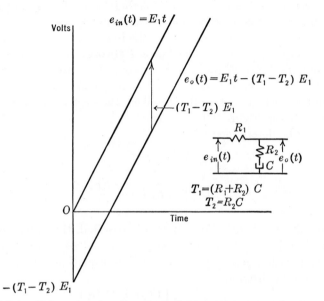

FIGURE 4.8–1.   Voltage input $e_{in}(t)$ and steady-state component of voltage output $e_o(t)$ for $RC$ network of Figure 4.4–2.

time. Not only is the expression for the transform simplified by virtue of the absence of the initial conditions, but also only those terms in the complete answer that are derived from the driving transform need have their inverse transform determined.

### 4.9   Application of the Laplace Transformation to Servomechanism Problems

In concluding this chapter on the use of the direct and inverse trans-formation for the solution of linear differential equations, it is worth while to describe briefly some of the types of servomechanism problems to which the Laplace transform method will be applied. The information sought from a problem solution has a pronounced effect on the extent to which the initial excitation and/or driving functions are important. By considering at the outset only those parts of the excitation function that will yield the required response information, that is, the transient and/or steady-state responses, the process of performing the Laplace transform may be shortened materially.

The excitation functions that are of interest in servomechanism problems tend to be of the following three types:

1. An external driving function is applied to a system in which the initial excitation function has a value. The transient response as well as the steady-state response are of interest in this case.

2. An external driving function is applied to a system that is initially at rest. As in the case above, transient and steady-state responses are desired.

3. An external driving function is applied to a system in which the value of the initial excitation function is immaterial. In this case only the steady-state performance is desired. Of particular importance here are the cases of a sinusoidal driving function, or driving functions consisting of a power series in time.

The first case above typifies the general problem, and it is necessary to include both the driving function and the initial excitation function. The initial energy stored in the individual elements of the system is represented by the initial conditions that appear in the initial excitation function. Both the steady-state and the transient responses can be determined by obtaining the inverse transform of the expression $F(s)$, as indicated by Equation 4.5–8. Those terms of the partial fractional expansion of $F(s)$ that have in their denominator factors of the system function yield transient response terms; those terms that have in their denominator factors of the excitation functions yield steady-state response terms. The complexity of this general solution frequently is not warranted.

In the second case the system is at rest and the initial values of the stored energy are zero. It is this type of solution that is more frequently performed when transient analyses are made. The Laplace transformations of the differentiation and integration processes of Section 4.3, Table 4.3–1, simplify down to

$$\mathcal{L}\left[\frac{df(t)}{dt}\right] = sF(s)$$

and

$$\mathcal{L}\left[\int f(t)\, dt\right] = \frac{F(s)}{s}$$

(4.9–1)

Hence the excitation function is merely that produced by the external driving forces, and a simpler response transform expression is obtained.

Since the transient and the steady-state responses are sought, it will be necessary to evaluate all the $C_k$ coefficients of Equation 4.5-3 and to perform the entire inverse transformation described by Equations 4.5-7 and 4.5-8.

For the third case where system performance is sought only after steady-state operating conditions have been obtained, simplification of both the direct and the inverse transformation is obtained as pointed out in Section 4.8. Since the value of the initial excitation function is immaterial, only the driving function appears in the excitation transform and a simpler response transform results. In performing the inverse transformation, only the $C_k$ coefficients of Equation 4.5-3, which are necessary for the $\mathcal{L}^{-1}$ transform of terms contributing to the steady-state solution, need be evaluated. The inverse transformations of the terms having $C_k$ coefficients derived for the factors of the system function all have time-decaying exponentials. It is not necessary to evaluate these coefficients or to perform the inverse transform if only the steady-state solution is required. Problems of this type are most frequently encountered in the study of servomechanisms and regulating systems.

It is of interest to note from the above comments that a close parallel exists in the general approach to the solution of linear differential equations by use of the Laplace transforms and the steady-state and transient methods described in the previous chapter. However, the completeness and the mathematical exactitude of the Laplace method make it preferable for general application. It provides a well-organized method in which the physical features of the problem are considered at the outset and the later algebraic manipulations are merely routine.

# 5

## STEADY-STATE OPERATION
## WITH SINUSOIDAL DRIVING FUNCTIONS

### 5.0 Introduction

The mathematical solution of the differential equations for a number of networks and servomechanism components, as they are subjected to various forms of driving functions, has been worked out in detail in Chapters 3 and 4. Although it was shown that the complete solution contains both transient and steady-state portions, it was indicated that the steady-state part could be obtained independently of the transient. The general form of the steady-state response for sinusoidal excitation was also found to be sinusoidal and of the same frequency as the driving function.

Because many of the useful concepts of servomechanism and regulator design are derived from the steady-state operation of networks with sinusoidal driving functions,[57] it is especially important that steady-state system performance for sinusoidal inputs be understood thoroughly. Not only should methods of simplifying the analysis for such cases be understood, but also a sufficient familiarity with this work should be obtained to facilitate synthesis of components to produce any desired performance. To these ends, this chapter further describes the impedance concept employed in obtaining steady-state response and indicates short-cut methods that can be performed by use of this concept.[5, 10, 19]

Since modern methods of servomechanism and regulator design involve a knowledge of the steady-state response of a system as a function of frequency,[26, 31] this aspect of steady-state performance is considered in detail for some simple elements in the latter portion of this chapter. Use is made of complex plane diagrams in which the magnitude and the angle of the output to input ratio are shown by a single line on the complex plane. Examples are also given in which separate plots are made of the magnitude and phase angle of the output-input ratio as a function of frequency. This attenuation-frequency concept is merely introduced in this chapter; it is discussed more thoroughly in Chapters 11, 12, and 13 where its application to servomechanism and regulator design is stressed.

As will be indicated later, a knowledge of the steady-state response of a system to a sinusoidal input can provide an indication of the characteristic form of the transient response of the system. Although this chapter deals only with the steady-state sinusoidal performance, it should not be inferred that transient performance is not important or that it should be neglected.

### 5.1 Impedance Concept

The term impedance was described in Section 3.6 for electrical networks, and it was shown that the expression for the impedance in complex form could be obtained by substituting $j\omega$ for $p$ in the reduced operational form of the polynomial in $p$ obtained from the differential equation. That this procedure may be used for obtaining the impedance of other types of circuits as well as for purely electrical ones was indicated in Section 3.8.

The Laplace transform is intimately related to the impedance concept when only steady-state excitation with sinusoidal driving forces are considered. For the Laplace transform also it will be found that $s$ may be replaced by $j\omega$. The similarity of the Laplace and steady-state methods of solution is described below.

When sinusoidal excitation is applied and only steady-state performance is desired, the initial excitation function in the Laplace transform can be set equal to zero. The general form of the response function as set forth in Section 4.4 is

Response function = (System function)(Excitation function)     (5.1–1)

Expressed in transform form, Equation 4.4–12 represents such a grouping of functions:

$$C(s) = \left[\frac{1}{Js^2 + Ds + K}\right][KR(s) + (Js + D)c(0) + Jc'(0)] \quad (4.4\text{–}12)$$

With only a sinusoidal driving force,

$$r(t) = R_0 \cos \omega t \quad (5.1\text{–}2)$$

and

$$R(s) = \mathcal{L}[R_0 \cos \omega t] = \frac{sR_0}{s^2 + \omega^2} \quad (5.1\text{–}3)$$

Thus Equation 4.4–12 becomes

$$C(s) = \left(\frac{1}{G(s)}\right) \frac{sKR_0}{s^2 + \omega^2} \tag{5.1-4}$$

where

$$\frac{1}{G(s)} = \frac{1}{Js^2 + Ds + K} \tag{5.1-5}$$

is the transform of the system function.

Since only the steady-state sinusoidal term in the response $c(t)$ is of interest, the methods for taking the inverse transform indicated in Equations 4.6–4, 4.6–6, and 4.6–7 apply. Hence

$$c(t) = \mathcal{L}^{-1}[C(s)] = I_m \left[\frac{KR_0}{G(j\omega)} je^{j\omega t}\right] \tag{5.1-6}$$

$$c(t) = \frac{KR_0}{|G(j\omega)|} \cos(\omega t - \theta_G) \tag{5.1-7}$$

where

$$|G(j\omega)| = \sqrt{(K - \omega^2 J)^2 + (\omega D)^2} \tag{5.1-8}$$

and

$$\theta_G = \tan^{-1}\left(\frac{\omega D}{K - \omega^2 J}\right) \tag{5.1-9}$$

Comparing Equations 5.1–7, 5.1–8, and 5.1–9 with Equation 3.8–10, in which $|Z|$ and $\theta_Z$ are as defined in Equations 3.8–7 and 3.8–8, one notices the identical nature of the magnitudes $|Z(j\omega)|$ and $|G(j\omega)|$, and the angles $\theta_Z$ and $\theta_G$. According to this example as well as the more rigorous analytical methods the mathematical manipulations for the Laplace and steady-state sinusoidal methods are apparently the same. It likewise appears that the substitution of $s$ or $p$ ($= j\omega$) for $d(\ )/dt$ in steady-state sinusoidal excitation may be of assistance in using the Laplace transform. The substitution is merely one of convenience to aid in the interpretation or handling of a problem; it is little more than a system of shorthand. This point is illustrated in the next two sections, where the impedance of individual elements and groups of elements is considered.

## 5.2  Impedance of Individual Elements

Not only may the total impedance, $Z(j\omega)$ or $G(j\omega)$, for a network or system be obtained by replacing $s$ by $j\omega$ throughout the system function of Equation 5.1–1, but also the impedance of each element in a group may be obtained by replacing $s$ in its transform by $j\omega$. Furthermore, the impedance concept need not be limited to electrical elements, but may also be used in conjunction with the differential equations of mechanical, thermal, hydraulic, or other physical systems when $s$ in a transform is replaced by $j\omega$.

Table 5.2–1 shows a summary of the voltage equations of electrical network elements in derivative, transform, and complex form associated

TABLE 5.2–1

SUMMARY OF VOLTAGE EQUATIONS AND COMPLEX QUANTITIES FOR ELECTRICAL NETWORK ELEMENTS

| Derivative Form | Transform Form | Complex Form | Complex Impedance |
|---|---|---|---|
| $L\dfrac{di(t)}{dt}$ | $LsI(s)$ | $j\omega LI(j\omega)$ | $j\omega L = jX_L$ |
| $Ri(t)$ | $RI(s)$ | $RI(j\omega)$ | $R$ |
| $\dfrac{1}{C}\int i(t)\,dt$ | $\dfrac{1}{C}\dfrac{I(s)}{s}$ | $\dfrac{I(j\omega)}{j\omega C}$ | $\dfrac{-j}{\omega C} = -jX_C$ |

with steady-state sinusoidal excitation. In addition, the impedance of each element is shown.

$X_L$ and $X_C$ are known as inductive and capacitive reactances, respectively, and are used to indicate those impedance components to sinusoidally varying currents that have their maximum values when the current has its greatest rate of change. The term impedance is general in that it describes both resistance and reactance elements.

In describing mechanical systems the term "motional impedance" is frequently employed, thus making it possible to distinguish between electrical and mechanical impedances in a system having a combination of these types of elements. Table 5.2–2 presents a set of force equations for mechanical elements analogous to those presented for electrical ele-

TABLE 5.2–2

SUMMARY OF FORCE EQUATIONS AND COMPLEX QUANTITIES FOR MECHANICAL SYSTEM ELEMENTS

| Derivative Form | Transform Form | Complex Form | Complex Impedance |
|---|---|---|---|
| $M\dfrac{dv(t)}{dt}$ | $MsV(s)$ | $j\omega MV(j\omega)$ | $j\omega M$ |
| $Dv(t)$ | $DV(s)$ | $DV(j\omega)$ | $D$ |
| $K\int v(t)\,dt$ | $\dfrac{KV(s)}{s}$ | $\dfrac{K}{j\omega}V(j\omega)$ | $-j\dfrac{K}{\omega}$ |

ments in Table 5.2–1.  The system constants used are the same as those used in the spring, mass, damper system of Section 3.8, namely, $M$ in slugs, $D$ in pounds per foot per second, and $K$ in pounds per foot.  The force equations have been written in terms of the velocity, $v(t)$, which corresponds to $(d/dt)x(t)$ of Section 3.8.  $V(s)$ is the $\mathcal{L}$ transform of $v(t)$, and $V(j\omega)$ is the corresponding complex velocity.  Comparison of Tables 5.2–1 and 5.2–2 serves to emphasize the similarity in form of the electrical and the mechanical systems of equations even though they differ markedly in their physical aspects.

The physical action of electrical and mechanical system elements is frequently described in terms of differential equations with the aid of such general physical laws as those described by Kirchhoff and Newton. The same physical phenomenon may also be accurately described in transform or complex forms, subject to the natural limitations listed by these universally accepted engineering laws.  When only the steady-state sinusoidal response is sought one generally deals with the transform or complex form of the equations rather than the derivative form.  Application of this principle is illustrated in the following section, where Kirchhoff's voltage and current laws are used extensively.

## 5.3  Aids to Simplifying Circuit Computations

The work required to solve complicated circuit configurations may be greatly reduced by using simplified expressions to represent various combinations of impedances and by using the various network theorems. The following material describes some of those network operations and theorems.[5, 10, 19]  The various voltages, currents, and impedances are all in the complex form.  For purposes of simplicity in symbolism, the complex form is indicated by the use of capital letters.

**Equivalent Impedance.**  In the remainder of this section it is assumed that steady-state sinusoidal excitation of a single frequency, $\omega$ radians

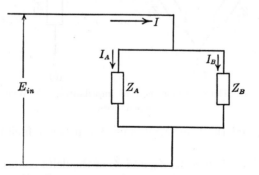

FIGURE 5.3–1.  Two impedances in parallel.

per second, is applied. Thus a current $I(j\omega)$ is represented as $I$ while the corresponding impedance $Z(j\omega)$ is indicated merely as $Z$.

The expression for the equivalent impedance of two impedances in parallel is readily derived by applying Kirchhoff's laws to Figure 5.3–1.

From the voltage law,

$$I_B Z_B - I_A Z_A = 0 \qquad (5.3\text{–}1)$$

The current law yields the equation

$$I - I_A - I_B = 0 \qquad (5.3\text{–}2)$$

Combining and solving for $I_A$ gives

$$I_A = \frac{Z_B I}{Z_A + Z_B} \qquad (5.3\text{–}3)$$

The total voltage drop across the two impedances is

$$E_{in} = Z_A I_A = \frac{Z_A Z_B}{Z_A + Z_B} I \qquad (5.3\text{–}4)$$

The equivalent impedance $Z$ is the impedance that, when multiplied by the total current $I$, gives the total voltage drop or

$$Z = \frac{Z_A Z_B}{Z_A + Z_B} \qquad (5.3\text{–}5)$$

**Wye-Delta Transformations.** In a way similar to that used above, the relationships between impedances connected in wye or delta, as shown in Figure 5.3–2 ($a$ and $b$), may be drawn. These groupings arise

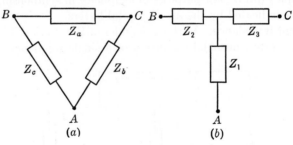

FIGURE 5.3–2. ($a$) Delta arrangement of impedances. ($b$) Wye arrangement of impedances.

occasionally, and the transformations shown below facilitate computation.

When the impedances $Z_a$, $Z_b$, and $Z_c$ of the delta connection shown in Figure 5.3–2a are known, the wye impedances $Z_1$, $Z_2$, and $Z_3$, which produce the same currents at terminals $A$, $B$, and $C$ for a given set of impressed voltage conditions, can be determined from Equations 5.3–6, 5.3–7, and 5.3–8.

Conversely, when the wye impedances $Z_1$, $Z_2$, and $Z_3$ shown in Figure 5.3–2b are known, the delta impedances $Z_a$, $Z_b$, and $Z_c$ of Figure 5.3–2a, which produce the same currents for the same terminal voltage conditions at $A$, $B$, and $C$, can be determined from Equations 5.3–9, 5.3–10, and 5.3–11.

$$Z_1 = \frac{Z_b Z_c}{Z_a + Z_b + Z_c} \qquad (5.3\text{–}6)$$

$$Z_2 = \frac{Z_a Z_c}{Z_a + Z_b + Z_c} \qquad (5.3\text{–}7)$$

$$Z_3 = \frac{Z_a Z_b}{Z_a + Z_b + Z_c} \qquad (5.3\text{–}8)$$

$$Z_a = \frac{Z_1 Z_2 + Z_2 Z_3 + Z_3 Z_1}{Z_1} \qquad (5.3\text{–}9)$$

$$Z_b = \frac{Z_1 Z_2 + Z_2 Z_3 + Z_3 Z_1}{Z_2} \qquad (5.3\text{–}10)$$

$$Z_c = \frac{Z_1 Z_2 + Z_2 Z_3 + Z_3 Z_1}{Z_3} \qquad (5.3\text{–}11)$$

**Superposition.**   Another aid to better understanding of circuit performance as well as to simplification of calculation is the principle of superposition.   This principle states that *in networks in which there is more than one source of voltage, the current produced by each voltage may be determined with the other voltages set equal to zero; the net current at any point is the algebraic sum of the currents produced by all the voltages.*   The

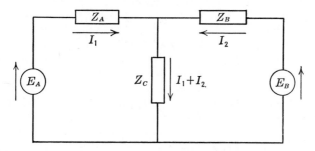

FIGURE 5.3–3.   Simple impedance network with two voltages impressed.

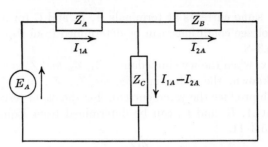

FIGURE 5.3–4.   Network of Figure 5.3–3 with only voltage $E_A$ impressed.

summation process is in effect the superposition of the currents produced by each voltage.

To illustrate this principle consider the network shown in Figure 5.3–3.   The customary circuit equations are

$$E_A = (Z_A + Z_C)I_1 + Z_C I_2 \qquad (5.3\text{–}12)$$

and

$$E_B = Z_C I_1 + (Z_B + Z_C)I_2 \qquad (5.3\text{–}13)$$

Solving for the currents $I_1$ and $I_2$ gives

$$I_1 = \frac{(Z_B + Z_C)E_A - Z_C E_B}{Z_A Z_B + Z_B Z_C + Z_C Z_A} \qquad (5.3\text{–}14)$$

and

$$I_2 = \frac{-Z_C E_A + (Z_A + Z_C)E_B}{Z_A Z_B + Z_B Z_C + Z_C Z_A} \qquad (5.3\text{–}15)$$

Using the principle of superposition, determine first the current components $I_{1A}$ and $I_{2A}$ that flow owing to the presence of $E_A$ alone.   Apply Kirchhoff's voltage law and Equation 5.3–5 to Figure 5.3–4.

$$I_{1A} = \frac{E_A}{Z_A + \dfrac{Z_B Z_C}{Z_B + Z_C}}$$

$$I_{1A} = \frac{(Z_B + Z_C)E_A}{Z_A Z_B + Z_B Z_C + Z_C Z_A} \qquad (5.3\text{–}16)$$

$$I_{2A} = \frac{Z_C}{Z_B + Z_C} I_{1A}$$

$$I_{2A} = \frac{Z_C E_A}{Z_A Z_B + Z_B Z_C + Z_A Z_C} \qquad (5.3\text{–}17)$$

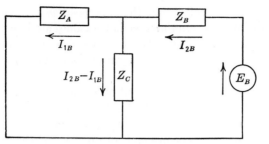

FIGURE 5.3–5.    Network of Figure 5.3–3 with only voltage $E_B$ impressed.

In similar fashion determine the current components $I_{1B}$ and $I_{2B}$, shown in Figure 5.3–5, for the case when only $E_B$ is applied.

$$I_{2B} = \cfrac{E_B}{Z_B + \cfrac{Z_A Z_C}{Z_A + Z_C}}$$

$$I_{2B} = \frac{(Z_A + Z_C)E_B}{Z_A Z_B + Z_B Z_C + Z_A Z_C} \tag{5.3–18}$$

$$I_{1B} = \frac{Z_C I_{2B}}{Z_A + Z_C}$$

$$I_{1B} = \frac{Z_C E_B}{Z_A Z_B + Z_B Z_C + Z_A Z_C} \tag{5.3–19}$$

Add the currents algebraically:

$$I_1 = I_{1A} - I_{1B}$$

$$I_1 = \frac{(Z_B + Z_C)E_A - Z_C E_B}{Z_A Z_B + Z_B Z_C + Z_A Z_C} \tag{5.3–20}$$

and

$$I_2 = -I_{2A} + I_{2B}$$

$$I_2 = \frac{-Z_C E_A + (Z_A + Z_C)E_B}{Z_A Z_B + Z_B Z_C + Z_A Z_C} \tag{5.3–21}$$

If the results of Equation 5.3–20 are compared with those of Equation 5.3–14, and those of Equation 5.3–21 with those of Equation 5.3–15, it is apparent that the same values for the currents $I_1$ and $I_2$ are obtained by either method of calculation. For the simple network chosen, the method of superposition holds no advantage; however, in more complicated networks its use is often quite advantageous.

It is important to realize that the *superposition principle can be used only* in those circuits where the impedance values are independent of the amplitudes of current or voltage, that is, *in systems with linear coefficients.* For many, but by no means all, cases in servomechanisms this condition is obtained.

By using the principle of superposition a number of network theorems can be derived that are helpful in solving complex circuit problems. Outstanding among them is Thévenin's theorem, which is described in the following material. The principle of superposing the effect of a number of driving functions to produce a single resultant can also be applied to advantage on mechanical as well as electrical systems.

**Thévenin's Theorem.** The effect of any impedance element in a circuit may be determined by replacing all the voltage sources in the system by one equivalent voltage source and all other impedances by one impedance in series with the impedance of interest. Thus any system reduces to a simple series circuit in which changes in the impedance being considered are readily determined. Figure 5.3–6a illustrates in block form a complex network whereas Figure 5.3–6b shows its simplified equivalent network.

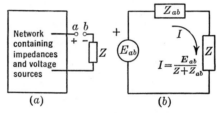

(a)                          (b)

FIGURE 5.3–6. (a) Block form of network containing a number of impedances and voltage sources. (b) Simplified equivalent voltage, equivalent impedance, and load impedance of (a).

The equivalent voltage $E_{ab}$ is equal to the open-circuit voltage that is present across the terminals $a$–$b$ with the circuit broken at this point. The equivalent impedance $Z_{ab} + Z$ is the impedance of the network that a voltage impressed across the terminals $a$–$b$ would see if all the voltage sources were replaced by their internal impedances. Since normally the internal impedances are represented as external impedances on a network diagram, this is the equivalent of replacing all voltage sources with short circuits.

In essence, the terminals $a$–$b$, which in the original system have no voltage across them, have a voltage $E_{ab}$ obtained from the other voltages and impedances with $a$–$b$ open. Superposed at $a$–$b$ is the negative of the same voltage, that is, $-E_{ab}$, impressed on the impedance of the network viewed from $a$–$b$ with all the other voltage sources removed. Thus the resultant voltage across $a$–$b$ is zero, as is actually the case, and the current through $Z$ is the correct value for the actual voltages and impedances of the system.

Use of Thévenin's theorem is illustrated in the simple problem that follows. In Figure 5.3–7, $Z_1$, $Z_2$, and $Z_3$ represent impedances of which

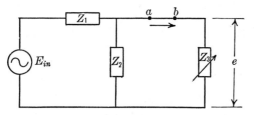

FIGURE 5.3–7.    Network used to illustrate application of Thévenin's theorem.

$Z_1$ and $Z_2$ are constant and $Z_3$ is adjustable. It is desired to determine the voltage $e$ as a function of the impedance $Z_3$ and the impressed voltage $E_{in}$.

With the circuit broken at $a$–$b$,

$$E_{ab} = \frac{Z_2}{Z_1 + Z_2} E_{in} \tag{5.3-22}$$

With the voltage source $E_{in}$ short-circuited, the impedance of the system viewed from $a$–$b$ is

$$Z_3 + \frac{Z_1 Z_2}{Z_1 + Z_2} = Z_3 + Z_{ab} \tag{5.3-23}$$

The current flowing through $Z_3$ is

$$I = \frac{E_{ab}}{Z_3 + Z_{ab}} = \frac{\dfrac{Z_2}{Z_1 + Z_2} E_{in}}{Z_3 + \dfrac{Z_1 Z_2}{Z_1 + Z_2}} \tag{5.3-24}$$

Since the desired voltage $e$ is equal to $I Z_3$,

$$e = \frac{Z_2 Z_3 E_{in}}{Z_3(Z_1 + Z_2) + Z_1 Z_2} = \frac{Z_2 E_{in}}{Z_1 + Z_2 + \dfrac{Z_1 Z_2}{Z_3}} \tag{5.3-25}$$

The result checks the voltage expression that is obtained from more straightforward methods of analysis for such a simple circuit.

Thévenin's theorem is applicable to both d-c and a-c voltages for steady-state conditions.

## 5.4  Performance as a Function of Frequency

In the preceding material the sinusoidal driving functions considered have been of a single frequency.  If, in the analysis of a system, calculations are made for only one frequency, the knowledge of the system performance will be limited to that frequency.  In certain cases this information may be sufficient.  However, in the study of servomechanisms and regulators one is frequently interested in knowing the response of the system over a considerable part or all of the frequency range.[26, 31, 62, 86] The remainder of this chapter will be devoted to analyzing steady-state system performance as a function of frequency.  Simple electrical circuits and electromechanical systems will be treated in this fashion.

**Resistance-Inductance Circuit.**     Figure  5.4–1 shows a series $RL$ circuit having a sinusoidal applied voltage.  This is similar to the cir-

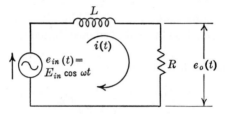

FIGURE 5.4–1.   Simple $RL$ circuit with sinusoidal voltage applied.

cuit  considered  in  Section  3.6.    It  is  now  desired  to  determine $E_o/E_{in}(j\omega)$, the ratio of the output voltage to the input voltage, as a function of frequency.  The steady-state expression for this ratio is

$$\frac{E_o}{E_{in}}(j\omega) = \frac{R}{R + j\omega L} \tag{5.4–1}$$

or

$$\frac{E_o}{E_{in}}(j\omega) = \frac{R}{\sqrt{R^2 + (\omega L)^2}} \bigg/ \tan^{-1} - \frac{\omega L}{R} \tag{5.4–2}$$

From these equations it can be seen that both the magnitude and the phase of the ratio $E_o/E_{in}(j\omega)$ are dependent on the excitation frequency, $\omega$.   The voltages across the resistance and inductance are shown on the complex plane in Figure 5.4–2 for a particular frequency $\omega$ and for that instant of time when $e_{in} = E_{in}$.

Note that at any frequency the angle between the voltage $RI(j\omega)$ and the voltage $j\omega LI(j\omega)$ is a right angle and that the sum of these two quantities is always real and equal to $E_{in}$.   Therefore the complex quantity $RI(j\omega)$ must lie on a semicircle.   But since $E_o(j\omega) = RI(j\omega)$ and since $E_{in}$ is real and constant, the ratio $E_o/E_{in}(j\omega)$ must always have the same orientation as $RI(j\omega)$, the only difference being in their magnitudes. Consequently, if $E_o/E_{in}(j\omega)$ is plotted on the complex plane, it also must lie on a semicircle for all values of $\omega$.

For convenience in describing the complex plane plot of Equation 5.4–1 the equation is written in terms of $\omega T$ where $T = L/R$ is the circuit time constant.

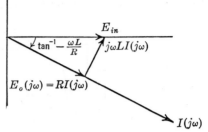

$$\frac{E_o}{E_{in}}(j\omega T) = \frac{1}{1 + j\omega T} \quad (5.4\text{–}3)$$

FIGURE 5.4–2. Voltages present in circuit of Figure 5.4–1 shown on complex plane when $e_{in} = E_{in}$.

The equation in this form is said to be non-dimensional since $\omega T$ is merely a numeric. As the value of the excitation frequency $\omega$ is varied from $\omega = 0$ to $\omega = \infty$, the complex quantity, $E_o/E_{in}(j\omega T)$ decreases in the manner shown in Figure 5.4–3. The locus of $E_o/E_{in}(j\omega T)$

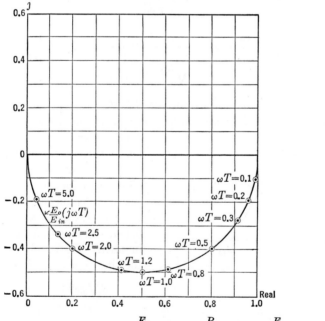

FIGURE 5.4–3. Complex-plane plot of $\dfrac{E_o}{E_{in}}(j\omega) = \dfrac{R}{R + j\omega L}$ where $\dfrac{E_o}{E_{in}}(j\omega)$ is expressed in the non-dimensionalized form

$$\frac{E_o}{E_{in}}(j\omega T) = \frac{1}{1 + j\omega T}$$

$$T = L/R \text{ seconds}$$

is a semicircle with its center on the real axis and with a radius equal
to one-half the value of the $E_o/E_{in}(j\omega T)$ ratio at $\omega = 0$.

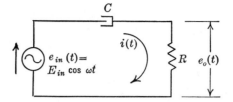

FIGURE 5.4–4.   Simple $RC$ circuit with sinusoidal voltage applied.

**Resistance-Capacitance Circuit.**   A series $RC$ circuit excited by a
sinusoidal voltage is shown in Figure 5.4–4.   The ratio of the output
voltage to the input voltage $E_o/E_{in}(j\omega)$ at steady state is

$$\frac{E_o}{E_{in}}(j\omega) = \frac{R}{R + \dfrac{1}{j\omega C}} \tag{5.4–4}$$

or

$$\frac{E_o}{E_{in}}(j\omega) = \frac{R}{\sqrt{R^2 + \dfrac{1}{(\omega C)^2}}}\ \bigg/ \tan^{-1}\frac{1}{\omega RC} \tag{5.4–5}$$

Equation 5.4–5 shows that, for the $RC$ circuit, the magnitude and
phase of $E_o/E_{in}(j\omega)$ are both functions of the frequency $\omega$.   Figure
5.4–5 shows the complex voltages
across the resistance and the capacitance elements for a particular excitation frequency $\omega$.

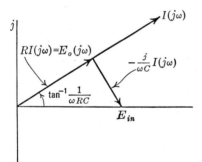

For convenience in representing
the complex plane plot of Equation
5.4–4, the equation may be written
in terms of $\omega T$, where $T = RC$ is
the time constant of the circuit.

$$\frac{E_o(j\omega T)}{E_{in}} = \frac{j\omega T}{1 + j\omega T} \tag{5.4–6}$$

FIGURE 5.4–5.   Voltages present in circuit of Figure 5.4–4 shown on complex
plane when $e_{in} = E_{in}$.

Figure 5.4–6 is a plot of Equation 5.4–6 and shows how the ratio
$E_o/E_{in}(j\omega T)$, expressed in non-dimensionalized form, varies as $\omega$ is
increased from 0 to $\infty$.   The locus of points described by $E_o/E_{in}(j\omega T)$

is a semicircle as indicated, the center of which is located on the real axis and the radius of which is equal to one-half the $E_o/E_{in}(j\omega T)$ ratio when $\omega = \infty$.

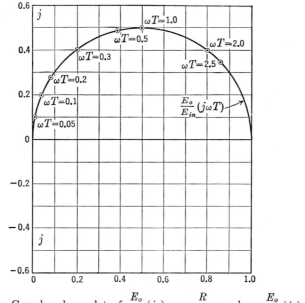

FIGURE 5.4–6.   Complex-plane plot of $\dfrac{E_o}{E_{in}}(j\omega) = \dfrac{R}{R + \dfrac{1}{j\omega C}}$ where $\dfrac{E_o}{E_{in}}(j\omega)$ is expressed in the non-dimensionalized form

$$\frac{E_o}{E_{in}}(j\omega T) = \frac{j\omega T}{1 + j\omega T} \qquad T = RC \text{ seconds}$$

**Direct-Current Shunt Motor with Constant Field Excitation.** In a manner similar to the treatment of simple electric circuits, the performance of other dynamic systems may be represented on the complex plane when sinusoidal driving forces are applied. Consider the d-c motor with constant field excitation shown in Figure 5.4–7. The

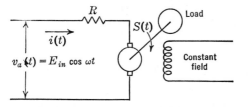

FIGURE 5.4–7.   Direct-current shunt motor with constant field excitation and variable armature voltage impressed.

following table of symbols applies:

$v_a(t)$ = applied voltage, volts

$R$ = armature circuit resistance including external resistance of brushes, lines, and internal resistance of voltage source, ohms

$i(t)$ = current, amperes

$K_e$ = voltage constant of motor, volts per radian per second

$K_T$ = torque constant of motor, pound-feet per ampere

$S(t)$ = angular velocity of motor, radians per second

$J$ = motor and load inertia referred to motor shaft, slug feet[2]

The voltage impressed across the motor is equal to the ohmic resistance drop plus the motor back emf.   Symbolically,

$$v_a(t) = Ri(t) + K_eS(t) \qquad (5.4\text{--}7)$$

The electromechanical torque accelerating the motor and load inertia is proportional to the motor current flowing.

$$\frac{J \, dS(t)}{dt} = K_T i(t) \qquad (5.4\text{--}8)$$

If the Laplace transform of Equations 5.4–7 and 5.4–8 is taken with the initial conditions set equal to zero,

$$V_a(s) = RI(s) + K_eS(s) \qquad (5.4\text{--}9)$$

and

$$JsS(s) = K_T I(s) \qquad (5.4\text{--}10)$$

Combining Equations 5.4–9 and 5.4–10 by eliminating $I(s)$ gives

$$V_a(s) = K_e \left[ \frac{JR}{K_T K_e} s + 1 \right] S(s) \qquad (5.4\text{--}11)$$

and the transform for the motor speed is

$$S(s) = \frac{V_a(s)}{K_e[T_m s + 1]} \qquad (5.4\text{--}12)$$

where the motor time constant $T_m$ is

$$T_m = \frac{JR}{K_T K_e} \qquad (5.4\text{--}13)$$

For the case of sinusoidal variation of the voltage $v_a(t)$ at a frequency $\omega$,

$$v_a(t) = E_{in} \cos \omega t \qquad (5.4\text{--}14)$$

and the ratio $S/E_{in}(j\omega)$ is

$$\frac{S}{E_{in}}(j\omega) = \frac{1}{K_e(1 + j\omega T_m)} \qquad (5.4\text{–}15)$$

or

$$\frac{S}{E_{in}}(j\omega) = \frac{1}{K_e\sqrt{1 + (\omega T_m)^2}} \underline{/\tan^{-1} - \omega T_m} \qquad (5.4\text{–}16)$$

The ratio $S/E_{in}(j\omega)$ of Equation 5.4–15 may be expressed as a function of $\omega T_m$ as

$$K_e \frac{S}{E_{in}}(j\omega T_m) = \frac{1}{(1 + j\omega T_m)} \qquad (5.4\text{–}17)$$

On Figure 5.4–8, Equation 5.4–17 is plotted on the complex plane as a function of $\omega T_m$.

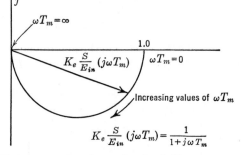

FIGURE 5.4–8. Plot on complex plane of ratio of $K_e \times$ motor speed to armature voltage of d-c motor shown on Figure 5.4–7 as a function of $\omega T_m$.

The effect of changing the frequency of excitation voltage on an electromechanical system is to produce a change in the magnitude and the phase angle of the output speed with respect to the input voltage. Although at low values of $\omega$ the speed $S(t)$ is in phase with the sinusoidally varying voltage $v_a(t)$, for higher values of frequency the maximum speed obtained is reduced in magnitude and occurs at a different time (that is, phase) from the time when the voltage is a maximum.

In the study of position-control servomechanism systems, the position $\theta(t)$ rather than the speed $S(t)$ is of major concern. Recalling that

$$S(t) = \frac{d\theta(t)}{dt} \qquad (5.4\text{–}18)$$

the transform $S(s)$ may be expressed in terms of $\theta(s)$ as

$$S(s) = s\theta(s) \qquad (5.4\text{–}19)$$

By substituting this value of $S(s)$ in Equation 5.4–12, the transform of the motor shaft position in terms of the applied voltage can be written as

$$\theta(s) = \frac{V_a(s)}{K_e s(T_m s + 1)} \qquad (5.4\text{–}20)$$

With a sinusoidal variation for $v_a(t)$, as given by Equation 5.4–14,

$$\frac{\theta}{E_{in}}(j\omega) = \frac{1}{K_e j\omega[1 + j\omega T_m]} \qquad (5.4\text{–}21)$$

and

$$\frac{\theta}{E_{in}}(j\omega) = \frac{1}{K_e \omega \sqrt{1 + (\omega T_m)^2}} \underline{/-90 + \tan^{-1}(-\omega T_m)}$$
$$(5.4\text{–}22)$$

Rewriting Equation 5.4–21 in terms of the quantity $\omega T_m$ gives

$$\frac{K_e}{T_m} \frac{\theta}{E_{in}}(j\omega T_m) = \frac{1}{j\omega T_m(1 + j\omega T_m)} \qquad (5.4\text{–}23)$$

Figure 5.4–9 is a plot of $\theta/E_{in}(j\omega T_m)$ in the non-dimensionalized form of Equation 5.4–23. As $\omega T_m$ approaches zero, the ratio of $K_e \theta/T_m E_{in}(j\omega T_m)$

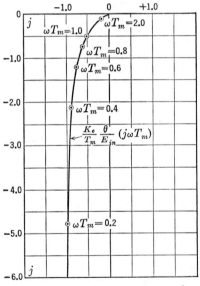

FIGURE 5.4–9.   Complex-plane plot of $\dfrac{\theta}{E_{in}}(j\omega) = \dfrac{1}{K_e j\omega(1 + j\omega T_m)}$ for d-c motor of Figure 5.4–7, where $\dfrac{\theta}{E}(j\omega)$ is expressed in the non-dimensionalized form

$$\left(\frac{K_e}{T_m}\right) \frac{\theta}{E_m}(j\omega T_m) = \frac{1}{j\omega T_m(1 + j\omega T_m)}$$

approaches infinity in magnitude and $-90°$ in phase angle. As $\omega T_m$ approaches infinity, the magnitude of $K_e\theta/T_mE_{in}(j\omega T_m)$ approaches zero and the phase angle is $180°$. At any frequency the phase angle of $K_e\theta/T_mE_{in}(j\omega T_m)$ is $-90°$ plus the corresponding phase angle of $K_eS/E_{in}(j\omega T_m)$ in Equation 5.4–17.

**Mechanical Spring-Mass System.** Figure 5.4–10 shows the spring-mass system considered in Section 3.8 for which the steady-state per-

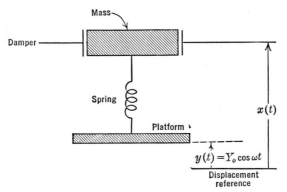

FIGURE 5.4–10.    Spring-mass system with sinusoidal driving motion.

formance with a sinusoidal displacement of the platform was given by Equation 3.8–9. This equation can be written as

$$\frac{X_s}{Y_0}(j\omega) = \frac{K\Big/\tan^{-1}\dfrac{-\omega D}{K - \omega^2 M}}{\sqrt{(K - \omega^2 M)^2 + (\omega D)^2}} \qquad (5.4\text{–}24)$$

To express $X_s/Y_0(j\omega)$ in a non-dimensionalized form, Equation 5.4–24 may be written in terms of the undamped natural frequency, $\omega_0 = \sqrt{K/M}$ so that the terms containing $\omega$ can be written as $\omega/\omega_0$. Employing this substitution in Equation 3.8–2 with only sinusoidal excitation considered gives

$$\frac{X_s}{Y_0}\left(j\frac{\omega}{\omega_0}\right) = \frac{1}{1 + \left(j\dfrac{\omega}{\omega_0}\right)^2 + j\dfrac{\omega}{\omega_0}\dfrac{D}{\sqrt{KM}}} \qquad (5.4\text{–}25)$$

or

$$\frac{X_s}{Y_0}\left(j\frac{\omega}{\omega_0}\right) = \frac{1}{\sqrt{\left[1 - \left(\dfrac{\omega}{\omega_0}\right)^2\right]^2 + \left[\dfrac{\omega}{\omega_0}\dfrac{D}{\sqrt{KM}}\right]^2}}\Bigg/\tan^{-1}\frac{\dfrac{-\omega}{\omega_0}\dfrac{D}{\sqrt{KM}}}{1 - \left(\dfrac{\omega}{\omega_0}\right)^2}$$

$$(5.4\text{–}26)$$

Allowing $\omega/\omega_0$ to take on values from zero to infinity, one obtains the plot of $X_s/Y_0(j\omega)$ as shown in Figure 5.4–11. It will be noted that, for $\omega/\omega_0 = 0$, $X_s/Y_0(j\omega/\omega_0)$ is of unit magnitude and has a phase angle of zero. The magnitude of $X_s/Y_0(j\omega/\omega_0)$ decreases as the frequency of $\omega$ increases and $X_s$, the position of the mass, lags behind the platform

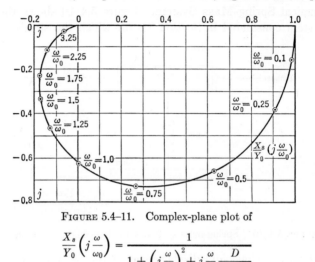

FIGURE 5.4–11.   Complex-plane plot of

$$\frac{X_s}{Y_0}\left(j\,\frac{\omega}{\omega_0}\right) = \frac{1}{1 + \left(j\,\dfrac{\omega}{\omega_0}\right)^2 + j\,\dfrac{\omega}{\omega_0}\,\dfrac{D}{\sqrt{KM}}}$$

for spring-mass system of Figure 5.4–10, where $\omega_0 = \sqrt{\dfrac{K}{M}}$, and $\dfrac{D}{\sqrt{KM}} = 1.6$ corresponding to $\zeta = 0.8$.

position in phase angle. As $\omega/\omega_0$ increases toward infinity, the mass moves with decreasing amplitude and is 180° out of phase with the platform motion.

Although the plot of $X_s/Y_0(j\omega/\omega_0)$ of Figure 5.4–11 does not describe a simple semicircular plot such as was obtained for the simple electrical networks previously considered, nevertheless this plot and that for the d-c shunt motor described above serve to show that the steady-state sinusoidal performance of both electrical and mechanical systems may be effectively presented on a complex plane plot.

## 5.5   Attenuation and Phase Angle Representation of System Performance for Sinusoidal Excitation

The preceding section has developed the equations and has indicated on the complex plane the steady-state performance of a few representative servomechanism elements when sinusoidal driving functions having frequencies over the entire range from zero to infinity are used.   Engineers skilled in communications techniques [43, 46, 56] have been instrumental in making widespread the usage of concepts that appear foreign to the control of mechanical, hydraulic, and electrical power for industrial and other purposes. Foremost among these concepts are the steady-state attenuation and phase representation of the performance of systems as a function of frequency. In the following sections some of the terms are presented, such as decibels, decade, and octave, that are used in this form of representation. Performance curves, which are the counterparts of the complex plane diagrams for the elements described in Section 5.4, are also shown.

**Definitions of Attenuation Terms.** The attenuation-frequency presentation of data consists of a plot of the magnitude of the sinusoidal response of a system versus the frequency of the sinusoidal excitation.[62, 86] The logarithm of the magnitude is plotted in units of decibels, and the frequency is plotted in radians per second on a scale that is logarithmic. Figures 5.5–1 through 5.5–5 described later show such plots.

The *decibel* is the unit used to describe the magnitude of a number; the value in decibels for a quantity having a magnitude $N$ is 20 times the logarithm to the base 10 of the magnitude $N$. Thus, if $n$ is the value in decibels of the number $N$,

$$n = 20 \log_{10} N \qquad (5.5\text{–}1)$$

The term decibel was used originally in communication engineering with a rather strict and limited meaning. As used in servomechanisms it is frequently applied rather loosely, and occasionally can be used so that the number $N$ need not be dimensionless. Needless to say, an over-all consistency of units must be maintained.

When the difference in decibels between the two numbers $N_1$ and $N_2$ is sought, the value in decibels of the resultant difference is the same as the decibels corresponding to the ratio of $N_1$ and $N_2$. Thus

$$20 \log_{10} N_1 - 20 \log_{10} N_2 = 20 \log_{10} \frac{N_1}{N_2} \qquad (5.5\text{–}2)$$

This difference will be positive or negative, depending on whether $N_1$ is greater or less than $N_2$, that is, whether $N_1/N_2$ is greater or less than 1. With a value of $N_1/N_2$ of unity, the decibel difference is zero. Hence by reference to the sign associated with a given number of decibels, one can determine whether $N_1$ is greater or less than $N_2$. Although strictly an *increase* in magnitude *is* termed a *gain* and a *decrease* is called an *attenuation*, the two terms gain and attenuation, as they are *frequently* used in servomechanisms work, are *applied interchangeably* when referring to diagrams or equations. By reference to the diagrams or equations, one can establish definitely whether there has been an increase or a decrease in magnitude.

Table 5.5–1 presents a tabulation of the magnitude and decibel value of some representative common numbers.

TABLE 5.5–1

MAGNITUDE AND DECIBEL VALUES OF REPRESENTATIVE COMMON NUMBERS

| Magnitude | Value in Decibels |
|:---:|:---:|
| 1 | 0 |
| 2 | + 6 |
| 10 | +20 |
| 100 | +40 |
| 0.1 | −20 |
| 0.2 | −14 |

Two units that are used extensively to describe the amount of change in the excitation frequency are *octave*, indicating a frequency change of 2 to 1, and *decade*, indicating a frequency change of 10 to 1.

The number of octaves represented by the difference in frequency from $f_2$ to $f_1$ is determined from the ratio

$$\frac{\log_{10} f_2/f_1}{\log_{10} 2} = 3.32 \log_{10} f_2/f_1 \text{ octaves} \qquad (5.5\text{–}3)$$

Since the logarithm to the base 10 of 10 is 1, the corresponding number of decades represented by the frequency ratio $f_2/f_1$ is

$$\log_{10} \frac{f_2}{f_1} \text{ decades} \qquad (5.5\text{–}4)$$

Thus Equations 5.5–3 and 5.5–4 permit one to calculate correctly the octaves or decades associated with a given change in frequency $f_2$ to $f_1$. Although much of the work associated with the use of the attenuation-frequency concept is graphical, the defining equations given above are important.

In Section 2.3 it was demonstrated by Equations 2.3–18 and 2.3–19 that to represent fully the logarithm of a complex number it was necessary to indicate not only the logarithm of its magnitude but also the size of its phase angle. The preceding definitions of decibel as describing a number by a constant times the common logarithm of another number permits one to represent only the magnitude of a complex number. To describe completely a complex number, however, it is also essential that the phase angle of the number be presented. The regular angular unit of degrees is used for the purpose of representing phase angles.

**Illustrations of Attenuation Phase Representation as a Function of Frequency.** The interrelation of the attenuation versus frequency characteristics and the phase versus frequency characteristics of physical systems has received extensive analytical study and will be the subject of some consideration later in Chapter 11. However, for the present purpose, it will be sufficient to describe by means of attenuation-and phase-frequency diagrams the performance of the systems analyzed in Section 5.4. The plots are made on semilog paper with the frequency plotted directly on the logarithmic scale for the abscissa, whereas the magnitude in decibels and the phase shift in angular degrees are plotted on the linear scales as ordinates.

The plot of the actual magnitudes of the quantities in decibels is shown by the solid lines, whereas the dotted lines represent straight-line approximations to the attenuation-frequency characteristics. The subject of approximate attenuation characteristics is discussed further in Chapters 11 and 12.

By reference to Figures 5.5–1 through 5.5–5 one is able to obtain an impression of some of the characteristics of this method of presentation of system performance for sinusoidal excitation over a whole range of frequencies. One should compare these figures with the appropriate figures in Section 5.4, where the corresponding complex plots are drawn.

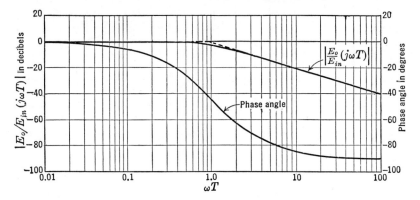

FIGURE 5.5–1. Attenuation and phase characteristics as a function of $\omega T$ for $LR$ system corresponding to Figure 5.4–3.

$$\frac{E_o}{E_{in}}(j\omega T) = \frac{1}{1 + j\omega T}$$

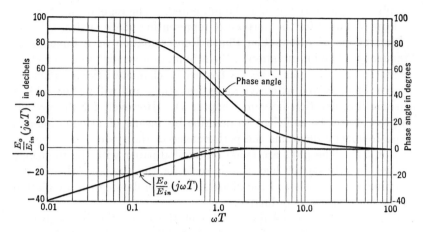

FIGURE 5.5–2.   Attenuation and phase characteristics as a function of $\omega T$ for $RC$ system corresponding to Figure 5.4–6.

$$\frac{E_o}{E_{in}}(j\omega T) = \frac{j\omega T}{1 + j\omega T}$$

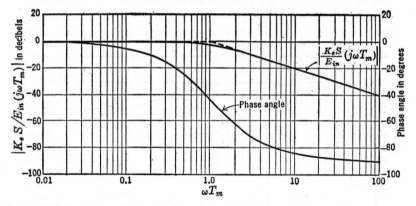

FIGURE 5.5–3.   Attenuation and phase characteristics as a function of $\omega T_m$ for

$$\frac{K_e S}{E_{in}}(j\omega T_m) = \frac{1}{1 + j\omega T_m}$$

corresponding to Figure 5.4–8.

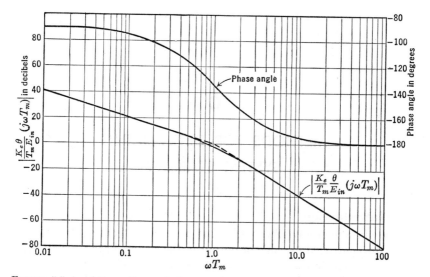

FIGURE 5.5-4. Attenuation and phase performance characteristics as a function of

$$\left(\frac{K_e}{T_m}\right)\frac{\theta}{E_{in}} = \frac{1}{j\omega T_m(1 + j\omega T_m)}$$

corresponding to Figure 5.4–9.

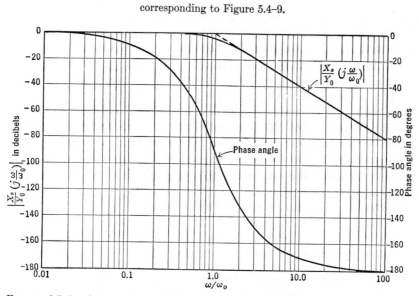

FIGURE 5.5-5. Attenuation and phase characteristics as a function of $\omega/\omega_0$ of

$$\frac{X_s}{Y_0}\left(j\frac{\omega}{\omega_0}\right) = \frac{1}{1 + \left(j\dfrac{\omega}{\omega_0}\right)^2 + j\dfrac{\omega}{\omega_0}\dfrac{D}{\sqrt{KM}}}$$

corresponding to Figure 5.4–11.

127

# 6

## METHODS FOR DETERMINING
## SYSTEM STABILITY

### 6.0  Introduction

The purpose of any servomechanism or feedback control system is to have the controlled variable or output of the system bear a definite and known relationship to the desired value or reference input.  To this end it is necessary that the transient response of the system to any temporary disturbance be a decaying one that vanishes a reasonable length of time after the cessation of the disturbance that caused the transient. Systems in which the motion of the controlled variable is random or erratic and not responsive to the reference input function or systems in which undesired self-sustained oscillations of the controlled variable are present are said to be unstable.  Instability is undesirable in that the controlled variable is not well controlled.  Frequently the condition of instability is dangerous because, if allowed to continue, it leads to undue wear or even failure of the system.

In the course of normal system design it is not merely necessary that the system be stable.  It is essential that the system be sufficiently stable so that transient disturbances will decay quickly enough to permit rapid recovery by the controlled variable.[88, 92]  In this chapter, however, the major emphasis is on the concept and methods of determining system stability.  Later chapters will indicate in suitable terms the amount of system stability that is required and desirable.

Because satisfactory system stability is imperative regardless of other considerations, a number of different methods of determining system stability have been developed as indicated below.

1. Determining the roots of the characteristic equation.

2. Determining the sign of the roots of the characteristic equation by Routh's criterion.

3. Determining the stability of the system from a complex plane plot and the use of the generalized form of Nyquist's criterion.

4. Determining graphically the locus of the roots for the closed-loop system starting with the poles and zeros of the open-loop system.

The attenuation and phase shift characteristics when plotted as a function of frequency provide a modified means for utilizing Nyquist's criterion. This procedure is described later in Chapter 11, where the attenuation and phase shift characteristics are explained more fully. The root locus method as developed by W. R. Evans [105] is a convenient graphical form for indicating the location of roots of the characteristic equation. Because of its strong dependence on the graphical significance of the mathematical expression for the open-loop control system characteristic, it warrants special attention rather than consideration as just another way of determining the roots of the characteristic equation. Although the stability of a number of the more standard control systems can be determined by limited forms of the stability criteria, the increasing complexity of controlled systems makes it desirable that a thorough understanding be obtained of the general methods of determining system stability.

## 6.1 Stability

The term stability can most easily be explained in terms of the response of the controlled variable to any sort of an input signal. A stable system is one in which the controlled variable has the ability to attain some constant value after responding to a temporary value of a reference input signal which then returns to zero.

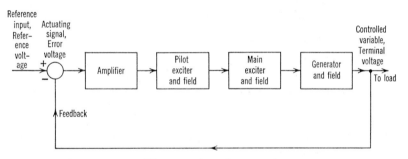

FIGURE 6.1–1.   Elements of a voltage regulator system.

If the system is unstable, the controlled variable motion may endeavor to follow the reference input motion, but the controlled variable may actually develop continued self-sustained oscillations of constantly increasing amplitude until some non-linearity or failure in the system brings a limit to the operation or to the magnitude of the oscillation. Although very small amplitudes of oscillation may sometimes be tolerated, in general this sort of operation is quite undesirable.

To obtain a clearer physical picture of the nature of the stability problem, consider a voltage regulator system like the one shown in block diagram form in Figure 6.1–1. The series arrangement of pilot exciter, main exciter, and generator, each having an inductive time constant associated with it, gives rise to the possibility of an unstable system. If the feedback of the output terminal voltage were disconnected and a small positive input of reference voltage occurred, the gain of the amplifier and the fields would produce a large positive change in output terminal voltage. However, without comparing the terminal voltage to the reference, the terminal voltage would rise to a value far in excess of the step-function disturbance that produced it. This is illustrated in Figure 6.1–2. The presence of the time constants in the fields prevents

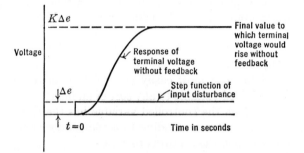

FIGURE 6.1–2.    Response of terminal voltage without feedback to step-function of input for voltage regulator system of Figure 6.1–1.

the rapid build-up of the terminal voltage following the input disturbance at time $t = 0$.

If now the case where the terminal voltage is fed back is considered, the *initial response* of the terminal voltage is very similar to that without feedback. However, as time passes the terminal voltage approaches the reference voltage, the actuating error signal goes to zero and then reverses sign increasing in value and with the opposite polarity from the initial error. Although at $t_1$ in Figure 6.1–3 the actuating error signal reverses, the time constants of the various generator fields tend to prevent the generator field current from decreasing. This current continues to drive the terminal voltage beyond the reference input signal until finally the terminal voltage comes to rest, $t_2$ on Figure 6.1–3. Since a difference in voltage $\Delta e'$ exists between the value of the controlled variable terminal voltage and the reference input voltage, the main generator field now starts to reduce the terminal voltage, and at time $t_3$ the actuating signal again goes through zero. The actuating signal now becomes of the opposite sense although the energy in the exciter and pilot fields continues to cause the terminal voltage to fall until $t_4$, when it differs from the reference voltage by $\Delta e''$. Since at successive times $t_0$, $t_2$, $t_4$, at which the rate of change of terminal voltage is zero, the absolute value of the actuating signal is increasing $\Delta e < \Delta e' < \Delta e''$, it appears that the controlled terminal voltage will not settle down to the value of

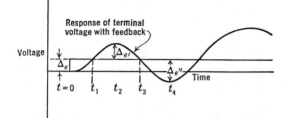

FIGURE 6.1–3.   Response of terminal voltage with feedback to a step-function of input for an unstable regulator system.

the reference voltage but will continue to oscillate with increasing amplitude until limited by saturation or failure of some of the system elements.   Such a system may be said to be unstable.

For a system similar to that shown in Figure 6.1–1, but having a lower gain and smaller or fewer time constants, the successive values of $\Delta e$, $\Delta e'$, and $\Delta e''$, at which the rate of change of terminal voltage is zero, will decrease.   Such a response for the controlled terminal voltage, shown in Figure 6.1–4, represents a stable system.

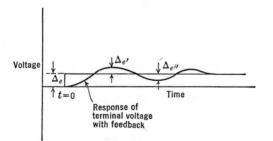
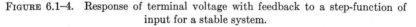

FIGURE 6.1–4.   Response of terminal voltage with feedback to a step-function of input for a stable system.

Experimental means of determining stability are time consuming and costly, if possible at all.   A qualitative physical approach is likewise unsatisfactory.   It is generally necessary to employ a quantitative method, either mathematical or graphical to determine system stability.

In Chapters 3 and 4, where the methods of solution of differential equations were discussed, it was pointed out that the transient form of the solution was $I_n e^{p_n t}$ or $C_k e^{s_k t}$, where $p_n$ and $s_k$ represented each of the roots of the characteristic equation of the system. For the transient terms to vanish with increasing values of time, it is necessary that the real part of all the roots of the characteristic equation be negative in sign. This is the mathematical condition for stability. Considered from the point of view of a plot of the location of these roots of the characteristic equation in the complex plane, this statement says in effect that for the system to be stable all the roots must lie in the area to the left of the origin. Conversely, a system having any roots of its characteristic equation lying to the right of the origin is an unstable system since its roots are positive. Figure 6.1–5 illustrates this division of the complex plane into the two areas corresponding to the location of the roots of the characteristic equation for stable ▨▨▨▨ and unstable ▨▨▨▨ systems.

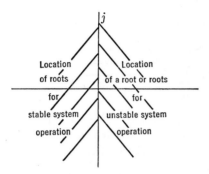

FIGURE 6.1–5.   Division of complex plane into regions for which the roots represent stable and unstable system operation.

The magnitude of the real part of the roots of the characteristic equations is inversely proportional to the time required for the transient disturbance to decay. Therefore, for stable, rapidly decaying transients, not only is it necessary that all the roots of the characteristic equation lie to the left of the imaginary axis, but these roots should lie as far to the left of the imaginary axis as possible.

This chapter considers only the stability of servomechanisms or regulators having linear elements. In Volume II, where non-linear operation is discussed, the effect of saturation on system stability is described in a qualitative fashion.

## 6.2   Determining the Roots of the Characteristic Equation

In Section 4.4 it was indicated that the characteristic equation and its roots are the same regardless of whether the characteristic equation is obtained from the Laplace transform or the operational approach. In this section the characteristic equation will be expressed in terms of the Laplace transform $s$.

The most straightforward but most time-consuming way of determining whether the roots of the characteristic equation have positive real parts is to evaluate the roots numerically.[27] It will be recalled that a root of the characteristic equation is that number, real or complex, that given to $s$ makes the equation equal to zero. Thus, if $(s - r)$ is a factor of the characteristic equation, $s = +r$ is a root of the equation. Hence it is necessary to determine the factors of the characteristic equation. This is essentially an algebraic process, and any one of a number of standard methods of determining the roots of a polynomial may be used.

Before describing some of the more simple methods whereby this can be done, the inverse process of forming the characteristic equation from a set of known roots will be performed. In this way certain useful properties will be revealed of the relationship between the *roots*, which are generally *unknown*, and the *coefficients* of the characteristic equation, which are generally *known*.

**Formation of the Characteristic Equation from Its Roots.** Suppose that there are three roots, $+r_1$, $+r_2$, and $+r_3$, where the $r$'s may be real or complex and may have the real part negative or positive.

$$(s - r_1)(s - r_2)(s - r_3) = 0 \tag{6.2-1}$$

Multiplying out the factors in Equation 6.2-1 yields

$$s^3 - (r_1 + r_2 + r_3)s^2 + (r_1r_2 + r_2r_3 + r_3r_1)s - r_1r_2r_3 = 0 \tag{6.2-2}$$

Let the roots be assigned the following values:

$$r_1 = a$$
$$r_2 = b + jc \tag{6.2-3}$$
$$r_3 = b - jc$$

where $a$, $b$, and $c$ are real numbers. Combining Equations 6.2-2 and 6.2-3 and simplifying gives

$$s^3 - (a + 2b)s^2 + (2ab + b^2 + c^2)s - a(b^2 + c^2) = 0 \tag{6.2-4}$$

From a study of the above equations and by employing the same approach to cases where there are more roots, the following relationships between the roots and the characteristic equations may be established.

1. The degree of the characteristic equation is equal to the number of the roots.

2. The roots, if complex, must occur in conjugate pairs so that the coefficients of the $s$ terms in the characteristic equation are real. The use of $j$ in the roots is a mathematical convenience, but $j$ cannot appear in the coefficients of the characteristic equation that have only real numerical values.

3. For the real parts of the roots to be negative as for a stable system, all the coefficients of the characteristic equation must have the same algebraic sign. This is a necessary, but not sufficient, condition.

4. Conversely, if not all the coefficients of the characteristic equation have the same sign or not all are present in the descending order of $s$, a root or roots must have a positive real part and the system is accordingly unstable.

These relationships provide a good basis for enabling one to determine whether a system may or may not be stable. Even though a system may have a characteristic equation that *may be* stable, it is not possible to tell by inspection if the system is definitely stable, that is, has all roots with negative real parts. The following sections indicate the process of evaluating the roots for equations from the second to fifth degree.

**Quadratic.** If the characteristic equation is the quadratic

$$as^2 + bs + c = 0 \qquad (6.2\text{-}5)$$

the roots are obtained by using the quadratic formula (developed in textbooks on advanced algebra). The solution for $s$ is

$$s_1, s_2 = -\frac{b}{2a} \pm \frac{1}{2a} \sqrt{b^2 - 4ac} \qquad (6.2\text{-}6)$$

If $b^2 > 4ac$, the two roots can be evaluated from Equation 6.2-6 directly. If $b^2 < 4ac$, the two roots are given by

$$s_1, s_2 = -\frac{b}{2a} \pm \frac{j}{2a} \sqrt{4ac - b^2} \qquad (6.2\text{-}7)$$

If $b^2 = 4ac$, the two roots are equal and are given by

$$s_1 = s_2 = -\frac{b}{2a} \qquad (6.2\text{-}8)$$

**Cubic.** If the characteristic equation is the cubic

$$as^3 + bs^2 + cs + d = 0 \qquad (6.2\text{-}9)$$

the information above reveals that there must be at least one real root and the other two may be real or they may be complex conjugates. The real root may be obtained by:

1. Plotting the value of the terms on the left side of the equation.
2. Factoring the polynomial if this is possible.
3. Performing synthetic division as indicated in the example below.

After the real root is factored out, the remaining quadratic may be evaluated as shown above.

*Example*

Find the roots of the following cubic equation:

$$s^3 + 9s^2 + 20s + 12 = 0$$

Take $(s + 1)$ as a trial factor and use synthetic division:

$$
\begin{array}{r}
1 + 9 + 20 + 12 \underline{\phantom{|}\;|\; -1} \\
-1 - \;\;8 - 12 \\
\hline
1 + 8 + 12 + \;\;0
\end{array}
$$

That $s_1 = -1$ is a root of the original equation is evidenced by the fact that the remainder for the last term is zero. Successive trials may be necessary to determine the value of this root when it is not an integer. The resulting quadratic,

$$s^2 + 8s + 12 = 0$$

may in this case be factored as $(s + 6)(s + 2)$. Hence the roots of the original equation are

$$s_1 = -1, \quad s_2 = -6, \quad \text{and} \quad s_3 = -2$$

**Quartic.** The following equation is a quartic:

$$as^4 + bs^3 + cs^2 + ds + e = 0 \qquad (6.2\text{--}10)$$

Since the roots may consist of two pairs of conjugates, there may be no direct method of obtaining the roots from plotting or synthetic division. A method that may be employed to advantage consists of factoring the quartic into two quadratics and determining the coefficients of the two quadratics that of course are real. The roots for each of the resultant quadratics are then evaluated independently.

Divide through by $a$, and the original quartic becomes

$$s^4 + \frac{b}{a}s^3 + \frac{c}{a}s^2 + \frac{d}{a}s + \frac{e}{a} = 0 \qquad (6.2\text{--}11)$$

Now assume Equation 6.2–11 to be factorable into two quadratics,

$$(s^2 + \alpha s + \beta)(s^2 + \gamma s + \delta) = 0 \qquad (6.2\text{--}12)$$

or

$$s^4 + (\alpha + \gamma)s^3 + (\beta + \delta + \alpha\gamma)s^2 + (\beta\gamma + \alpha\delta)s + \beta\delta = 0$$

Hence, by comparing coefficients, four simple equations are obtained:

$$\alpha + \gamma = \frac{b}{a} \qquad (6.2\text{--}13)$$

$$\beta + \delta + \alpha\gamma = \frac{c}{a} \qquad (6.2\text{--}14)$$

$$\beta\gamma + \alpha\delta = \frac{d}{a} \qquad (6.2\text{--}15)$$

$$\beta\delta = \frac{e}{a} \qquad (6.2\text{--}16)$$

The quantities on the right of each equal sign are known. By assuming a value of $\alpha$, the first three equations permit the evaluation of $\beta$, $\gamma$, and $\delta$. The fourth equation serves as a check of the original assumption of $\alpha$. An intermediate check of course is available from the fact that $\alpha$, $\beta$, $\gamma$, and $\delta$ must all be positive for a stable system. This method, suggested by A. Porter of England, permits rapid evaluation of the roots of a quartic equation. A variation of the method of factoring a quartic or higher degree equation by a quadratic is suggested by Brown and Campbell,[86] who indicate the process to be rapidly convergent.

*Example*

Find the roots of the following characteristic equation:

$$0.0039s^4 + 0.1037s^3 + 0.992s^2 + 2.264s + 3.190 = 0$$

$$0.0039[s^4 + 26.6s^3 + 254.4s^2 + 581.0s + 818.0] = 0$$

Compare the coefficients of the pair of quadratics with the coefficient of the equation above:

$$\alpha + \gamma = 26.6$$

$$\beta + \delta + \alpha\gamma = 254.4$$

$$\beta\gamma + \alpha\delta = 581$$

$$\beta\delta = 818$$

Solving these simple simultaneous equations yields the following values:

$$\alpha = 24.08$$

$$\gamma = 2.52$$

$$\beta = 190.0$$

$$\delta = 4.31$$

Hence
$$s^2 + 24.08s + 190 = 0$$
and
$$s^2 + 2.52s + 4.31 = 0$$

Solving for the four roots gives
$$s_1, s_2 = -12.04 \pm j6.75$$
and
$$s_3, s_4 = -1.26 \pm j1.65$$

**Quintic.**
$$as^5 + bs^4 + cs^3 + ds^2 + es + f = 0 \qquad (6.2\text{--}17)$$

By factoring out the real roots of the quintic, the characteristic equation is reduced to a quartic, which may be handled by the method outlined above.

*Example*

Reduce the following fifth-order characteristic equation to a fourth-order by obtaining a real root:

$$0.0039s^5 + 0.10565s^4 + 1.0438s^3 + 2.760s^2 + 4.322s + 1.595 = 0$$

Take $(s + 0.5)$ as a trial factor and use synthetic division.

$$
\begin{array}{l}
\underline{0.0039 + 0.10565 + 1.0438 + 2.76 \ \ + 4.322 + 1.595 \,\big|{-}\,0.5} \\
\qquad\quad\; -0.00195 - 0.0518 - 0.496 - 1.132 - 1.595 \\
\hline
0.0039 + 0.1037 \ \ + 0.992 \ \ + 2.264 + 3.190 + 0
\end{array}
$$

Since the remainder is zero, $s = -0.5$ is a root of the original quintic. The remaining quartic becomes

$$0.0039s^4 + 0.1037s^3 + 0.992s^2 + 2.264s + 3.190 = 0 \quad (6.2\text{--}18)$$

Note that this quartic equation is the same as that factored in the preceding example. Hence the remaining roots are those indicated for that example.

The labor involved in obtaining the roots of equations higher than a quintic is considerable. The methods outlined will be of assistance in obtaining the roots of higher degree equations if it is necessary to do so. Reference to the discussion of Graeffe's Root Squaring Method in *Mathematics of Modern Engineering*, Volume I, by Doherty and Keller,[12] or other textbooks will also prove profitable.

## 6.3   Routh's Criterion for Stability

As has been pointed out previously, it is not necessary to evaluate the actual magnitude of the roots to determine if a system is stable or not. However, it is essential to determine whether there are any roots that are real and positive or that have positive real parts.  This may be done quite directly by a process known as Routh's criterion outlined below. Although the process is rapid and exact, it suffers from one drawback in that no direct measure of stability is obtained as would be the case if the values of the real portions of the roots were known.  However, by determining the range of values of a system parameter over which stable operation is obtained some indication of the degree of stability can be given.

Consider a system to have a characteristic equation with constant coefficients, such as

$$a_0 s^n + a_1 s^{n-1} + a_2 s^{n-2} + \cdots + a_{n-1} s + a_n = 0 \qquad (6.3\text{-}1)$$

where $a_0$, $a_1$, $a_2$ $\cdots$ $a_{n-1}$, $a_n$ are the coefficients of the powers of $s$, and *all* coefficients of the decreasing powers of $s$ from $n$ to 0 are *present*.  It was shown previously in Section 6.2 that, if not all the coefficients have the same algebraic sign or not all are present, the system is unstable.

For convenience in having a definite number of coefficients to consider, let $n = 7$ in Equation 6.3-1.  Arrange the coefficients of the characteristic equation in the following array, where the order of the arrangement of the coefficients in the array is indicated by the direction of the arrows.

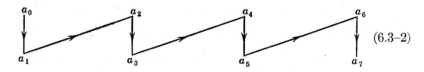

$$(6.3\text{-}2)$$

From this array calculate, in the fashion described below, the remaining terms of the array:

$$
\begin{array}{llll}
a_0 & a_2 & a_4 & a_6 \\
a_1 & a_3 & a_5 & a_7 \\
b_1 & b_3 & b_5 \\
c_1 & c_3 & c_5 \\
d_1 & d_3 \\
e_1 & e_3 \\
f_1 \\
g_1
\end{array}
\qquad (6.3\text{-}3)
$$

*Routh's criterion states that the system* represented by the characteristic Equation 6.3–1 *is stable if all the terms in the left column of the array* 6.3–3 *have the same algebraic sign.*

The additional coefficients that must be calculated are determined in the following fashion:

$$b_1 = \frac{\begin{array}{cc} a_0 & a_2 \\ a_1 & a_3 \end{array}}{a_1} = \frac{a_1 a_2 - a_0 a_3}{a_1} \qquad (6.3\text{–}4)$$

$$b_3 = \frac{\begin{array}{cc} a_0 & a_4 \\ a_1 & a_5 \end{array}}{a_1} = \frac{a_1 a_4 - a_0 a_5}{a_1} \qquad (6.3\text{–}5)$$

$$c_1 = \frac{\begin{array}{cc} a_1 & a_3 \\ b_1 & b_3 \end{array}}{b_1} = \frac{b_1 a_3 - a_1 b_3}{b_1} \qquad (6.3\text{–}6)$$

$$d_1 = \frac{\begin{array}{cc} b_1 & b_3 \\ c_1 & c_3 \end{array}}{c_1} = \frac{c_1 b_3 - b_1 c_3}{c_1} \qquad (6.3\text{–}7)$$

The processes of multiplication, subtraction, and division indicated above are continued until only zeros are obtained for any additional coefficients. From the nature of this process it is apparent that it is immaterial whether $n$ is an odd or an even number; the only effect is to increase or lessen the number of rows to the array of Equations 6.3–2 or 6.3–3.

The statement of Routh's criterion above is based on the assumption that all powers of $s$, from $n$ to 0, inclusive, are present in Equation 6.3–1. As indicated previously in Section 6.2, if not all the powers of $s$ are present or if not all the coefficients have the same sign, the system is known to be unstable by inspection and it is not necessary to calculate the Routh array. If the Routh array indicates the system to be unstable, the number of changes of sign of the first column indicates the number of roots with positive real parts.

**Examples of the Use of Routh's Stability Criterion.**

*Example 1*

$$s^4 + 2s^3 + 8s^2 + 4s + 3 = 0$$

| 1 | 8 | 3 |
|---|---|---|
| 2 | 4 | |
| 6 | 3 | |
| 3 | | |
| 3 | | |

Since all terms in the first column are positive, the system is stable.

*Example 2*

$$s^4 + 2s^3 + s^2 + 4s + 2 = 0$$

| 1 | 1 | 2 |
|---|---|---|
| 2 | 4 | |
| -1 | 2 | |
| 8 | | |
| 2 | | |

Not all the terms in the first column are positive, and the system is unstable. There are two changes of sign, $+2, -1, +8$; hence there are two roots with positive real parts.

*Example 3*

$$s^5 + s^4 + 3s^3 + 4s^2 + s + 2 = 0$$

| 1 | 3 | 1 |
|---|---|---|
| 1 | 4 | 2 |
| -1 | -1 | |
| 3 | 2 | |
| -⅓ | | |
| 2 | | |

Since there are four changes in sign, the system is unstable and has four roots with positive real parts.

**Change in Scale Factor of Characteristic Equation.** The amount of labor involved in using Routh's criterion is considerably shortened through use of scale factor changes that present the characteristic equation in a more usable form. First, since the characteristic equation is equal to zero, it may be divided by a constant without disturbing the equality. Thus, if the characteristic equation is

$$a_0 s^n + a_1 s^{n-1} + a_2 s^{n-2} + \cdots + a_{n-2} s^2 + a_{n-1} s + a_n s^0 = 0 \qquad (6.3\text{-}8)$$

$$\frac{a_0 s^n}{g} + \frac{a_1 s^{n-1}}{g} + \frac{a_2 s^{n-2}}{g} + \cdots + \frac{a_{n-2} s^2}{g} + \frac{a_{n-1} s}{g} + \frac{a_n s^0}{g} = 0 \qquad (6.3\text{-}9)$$

In addition, if the substitution

$$s = V\lambda \qquad (6.3\text{--}10)$$

is made, the modified equation is either stable or unstable, depending on whether the original equation was stable or unstable; that is, the modified equation when tested by Routh's criterion yields the same result as the original equation. Hence the foregoing equations may be written in the form

$$\frac{a_0 V^n \lambda^n}{g} + \frac{a_1 V^{n-1}\lambda^{n-1}}{g} + \frac{a_2 V^{n-2}\lambda^{n-2}}{g} + \cdots$$

$$+ \frac{a_{n-2} V^2 \lambda^2}{g} + \frac{a_{n-1} V\lambda^1}{g} + \frac{a_n \lambda^0}{g} = 0 \quad (6.3\text{--}11)$$

If $a_n/g$ is set equal to 1 by letting $g = a_n$, and $a_0 V^n/g$ is made about equal to 1 by a convenient choice of $V$, the resultant equations are of a more easily manageable form. An example of the use of this method is given here.

*Example*

Given the characteristic equation

$$100s^5 + 1100s^4 + 9000s^3 + 105{,}000s^2 + 1{,}200{,}000s + 10{,}000{,}000 = 0$$

Obviously, the Routh array formed from this equation as it stands would be exceedingly unwieldy. Proceeding as outlined above, let $g = a_n = 10{,}000{,}000$ and let

$$\frac{a_0 V^n}{g} = 1$$

Solve for $V$:

$$V = \left[\frac{g}{a_0}\right]^{1/n} = \left[\frac{10{,}000{,}000}{100}\right]^{1/n} = [100{,}000]^{1/5} = 10$$

Substituting these values in Equation 6.3–11 yields

$$\frac{10^2 10^5}{10^7}\lambda^5 + \frac{(1.1)10^3 10^4}{10^7}\lambda^4 + \frac{(0.9)10^4 10^3}{10^7}\lambda^3$$

$$+ \frac{(1.05)10^5 10^2}{10^7}\lambda^2 + \frac{(1.2)10^6 10}{10^7}\lambda + \frac{10^7}{10^7}\lambda^0 = 0$$

The simplified equation is then

$$\lambda^5 + 1.1\lambda^4 + 0.9\lambda^3 + 1.05\lambda^2 + 1.2\lambda + 1 = 0$$

for which the Routh array can be readily calculated.

### 6.4   The Nyquist Stability Criterion

The two methods of studying stability just mentioned are largely mathematical, whereas the Nyquist stability criterion [6] lends itself more easily to a physical interpretation. If in a closed-loop control system with sinusoidal excitation the feedback signal from the controlled variable is in phase and is equal or greater in magnitude to the reference input at any one frequency, the system is unstable. The Nyquist stability criterion presents this fact in a rigorous mathematical form. In addition, it permits one to determine the stability of systems for which the simpler physical approach is inadequate. An example of such a system is one that is stable even though the amplitude of the feedback signal is greater than, and in phase with, the reference input at more than one frequency.

The Nyquist stability criterion possesses a number of features that make it particularly desirable for the determination of feedback control system stability. First, it provides definite information as to whether there are any roots of the characteristic equation that lie in the positive half plane. Second, the same plot that is employed to indicate the stability of the system may also be employed to give quantitative data regarding the performance of the system to steady-state sinusoidally varying inputs. In addition the plot also provides an indication of the degree of stability as well as points the way toward improving the stability of the system when this is necessary. To a greater degree than is possible through the use of Routh's criterion, the Nyquist stability criterion permits the effect of various system elements on stability to be considered independently. For these reasons, the Nyquist stability criterion developed in the Bell Laboratories in 1932 for use in feedback amplifier design and used extensively in the servomechanisms field from 1940 on has become the most widely used criterion of stability. Originally limited to control systems that are inherently stable, the Nyquist criterion has been generalized to indicate the stability of systems that are unstable without the benefit of closed-loop operation.[41, 43, 62, 86, 123]

Later extensions of the Nyquist approach by J. R. Moore, W. R. Evans,[105] and others make it possible to determine the magnitude of the real parts of the negative roots. By these methods it is possible to determine the absolute decrement rate of the exponential factors and also the decay time expressed in terms of frequency of oscillation. For those applications where transient response is of paramount importance, these methods provide a direct design aid.

The approach to the subject of system stability afforded by the Nyquist criterion is of sufficient importance to warrant presenting first a description of its mathematical background and method of application.

After this, a statement of the Nyquist criterion itself is given in the general and limited forms. Finally, the criterion is applied to the transfer function of a number of representative feedback control systems.

**Development of the Characteristic Equation in Terms of Transfer Functions.** Shown in block diagram form in Figure 6.4–1 is a servomechanism or feedback control system in which it is desired to determine

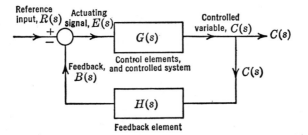

FIGURE 6.4–1. Feedback control system with control and feedback elements.

its stability. The transform expression relating the controlled variable in terms of the actuating signal and the control system elements is

$$C(s) = G(s)E(s) \qquad (6.4\text{–}1)$$

where $G(s)$ represents the transfer function of the forward control elements. It includes the over-all gain coefficient of the control elements and the transformed terms containing $s$ in the control elements. $G(s)$ is in general a fraction containing a sum of terms of whole powers of $s$ in both numerator and denominator.

Although the controlled variable may be compared directly to the reference input $R(s)$ by means of the differential, in the more general case it is a feedback quantity $B(s)$ related to the controlled variable that is compared to the reference input. The difference forms the signal $E(s)$. Thus

$$R(s) - B(s) = E(s) \qquad (6.4\text{–}2)$$

and

$$B(s) = H(s)C(s) \qquad (6.4\text{–}3)$$

where $H(s)$ represents the transfer function of the feedback elements. It includes the gain coefficient and the terms containing $s$ in the feedback element. It is similar in nature to $G(s)$ from a mathematical standpoint.

If Equations 6.4–1, 6.4–2, and 6.4–3 are combined, the resulting equation for controlled variable in terms of the reference input signal $R(s)$ is

$$C(s) = \frac{G(s)R(s)}{1 + G(s)H(s)} \qquad (6.4\text{–}4)$$

Because both $G(s)$ and $H(s)$ may be fractions, it is necessary to write them in fractional form and then clear the fractions in order to produce an expression for $C(s)$, from which the characteristic equation can be obtained. Thus, if

$$G(s) = \frac{N_1(s)}{D_1(s)} \tag{6.4-5}$$

and

$$H(s) = \frac{N_2(s)}{D_2(s)} \tag{6.4-6}$$

Equation 6.4–4 may be written in the form

$$[D_1(s)D_2(s) + N_1(s)N_2(s)]C(s) = N_1(s)D_2(s)R(s) \tag{6.4-7}$$

From the definition of the characteristic equation in Section 3.2 it is evident that those values of $s$ from which the transient forms of solution are determined by the characteristic equation are

$$D_1(s)D_2(s) + N_1(s)N_2(s) = 0 \tag{6.4-8}$$

In terms of the roots of the characteristic equation, Equation 6.4–8 may also be written as

$$D_1(s)D_2(s) + N_1(s)N_2(s) = (s - r_1)(s - r_2) \cdots (s - r_n) = 0 \tag{6.4-9}$$

where $+r_1, +r_2, + \cdots + r_n$ are the roots of the characteristic equation.

If now Equation 6.4–9 is divided by $D_1(s)D_2(s)$ to obtain the left term in the form of $1 + G(s)H(s)$, then

$$1 + G(s)H(s) = \frac{(s - r_1)(s - r_2) \cdots (s - r_n)}{D_1(s)D_2(s)} = 0 \tag{6.4-10}$$

This is done since the function $G(s)H(s)$ is composed of the product of two terms that can be directly determined from physical elements.

Finally, since the product $D_1(s)D_2(s)$ may itself be factored into a number of terms of the form $(s - r_a)(s - r_b)$, etc., where $+r_a, +r_b$ are the roots of $D_1(s)D_2(s)$, Equation 6.4–10 can be expressed as

$$1 + G(s)H(s) = \frac{(s - r_1)(s - r_2) \cdots (s - r_n)}{(s - r_a)(s - r_b) \cdots (s - r_m)} = 0 \tag{6.4-11}$$

For a stable system it is necessary that none of the roots $r_1, r_2, \cdots, r_n$ have positive real parts; there is no particular restriction on the other roots, $r_a, r_b, \cdots, r_m$. However, since it is desirable to use the expression $G(s)H(s)$ alone as a measure of system stability, a knowledge of the characteristics of the $r_1, r_2, \cdots, r_n$ roots as well as the $r_a, r_b, \cdots, r_m$ roots must be obtained.

**Method of Applying the Nyquist Stability Criterion.** The generalized form of the Nyquist criterion can be applied as follows:

For a feedback control system shown in the form of Figure 6.4–1, plot the $G(s)H(s)$ function in the complex plane for $s = j\omega$ with all values of $\omega$ from $-\infty$ to $+\infty$. It will be noted that the plot from $-\infty < \omega < 0$ is the conjugate of the plot from $+\infty > \omega > 0$.     (6.4–12)

Draw the vector from the $-1 + j0$ point to a point on this curve, and observe the rotation of this vector as $\omega$ varies from $-\infty$ to $+\infty$. Let $[R]$ be the net *counterclockwise rotation expressed in revolutions.*     (6.4–13)

Express $G(s)H(s)$ as the ratio of the two polynomials: $\dfrac{N_1(s)N_2(s)}{D_1(s)D_2(s)}$.

$$(6.4–14)$$

Check to see that the degree of the polynomial $N_1(s)N_2(s)$ is less than or equal to the degree of $D_1(s)D_2(s)$. Find the number of roots of the equation $D_1(s)D_2(s) = 0$, whose real parts are positive. Call this number, $[P]$. The system will be stable if, and only if, $[R] = [P]$.     (6.4–15)

The common form of the Nyquist stability criterion involves one major assumption that is frequently present in the simpler form of servomechanisms, namely, that the transfer function, $G(s)H(s)$, of the forward and feedback circuits is by itself stable.

This assumption means that the denominator of $G(s)H(s)$ has no positive roots so that $[P] = 0$. Hence the generalized stability criterion can be abbreviated to the following:

For a feedback control system shown in the form of Figure 6.4–1, plot the $G(s)H(s)$ function in the complex plane for $s = j\omega$ with all values of $\omega$ from $-\infty$ to $+\infty$.     (6.4–16)

Draw the vector from the $-1 + j0$ point to a point on this curve, and observe the rotation of this vector as $\omega$ varies from $-\infty$ to $+\infty$. $[R]$, the net counterclockwise rotation, must be zero for the system to be stable.

$$(6.4–17)$$

**Limitations to the Generalized Nyquist Stability Criterion.** The two limitations to the generalized Nyquist stability criterion are:

1. The system must be capable of being represented by a system of linear differential equations with constant coefficients.

2. The limit of $G(s)H(s)$ must approach a constant or zero as $s$ approaches $\infty$.

The first limitation is implied when the system is represented in Laplace transform form with constant coefficients. Frequently, although the coefficients of the system may not be constant throughout the entire operating region, it is possible to "linearize" the equations by considering the system operation for small departures from a mean operating point. The process whereby this linearization may be performed is discussed in Volume II.

The second limitation is inherent in the physical make-up of feedback control systems. Note in Figure 6.4–1 that the product $G(s)H(s)$ represents the net transfer function around the loop from $E(s)$ to $B(s)$. In any practical system there are losses, series inductive effects, and shunt capacitance effects that limit the transmission around this loop to a finite value as the frequency approaches infinity. This practical condition is present in all physical systems and at the same time produces a condition necessary for the mathematical proof that follows. This condition is that the highest power of $s$ in the denominator $D_1(s)D_2(s)$ is equal to or greater than the highest power of $s$ in the numerator $N_1(s)N_2(s)$.

**Angular Change Produced by the Presence of Roots in the Positive Real Portion of the Complex Plane.** This approach to the problem of determining the presence of roots in the positive real portion of the complex plane was described by F. H. Andrix. It indicates a simplified explanation of the classical method of complex plane integration.

Consider the fraction of Equation 6.4–11 to be represented by the function $S(s)$, where

$$S(s) = 1 + G(s)H(s) = \frac{(s - r_1)(s - r_2)(s - r_3) \cdots (s - r_n)}{(s - r_a)(s - r_b)(s - r_c) \cdots (s - r_m)} \quad (6.4\text{–}18)$$

where         $s = a + jb$.

$r_1, r_2, r_3, \cdots r_n$ = roots of the characteristic equation and values for which the numerator of $S(s)$ is equal to zero. *These roots are called zeros of $S(s)$.*

$r_a, r_b, r_c, \cdots r_m$ = roots of the denominator of $S(s)$ and values for which the $G(s)H(s)$ function is infinite. *These roots are called poles of the function $G(s)H(s)$.*

Figure 6.4–2 shows a plot on the complex plane of the values of $r_1$, $r_2$, $r_a$, $r_b$ etc., where $r_a$, $r_1$, $r_2$ have been chosen so as to have positive real parts. Also on this plot is an arbitrary closed curve drawn in the positive half plane; $P$ is a point on this curve the coordinates of which are $s$ ($= a + jb$). The distance from the root $r_1$ to the point $P$ is $(s - r_1)$, from root $r_a$ to the point $P$ is $(s - r_a)$; and in similar fashion the terms

$(s - r)$ are the distances from the other roots to $P$, although all are not shown on Figure 6.4–2.

One will observe that as the point $P$ travels clockwise once completely around the curve that has encircled $r_1$, the quantity $(s - r_1)$ rotates through an angle of 360° clockwise, whereas all the other $(s - r)$ factors rotate through a net angle of zero degrees. Thus the presence of a root

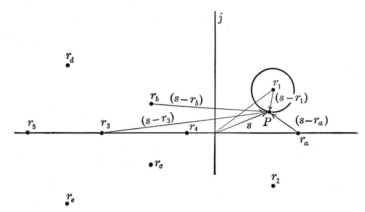

FIGURE 6.4–2.   Values of $r$'s of Equation 6.4–11 on complex plane.

in the numerator with a positive real part is indicated by the net angular rotation of 360° clockwise as the point $P$ traverses the closed path. Since from Equation 6.4–18,

$$S(s) = \frac{(s - r_1)(s - r_2)(s - r_3) \cdots (s - r_n)}{(s - r_a)(s - r_b)(s - r_c) \cdots (s - r_m)}$$

it follows that the net angular rotation of 360° clockwise must also be experienced by $1 + G(s)H(s)$ for the encirclement of $r_1$.

If, instead of the curve shown in Figure 6.4–2, a larger one that encircles $r_1$ and $r_2$ were chosen, one can see that $S(s)$ would rotate through 720° clockwise, the net angular rotation contribution of $r_1$ and $r_2$ each being 360°. In general, one clockwise rotation will result from each root of the numerator of Equation 6.4–18, which is encircled by the arbitrary curve.

Likewise, if $r_a$ alone were encircled by the original closed curve, the quantity $(s - r_a)$ would rotate 360° clockwise. However, since $(s - r_a)$ appears in the denominator of Equation 6.4–18, the quantity $S(s)$ must rotate through an angle of 360° counterclockwise for a 360° clockwise rotation of $(s - r_a)$. Had the curve enclosed both $r_1$ and $r_a$, the net rotation of $S(s)$ would have been zero since the clockwise rotation of

$(s - r_1)$ would just cancel the counterclockwise rotation caused by $(s - r_a)$.

It will be noted that the quantities $(s - r_3)$ and $(s - r_b)$, for which the real parts of $r_3$ and $r_b$ are negative, have zero degrees net angular rotation as the point $P$ encircles any closed path in the right-hand portion of the complex plane.

Now if the arbitrary curve is extended so that the entire positive part of the complex $s$ plane is encircled by the path of the point $P$, every root of the numerator and the denominator of Equation 6.4–18 that has a

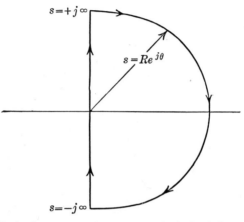

FIGURE 6.4–3.  Path chosen to enclose entire right half of the complex plane for determining system stability.

positive real part would be encircled.  $S(s)$ would make a number of counterclockwise revolutions equal to the number of roots of the denominator of $G(s)H(s)$ minus the numerator of $S(s)$ within the region.

If the system is stable, there can be no roots of the numerator of Equation 6.4–18 that have positive real parts, that is, zeros in the positive half plane.  Hence for a stable system there must be no net clockwise rotation of $S(s)$ as the point $P$ traverses a path encircling the entire positive portion of the $s$ plane in the clockwise direction.  To encircle the entire positive portion of the $s$ plane in the clockwise direction, the path of the point $P$ lies along the imaginary axis of the $s$ plane from $-j\infty$ to $+j\infty$; it is then completed around a semicircular path of infinite radius enclosing the right half of the $s$ plane.  Mathematically that portion of the path along the imaginary axis from $-j\infty$ to $+j\infty$ may be represented by replacing $s$ in Equation 6.4–18 by $j\omega$ and allowing $\omega$ to take on all values from $-\infty$ to $+\infty$.  Figure 6.4–3 illustrates the path of $P$ that enclosed the right half of the $s$ plane.

By taking the path for $P$ only along the imaginary axis of the $s$ plane from $-\infty$ to $+\infty$, the net angular rotation obtained is the same as is obtained by encircling the entire positive half plane in the clockwise direction. This follows from the fact that, by the second limiting assumption above, the value of $G(s)H(s)$ approaches a constant or zero as $s$ approaches infinity. If $G(s)H(s)$ is equal to zero at $s = \infty$, $1 + G(s)H(s)$ $= S(s) = 1$ at all points for which $s = \infty$. If $G(s)H(s)$ is a constant at $s = \infty$, $S(s)$ is 1 plus that constant. In either event, if $S(s)$ is equal to a constant for all points on the semicircle corresponding to values of $s$ equal to infinity, the quantity $S(s)$ plotted on the complex plane must undergo no rotation while the semicircular path is being traversed. Therefore, *all* the rotation of $S(s)$ must occur while the imaginary axis is being traversed, that is, $s = j\omega$ where $-\infty < \omega < +\infty$.

If $S(s)$ has a net clockwise rotation, the system is known to be unstable since a clockwise rotation is produced only by zeros in $S(s)$. If the net rotation of $S(s) = S(j\omega)$ is zero, the number of zeros with positive real parts equal the number of poles of $G(s)H(s)$ with positive real parts. It is still necessary to show that there are no poles of $G(s)H(s)$ with positive real parts. If there is a net counterclockwise rotation for $S(j\omega)$, the number of poles with positive real parts exceeds the number of zeros with positive real parts by the number of the counterclockwise rotations. If there are to be no zeros with positive real parts, the number of counterclockwise revolutions must equal the number of poles with positive real parts.

To find the number of roots with positive real parts in the denominator of $S(s)$, it is merely necessary to investigate the roots of $D_1(s)D_2(s)$ from Equation 6.4–10 by means of Routh's criterion. It will be recalled that in Section 6.3 the Routh array not only shows whether the system is stable but also indicates the number of roots with positive real parts from the number of changes of sign of the first column.

*Summarizing*: *If* $[R]$ *is the number of counterclockwise revolutions of* $S(s)$ *and* $[P]$ *is the number of poles of* $G(s)H(s)$ *with positive real parts, then* $[R]$ *must equal* $[P]$ *for the system to be stable.*

Before leaving the matter of the number of net rotations of $S(s)$, it is worth while to emphasize that common practice consists of plotting only $G(s)H(s)$ for $s = j\omega$ from $-\infty < \omega < +\infty$. The effect of the 1 in $S(s) = 1 + G(s)H(s)$ is taken into account by measuring the rotations of $G(j\omega)H(j\omega)$ with respect to the point $-1 + j0$. For a plot of $1 + G(j\omega)H(j\omega)$ to have any net rotations, this function must encircle the origin $(0,0)$. The number of times that $1 + G(j\omega)H(j\omega)$ encircles the point $(0,0)$ is exactly equal to the number of times $G(j\omega)H(j\omega)$ encircles the $-1 + j0$ point. Hence by plotting $G(j\omega)H(j\omega)$ directly and using the point $-1 + j0$ as a reference for determining the net number of en-circlements, the number of rotations of $S(j\omega)$ is also determined. Figures 6.4–4 and 6.4–5 illustrate plots of $1 + G(j\omega)H(j\omega)$ and $G(j\omega)H(j\omega)$ for a particular system and show the change of reference to be merely one of calculating convenience.

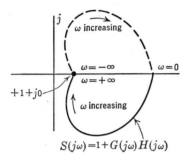

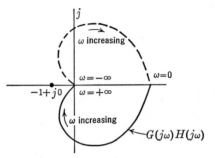

FIGURE 6.4–4.  Representative function for $1 + G(j\omega)H(j\omega)$ on complex plane.

FIGURE 6.4–5.  $G(j\omega)H(j\omega)$ on complex plane for same function as shown in Figure 6.4–4.

In Section 6.5 a number of typical plots of $G(j\omega)H(j\omega)$ functions are shown for various representative control systems. On these plots it is indicated whether or not the plots represent stable or unstable systems.

**Angular Change Produced by the Presence of Poles at the Origin.** Frequently functions occur for $G(s)H(s)$, where $s = 0$ is a root of the denominator. For example,

$$G(s)H(s) = \frac{K(1 + T_2 s)}{s(1 + T_1 s)(1 + T_3 s)} \qquad (6.4–19)$$

If $s$ is allowed to equal $j\omega$, $+$ and $-$ infinite values of $G(j\omega)H(j\omega)$ are indicated as $\omega$ approaches zero from the negative and the positive directions, respectively. Figure 6.4–6 illustrates a complex plot of the corresponding $G(j\omega)H(j\omega)$ function for Equation 6.4–19,

$$G(j\omega)H(j\omega) = \frac{K(1 + j\omega T_2)}{j\omega(1 + j\omega T_1)(1 + j\omega T_3)} \qquad (6.4–20)$$

It is important to determine how this plot is joined from $\omega = 0-$ to $\omega = 0+$ since, if the $G(j\omega)H(j\omega)$ contour is closed around the $-1 + j0$ point to the left, the system is unstable. This follows from the fact that a counterclockwise rotation of the $-1$ point would be realized as $\omega$ changed from $-\infty$ to $+\infty$ whereas Equation 6.4–19 shows that there are no roots with positive real parts, that is, poles, in the denominator.

The nature of the plot in the neighborhood of $\omega = 0$ may be resolved by considering the path of the point $P$ to be along the negative imaginary axis from $s = -j\infty$ until $s = -j\omega$ gets very small. Then let the path be semicircular *in the positive half plane* of a very small radius until it

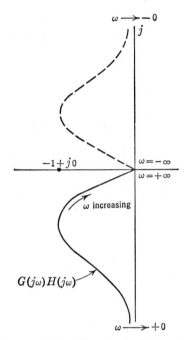

FIGURE 6.4–6.   Plot of transfer function

$$G(j\omega)H(j\omega) = \frac{K(1 + j\omega T_2)}{j\omega(1 + j\omega T_1)(1 + j\omega T_3)}$$

reaches the positive imaginary axis at $s = +j\omega$, after which it continues along the positive imaginary axis until $s = +j\infty$.

For the semicircular portion of the path

$$s = \delta e^{j\theta} \tag{6.4–21}$$

where $\delta \to 0$ and $-\pi/2 < \theta < \pi/2$.

Figure 6.4–7 shows a plot of this portion of the path in the $s$ plane.

It is evident that only a very small portion of the positive half plane is not encircled, the area of this portion approaching zero as $\delta \to 0$.

Now consider Equation 6.4–19 for $s \to 0$.

$$G(s)H(s) = \frac{K}{s} \tag{6.4–22}$$

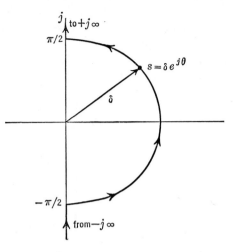

FIGURE 6.4–7.  Plot to an enlarged scale of the locus of the point $P$ as $s$ passes in the vicinity of zero ($s = 0$) in going from $-j\omega$ to $+j\omega$ for the transfer function

$$G(s)H(s) = \frac{K(T_2s + 1)}{s(T_1s + 1)(T_3s + 1)}$$

Substituting Equation 6.4–21 in Equation 6.4–22 gives

$$G(s)H(s) = \frac{K}{\delta e^{j\theta}} = \frac{K}{\delta} e^{-j\theta} \tag{6.4–23}$$

for $-\pi/2 < \theta < \pi/2$ and $\delta \to 0$.

The magnitude of $K/\delta \to \infty$ as $\delta \to 0$, and the angle of Equation 6.4–23 goes from $\pi/2$ to 0 to $-\pi/2$ as $\theta$ goes through values of $-\pi/2$ to 0 to $+\pi/2$. In Figure 6.4–6 this means that the points for $\omega \to -0$ and $\omega \to +0$ are joined by means of a semicircle of infinite radius in the first and fourth quadrants. Figure 6.4–8 shows the completed plot of $G(s)H(s)$ of Figure 6.4–6 and indicates the system to be stable.

By reasoning similar to that used above, the complex plane plot for other cases where $s^n$ occurs in the denominator of $G(s)H(s)$ can be determined. Such analysis shows that when $\omega$ passes through zero, the $G(s)H(s)$ plot makes $n$ clockwise semicircles of infinite radius about the origin.

The conjugate nature of the $G(+j\omega)H(+j\omega)$ and $G(-j\omega)(H(-j\omega)$ means that the plot of $G(s)H(s)$ for values of $-\infty < \omega < 0$ and $+\infty > \omega > 0$ is symmetrical about the real axis, as has been illustrated by the functions drawn for Figures 6.4–5 and 6.4–8. Hence, if the shape of the

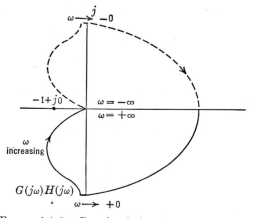

FIGURE 6.4–8.    Completed plot of transfer function

$$G(j\omega)H(j\omega) = \frac{K(1 + j\omega T_2)}{j\omega(1 + j\omega T_1)(1 + j\omega T_3)}$$

on complex plane.

plot of $G(s)H(s)$ is known for the range of values of $0 < \omega < +\infty$, it is not essential to calculate the data for the range $-\infty < \omega < 0$. In fact, the plot of $G(j\omega)H(j\omega)$ is generally not completed for the range of negative frequencies since the portion of the data has only mathematical significance. If only the range of frequencies from 0 to $+\infty$ is plotted on the complex plane, the counterclockwise rotations shown by the plot is $[R/2]$ rather than $[R]$, which is the net counterclockwise rotation when the range of $\omega$ is from $-\infty$ to $+\infty$.

Other criteria for stability have been derived from the Nyquist criterion that are convenient for use with other methods of presenting information on system performance. Two of these, the inverse transfer function method and the attenuation and phase margin versus frequency method, are described in later chapters of this book. The mathematical background for the criteria used with these methods is the same as that for the Nyquist criterion; it is merely the form of representation of the information that alters the statement of the conditions for stability.

## 6.5  Application of the Nyquist Stability Criterion to Typical System Transfer Functions

In this section the transfer function $G(s)H(s)$ of a number of examples of control systems is sketched on the complex plane. It should be noted that no consistent scale of magnitudes has been used. The numerical values of the transfer functions are shown in addition to the form of the functions. Also a brief description is given of the type of control system for which the transfer functions and plots are representative.

*Example 1*

$$G(s)H(s) = \frac{K}{(T_1 s + 1)(T_2 s + 1)} \qquad (6.5\text{-}1)$$

Typical systems having such a transfer function are voltage regulators, speed regulators, and meter elements. Figure 6.5–1 shows the complex plane plot of such a transfer function ($s = j\omega$). With $s^2$ the highest

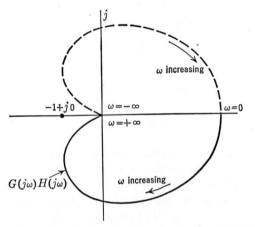

FIGURE 6.5–1. Transfer function of stable regulator type system.

$$G(j\omega)H(j\omega) = \frac{20}{(1 + j0.5\omega)(1 + j0.04\omega)}$$

power of $s$ in the denominator and there being no $s$ terms in the numerator, the system cannot encircle the $-1 + j0$ point and it must be stable. However, with additional $(Ts + 1)$ factors in the denominator, it is possible to encircle the $-1 + j0$ point and to obtain an unstable system.

*Example 2*

$$G(s)H(s) = \frac{K}{s(T_1 s + 1)(T_2 s + 1)} \qquad (6.5\text{-}2)$$

Typical systems having such a transfer function with a single integrating element are position controls that may be driven, for example, by an electric motor or a hydraulic motor.

Since the highest power of $s$ for the transfer function is $1/s^3$, the net angular rotation of this term from $0 < \omega < \infty$ is $-270°$. Depending on the magnitude of the gain $K$ and the time constants $T_1$ and $T_2$, the system may be stable or not. On Figure 6.5–2 are shown sketches of such a transfer function having the same time constants but with low and high values of gain corresponding to stable and unstable systems.

*Example 3*

$$G(s)H(s) = \frac{K(T_3s + 1)(T_4s + 1)}{s(T_1s + 1)(T_2s + 1)(T_5s + 1)(T_6s + 1)} \qquad (6.5\text{–}3)$$

This transfer function is typical of a more complicated position control of the type considered in the previous example, and the additional terms

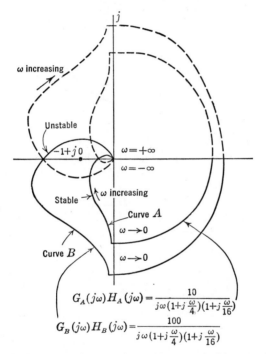

$$G_A(j\omega)H_A(j\omega) = \frac{10}{j\omega(1+j\frac{\omega}{4})(1+j\frac{\omega}{16})}$$

$$G_B(j\omega)H_B(j\omega) = \frac{100}{j\omega(1+j\frac{\omega}{4})(1+j\frac{\omega}{16})}$$

FIGURE 6.5–2.   Position control system for stable and unstable operating conditions.

may represent the contribution of stabilizing factors. Since the power of $s$ that $G(s)H(s)$ approaches as $s = j\omega \to \infty$ is $1/s^3$, the net angular rotation of the transfer function at large values of $+\omega$ is $-270°$. Figure 6.5–3$a$ shows a plot of such a transfer function for a stable system. Although the plot of the transfer function has a negative real value in excess of $-1 + j0$ for some lower frequencies at still higher frequencies, and in particular in the range of $\omega$'s where the magnitude is about unity, the phase angle is not as negative as $-180°$. Hence the $-1 + j0$ point is not encircled, and the system is stable. Many high performance

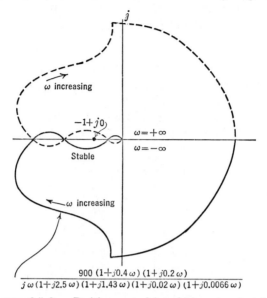

FIGURE 6.5–3a.   Position control for which system is stable.

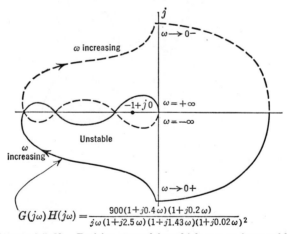

FIGURE 6.5–3b.   Position control for which system is unstable.

systems have this general shape when plotted on the complex plane. Such a system is said to be *conditionally stable*.

It will of course be understood that by improper choice of gain or time constants, systems having this form of transfer function may be unstable. Figure 6.5–3*b* shows the complex plane plot of an unstable system of this type.

*Example 4*

$$G(s)H(s) = \frac{K(T_1s + 1)}{s^2(T_2s + 1)(T_3s + 1)} \qquad (6.5\text{--}4)$$

This type of transfer function is obtained in a position control having a torque motor element or having two single motor integrating elements

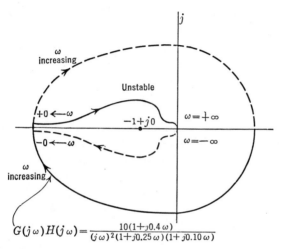

$$G(j\omega)H(j\omega) = \frac{10(1+j0.4\,\omega)}{(j\omega)^2(1+j0.25\,\omega)(1+j0.10\,\omega)}$$

FIGURE 6.5–4*a*. Position control system containing torque motor shown for unstable condition of operation.

arranged in series. The additional time constants present may be due to the nature of the motor design or they may be introduced into the control to insure stable operation. As in the previous example, the net angular rotation of the transfer function at large values of $\omega$ is $-270°$. However, the initial angle corresponding to very low values of $\omega$ is $-180°$. This means that if $T_1$ does not exceed $T_2$ plus $T_3$, and the gain is not sufficiently low, the $-1 + j0$ point is encircled and an unstable system results. Figure 6.5–4 shows complex plane plots of two transfer functions of this form. Figure 6.5–4*a* is of an unstable system, Figure 6.5–4*b* is of a stable system.

*Example 5*

$$G(s)H(s) = \frac{K_1}{s(T_1s + 1)(T_2s + 1) + \dfrac{K_2s^3}{(T_3s + 1)(T_4s + 1)}}$$

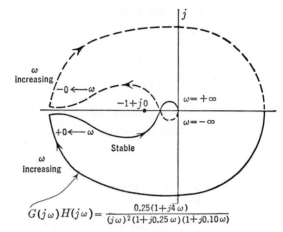

$$G(j\omega)H(j\omega) = \frac{0.25(1+j4\omega)}{(j\omega)^2(1+j0.25\omega)(1+j0.10\omega)}$$

FIGURE 6.5–4b.   Position control system for stable condition of operation.

A position control having a motor as a power element and using tachometer or rate feedback through a double $RC$ resistance-capacitance network may have the transfer function shown above.   A stable system of this kind has a complex plane plot similar to that shown for Example 3 on Figure 6.5–3a whereas unstable systems may have a complex plane plot of the form shown for Example 3 on Figure 6.5–3b.

Representative transfer functions for stable and unstable systems of this form are:

*Stable*

$$G(s)H(s) = \frac{500}{s(0.5s+1)(0.08s+1) + \dfrac{8.16s^3}{(0.6s+1)(0.3s+1)}}$$

*Unstable*

$$G(s)H(s) = \frac{500}{s(0.5s+1)(0.08s+1) + \dfrac{2.04s^3}{(0.6s+1)(0.3s+1)}}$$

*Example 6*

$$G(s)H(s) = \frac{K_1}{s(T_1s+1)(T_2s+1) + \dfrac{K_2s^4}{(T_3s+1)^2(T_4s+1)}}$$

The system represented in this example is similar in form to that described in Example 5, except that the $s^4$ term in the denominator of this example is of higher power than that of the $s^3$ term in Example 5.   This is obtained practically by the use of a tachometer and a triple $RC$ resistance-capacitance network. Figure 6.5–5 shows a form that the complex plane plot of such a transfer function may have. Despite the fact that the $-1 + j0$ point is encircled as the value of $\omega$ is increased from $-\infty$ to $0 + \infty$, it will be noted that the rotation is a counterclockwise one corresponding to the presence of poles in the denominator. This

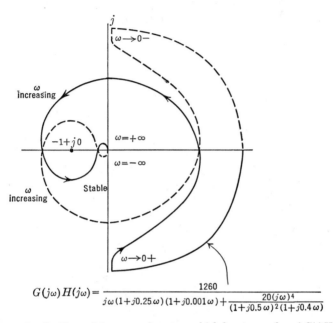

$$G(j\omega)H(j\omega) = \frac{1260}{j\omega(1+j0.25\omega)(1+j0.001\omega) + \dfrac{20(j\omega)^4}{(1+j0.5\omega)^2(1+j0.4\omega)}}$$

FIGURE 6.5–5.   Stable position control system which has two poles of $G(s)H(s)$ with positive real parts.

system shown is a stable one, although the tachometer feedback loop is unstable when the major feedback loop is not closed. It is of interest that the $-1 + j0$ point is encircled in a counterclockwise sense as $\omega$ is increased for this case; for previous examples where the systems were unstable the $-1 + j0$ point was encircled in a clockwise fashion.

If Routh's criterion is applied to the denominator of the fraction representing $G(s)H(s)$ it will be found that two roots have positive real parts corresponding to the two times the $-1 + j0$ point is encircled in Figure 6.5–5.

*Example 7*

$$G(s)H(s) = \frac{K(T_1s + 1)}{(T_0^2s^2 + 2\zeta T_0s + 1)(T_2s - 1)} \times \frac{(T_3s + 1)}{(T_4s + 1)}$$

The complex transfer function shown above consists of two parts as shown by the product terms. The first portion represents the transfer function of a missile under certain conditions of flight; the second represents a suitable stabilizing network. The presence of the minus term indicates an inherent instability of the missile in uncontrolled flight, but this does not prevent the missile having stable flight with suitable control. Figure 6.5–6, showing such a transfer function on the complex plane, indicates a finite negative value for $\omega = 0$.

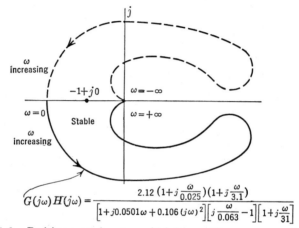

$$G(j\omega)H(j\omega) = \frac{2.12\left(1+j\frac{\omega}{0.025}\right)\left(1+j\frac{\omega}{3.1}\right)}{\left[1+j0.0501\omega + 0.106\,(j\omega)^2\right]\left[j\frac{\omega}{0.063}-1\right]\left[1+j\frac{\omega}{31}\right]}$$

FIGURE 6.5–6.    Position control system which is unstable as an unregulated system but is stable when control is employed.

It is worthy of note that this example of a missile transfer function is not a particularly representative one but is rather a special case used to illustrate the fact that stable operation is possible for a system that is unstable when unregulated. Many of the previous examples of "position controls" are valid for controlled steering systems in which the heading being maintained is the "position" being controlled. As such, these earlier examples may be considered as illustrating more representative steering system controls.

## 6.6   Root Locus for Determining Stability [120, 122]

The methods of determining stability described previously have shown how to (a) determine mathematically the location of the roots by numerical computation or by Routh's criterion, or (b) establish whether or not the roots of the closed-loop system are in the positive or negative part of the complex plane as by Nyquist. Now a way will be established for determining the locus of the roots (poles) of the closed-loop system from the location of zeros and poles of the open-loop system. This method of analyzing the stability of a control system from the locus of its roots is known as the root locus method and was first described by W. R. Evans [105] who has done a great deal to demonstrate its full effectiveness. The *root locus method* lends itself to a greater understanding of the transient response performance of a system rather than its frequency response as does the Nyquist criterion. It *has the ability to demonstrate* directly *the effect on the closed-loop response of the changes in system gain from 0 to ∞.* Although changes in the time constants or complex roots of the open-loop are not directly indicated, their effects are generally fairly evident from the original plot. From this method it is possible to determine the absolute decrement rate of exponential factors and also the decay time expressed in terms of its ratio to the frequency oscillation. In Chapter 13 are presented more data on the interpretation of the information that can be obtained from the root locus plot.

**Description of Root Locus.**   Since the root locus solves the stability problem for the general control system as was set forth in Figure 6.4–1, let us consider the general equation for the controlled variable in terms of the reference input signal $R(s)$ and the transfer functions as was done in Equation 6.4–4.

$$C(s) = \frac{G(s)R(s)}{1 + G(s)H(s)} \qquad (6.6\text{–}1)$$

The denominator, $1 + G(s)H(s)$, of this equation has the value of zero for all the same values of $s$ as does the characteristic equation of this system. Thus,

$$1 + G(s)H(s) = \frac{(s + r_1)(s + r_2) \cdots (s + r_n)}{(s + r_a)(s + r_b) \cdots (s + r_m)} = 0 \qquad (6.6\text{–}2)$$

To determine that the system is stable, it is necessary to establish that none of the roots of the characteristic equation has positive real parts. This can be done by looking at those values of $s$ for which $1 + G(s)H(s)$ is equal to zero and seeing if the real parts of $s$ are negative or positive. The condition for which $s$ must be evaluated is therefore,

$$G(s)H(s) = -1 = |1| \underline{/180°} \qquad (6.6\text{–}3)$$

For complex values of $s$ ($= a + jb$), $G(s)H(s)$ can have both magnitude and phase. The root locus approach places greatest emphasis on the establishing of the locus for all those values of $s$ for which the phase angle of $G(s)H(s)$ is equal to 180° or odd multiples thereof. This is the so-called root locus for values of $s$. On this locus the values of $s$ having positive real parts and therefore an unstable operating condition are revealed. With the shape of this locus, one can establish the value of the gain term associated with each value of $s$ on the $G(s)H(s)$ curve for which the *magnitude* of $G(s)H(s)$ equals 1.

The process of establishing those values of $s$, real and/or complex, for which the 180° or odd multiples thereof will be obtained is essentially

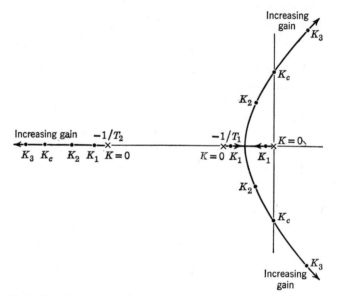

FIGURE 6.6–1. Root locus plot of simple servomechanism showing the effect of increasing system gain.

$$G(s)H(s) = \frac{K}{s(T_1 s + 1)(T_2 s + 1)}$$

a cut-and-try one, but the process is one for which the mathematical logic involved makes possible only a few choices of values of $s$. Thus the process of plotting the root locus can be a fairly straightforward one despite the seemingly limitless choice of values of $s$ possible.

Figure 6.6–1 shows the root locus plot of a simple servomechanism system.

The open-loop root locations at the origin, $-1/T_1$ and $-1/T_2$, correspond to the condition for zero gain. As the gain is increased somewhat to the low value $K_1$, the roots of the closed-loop system all have negative real values as shown, the two lowest values being intermediate between 0 and $-1/T_1$. As the gain is increased to $K_2$, the two closed-loop poles nearest the origin become oscillatory as shown by their having locations off the negative real axis. The third root is still real and has a larger negative value.

For some value of gain, $K_c$, the two closed-loop poles nearest the origin have no negative real part and the system is at the stability limit. The third closed-loop pole remains real and is more negative. Further increases in gain to $K_3$ will produce an unstable system as indicated by the two oscillatory roots having positive real parts.

To utilize the root locus concept most effectively, it is helpful for one to understand the angular and magnitude contribution of the various terms to the over-all root locus. $G(s)H(s)$ is generally of the form of a fraction with a product of factors in both numerator and denominator, as

$$G(s)H(s) = \frac{K(T_a s + 1)(T_b s + 1) \cdots}{s^n(T_1 s + 1)(T_2 s + 1) \cdots} \tag{6.6--4}$$

Each term of the form $(T_n s + 1)$ can be expressed as $T_n(s + 1/T_n)$, where $s_n = -1/T_n$ is equal to the root associated with this term. For some value of $s = -a + jb$, the vector associated with $(s + 1/T_n)$ has a magnitude

$$| s + 1/T_n | = | (1/T_n - a) + jb |$$

and a phase angle                                                                        (6.6--5)

$$\phi = \tan^{-1}\left(\frac{b}{1/T_n - a}\right)$$

Figure 6.6–2 shows graphically the relationship involved. The proper

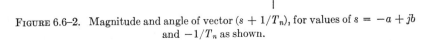

FIGURE 6.6–2.  Magnitude and angle of vector $(s + 1/T_n)$, for values of $s = -a + jb$ and $-1/T_n$ as shown.

sense and magnitude of the vector term for $s = -a + jb$ is indicated
by drawing an arrow from the value of the root of $s_n$ $(= -1/T_n)$ with
its head to the value of $s$ $(= -a + jb)$.

Quadratic terms, $(As^2 + Bs + 1)$, can be factored as

$$As^2 + Bs + 1 = A\left[s^2 + \frac{Bs}{A} + \frac{1}{A}\right] = A[s + \alpha - j\beta][s + \alpha + j\beta]$$

$$(6.6-6)$$

where $\alpha = \dfrac{B}{2A}$

and $\beta = \dfrac{1}{2A}\sqrt{4A - B^2}$

For a value of $s = -a + jb$, the values of the general terms $(s + \alpha + j\beta)$ and $(s + \alpha - j\beta)$ are as shown in Figure 6.6–3.

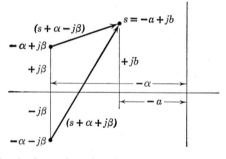

FIGURE 6.6–3.   Magnitudes and angles of vectors $(s + \alpha - j\beta)$ and $(s + \alpha + j\beta)$, for values of $s = -a + jb$ and $-\alpha$ and $\pm j\beta$ as shown.

Referring to Equation 6.6–4, it can be seen that each of the terms of
the numerator contributes positive phase angles to the net angle of
$G(s)H(s)$, whereas each of the denominator terms contributes a negative
phase angle to the net phase angle of $G(s)H(s)$.

That value of s that makes the numerator of a polynominal in s, say
$G(s)H(s)$, equal to zero is known as a zero of this polynomial. A value of s
that makes the denominator of a polynomial in s equal to zero is known as a
pole of this polynomial. Thus, in Equation 6.6–4, $-1/T_a$ and $-/1T_b$
are zeros, while $0$, $-1/T_1$ and $-1/T_2$ are poles.

**Rules Helpful for Drawing the Root Locus.** [120, 122, 134]   Figure 6.6–4
shows the root locus for a system having the loop-gain characteristic

$$G(s)H(s) = \frac{K(T_2s + 1)}{s(T_1s + 1)(T_3s + 1)}$$

$$(6.6-7)$$

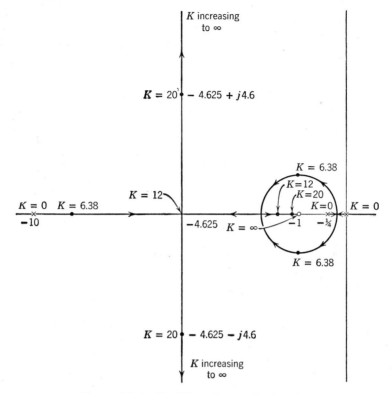

FIGURE 6.6–4.   Root locus for transfer function.

$$G(s)H(s) = \frac{K(T_2 s + 1)}{s(T_1 s + 1)(T_3 s + 1)} = \frac{K(s + 1)}{s(4s + 1)(0.1s + 1)}$$

This equation may be rewritten in the form

$$G(s)H(s) = \frac{KT_2(s + 1/T_2)}{T_1 T_3 s(s + 1/T_1)(s + 1/T_3)} \qquad (6.6\text{–}8)$$

for more convenient plotting on the complex plane.  Study of this root
locus plot reveals the validity of the following general rules helpful for
drawing all root locus plots.   In Section 13.4 are presented additional
aids which are of considerable help for constructing root locus plots.

1. *The number of branches of the root locus is equal to the number of
closed-loop poles.*

A branch is a separate portion of the root locus which represents all
values of $K$ on it from 0 to $\infty$.   Each branch contributes one closed-loop
pole to the system performance characteristic for any particular value

of loop gain, although sometimes a pair of poles work in concert to produce a pair of branches. Therefore, the number of branches must be equal to the number of closed-loop poles of the system. In this case, as shown in Figure 6.6–4, the number of branches is three corresponding to a third-order characteristic equation that would be derived from Equation 6.6–7.

2. *Each branch of the root locus starts at an open-loop pole (with $K = 0$) and ends at an open-loop zero or infinity (with $K = \infty$).*

Referring to Equation 6.6–7, it will be noted that at each open-loop pole, zero, $-1/T_1$ and $-1/T_3$, the value of the denominator is equal to zero. To make the ratio of $G(s)H(s)$ equal $-1$, it is necessary for $K$ also to equal zero.

At the closed-loop zero, $-1/T_2$, the numerator would have a value of zero were it not that $K$ can have a value of infinity and the resultant $G(s)H(s)$ ratio can again equal $-1$. As $s$ takes on values approaching infinity, it again is necessary for $K \rightarrow \infty$ so as to make $G(s)H(s) = -1$.

3. *For a locus to exist on the real axis, the sum of the poles and zeros to the right of the point on the axis must be odd.*

Each pole or zero to the right of a point on the real axis has an angle of 180° associated with it. With an odd number of poles and zeros to the right of a point, 180° or odd multiples thereof result.

With an even number of poles and zeros to the right of the point, 0° or even multiples of 180° result and the $-1$ condition for $G(s)H(s)$ cannot be obtained. Applying this criterion to Figure 6.6–4, from 0 to $-1/T_1$ and from $-1/T_2$ to $-1/T_3$, the locus exists along the real axis, while from $-1/T_1$ to $-1/T_2$ and from $-1/T_3$ to $\infty$ no locus exists.

Since complex roots occur in conjugate pairs, the contribution of either complex poles or zeros does not produce any net angular contribution to a point along the real axis.

4. *The root locus is symmetrical with respect to the real axis.*

The angular contribution of each open-loop pole or zero to a point on the positive branch of the root locus is the negative of the angular contribution of these same poles and zeros to the corresponding point on the negative branch. Furthermore, since the complex roots of the characteristic equation must occur in conjugate pairs, it is again apparent that the root locus is symmetrical with respect to the real axis. Figure 6.6–4 illustrates the nature of the symmetry that is obtained in a root locus.

5. *The angle by which the root locus leaves an open loop pole or approaches an open-loop zero is in the direction $\pm 180°$ q minus the sum of the angles of the vectors from the remaining poles and zeros to the pole or zero in question where q is an odd integer.*

The direction of departure from a pole or approach to a zero helps establish the root locus in the immediate vicinity of this pole or zero. The angle contribution of each of the other open-loop poles and zeros to the over-all resultant is very slightly affected by the direction with which the root locus leaves a particular pole or zero. However, the angle contribution of the vector associated with that particular pole or zero can vary from 0 to ±180°, depending on the direction of the departure from the pole or the approach to the zero. Since the angle contributions from all the other poles or zeros are essentially independent of the direction of departure or approach, the angle contribution of the pole or zero in question must provide the angle necessary to satisfy the ±180° $q$ angle condition required by the root locus. Figure 6.6–5 shows how this rule is applied to a transfer function having complex open-loop poles.

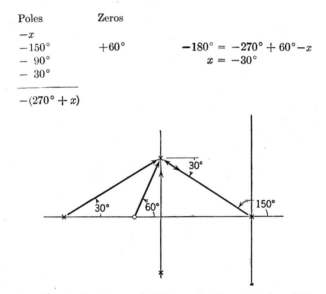

| Poles | Zeros | |
|---|---|---|
| $-x$ | | |
| $-150°$ | $+60°$ | $-180° = -270° + 60° - x$ |
| $-\ 90°$ | | $x = -30°$ |
| $-\ 30°$ | | |
| $-(270° + x)$ | | |

FIGURE 6.6–5. Sketch showing method for evaluating angle by which root locus leaves an open-loop pole.

6. *The point at which the root locus leaves the real axis is determined by equating the reciprocals of the distances from the poles and zeros on the real axis to zero.*

Referring to Figure 6.6–6, one notes that for a point on the root locus just off the real axis, the value of $\Delta$ will be very small and the angular contribution associated with each pole or zero on the real axis will be essentially equal to its tangent. Further, the net angular contribution

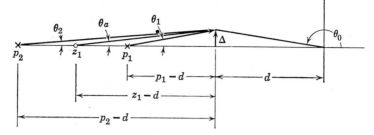

FIGURE 6.6–6. Sketch showing method for locating point on real axis at which the root locus leaves the real axis.

of the complex poles and zeros will be zero so their effect can be disregarded in establishing the point at which the root locus leaves the axis.

From the angle criterion at departure,

$$\theta_0 + \theta_1 + \theta_2 - \theta_a = 180° \qquad (6.6\text{–}9)$$

where $\theta_0 = \tan^{-1}\left(180 - \dfrac{\Delta}{d}\right)$

$$\theta_1 = \tan^{-1}\left(\frac{\Delta}{p_1 - d}\right)$$

$$\theta_2 = \tan^{-1}\left(\frac{\Delta}{p_2 - d}\right)$$

$$\theta_a = \tan^{-1}\left(\frac{\Delta}{z_1 - d}\right)$$

Replacing the angles by their tangents,

$$\Delta\left(-\frac{1}{d} + \frac{1}{p_1 - d} + \frac{1}{p_2 - d} - \frac{1}{z_1 - d}\right) = 0 \qquad (6.6\text{–}10)$$

or

$$-\frac{1}{d} + \frac{1}{p_1 - d} + \frac{1}{p_2 - d} - \frac{1}{z_1 - d} = 0 \qquad (6.6\text{–}11)$$

From this relationship it is evident that the poles and zeros close to the point of departure from the real axis are the most effective in establishing the location of the departure point.

7. *The direction of the asymptote lines to the root locus is given by* $\dfrac{\pm 180° \, q}{n - m}$ *where n is the number of the open-loop poles, m is the number of the open-loop zeros and q is an odd integer.*

The asymptote lines to the root locus describe the limits to which root loci approach when far distant from the open-loop poles and zeros themselves. For these distant regions, the angle contribution of each pole and zero is essentially the same so that $G(s)H(s)$ reduces approximately to

$$G(s)H(s) = \frac{s^m}{s^n} \tag{6.6–12}$$

Referring to Equation 6.6–7, where $m = 1$ and $n = 3$ the direction of the asymptotes is $\dfrac{180°}{2} = \pm 90°$ as is shown in Figure 6.6–4.

8. *The asymptote lines cross the real axis at the point determined by the relationship (sum of real parts of the poles − sum of the real parts of the zeros)/(total number of poles − total number of zeros).*

This point is important for it establishes the intersection of the asymptote lines and, with the slope of the asymptote lines, helps to block out the over-all form of the loci remote from the origin.

The significance of the above expression can be obtained from the following consideration. With the transfer function written as

$$G(s)H(s) = \frac{K[s^m + (a_{m-1})s^{m-1} + (a_{m-2})s^{m-2} + \cdots a_0]}{s^n + (b_{n-1})s^{n-1} + (b_{n-2})s^{n-2} + \cdots b_0} \tag{6.6–13}$$

the numerator is divided into the denominator to obtain the expression

$$G(s)H(s) = \frac{K}{s^{n-m} + (b_{n-1} - a_{m-1})s^{(n-m-1)} + \cdots} \tag{6.6–14}$$

When $s$ is very large, the transfer function behaves like the polynomial of degree $n - m$ with the combined resultant poles of $(b_{n-1} - a_{m-1})$. Thus, the resultant asymptotes meet at the point on the real axis given by

$$\frac{(b_{n-1} - a_{m-1})}{n - m} \tag{6.6–15}$$

Hence, with

$$G(s)H(s) = \frac{KT_2(s + 1/T_2)}{T_1 T_3 \left[ s^3 + \left( \dfrac{1}{T_1} + \dfrac{1}{T_3} \right) s^2 + \dfrac{1}{T_1 T_3} s \right]} \tag{6.6–16}$$

the point where the asymptotes intersect the real axis is

$$+ \frac{\left(\dfrac{1}{T_1} + \dfrac{1}{T_3}\right) - \dfrac{1}{T_2}}{3 - 1} = \frac{-(10 + \frac{1}{4}) + 1}{2} = -4.625 \qquad (6.6\text{-}17)$$

as shown in Figure 6.6–4.

Examples of the use of the root locus for determining stability are contained in the following section and further explanation of the root locus method is contained in Chapter 13.

## 6.7   Application of Root Locus to Typical Control System Transfer Functions

In this section the root locus plots will be drawn for a number of the transfer functions considered in Section 6.5.  In addition to providing a comparison of the results obtained from analyzing the same transfer functions by the root locus and the complex plane approaches, these plots will serve to illustrate some of the rules helpful in drawing root locus plots.

*Example 1*

$$G(s)H(s) = \frac{K}{(T_1 s + 1)(T_2 s + 1)} \qquad (6.7\text{-}1)$$

For this regulator type characteristic, the two poles of the open-loop transfer functions are on the negative real axis, as shown in Figure 6.7–1. Corresponding to these two poles are the two branches 1 and 2 which start at the poles $-2$ and $-25$ for $K = 0$ and increase until they meet at $s = -13.5 + j0$ for $K = 2.66$.  For larger values of gain, the closed loop poles leave the negative real axis at right angles to form the branches $1'$ and $2'$ which continue on asymptotic to $\dfrac{180°}{2} = \pm 90°$.  The point on real axis at which the asymptotes cross is given by

$$-\frac{(25 + 2)}{2} = -13.5$$

For the actual value of gain of the system, $K = 20$, the closed-loop poles are located at $-13.5 \pm j\,29.5$.

*Example 2*

$$G(s)H(s) = \frac{K}{s(T_1 s + 1)(T_2 s + 1)} \qquad (6.7\text{-}2)$$

The presence of the integrator in this transfer function representing a simple position control produces an open-loop pole at the origin.  Figure

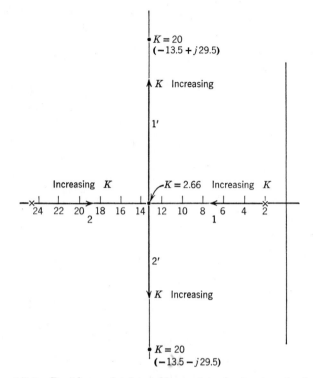

FIGURE 6.7–1.   Root locus plot for stable regulator having transfer function.

$$G(s)H(s) = \frac{20}{(1 + 0.5s)(1 + 0.04s)}$$

$$= \frac{50K}{(s + 2)(s + 25)}$$

6.7–2 shows the root locus plot for this control.   Note that for the three poles there are three branches each originating at a pole.   For low gains there are three real closed-loop poles, two on the axis between $s = 0$ and $s = -2$, where there exists an open-loop pole to the right, and the third real pole to the left of $s = -16$, where there is again an odd number of open-loop poles on the real axis to the right.

The point of departure of the root locus from the real axis is determined from the equation obtained from the rules of the previous section:

$$-\frac{1}{d} + \frac{1}{4 - d} + \frac{1}{16 - d} = 0$$

from which the value of $d$ is found to be 1.86 corresponding to a gain of $K = 0.87$ and $s = -1.86$.

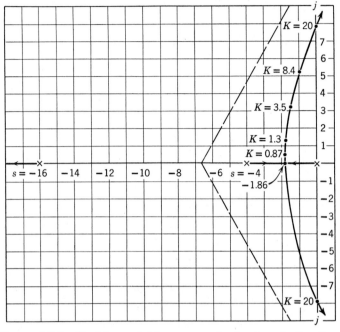

FIGURE 6.7-2.  Root locus plot for servomechanism transfer function.

$$G(s)H(s) = \frac{K}{s(1 + s/4)(1 + s/16)} = \frac{64K}{s(s + 4)(s + 16)}$$

By setting $s = j\omega$, the value of the intersection of the root locus with the imaginary ($j$) axis is found to occur at $\omega = \pm 8$. At this intersection point $K = 20$ corresponding to an intermediate value of gain between $K = 10$ of the stable system and $K = 100$ of an unstable system. These results verify the conclusions as to the system stability for these gains previously illustrated in Figure 6.5–2.

The asymptotes for the root locus are at angles $\frac{\pm 180}{3} = \pm 60°$ and at $\frac{\pm 180 \times 3}{3} = \pm 180°$ as shown by the dotted lines in Figure 6.7–2. The intersection of the asymptotes with the real axis is at $\frac{-(16 + 4)}{3} = -6\frac{2}{3}$.

*Example 3*

$$G(s)H(s) = \frac{K(T_3 s + 1)(T_4 s + 1)}{s(T_1 s + 1)(T_2 s + 1)(T_5 s + 1)(T_6 s + 1)}$$

This more complicated transfer function has additional poles and zeros located along the negative real axis as is indicated in an approximate fashion on Figure 6.7–3($a$). The presence of these additional terms as

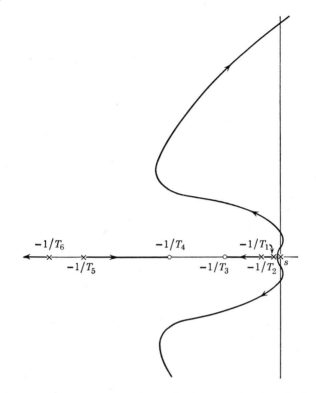

FIGURE 6.7–3($a$). Approximate root locus plot for control system having transfer function.

$$G(s)H(s) = \frac{900(1 + s/2.5)(1 + s/5.0)}{s(1 + 2.5s)(1 + 1.43s)(1 + s/50)(1 + s/152)}$$

$$= \frac{170K(s + 2.5)(s + 5.0)}{s(s + 0.4)(s + 0.74)(s + 50)(s + 152)}$$

caused by including more factors such as stabilizing means results in a more complex shape for the root locus plot. The five branches are indicated by the five poles and their location along the real axis follows the rules set forth in the previous section. It will again be noted that the branches start at the poles and end at the zeros or at infinity.

The directions for the asymptote lines to the root locus are given by $\frac{\pm 180°}{5 - 2} = \pm 60°$ and by $\frac{\pm 180 \times 3}{5 - 2} = \pm 180°$. These asymptote lines cross the real axis at the point $\frac{-195.6}{3} = -65.2$.

Figure 6.7–3(b) shows the root locus plot to a proper scale for the control system shown in approximate form in Figure 6.7–3(a). When

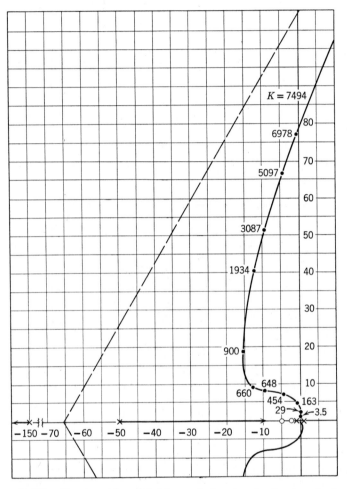

FIGURE 6.7–3(b).   Exact root locus plot for control system having transfer function.

$$G(s)H(s) = \frac{170K(s + 2.5)(s + 5.0)}{s(s + 0.4)(s + 0.74)(s + 50)(s + 152)}$$

the root locus for a high-gain system such as this one being considered is shown to the proper scale, the shape of the characteristic near the origin is apt to be obscured. Since the highest value of gain at which the locus crosses the imaginary axis is about 7000 and the value of $\omega$ for this gain is 80, it is evident that the root locus near the origin cannot be clearly represented.   In addition to the imaginary axis crossing depicted, two other crossings take place at $\omega = 0.9$ and 2.2.   These three crossings correspond to the three crossings of the negative real axis on the Nyquist stability plot of Figure 6.5–3(a).

*Example 4*

$$G(s)H(s) = \frac{K(T_1 s + 1)}{s^2(T_2 s + 1)(T_3 s + 1)}$$

As was noted in connection with other methods of determining stability, the presence of the $1/s^2$ term causing two poles at the intersection of the axes tends to decrease the stability of such a system for very low values of gain.   However, stable operation is possible as shown in Figure 6.7–4.   The presence of the four poles produces four branches to the

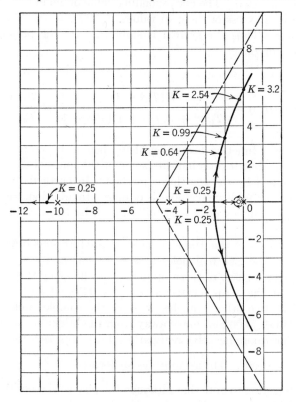

FIGURE 6.7–4.   Root locus plot for control system having a transfer function.

$$G(s)H(s) = \frac{1/4(1 + 4s)}{s^2(1 + s/4)(1 + s/10)} = \frac{160K(s + 1/4)}{s^2(s + 4)(s + 10)}$$

root locus plot, two of which start at the origin. The other two branches, starting at the poles $s = -4$ and $s = -10$, lie along the negative real axis and approach the zero at $s = -0.25$ and approach infinity, respectively.

There are three asymptotes for the root locus corresponding to $\dfrac{\pm 180°}{4 - 1}$ = $\pm 60°$ and $\dfrac{\pm 180° \times 3}{3} = \pm 180°$. The intersection of these asymptotes occurs at $\dfrac{-14 + 0.25}{3} = -4.6$ on the negative real axis.

By substituting $s = j\omega$ into the expression for the transfer function and setting the real part of the resultant expression equal to zero, the value of $\omega$ at the intersections of the root locus and the imaginary axis is found to be $\pm 6.0$. The corresponding value of gain at these points is 3.2 which is in excess of the gain values of 0.25 that the control system actually has. Thus the system is stable despite the presence of two poles at the origin.

*Example 5*

$$G(s)H(s) = \frac{K(T_2 s + 1)}{(T_0^2 s^2 + 2\zeta T_0 s + 1)(T_1 s - 1)} \times \frac{T_3 s + 1}{T_4 s + 1}$$

The transfer function being considered here is by no means a representative one, but it does indicate some of the unusual effects that can also be handled by the root locus method. In particular the presence of a pole on the positive real axis is of note. In addition, the method of handling the complex poles is also illustrated by this example shown on Figure 6.7–5(a).

The four poles of this transfer function produce four branches to the root locus. The two real poles at $s = +0.063$ and $s = -31$ are the starting point for two of these branches that lie along the real axis and terminate at the zeros located at $s = -0.025$ and $s = -3.1$, respectively. The two other branches start at the complex poles located at $s = -0.236 \pm j3.06$ and move away from the origin in the direction so as to produce more negative real parts. They approach the asymptotes at $\dfrac{\pm 180°}{4 - 2} = \pm 90°$. The asymptotes are located at $\dfrac{-28.38}{4 - 2} = -14.19$.

It is interesting to note that although the pole with a positive real part would produce an unstable system with low system gains, the presence of a zero on the negative real axis is able to attract this branch at higher gains and thus produce a stable loop pole. The two complex poles serve

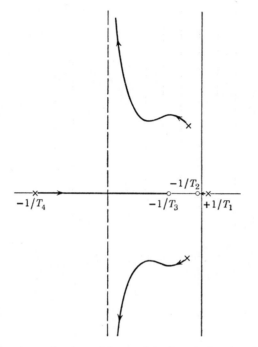

FIGURE 6.7–5(a).   Approximate root locus plot of control system having transfer function,

$$G(s)H(s) = \frac{2.12(1 + s/0.025)(1 + s/3.1)}{(1 + 0.0501s + 0.106s^2)(s/0.063 - 1)(1 + s/31)}$$

$$= \frac{237.K(s + 0.025)(s + 3.1)}{(s^2 + 0.473s + 9.44)(s - 0.063)(s + 31)}$$

as starting points for the other two branches. Although the initial direction of these branches is readily established as by the fifth rule of the preceding section, the intermediate points on the root locus can be determined readily, with the aid of methods described in Section 13.4.

Figure 6.7–5(b) shows a more exact plot of the root locus of the transfer function shown on Figure 6.7–5(a). For the stipulated value of gain of 2.12, the poles of the closed-loop system are found to be $-0.01$, $-4.66$, and $-13.4 \pm j14.6$ corresponding to a stable system.

The purpose of the above examples is to show the root locus of some typical control problems such as were worked out in Section 6.5, and to indicate the use of the root locus plots in showing control system stability. Chapter 13 contains much more detailed explanations of the construction and use of root locus plots for the design and synthesis of

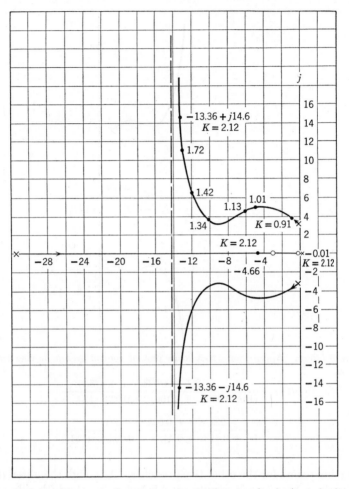

FIGURE 6.7–5(b).   Exact root locus point of control system having transfer function.

$$G(s)H(s) = \frac{2.12(1 + s/0.025)(1 + s/3.1)}{(1 + 0.0501s + 0.106s^2)(s/0.063 - 1)(1 + s/31)}$$

$$= \frac{237.K(s + 0.025)(s + 3.1)}{(s^2 + 0.473s + 9.44)(s - 0.063)(s + 31)}$$

control systems.  At that time, examples such as those represented by 5 and 6 of Section 6.5 as well as many others will be considered in detail.

# 7

## TYPICAL CONTROL ELEMENTS
## AND THEIR TRANSFER FUNCTIONS

### 7.0 Introduction

The preceding chapters have emphasized the mathematical background that is so important in establishing a firm basis for studying feedback control systems.[26, 31] The remaining chapters of this volume deal primarily with the methods of servomechanism, regulator, and control system analysis that have developed from the treatment of linear feedback control systems with constant coefficients. Although the complex plane ideas of Nyquist,[6] the attenuation-frequency concepts of Bode,[14] and the root locus methods of Evans [105, 120] will be presented as *analytical* tools for servomechanism and regulator study, the usefulness of these ideas for purposes of *synthesis* [122] will also be stressed. Despite the fact that the main objective of this volume is to describe clearly the basic analytical methods of servomechanism and regulator design, an endeavor is made continually to present the physical reasoning involved in the synthesis of these feedback control systems.

To provide a background of understanding of the types of problems that may be encountered in the feedback control system fields, this chapter presents a physical or qualitative picture and a mathematical or quantitative presentation of representative control elements.

### 7.1 Description of the Control Problem

Basically a control system is one in which the controlled variable bears a close and intimate relationship to the desired value. In general the controlled variable is at a higher power level and is somewhat removed from the desired value. It is the purpose of the control to maintain the desired relationship between the controlled variable and the desired value with a minimum of discrepancy between the two. As examples of the sort of relationships that may be desired between these two quantities, consider the various control systems shown in simplified form in Figures 7.1–1 through 7.1–5.

Figure 7.1–1 shows a gun-positioning control system in which an electrical signal proportional to the desired gun position is the reference input and the actual gun position is the indirectly controlled quantity.[80]

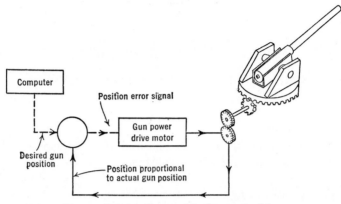

FIGURE 7.1–1.   Gun-positioning power drive.

The controlled variable is a position proportional to the actual gun position. In this sort of system the control endeavors to maintain at all times the control variable position equal to the desired input position. Hydraulic or electric motors generally are the controlled system used to provide the main power for moving the gun carriage.

Figure 7.1–2 illustrates a mill motor speed control system in which it is desired to operate the second drive motor at the same speed as the main

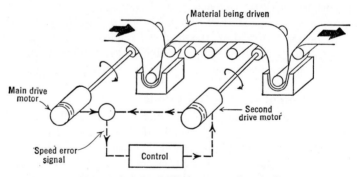

FIGURE 7.1–2.   Mill motor speed control.

drive motor.[98, 104]   Frequently a d-c voltage proportional to the main d-c motor speed is the reference input whereas the speed of the second d-c motor is the controlled variable output.   A d-c tachometer used to indicate the output speed provides the feedback signal.

The basic elements of a ship's steering control system [1] are shown in Fig. 7.1–3. The desired ship's angular heading is used to provide the reference input signal. The actual ship's angular heading is the con-

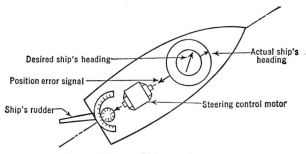

Desired ship's heading

Position error signal

Ship's rudder

Actual ship's heading

Steering control motor

FIGURE 7.1–3.   Ship-steering system.

trolled variable. A signal proportional to the actual ship's heading provides the feedback that is compared to the reference input signal. The error signal proportional to the angular difference between the desired and the actual ship's heading is used to actuate the steering control motor. The steering motor, hydraulic or electric, positions the ship's rudder that causes the ship to turn to the desired heading.

Another type of position control is shown in Figure 7.1–4 where a machine tool cutter control is indicated. The reference input is the position of the edge of the template at the longitudinal position of the car-

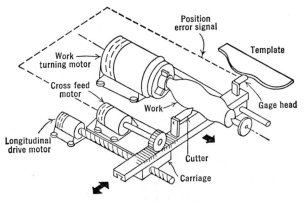

Position error signal

Template

Work turning motor

Cross feed motor

Work

Gage head

Longitudinal drive motor

Cutter

Carriage

FIGURE 7.1–4.   Machine tool cutter control.

riage carrying the cross-feed motor, the cutter, and the gage head. The indirectly controlled quantity position is the distance from the axis to the edge of the work being turned for the same longitudinal position of the carriage. By careful initial alignment, a gage head mounted on the carriage can be made to yield a signal proportional to the difference in position between the desired value and the indirectly controlled quantity. Pneumatic, hydraulic, and electric motors have been used for driving the cross-feed in installations of this type.

Figure 7.1–5 shows a simple form of temperature control for use as part of a process control system.[42]   The reference input is a signal proportional to the process temperature desired.   The indirectly controlled quantity is the actual temperature of the processed material.   A signal proportional to the process temperature is fed back and compared

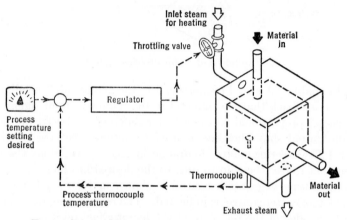

FIGURE 7.1–5.   Temperature regulator on process control.

with the signal proportional to the desired temperature.   The difference signal, actuating error, operates the regulator that positions the throttling valve that controls the amount of steam flow to heat the material contained in the process.   The addition or withdrawal of material from the process may be considered to be a disturbing function that acts to alter the value of the temperature being controlled.   Pneumatic control of the throttling valve is frequently employed.

These five examples are merely illustrative and are chosen to indicate a few of the many different types of systems for which control is used.[9, 13, 16, 22, 24, 25, 36, 37, 39, 44, 58, etc.]   They also serve to indicate the high degree of similarity in form among these seemingly different controls.

In addition to controls that endeavor to maintain a direct relationship between similar quantities such as position and position, speed and speed, it is frequently desirable and/or necessary to obtain controls or control elements for which the controlled variable is proportional to such time functions as the time rate of change (that is, the derivative) of a quantity, or to the rate of change of the rate of change (that is, the second derivative) of the reference input.   Likewise it may be desirable to obtain as an indirectly controlled quantity an output proportional to the single or double integral of a reference input quantity.

Because the field of usefulness of the theory that is developed in the succeeding chapters is not limited to the electromechanical systems around which it is presented, this chapter describes some of the qualitative and the analytical performance characteristics of typical electrical, mechanical, hydraulic, and steering system elements. In this way the basic similarity of the control problems in these various fields will be clarified further.

## 7.2   Definition of Control System Element Transfer Function

A *control system element* may be defined as one of a number of parts that, when connected together, form the feedback control system. Ideally each control system element performs some specific function that is necessary to the over-all performance of the system.

In general, a control system element receives an input signal from another element or group of elements and transmits its output to another control system element or group of elements. Although the nature of the output depends on the input and the characteristics of the control system element, the output is very often a function of the characteristics of the control element that supplies the input and also a function of the control element that serves as its load. As an example, the transfer function of a particular power source may vary appreciably with the means used to interconnect it to its load, or with the means used for driving it. The loading and regulation effects may mean that a given control element will have one set of values (constants) for one set of input and output operating conditions and another set of values for another set of input and output operating conditions. For this reason it is frequently necessary to group together a number of control elements to develop an equivalent transfer function that contains the actual system configuration of control elements and their interconnections.

Having grouped together control system elements to form an equivalent transfer function, it is important to continue to be cognizant of the actual physical characteristics represented by the equivalent transfer function. For example, some of the electrical networks added for stabilizing purposes, unless care is taken, have impedance values which are incompatible with the circuit elements they are being driven from. The desired effects of such stabilizing means are achieved when due attention is given to the basic physical laws involved. Another matter requiring attention is the fact that many control elements and devices are bilateral in their action. Although the arrows drawn on block diagrams indicate a flow of signals or information in only one direction, actually the signals may in reality be feeding networks and impedances as described in section 5.3 such that superposition effects play a dominant role. In fact, a number of control engineers have advocated representing transfer functions as four-terminal networks rather than unilateral block diagrams.

In the examples that follow it will be noted that the *physical laws dictate what the transfer function of a group of interconnected control elements will be rather than what the characteristic transfer function of each of them is separately.* The d-c generator-motor combination, the hydraulic pump-motor, and the steering systems all illustrate this point. In addition to the effect of interconnection on the transfer function of a control element, nonlinearities and other effects may cause the transfer function of a control element to be different under different regions of operation. From the above it is evident that there are frequently a large number of assumptions that are contained in the statement of a given transfer function. These assumptions should be kept in mind throughout lest the mathematical exactness of some of the work that is performed on transfer functions create a false feeling of confidence that the results are better than the validity of the original assumptions.

The output of a control system element may differ from the input in three ways: (1) form, (2) time relationship, and (3) energy level. *Form* means the physical nature of the quantities involved; that is, the input may be a voltage whereas the output may be a voltage, a current, a position, or vice versa. *Time relationship* is used to indicate the effect of time constants, phase shift, integration, or differentiation that may take place in the control system element. *Energy level* is a measure of the ability of the system to perform external work; it includes the effect of change of magnitude between input and output when both are of the same type. Energy level is an essential factor to be considered when a control system element used in one application is considered for use in another; in purely analytical studies this factor seldom appears per se.

A transfer function of a control system element is a mathematical expression that indicates the dynamic characteristics of the element in terms of the ratio of the output to the input of the element. In much of the discussion that follows, a *transfer function, G(s), is expressed in the form of the Laplace transform of the output to input ratio in which all the initial values are set equal to zero.* Thus

$$O(s) = G(s)I(s) \qquad (7.2\text{--}1)$$

where $I(s)$ is the Laplace transform of the input,
$O(s)$ is the Laplace transform of the output, and
$G(s)$ is the transfer function.

The transfer function expresses both the magnitude and the units necessary to relate the input to the output.   It also expresses the dynamic characteristics of the element in terms of its parameters.

An alternate method of describing the transfer function sometimes employed expresses this ratio in operational form.   Since the initial conditions have been set equal to zero when obtaining the Laplace transform for the transfer function, *the operational and the Laplace transform forms differ in appearance only by the substitution of p for s.*

Solving for the ratio of $O(s)/I(s)$ in Equation 7.2–1 gives

$$\frac{O(s)}{I(s)} = G(s) \tag{7.2-2}$$

which is the defining relation for the transfer function.   Equations 7.2–1 and 7.2–2 show that, physically, the transfer function is that dynamic characteristic that modifies the input quantity in transferring it to become the output quantity.

When the input to a control system element is varying sinusoidally, the output to input ratio, which is the transfer function, may be determined by replacing $s$ by $j\omega$.   It will be recalled from Chapters 4 and 5 that this procedure is what takes place when the inverse Laplace transform is performed.   The transfer function is then said to be in its complex or sinusoidal form.   Corresponding to Equation 7.2–3, the sinusoidal form of this transfer function is

$$\frac{O}{I}(j\omega) = G(j\omega) \tag{7.2-3}$$

It is evident that Equations 7.2–2 and 7.2–3 are merely alternate forms of the same equation, the use of $G(s)$ or $G(j\omega)$ serving primarily to indicate the general transfer function or the specific case of sinusoidal excitation.   Figure 7.2–1 is a block diagram used to indicate the relationship of Equation 7.2–2.

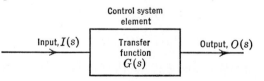

Figure 7.2–1.   Block diagram representation of control system element transfer function.

## 7.3    Combination of Control System Elements in Series

The grouping of control system elements in a control system is often a series arrangement whereby the output of one system element serves as the input to the next system element, the output of the second element serving as the input for the third, and so on.    Figure 7.3–1 is a block diagram of such a series or cascade-type connection, as this is sometimes called.

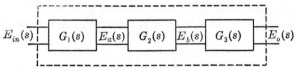

FIGURE 7.3–1.    Block diagram of a series of control system elements.

*It is important that the loading effect of the succeeding control elements be included in the expression for the transfer function of the control system element that precedes it, or, conversely, the regulation effect of one element should be included with the transfer function of the element that follows it.*    This results in the transfer function of a system element depending upon the element it supplies.    For example, consider an electronic amplifier supplying a load with an impedance comparable to the amplifier internal impedance.    The voltage or current through the load will depend on the load impedance as well as the amplifier characteristics.    Frequently, in such a case, it is convenient to group the two elements, amplifier and load, into one more inclusive, equivalent system element for which the transfer function is determined.

By assuming that Figure 7.3–1 represents a series of control system elements in which loading effects have already been taken into account, and by using the definition of transfer function, the output of each element may be written in terms of its input.    Thus

$$E_a(s) = G_1(s)E_{in}(s) \qquad (7.3–1)$$

$$E_b(s) = G_2(s)E_a(s) \qquad (7.3–2)$$

$$E_o(s) = G_3(s)E_b(s) \qquad (7.3–3)$$

By eliminating $E_a(s)$ and $E_b(s)$ in the foregoing equations, the over-all transfer function from input to output of the group of elements shown in the dotted block on the diagram can be obtained.

$$\frac{E_o(s)}{E_{in}(s)} = G_1(s)G_2(s)G_3(s) \qquad (7.3–4)$$

This expression may be written in the general form

$$\frac{E_o(s)}{E_{in}(s)} = G(s) \qquad (7.3\text{--}5)$$

where $G(s) = G_1(s)G_2(s)G_3(s)$.

Thus the over-all transfer function for a group of elements in series may be expressed in the same form as the transfer function of a single control system element. It will be shown later that the over-all transfer function can be expressed as a $G(s)$ for groupings of servomechanism elements other than the series arrangement considered here. However, the relationship between the over-all transfer function and that of the individual components is not so direct as that obtained when all series elements are employed.

## 7.4 Transfer Functions of Typical Mechanical Control Elements

As indicated in Figures 7.1–1 through 7.1–4 a number of common servomechanisms and regulators involve control of mechanical elements to obtain accurate positioning or speed control of a load. To illustrate this further, the nature of the physical and mathematical relationships will be developed between such input quantities as torque and the output angular position on a rotational control system or the input force and the output position in a translational control. In addition such mechanical and hydraulic means as spring-dashpot combinations for obtaining differentiation and integration effects will be described.

**Mechanical Elements Having Rotary Motion.** Rotary motion is defined by Newton's second law of motion as the angular acceleration of a body, which is directly proportional to the sum of the applied torques and is inversely proportional to the moment of inertia of the body. Stated mathematically,

$$\text{Angular acceleration} = \frac{d^2\theta}{dt^2} = \frac{\Sigma \text{ torques}}{J} \qquad (7.4\text{--}1)$$

where $\theta$ = angular position of the body,
  $J$ = moment of inertia.

In more familiar form Equation 7.4–1 generally appears as

$$J\frac{d^2\theta}{dt^2} = \Sigma \text{ torques} \qquad (7.4\text{--}2)$$

For use in the English system, the consistent units are:

Angular acceleration = radians per second per second
Angular position     = radians
Torques              = pound-feet
Moment of inertia    = slug feet squared

The torques may be produced by external sources such as electric or hydraulic motors, by load torques, by spring reaction, or by viscous or other forms of damping. In later sections the transfer functions of electric and hydraulic motors will be described. The nature of the load torques is varied. In certain cases the load torque is a function of time. The firing of a gun that introduces a large unbalance torque if the direction of the reaction force does not pass through the center of rotation of the gun carriage is an example. The load torque on a motor controlling the speed of a steel rolling mill as a large billet passes through the rollers is another example of a time-varying disturbance torque. Other load torques, such as windage loads, are functions of the position or velocity of the controlled element or of another system of which it is a part.

The characteristic of a spring-type torque is that the magnitude of the torque is proportional to the angular deflection of the load from its neutral or reference position, and the direction of the torque is such as to restore the load to the reference position of zero spring torque. Thus, mathematically, the spring torque is expressed as

$$T_s = K_s(\theta_r - \theta_l) \qquad (7.4\text{--}3)$$

where $T_s$ = spring torque in pound-feet,
$\quad K_s$ = spring torque coefficient in pound-feet per radian,
$\quad \theta_r$ = reference angular position in radians, and
$\quad \theta_l$ = load angular position in radians.

Spring torques may enter into the performance of servomechanisms in a number of different ways. For example, if the reference angle is held fixed at zero, and a torque $T_s$ is applied to the load, the load position $\theta_l$ can be used to indicate the amount of the restoring torque acting on the load. Thus

$$T_s = -K_s\theta_l \qquad (7.4\text{--}4)$$

Another instance of spring torques acting on a servomechanism system is the transmission of large torques through shafts or structural members in which torsional deflection occurs. Figure 7.4–1 illustrates an example of this condition.

It is desired to control the load position $\theta_l$ by positioning the angle $\theta_r$ at the driving end of the shaft.  By rewriting Equation 7.4–3 in the form,

$$\theta_r - \theta_l = \frac{T_s}{K_s} \qquad (7.4\text{–}5)$$

it can be seen that there will be a difference between the reference and load positions directly proportional to the torque and inversely proportional to the shaft stiffness.

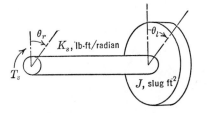

The characteristic of a spring that produces a force or a torque proportional to displacement has given rise to the use of the term "spring torque" or "spring force" in other instances.  Such cases occur where there is no torque produced by an actual spring but where there is a torque produced proportional to the displacement of the load from its neutral position.  Examples of this are encountered in aerodynamic and hydraulic problems, as will be seen later.

FIGURE 7.4–1.  Load of inertia $J$ being driven by torque $T_s$ through shaft of stiffness coefficient $K_s$.

Viscous or damping torques are characterized by being proportional to the rate of change of load position, that is,

$$T_D = K_D \frac{d\theta_l}{dt} \qquad (7.4\text{–}6)$$

where $T_D$ = damping torque in pound-feet and
$\quad\;\; K_D$ = damping torque coefficient in pound-feet per radian per second.

Occasionally hydraulic devices used for damping purposes have such a characteristic as is described by Equation 7.4–6.  Windage characteristics of rotating equipment can frequently be approximated by such an equation as Equation 7.4–6.  It is this sort of torque that absorbs energy from the system and thus tends to damp out disturbances to the system. In view of the fact that this sort of damping represents an actual power loss to the system, this sort of torque is generally minimized by good mechanical design.  However, there are other means of obtaining torques proportional to load speed, and in common parlance they are called "damping" torques because of the similarity of the effect produced by them and by damping torques.

An example of a mechanical servomechanism element that has rotary motion of the sort just described is the power portion of a gun-positioning power drive such as was shown in Figure 7.1–1. This system, illustrated in Figure 7.4–2, is one in which there are two guns mounted on a common

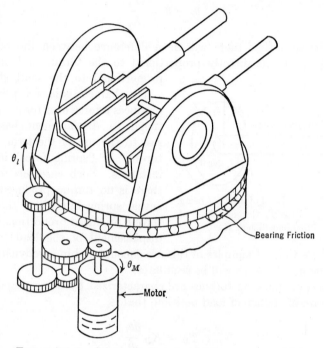

FIGURE 7.4–2.   Schematic diagram of twin-gun power drive.

gun carriage so that when only one gun is fired the motor positioning the mount has to supply sufficient torque not only to follow accurately the desired signal motion but also to counteract the firing torque. Figure 7.4–3 shows schematically the salient features of the systems.

The torques acting on the inertia of the mount are the following.

*Firing torque, f(t).* This is a disturbance function that is a function of time, the exact nature of which may be obtained from oscillographic records with the gun locked in position or from other more approximate means.

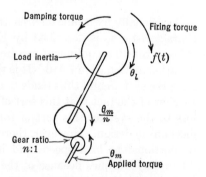

FIGURE 7.4–3.   Salient features of power drive of Figure 7.4–2.

*Shaft spring torque*, $K_s\left(\dfrac{\theta_m}{n} - \theta_l\right)$. This is the torque transmitted to the load by the drive shaft, and it is proportional to the difference in position between the load and the motor ends of the shaft, which has a spring constant, $K_s$ pounds per radian. Since the torque applied by the motor is also a function of the motor position $\theta_m$, the applied torque is not simply expressible as a function of time. Because of the gear mesh, with ratio $n:1$, the motor position $\theta_m$ appears as an angle $\theta_m/n$ on the motor end of the shaft. The load is located at $\theta_l$. In general the effect of the shaft inertia is small compared to that of the load or motor.

*Damping torque*, $K_D \dfrac{d\theta_l}{dt}$. This torque represents the action of friction of the gun carriage as it rolls on its bearings and other similar torques proportional to load speed. Since it represents an energy loss to the system, its direction is such as to oppose the velocity of the load.

The resultant of these torques causes the acceleration of the load inertia. Thus

$$J\frac{d^2\theta_l}{dt^2} = f(t) + K_s\left(\frac{\theta_m}{n} - \theta_l\right) - K_D\frac{d\theta_l}{dt} \qquad (7.4\text{--}7)$$

By grouping together the terms containing the load motion and performing the Laplace transformation with initial conditions set equal to zero,

$$(Js^2 + K_D s + K_s)\theta_l(s) = F(s) + \frac{K_s}{n}\theta_m(s) \qquad (7.4\text{--}8)$$

where $\theta_l(s) = \mathcal{L}[\theta_l]$,
$F(s) = \mathcal{L}[f(t)]$,
$\theta_m(s) = \mathcal{L}[\theta_m]$.

If the performance of the servomechanism element is considered in the absence of the firing torque, Equation 7.4–8 may be rewritten as

$$(Js^2 + K_D s + K_s)\theta_l(s) = \frac{K_s}{n}\theta_m(s) \qquad (7.4\text{--}9)$$

and $G(s)$ the transfer function, the ratio of output motion $\theta_l$ to input motion $\theta_m$ is

$$G(s) = \frac{\theta_l(s)}{\theta_m(s)} = \frac{1/n}{\left[\dfrac{J}{K_s}s^2 + \dfrac{K_D}{K_s}s + 1\right]} \qquad (7.4\text{--}10)$$

The corresponding operational form of this transfer function is

$$G(p) = \frac{1/n}{\left[\dfrac{J}{K_s} p^2 + \dfrac{K_D}{K_s} p + 1\right]} \qquad (7.4\text{--}10a)$$

**Mechanical Elements Having Translatory Motion.** The equations of translatory motion of a rigid body are analogous to the equations of rotary motion. Corresponding to Equation 7.4–1 is this equation for translation:

$$m \frac{d^2x}{dt^2} = \Sigma \text{ forces} \qquad (7.4\text{--}11)$$

where $x$ = translatory position of the body,
   $m$ = mass of body,
   and the forces are all external ones.

The external forces are produced by load reactions, by spring forces, and by damping and friction forces as was the case for rotary motion. Load reactions may be forces that are expressible as functions of time or they may be forces that are proportional to the difference in position between the load and other objects. These latter forces may be of the nature of spring forces. In addition to friction forces that are proportional to the speed of motion of the load, frequently there are present non-linear forces such as static or coulomb, friction or backlash effects that are also non-linear. These non-linear effects will not be included in the discussion.

An example of a mechanical servomechanism element in which translatory motion is of major importance has been described in the spring-mass system of Section 3.8.

Equation 3.8–1, which presents the summation of forces acting on the platform, is repeated here.

$$M \frac{d^2x}{dt^2} = -K(x - X_o - y) - D \frac{dx}{dt} - Mg \qquad (7.4\text{--}12)$$

By proper selection of the reference point for $x$, the value of $KX_o = Mg$ so that Equation 7.4–12 can be written as

$$M \frac{d^2x}{dt^2} + D \frac{dx}{dt} + Kx = Ky \qquad (7.4\text{--}13)$$

Performing the transformation of Equation 7.4–13 with the initial conditions zero gives

$$[Ms^2 + Ds + K]X(s) = KY(s) \qquad (7.4\text{--}14)$$

The corresponding ratio of output to input is

$$\frac{X(s)}{Y(s)} = \frac{1}{\dfrac{M}{K}s^2 + \dfrac{D}{K}s + 1} \qquad (7.4\text{--}15)$$

Hence the transfer function $G(s)$ for the $X(s)/Y(s)$ ratio is

$$G(s) = \frac{X(s)}{Y(s)} = \frac{1}{\dfrac{M}{K}s^2 + \dfrac{D}{K}s + 1} \qquad (7.4\text{--}16)$$

**Spring-Dashpot Elements Used to Obtain Mechanical Displacements.**
In all-mechanical, mechanical-hydraulic, or in mechanical-pneumatic

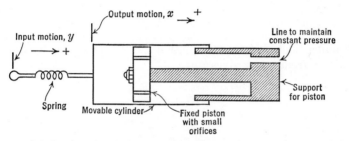

FIGURE 7.4–4.  A spring-dashpot arrangement used for stabilizing purposes.

control systems it is frequently desirable to obtain an output motion
that has a different type of response to slowly changing input motions
from its response to rapidly changing input motions.[34]  Mechanisms that
can be used to advantage for such a purpose are a combination of spring
and dashpot, such as are shown in Figures 7.4–4 and 7.4–5.  The action

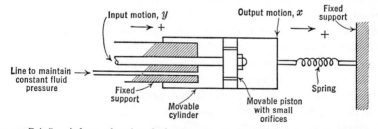

FIGURE 7.4–5.  A form of spring-dashpot arrangement alternate with that of Figure
7.4–4.

of the dashpot with the piston containing small orifices is to produce a
reaction force proportional to the speed of motion of the movable cyl-

inder, that is, the speed with which oil or fluid is being forced through the orifices as the pressure on both sides of the piston strives for equality.

Thus for the arrangement shown in Figure 7.4–4, the following forces are present:

$$\text{Spring force} = K_s(y - x) \qquad (7.4\text{–}17)$$

where $K_s$ is the force per unit relative motion of the input position $y$ with respect to output position $x$.

$$\text{Viscous force} = D\frac{dx}{dt} \qquad (7.4\text{–}18)$$

where $D$ is the force per unit speed of the output. If the cylinder inertia is small, these forces must be equal, and

$$K_s(y - x) = D\frac{dx}{dt} \qquad (7.4\text{–}19)$$

Obtaining the transform of Equation 7.4–19 and solving for the transfer function from $y$ to $x$ gives

$$\frac{X(s)}{Y(s)} = G(s) = \frac{1}{\dfrac{D}{K_s}s + 1} \qquad (7.4\text{–}20)$$

When the input position $y$ changes slowly, the output position $x$ is essentially equal to the input for there is time for the flow through the orifices to equalize the pressure across the piston. However, if $y$ changes very rapidly, the output does not follow quickly for the action of the orifices is to tend to maintain a large pressure differential across the piston and thus restrain the motion of the cylinder. For rapid motion of $y$, the spring stretches or compresses to make up the difference displacement.

With a sinusoidal input displacement, the output motion lags behind the input. This characteristic is therefore termed a *phase lag* characteristic. Further discussion of phase lag and phase lead characteristics will be found in Chapter 10.

By contrast, for the spring-dashpot arrangement shown in Figure 7.4–5, slowly changing input displacements result in little output motion whereas rapidly changing input positions produce almost equal displacement of the output. This is shown mathematically as follows:

$$\text{Spring force} = K_s x \qquad (7.4\text{–}21)$$

where $K_s$ is the force per unit displacement of $x$.

$$\text{Viscous force} = D \frac{d}{dt} (y - x) \qquad (7.4\text{--}22)$$

where $D$ is the force per unit velocity difference between piston and cylinder.

Transforming Equations 7.4–21 and 7.4–22 and grouping terms to form the transfer function from $y$ to $x$ gives

$$\frac{X(s)}{Y(s)} = G(s) = \frac{\dfrac{D}{K_s} s}{\left( \dfrac{D}{K_s} s + 1 \right)} \qquad (7.4\text{--}23)$$

If the input motion $y$ is sinusoidal, the transfer function of Equation 7.4–23 becomes

$$\frac{X}{Y} (j\omega) = \frac{\dfrac{j\omega D}{K_s}}{1 + \dfrac{j\omega D}{K_s}} \qquad (7.4\text{--}24)$$

A direct comparison will be noted between this equation and Equation 5.4–6 for the output to input voltage ratio for the $RC$ electrical network of Figure 5.4–4. The characteristic of the output to lead the input for sinusoidal inputs to this type of transfer function is shown in Figure 5.4–6. Hence the term *phase lead* is applied to this type of transfer function.

Equation 7.4–20, when expressed in terms of a sinusoidal driving function, becomes identical in form with Equation 5.4–3 for an $RL$ electrical network. Likewise, many of the transfer functions described for electrical networks in later chapters may be obtained mechanically by spring-dashpot combinations suitably applied.

### 7.5  Transfer Functions of Typical Electrical Control System Elements

Some of the most flexible power sources for servomechanism and regulator system use are electrical in nature. Although frequently the indirectly controlled quantity is mechanical, the source of the control power is an electric motor, with d-c machines one of the more common types. Through control of a d-c generator field with a comparatively small amount of power, it is possible to obtain a d-c generated voltage with much larger power capacity at the generator terminals. When this voltage is impressed on a d-c motor with constant field excitation, a motor speed is obtained that is roughly proportional to the voltage impressed and therefore approximately proportional to the control signal initially applied to the generator control field. Such a servomechanism element is frequently used in a mill motor speed-regulator drive, as shown in Figure 7.1–2. This type of controlled power source is also common in position control servomechanisms, such as is illustrated by the gun positioning drive of Figure 7.1–1 and by the machine tool cutter control in Figure 7.1–4.

In addition to providing the controlled system of many feedback control applications, electrical control elements in the form of valve controls provide accurate and rapid positioning of mechanical elements for use with hydraulic and pneumatic power elements. Furthermore, the use of electric networks to obtain differentiation and integration actions for insuring stable system operation is simple, cheap, and effective.

The transfer functions of many electrical elements such as motors, generator fields, as well as other simple networks have previously been discussed. In the following paragraphs some of these expressions as well as those for other electrical elements are presented in the form of transfer functions.

**Direct-Current Motor-Generator Control.** In Section 5.4 the equations that describe the performance of a d-c motor with constant field excitation were developed. For such a motor the ratio of the transform of motor speed $S(s)$ to the transform of the applied voltage $V_a(s)$ from Equation 5.4–12 is

$$\frac{S(s)}{V_a(s)} = \frac{1}{K_e[T_m s + 1]} \tag{7.5–1}$$

whereas the transfer function between the motor shaft position $\theta(s)$ and the applied voltage $V_a(s)$ from Equation 5.4–20 is

$$\frac{\theta(s)}{V_a(s)} = \frac{1}{K_e s(T_m s + 1)} \tag{7.5–2}$$

In Equations 7.5–1 and 7.5–2 the symbols used have the same significance as those used in Section 5.4, where these equations were derived.

The voltage $v_a$ applied to the motor terminals may itself be a controlled quantity; hence it can be expressed as the output of a control system element consisting of a d-c generator. The d-c generator, as shown in Figure 7.5–1, has as its input the control voltage $e_c$. The magnitude of the voltage output of the generator as impressed on the motor is a function of both the control voltage and also the nature of the motor and

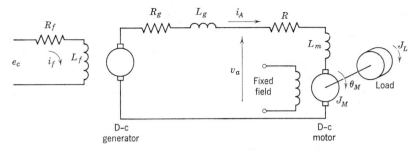

FIGURE 7.5-1.   Schematic diagram of d-c generator supplying at d-c motor with an attached inertia load.

its load as reflected in the armature current, $i_a$.   Although the internal voltage of the generator may for present purposes be assumed to be independent of the armature current, the voltage, $v_a$, impressed on the terminals of the motor will be affected by generator $i_a R_g$ drop and any series generator field inductive voltage.   In this respect, the d-c motor generator characteristic is a function of both motor and generator as interconnected rather than the product of the two of them considered separately.

The generator is assumed to be operating at constant speed and to be unsaturated.   The voltage constant of the generator is $K_g$ volts per ampere of field current.

The voltage equation of the field circuit is

$$L_f \frac{di_f}{dt} + R_f i_f = e_c \qquad (7.5\text{–}3)$$

Considering the armature resistance of the generator and associated conductors from the generator to the motor to be $R_g$, and the armature inductance of the generator to be $L_g$, one can express the motor terminal voltage as

$$v_a = K_g i_f - \left[ L_g \frac{di_a}{dt} + R_g i_a \right] \qquad (7.5\text{–}4)$$

For many d-c motors with fixed field excitation, the motor armature resistance, $R_m$, and the motor armature inductance are not negligible, so that the motor terminal voltage is equal to

$$v_a = L_m \frac{di_a}{dt} + R_m i_a + K_e \frac{d\theta_m}{dt} \qquad (7.5\text{–}5)$$

where $K_e$ is the motor voltage constant in volts per radian per second and $\frac{d\theta_m}{dt}$ is the motor speed in radians per second.

Assuming no external torques, one may express the torques acting on the motor as

$$K_T i_a = (J_M + J_L) \frac{d^2\theta_m}{dt^2}, \qquad (7.5\text{--}6)$$

where $K_T$ is the motor torque constant in pound-feet per ampere,

$J_M$ is the motor inertia in slug-feet$^2$, and

$J_L$ is the equivalent inertia of the load referred to the motor in slug-feet$^2$.

Taking the transform of Equations 7.5–3 through 7.5–6, one can express the over-all transfer functions from control field voltage to motor shaft position as

$$\frac{\theta_M(s)}{E_c(s)} = \frac{K_g}{K_e R_f s [T_f s + 1][T_e T_{mc} s^2 + T_{mc} s + 1]} \qquad (7.5\text{--}7)$$

where $T_f = L_f/R_f$ is the control field time constant,

$T_e = \dfrac{L_g + L_m}{R_g + R_m}$ is the combined motor generator electrical time constant,

$T_{mc} = \dfrac{(J_M + J_L)(R_g + R_m)}{K_e K_T}$ is the combined motor-generator load mechanical time constant.

It is of importance to note that, although the effect of the control field shows up as a separate time constant, the generator, motor, and load inertia produce a combined effect which appears as a quadratic term. Depending on the relative values of $T_e$ and $T_{mc}$, this quadratic may factor into two real or two complex values. In any event, each of the values for the factors will be a function of all three units, namely, the generator, motor, and load. From this it is evident that the designer needs to know the characteristics of each element before he can determine their interrelated effect.

Also worthy of mention is the fact that the time constants $T_e$ and $T_{mc}$ are "combined" or "equivalent" time constants in which some of the parameters, $R_g$ and $L_g$ for example, are associated with one machine, while others, $R_m$ and $L_m$, are associated with another. Since one manufacturer or company may supply one unit and not the other, it is important that the system's designer establish the effect of interconnecting the machines to form the resultant transfer function.

The combined transfer function of Equation 7.5–7 may be shown in block diagram form, Figure 7.5–2, where the effects of the control field and the generator, motor, and load are indicated separately despite the very real interrelationship. It is of interest to note that for negligible armature inductance, $T_e = 0$, and the right-hand block represents the motor time constant term alone.

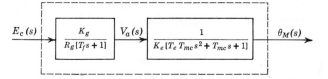

Figure 7.5–2.   Block diagram of transfer function of a d-c generator-motor and associated inertia load.

When it is desired to obtain higher performance systems, the concept of the generator merely having a single field time constant is not always valid. Unless the field structure is laminated quite thoroughly, the effect of eddy currents in the iron of the machine tends to produce an additional short-circuited winding that delays the build-up of the field current and hence the generated voltage. For systems where rapid voltage and current reversals are required, this additional time delay may prove objectionable. Some machines such as amplidynes and multi-field generators purposely use one or more added fields for obtaining higher gain or in providing a means for summing of a number of signals. For these machines additional time constants and gain terms appear in the transfer function expressions.

The presence of armature reaction in both motor and generator may affect the gain and linearity of the machine characteristics such that the relationships established for small loads are somewhat different than for large loads. Consideration should be given to the values of the various coefficients $K_e$, $K_T$, and $K_g$ at a number of machine-operating points.

From the above, it is again evident that a thorough understanding of the physics of the equipment is essential for one to derive a satisfactory transfer function expression.

**Torque Motor Type Servomechanism Elements.** The use of electrical instruments in servomechanism systems to obtain a torque proportional to a current signal is widespread. Two examples of such instruments are galvanometers, such as are used in photoelectric recorders, and gyroscopes, where precession rates or precession torques are used for rate-measuring purposes. The basic electrical relationship involved is that torque is proportional to the product of a flux times a current. By maintaining the flux constant as in a permanent magnet or in an electromagnetic field with fixed d-c excitation and by insuring that negligible demagnetization is produced by the signal current, the torque becomes directly proportional to the current signal. Thus

$$T = K_T i \qquad (7.5\text{–}8)$$

where  $T$ = torque in pound-feet,
   $i$ = signal current in amperes, and
   $K_T$ = torque coefficient in pound-feet torque per ampere.

Applying such a torque to a simple inertia, as in an undamped galvanometer element with a negligible spring coefficient, gives

$$T = J \frac{d^2\theta}{dt^2} \qquad (7.5\text{-}9)$$

where $J$ = moment of inertia of the galvanometer element and
$\theta$ = position of the galvanometer element in radians.

Taking the transform of Equations 7.5–8 and 7.5–9 and combining the resultant equations gives

$$s^2\theta(s) = \frac{K_T}{J} I(s) \qquad (7.5\text{-}10)$$

If the galvanometer position (that is, the output of the galvanometer as indicated by a mirror mounted on the element) is expressed in terms of the current (that is, the input to the galvanometer), the transfer function of the galvanometer is

$$\frac{\theta(s)}{I(s)} = \frac{K_T}{Js^2} \qquad (7.5\text{-}11)$$

Use of the torque motor principle as applied to gyroscopes involves establishing an angular rate proportional to the current signal. In this case Equation 7.5–8 is written in the form

$$T = J \frac{d\Omega}{dt} \qquad (7.5\text{-}12)$$

where $\Omega = d\theta/dt$, the angular velocity of the galvanometer element.

Equations 7.5–8 and 7.5–12 combine to yield for the transform of the transfer function of the gyroscope,

$$\frac{\Omega(s)}{I(s)} = \frac{K_T}{Js} \qquad (7.5\text{-}13)$$

If the coils and the circuits through which the current $i$ flows have time constants associated with them that are not negligible, the more common form for the transfer functions of Equations 7.5–11 and 7.5–13 are obtained, namely,

$$\frac{\theta(s)}{I(s)} = \frac{K_1}{s^2(T_1 s + 1)} \qquad (7.5\text{-}11a)$$

and

$$\frac{\Omega(s)}{I(s)} = \frac{K_2}{s(T_2 s + 1)} \qquad (7.5\text{-}13a)$$

where $K_1$ is the angular acceleration of the galvanometer mirror per volt input to the galvanometer coil circuit,
$T_1$ is the time constant of the galvanometer coil circuit,
$K_2$ is the angular velocity of the gyroscope per volt input to the gyroscope precession coil circuit, and
$T_2$ is the time constant of the gyroscope precession coil circuit.

**Electrical Networks Used for Stabilizing Purposes.**   In connection with the spring-dashpot combinations of Section 7.4 it was noted that the action of these combinations could be made to produce output motions that were a function of the input position and its rates.   It was also noted that these transfer functions were similar in nature to some of the electrical networks that were previously described in Chapters 3, 4, and 5 and that they might be useful for stabilizing purposes.   Although the majority of the servomechanism systems discussed in the following chapters employ electrical networks for such stabilizing means, a brief summary will be given here of some of the more common types of $RC$ stabilizing networks.   The methods of network analysis outlined in Chapters 3, 4, and 5 are employed in obtaining the following transfer functions.

*Networks Proportional to Rate of Change of Input Voltage.*   The network shown in Figure 5.4–4 is one that is capable of producing an output voltage proportional to the rate of change of input voltage to some extent.   The transfer function of this network can be written as

$$\frac{E_o(s)}{E_{in}(s)} = \frac{Ts}{Ts+1} \qquad (7.5\text{–}14)$$

where $T = RC$.

The transform of the output voltage is therefore

$$E_o(s) = \frac{TsE_{in}(s)}{Ts+1} \qquad (7.5\text{–}15)$$

Recalling that $\mathcal{L}^{-1}[sE_{in}(s)] = (d/dt)e_{in}$ when the initial conditions are neglected, one realizes that some proportionality exists between the output and the rate of change of input.

A modification of the rate network of Figure 5.4–4 is shown in Figure 7.5–3.   In addition to the output voltage being somewhat proportional to the rate of change of the input voltage, the output voltage is also proportional to the actual magnitude of the input voltage.   The transfer function for Figure 7.5–3 is

$$\frac{E_o(s)}{E_{in}(s)} = \frac{T_2}{T_1}\left[\frac{T_1 s + 1}{T_2 s + 1}\right] \qquad (7.5\text{–}16)$$

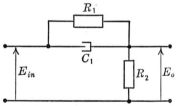

FIGURE 7.5–3.   Modified rate network (phase lead).

$$\frac{E_o(s)}{E_{in}(s)} = \frac{T_2}{T_1}\left[\frac{T_1 s + 1}{T_2 s + 1}\right]$$

$$T_1 = R_1 C_1$$

$$T_2 = \frac{R_1 R_2}{R_1 + R_2} C_1$$

Networks that have an output proportional to the rate of change of the input have the phase-lead characteristic for sinusoidal inputs as previously noted.

*Networks Proportional to the Integral of the Input Voltage.*   The network shown in Figure 4.4–2 is one in which the output voltage is somewhat a function of the integral of the input current.   With initial conditions set equal to zero, the transfer function as obtained from Equation 4.4–19 is

$$\frac{E_o(s)}{E_{in}(s)} = \frac{T_2 s + 1}{T_1 s + 1} \qquad (7.5\text{--}17)$$

where $T_2 = R_2 C$, and
$$T_1 = (R_1 + R_2)C.$$

With $R_2$ of Figure 4.4–2 set equal to zero, the transfer function of Equation 7.5–17 reduces to

$$\frac{E_o(s)}{E_{in}(s)} = \frac{1}{T_1 s + 1} \qquad (7.5\text{--}18)$$

For large values of $T_1$ this network has properties similar to those of an integrating element.   Networks that have an output proportional to the integral of the input have for sinusoidal inputs a phase lag characteristic.

*Combined Rate and Integral Network.*   An illustration of a network having some properties similar to individual rate and integrating networks is shown in Figure 7.5–4.   Since initial conditions are considered to be zero in determining the transfer function, the over-all transform

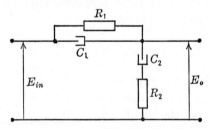

FIGURE 7.5–4.   Combined rate and integral network.

$$\frac{E_o(s)}{E_{in}(s)} = \frac{T_1 T_2 s^2 + (T_1 + T_2)s + 1}{T_1 T_2 s^2 + (T_1 + T_2 + T_{12})s + 1}$$

$$T_1 = R_1 C_1$$

$$T_2 = R_2 C_2$$

$$T_{12} = R_1 C_2$$

can be obtained readily by proper grouping of the transforms of the individual elements. In this fashion, one can determine that

$$\frac{E_o(s)}{E_{in}(s)} = \frac{\dfrac{1}{C_2 s} + R_2}{\dfrac{R_1\left(\dfrac{1}{C_1 s}\right)}{R_1 + \dfrac{1}{C_1 s}} + \dfrac{1}{C_2 s} + R_2} \tag{7.5-19}$$

or

$$\frac{E_o(s)}{E_{in}(s)} = \frac{T_1 T_2 s^2 + (T_1 + T_2)s + 1}{T_1 T_2 s^2 + (T_1 + T_2 + T_{12})s + 1} \tag{7.5-20}$$

The properties and field of usefulness of such a network are described more fully in Chapters 10 and 12.

*Stabilizing Transformers.* Another electrical means commonly used for providing stabilizing signals in some control systems is the stabilizing transformer. In Section 13.3 an illustrative example is presented that shows the nature of the derivative action of this kind of network.

## 7.6 Transfer Functions of Typical Hydraulic Control Elements

The ability of hydraulic systems to develop a large amount of power in a small volume with comparatively light moving parts has made them particularly attractive for large servomechanism applications.[73] Some of the largest naval shipboard guns are hydraulically positioned, and ship-steering systems such as that described in Figure 7.1–3 frequently have at least one stage of power amplification that is hydraulically controlled. The wealth of favorable experience in hydraulic control is another reason for the widespread acceptance of the hydraulic form of servomechanism elements.

In the section that follows the fundamentals of hydraulic valve-piston operation are described briefly for two common conditions of load reactions. The use of a few different valve piston arrangements to produce desirable forms of transfer functions is discussed next. Finally a common form of hydraulic power element, the fixed displacement motor operating with a variable displacement pump, is described.

**Hydraulic Valve-Piston Transfer Functions for Two Common Types of Operation.** Figure 7.6–1 shows schematically a simple valve-piston arrangement where the valve position $y$ regulates the flow of oil from the

inlet source to the piston.  As the inflowing oil at high pressure causes
the piston to move, the fluid displaced is permitted to empty into the
drain at low pressure to a sump, from which it is recompressed by a pump
and returns to the high inlet pressure source.  Attached to the piston is
the load that moves an amount $x$, which is proportional to the piston
motion.  Compared with the forces involved, the inertia of the piston
and the load is frequently so small as to be neglected.  Two common
conditions of operation for this type of system are (1) load reaction
negligible and (2) load reaction entirely dominated by heavy spring
force (shown by dotted spring in Figure 7.6–1).

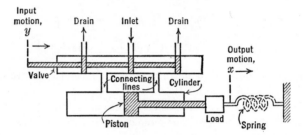

FIGURE 7.6–1.   Simple hydraulic valve-piston arrangement.

When the load reaction is negligible, the amount of oil flowing through
the valve and into the cylinder is proportional to the displacement of the
valve from the neutral position with the direction of oil flow into the
cylinder being dependent upon the direction of the valve displacement.
Since the cylinder has a constant area, the rate of displacement of the
piston is proportional to the oil flow rate through the valve and therefore
to the valve position.  Thus

$$\frac{dx}{dt} = C_1 y \qquad\qquad (7.6\text{--}1)$$

where $C_1$ is a constant having the dimensions of displacement per second
of the piston per unit displacement of the valve.

Transforming Equation 7.6–1 into a transfer function from $y$ to $x$ gives

$$\frac{X(s)}{Y(s)} = \frac{C_1}{s} \qquad\qquad (7.6\text{--}2)$$

The similarity between the action of a valve-piston combination and an
electric motor with a negligible time constant is apparent by comparing
Equations 7.6–2 and 7.5–2.  In ideal form both elements produce an
integrating action in that their output is the integral of the input posi-

tion.  This may be seen from Equation 7.6–1, where if both sides of the equation are integrated with respect to time

$$x = C_1 \int y \, dt \qquad (7.6\text{–}3)$$

The other important case of valve piston operation occurs when the load reaction is dominantly a spring force, that is, one in which the displacement of the piston produces a force proportional to the piston displacement and opposite in sign.  In this type of operation, the valve construction is such that some oil can by-pass the main piston by leaking around the valve.  By this means the pressure drop across the piston is made proportional to the valve displacement.  Hence a given valve position produces a force on the piston that is equal and opposite to the restraining spring force that in turn is proportional to the spring (and piston) displacement.  Thus

$$x = C_2 y \qquad (7.6\text{–}4)$$

or

$$X(s) = C_2 Y(s) \qquad (7.6\text{–}5)$$

where $C_2$ is the displacement of the output per unit displacement of the valve.

Although a short time may be required for the piston and output to reach the position indicated by Equation 7.6–4 because of the mass of the piston or the flow of oil in the lines, for the light high-pressure valves and the short lines generally employed this effect is frequently negligibly small.

**Transfer Functions for Various Valve-Piston Linkage Combinations.** Although the valve-piston arrangement is useful for power amplification and integration applications, there are types of applications where other desirable characteristics can be obtained by the addition of a common link applied to piston and valve.  Figure 7.6–2 indicates such a hydraulic control element.

A rigid bar is used to connect the input, the valve stem, and the piston-output member.  Motion of the input $y$ in the direction indicated by the arrow tends to produce a displacement of the valve $v$ in the same direction, as shown by the arrow at $v$.  Displacement of the valve $v$ from the neutral position produces a rate of motion of the piston and load

$$C_1 v = \frac{dx}{dt} \qquad (7.6\text{–}6)$$

which is dependent solely on the valve-piston characteristics.  By virtue

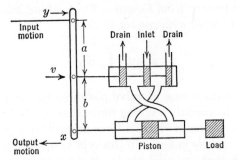

FIGURE 7.6-2.  A valve-piston-linkage arrangement.

$y$ = displacement of input from neutral
$v$ = displacement of valve from neutral
$x$ = displacement of piston from neutral

$C_1$ = velocity of piston per valve displacement
$a, b$ = lengths of linkage distance

of the fact that the bar remains straight, the following relationship exists between the $y$, $v$, and $x$ displacements:

$$\frac{y - v}{a} = \frac{y + x}{a + b} \qquad (7.6\text{-}7)$$

By taking the transforms of Equations 7.6–6 and 7.6–7 and combining, the displacement of the piston may be expressed in terms of the input displacement alone:

$$X(s) = \frac{(b/a)Y(s)}{\left(\dfrac{a + b}{aC_1} s + 1\right)} \qquad (7.6\text{-}8)$$

From this equation the transfer function may be written as

$$\frac{X(s)}{Y(s)} = \frac{b/a}{T_v s + 1} = G(s) \qquad (7.6\text{-}9)$$

where $T_v = \dfrac{a + b}{a\,C_1}$ , the valve effective time constant.

The power amplification of the valve-piston combination has been maintained, but the motion of the load has been made proportional to the input motion for slowly changing input motions.  Furthermore, since the constant $C_1$ may be made large, the time constant $T_v$ may be made small; the load motion then can reproduce the form of the input motion for fairly fast input speeds. Equation 7.6–9 indicates a phase lag characteristic for this arrangement.

Another useful form of valve-piston linkage combination is shown in Figure 7.6–3. The object of this arrangement is to produce an output displacement $x$, which is a function of the speed of the input motion $y$, as well as its amplitude; hence it is useful for stabilization purposes.

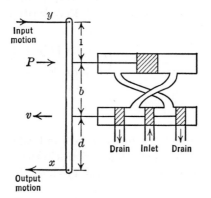

FIGURE 7.6–3.    A hydraulic valve-piston-linkage combination useful for stabilization purposes.

$y$ = displacement of input from neutral
$v$ = displacement of valve from neutral
$P$ = displacement of piston from neutral
$x$ = displacement of output from neutral

$C$ = velocity of piston per unit valve displacement
1, $b$, $d$ = ratio of lengths of various sections of bars

A rigid bar connects $x$, $y$, the valve, and the piston. Hence the relationships existing between the motion at the various points of the bar are

$$y - P = \frac{y + v}{1 + b} \qquad (7.6\text{–}10)$$

and

$$y - P = \frac{y + x}{1 + b + d} \qquad (7.6\text{–}11)$$

The velocity of the piston is determined by the valve displacement,

$$Cv = \frac{dP}{dt} \qquad (7.6\text{–}12)$$

By taking the transforms of Equations 7.6–10 and 7.6–12 the relationship between $Y(s)$ and $P(s)$ is found to be

$$\left(\frac{b}{1+b}\right) Y(s) = (T_v s + 1)P(s) \qquad (7.6\text{–}13)$$

where $T_v = 1/(1+b)C$.

Combining Equation 7.6–13 and the transform of Equation 7.6–11 gives an expression between $X(s)$ and $Y(s)$, written in the form of a transfer function

$$\frac{X(s)}{Y(s)} = G(s) = \left(\frac{d}{1+b}\right)\frac{[T_3 s + 1]}{T_v s + 1} \qquad (7.6\text{–}14)$$

where $\dfrac{T_v(1+b)(b+d)}{d} = T_3$.

This transfer function for values of $b > 1$ and values of $d < 1$ is found to have desirable stabilization characteristics in that rapid input motions tend to produce larger outputs than are produced for slowly moving inputs of the same amplitude.

**Hydraulic Motor with Variable Displacement Hydraulic Pump.** A commonly used hydraulic servomechanism power element employs a variable displacement pump in which the quantity of oil pumped is proportional to the displacement of the pump control from the neutral, and the direction of oil flow is determined by the direction of the displacement of the pump tilt plate from neutral. Figure 7.6–4 indicates

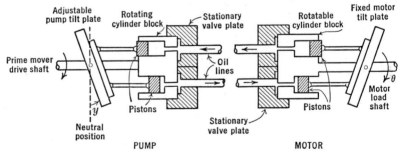

FIGURE 7.6–4.   Hydraulic pump and motor.

such a hydraulic pump and motor combination. The oil from the pump is supplied by a hydraulic motor that has a speed proportional to the magnitude and direction of the oil flow to it. The presence of oil leakage around the valves in the pump when the pressure in the lines is high, as during rapid acceleration periods, means that the inertia of the load being driven produces an effective time constant for the hydraulic motor.

The development of the transfer function for a hydraulic motor as is given below follows directly the analysis described by Brown and Campbell in *Principles of Servomechanisms.*[86]

The volume of oil $Q_p$ flowing from the pump appears in varying amounts in the following forms:

$$Q_m = \text{flow of oil through motor}$$
$$Q_l = \text{leakage flow around motor}$$
$$Q_c = \text{compressibility flow}$$

Thus

$$Q_p = Q_m + Q_l + Q_c \qquad (7.6\text{--}15)$$

If $y$ is the displacement of the pump stroke from the neutral and $S_p$ is the cubic feet of flow per second from the pump per unit displacement of $y$, then

$$Q_p = S_p y \qquad (7.6\text{--}16)$$

The motor flow is equal to $d_m$, the displacement of the motor in cubic feet, times $d\theta/dt$, the motor speed.

$$Q_m = d_m \frac{d\theta}{dt} \qquad (7.6\text{--}17)$$

The leakage flow is proportional to $L$, the leakage coefficient in cubic feet per second, per pound, per square foot of pressure, times the differential line pressure $P$. This pressure is equal to the torque accelerating the combined motor and associated load inertia $J$ divided by the motor displacement. Thus

$$P = \frac{J}{d_m} \frac{d^2\theta}{dt^2} \qquad (7.6\text{--}18)$$

and

$$Q_l = \frac{LJ}{d_m} \frac{d^2\theta}{dt^2} \qquad (7.6\text{--}19)$$

$\Delta V$, the change in $V$, the total volume of oil under compression, is proportional to the differential pressure $P$. The proportionality constant is $V/B$, where $B$ is the bulk modulus of oil that has the units of pounds per unit area. Hence

$$\Delta V = \frac{V}{B} P \qquad (7.6\text{--}20)$$

$V$, the total volume of oil under compression, is a factor that deserves additional attention and emphasis in that it is dependent on the physical location of the pump and motor. As such, it is not under the control of the pump and motor designers. Use of short lines between these two units permits the volume $V$ to be kept to a minimum. Use of long lines between pump and motor may result in marked degradation of the inherent capabilities of the pump and motor alone. This again serves to emphasize the responsibility of the system's designer to be aware of the effect of his decisions on the over-all system's performance.

The compressibility flow is the amount by which $\Delta V$ changes with time, thus

$$Q_c = \frac{\Delta V}{\Delta t} = \frac{VJ}{Bd_m} \frac{d^3\theta}{dt^3} \qquad (7.6\text{--}21)$$

Taking the transform of Equations 7.6–15, 7.6–16, 7.6–17, 7.6–19 and 7.6–21, and combining the results, gives

$$S_p Y(s) = \left[ \frac{VJ}{Bd_m} s^3 + \frac{LJ}{d_m} s^2 + d_m s \right] \theta(s) \qquad (7.6\text{--}22)$$

Expressing the relationship of Equation 7.6–22 in the form of a transfer function from input $y$ to output $\theta$ gives

$$\frac{\theta(s)}{Y(s)} = G(s) = \frac{S_p/d_m}{s\left[ \dfrac{VJ}{Bd_m{}^2} s^2 + \dfrac{LJ}{d_m{}^2} s + 1 \right]} \qquad (7.6\text{--}23)$$

The presence of the bracketed term in the denominator of this equation indicates the possibility of an oscillatory form for the motor speed when subjected to input changes. The oscillation is caused by the fluctuation in hydraulic pressure in the motor lines brought about by the compressibility of the oil. Generally this oscillation is of fairly high frequency of the order of 5 to 10 cycles per second or higher. If the bulk modulus is very high compared to the volume of the oil in the system, Equation 7.6–23 may be simplified to

$$\frac{\theta(s)}{Y(s)} = \frac{S_p/d_m}{s\left( \dfrac{LJ}{d_m{}^2} s + 1 \right)} \qquad (7.6\text{--}24)$$

If Equation 7.6–24 is compared with the corresponding transfer function for an electric motor, Equation 7.5–2, it will be noted that the two expressions are similar, and the performance for each will be the same if $(S_p/d_m) = (1/K_e)$, $(LJ/d_m{}^2) = T_m$, and the applied voltage $v_a$ is proportional to the stroke position $y$. Thus the transfer functions and the performance of these two types of motors can be very similar despite the vast difference in the physical means used to bring about that performance. This fact is of great importance for it points the way to the use of desirable operating characteristics developed for the electric or the hydraulic type of system to be used advantageously on the other type of physical system.

## 7.7 Transfer Functions of Steering Systems

A form of control problem in which the control of a position or a speed by means of a motor is only a part of the over-all system control is encountered in the steering systems for such vehicles as ships, aircraft, and guided missiles. Although these more comprehensive steering control systems are subject to the same type of analysis as was described for purely translatory or purely rotary servomechanism systems, the interaction of the two degrees of freedom, the non-linearity of the coefficients, and the time variation of the constants in some cases combine to provide a control problem worthy of special mention. For the present purpose it will suffice to consider the system to be linear and have constant coefficients; only the interaction of translatory and rotary motions will be investigated. Although this is a considerable simplification, nevertheless, the results are valid for approximating the basic steering control problems. In addition they serve to illustrate further that simple time constants are not always adequate to describe a system transfer function.

**Ship-Steering Transfer Function.** The problem of automatically steering a ship is one of controlling the direction of the ship's forward motion as well as controlling the position of the center of gravity of the ship with respect to the desired course. The control means is the ship's rudder (or rudders) located at the stern of the ship. Figure 7.7–1 shows the significant angles and forces acting on the ship. Distinction is made between $\theta_p$, the direction in which the ship is moving, and $\theta_m$, the direction in which the ship is headed. The difference angle, $\alpha$, is the angle of attack, and the lateral force, acting on the ship perpendicular to the ship's velocity at the center of pressure, is proportional to this angle for small values of $\alpha$ (less than $10°$). In addition, for these small values of $\alpha$, the drag force is practically constant and acts at the center of pressure. The direction of this drag force is parallel to velocity vector. The rudder force, produced by rudder deflection $\delta$, is perpendicular to the rudder. The main driving force maintains the forward speed approximately constant and acts through the center of gravity of the ship.

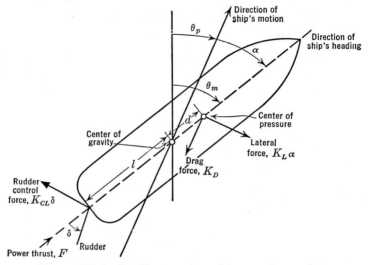

FIGURE 7.7–1.   Significant angles and forces acting on ship.

The forces acting perpendicular to the ship's velocity produce an acceleration of the center of gravity of the ship and cause it to change its direction of motion.  Thus, if the angle of attack is reasonably small,

$$mV \frac{d\theta_p}{dt} = K_L\alpha + F\alpha - K_{CL}\delta \qquad (7.7\text{–}1)$$

where $m$ = mass of ship in slugs,
$V$ = velocity of ship in feet per second,
$K_L$ = pounds of lateral force per unit of $\alpha$,
$F$ = forward thrust of main drive, and
$K_{CL}$ = pounds of lateral force per unit of $\delta$.

The torques tending to rotate the ship produce an angular acceleration of the ship's inertia:

$$J \frac{d^2\theta_m}{dt^2} = K_L\,d\alpha + K_D\,d\alpha + K_{CL}l\delta - K_f \frac{d\theta_m}{dt} \qquad (7.7\text{–}2)$$

where $J$ = effective moment of inertia of ship in slug feet squared,
$d$ = distance in feet from center of gravity to center of pressure,
$K_D$ = drag force on ship in pounds,
$l$ = distance in feet from center of gravity to rudder, and
$K_f$ = damping torque in pound-feet per radian per second of ship's motion.

In the foregoing equations the angles $\alpha$ and $\delta$ have been considered to be sufficiently small so that $\sin \alpha = \alpha$ and $\cos \alpha = 1$ and a similar approximation used for $\delta$.

An additional equation is the defining relationship between $\theta_m$, $\theta_p$, and $\alpha$, namely,

$$\theta_m - \theta_p = \alpha \qquad (7.7\text{--}3)$$

By performing the transform of Equations 7.7–1 through 7.7–3, and neglecting the initial conditions, the ship's heading may be expressed in terms of the control rudder deflection. The resultant expression is

$$\frac{\theta_m(s)}{\delta(s)} = \frac{K_{CL}[lmVs + (K_L + K_D)d + (K_L + F)l]}{s\left\{\begin{array}{l} JmVs^2 + [J(K_L + F) + K_fmV]s \\ + K_f(K_L + F) - mV(K_L + K_D)d \end{array}\right\}}$$

or

$$\frac{\theta_m(s)}{\delta(s)} = G_m(s) \qquad (7.7\text{--}4)$$

Another relationship of interest is that comparing the path angle $\theta_p$ to the heading angle $\theta_m$. Again, using the transforms of Equations 7.7–1 through 7.7–3 gives

$$\frac{\theta_p(s)}{\theta_m(s)} = \frac{-Js^2 - K_fs + (K_L + K_D)d + (K_L + F)l}{mVls + (K_L + K_D)d + (K_L + F)l} = G_p(s) \quad (7.7\text{--}5)$$

Equations 7.7–4 and 7.7–5 are of interest not only for their value in the ship-steering problem but also for the information they provide on the sort of transfer functions that can arise in controlled systems. It will be noted in Equation 7.7–4 that the bracketed term in the denominator may be such that the net value of the constant term is positive or negative, depending on whether $K_f(K_L + F)$ is greater than or less than $mV(K_L + K_D)d$. Should the resultant constant term be negative, it is evident that a root or roots with positive real parts is indicated with the accompanying problem of instability for the uncontrolled ship. The tendency for instability arises from the fact that the center of pressure for a normal ship design is forward of the center of gravity of the ship (see Figure 7.7–1). When the ship has an angle of attack the lateral forces tend to increase the angle of attack; thus the lateral force and the angle of attack are increased further.

Although $\theta_p(s)/\theta_m(s)$ from Equation 7.7–5 indicates no stability problem, nevertheless, the presence of the negative coefficients of the $s^2$ and $s$ terms in the numerator indicates that on a transient basis the ship's path angle is opposite in sign to the final path angle for the same steady-state ship's heading angle. Also of interest is the fact that $\theta_p(s)/\theta_m(s)$ has a higher power of $s$ in the numerator than in the denominator. However, this is not the case when the over-all transfer function from $\delta$ to $\theta_p$ is considered. The form of Equations 7.7–4 and 7.7–5 is such as to lend itself to the block diagram representation shown in Figure 7.7–2.

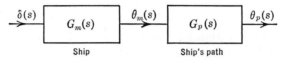

FIGURE 7.7–2. Block diagram of transfer functions for ship-steering characteristics.

It should be noted that the block diagram and the transfer functions used therein are outgrowths of the equations describing the performance of the system. The block diagram and transfer functions are merely conveniences to aid in the presentation of the equations and are not the primary source of the equations of performance. In practice Equations 7.7–4 and 7.7–5 are generally expressed more simply by grouping the system parameters in terms of equivalent system time constants.

**Transfer Function of Controlled Missile in Vertical Flight.** The diagram of forces on a missile using tail-steering means is similar to that of the ship shown in Figure 7.7–1 if the missile motion is considered to be in the horizontal plane. However, when motion in the vertical plane is considered, the presence of the gravity force acting on the missile alters the missile control equations and produces a definite destabilizing effect. Figure 7.7–3 shows the forces acting on a controlled missile in vertical flight. It will be noted that for controlled missiles the center of pressure is generally located behind the center of gravity in an effort to avoid the inherent instability that was noted for ship steering. With the two exceptions noted above, the force and torque equations are quite similar to those for the ship-steering problem previously described.

For small angles of attack, the summation of forces perpendicular to the velocity vector yields

$$mV\frac{d\theta_p}{dt} = K_L\alpha + F\alpha - K_{CL}\delta + mg\sin\theta_p \qquad (7.7\text{–}6)$$

which, with small values of $\theta_p$, may be written as

$$mV\frac{d\theta_p}{dt} - mg\theta_p = (K_L + F)\alpha - K_{CL}\delta \qquad (7.7\text{–}7)$$

The summation of torques about the center of gravity can be written as

$$J\frac{d^2\theta_m}{dt^2} = -K_L\,d\alpha - K_D\,d\alpha + K_{CL}l\delta - K_f\frac{d\theta_m}{dt} \qquad (7.7\text{–}8)$$

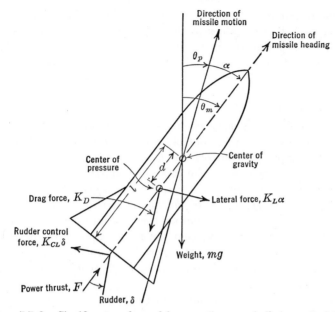

FIGURE 7.7–3.   Significant angles and forces acting on missile in vertical flight.

which with the exception of the sign of the lift and drag term is identical with Equation 7.7–2 for the ship steering.  From Figure 7.7–3,

$$\theta_m - \theta_p = \alpha \qquad (7.7\text{–}9)$$

Taking the transform of Equations 7.7–7, 7.7–8, and 7.7–9 with the initial conditions zero, the ratios $\theta_m(s)/\delta(s)$ and $\theta_p(s)/\theta_m(s)$ are found to be

$$\frac{\theta_m(s)}{\delta(s)} = \frac{K_{CL}[lmVs - (K_L + K_D)d + (K_L + F - mg)l]}{\begin{bmatrix} JmVs^3 + [J(K_L + F - mg) + K_f mV]s^2 \\ + [K_f(K_L + F - mg) + d(K_L + K_D)mV]s \\ - d(K_L + K_D)mg \end{bmatrix}}$$

$$(7.7\text{–}10)$$

and

$$\frac{\theta_p(s)}{\theta_m(s)} = \frac{-Js^2 - K_f s + (K_L + F)l - (K_L + K_D)d}{lmVs + l(K_L + F - mg) - (K_L + K_D)d} \qquad (7.7\text{–}11)$$

From the denominator of Equation 7.7–10 the presence of the negative sign for the constant term, that is, the missile weight, indicates definite instability.  Although the denominator of Equation 7.7–11 indicates the amount that there might be a chance for instability for this transfer function as well, the values of the physical quantities involved when $F > mg$ are such that this instability is not obtained. Equations 7.7–10 and 7.7–11 may also be written in simpler form in terms of system time constants.

## 7.8  Conclusions

The list of examples of types of transfer functions could be extended greatly to cover such other control means as electronic amplifiers, thermal and other process controls, and a host of regulating devices. However, the main objective of the preceding illustrations will have been achieved if it is fully appreciated that *the physics of the problem determines the equations of performance of the control element.* The performance equations relating output to input are the basis for the transfer functions. It is these transfer functions that must then appear in the block diagrams. *The block diagrams are pictorial representations of the physical relationships involved; the diagrams must conform to the physics for the diagrams to be correct.*

Table 7.8–1 presents a summary of the transfer functions derived in this chapter for representative mechanical, electrical, and hydraulic elements.

TABLE 7.8–1

Summary of Transfer Functions Derived for Representative Mechanical, Electrical, and Hydraulic Elements

I. *Mechanical Elements*
Rotation
  Spring-mass-damper

$$\frac{\theta_l(s)}{\theta_m(s)} = \frac{1/n}{\dfrac{J}{K_s}s^2 + \dfrac{K_D}{K_s}s + 1}$$

Translation
  Spring-mass-damper

$$\frac{X(s)}{Y(s)} = \frac{1}{\dfrac{M}{K}s^2 + \dfrac{D}{K}s + 1}$$

Spring-dashpot (phase lag)

$$\frac{X(s)}{Y(s)} = \frac{1}{\dfrac{D}{K_s}s + 1}$$

Spring-dashpot (phase lead)

$$\frac{X(s)}{Y(s)} = \frac{\dfrac{D}{K_s}s}{\dfrac{D}{K_s}s + 1}$$

II. *Electrical Elements*
D-c motor
  For speed control

$$\frac{S(s)}{V_a(s)} = \frac{1}{K_e[T_m s + 1]}$$

TABLE 7.8–1 (*Continued*)

II. *Electrical Elements—Continued*

For position control

$$\frac{\theta(s)}{V_a(s)} = \frac{1}{K_e s[T_m s + 1]}$$

D-c generator and motor
For position control

$$\frac{\theta(s)}{E_c(s)} = \frac{K_g}{K_e R_f s[T_f s + 1][T_e T_{mc} s^2 + T_{mc} s + 1]}$$

Galvanometer

$$\frac{\theta(s)}{I(s)} = \frac{K_1}{s^2(T_1 s + 1)}$$

Gyroscope

$$\frac{\Omega(s)}{I(s)} = \frac{K_2}{s(T_2 s + 1)}$$

Stabilizing networks
For rate signals (phase lead)

$$\frac{E_o(s)}{E_{in}(s)} = \frac{Ts}{Ts + 1}$$

$$\frac{E_o(s)}{E_{in}(s)} = \frac{T_2}{T_1}\left[\frac{T_1 s + 1}{T_2 s + 1}\right]; \quad T_1 > T_2$$

For integral signals (phase lag)

$$\frac{E_o(s)}{E_{in}(s)} = \frac{T_2 s + 1}{T_1 s + 1}; \quad T_1 > T_2$$

$$\frac{E_o(s)}{E_{in}(s)} = \frac{1}{T_1 s + 1}$$

For rate and integral (lead-lag)

$$\frac{E_o(s)}{E_{in}(s)} = \frac{T_1 T_2 s^2 + (T_1 + T_2)s + 1}{T_1 T_2 s^2 + (T_1 + T_2 + T_{12})s + 1};$$

$$T_{12} \gg T_1 + T_2$$

III. *Hydraulic Elements*
Valve-piston
Load reaction negligible

$$\frac{X(s)}{Y(s)} = \frac{C_1}{s}$$

Spring load dominant

$$\frac{X(s)}{Y(s)} = C_2$$

Valve-piston linkage
For phase lag

$$\frac{X(s)}{Y(s)} = \frac{b/a}{T_v s + 1}$$

For phase lead

$$\frac{X(s)}{Y(s)} = \frac{d}{1 + b}\left[\frac{T_3 s + 1}{T_v s + 1}\right]; \quad T_3 > T_v$$

Hydraulic motor
With compressibility

$$\frac{\theta(s)}{Y(s)} = \frac{S_p/d_m}{s\left[\dfrac{VJ}{Bd_m{}^2}s^2 + \dfrac{LJ}{d_m{}^2}s + 1\right]}$$

With negligible compressibility

$$\frac{\theta(s)}{Y(s)} = \frac{S_p/d_m}{s\left[\dfrac{LJ}{d_m{}^2}s + 1\right]}$$

# 8

## TYPES OF SERVOMECHANISM

## AND CONTROL SYSTEMS

### 8.0 Introduction

In the preceding chapter the transfer functions for a number of physically different types of control elements and servomechanism motors were developed. It was shown that there was a certain similarity between a number of these various elements when considered from the analytical viewpoint, as was indicated by many of these elements having similar forms for their transfer functions.

In this chapter is described the form of representative servomechanisms and regulators typical of some control systems in which the elements previously described might be employed. Definitions of the various portions of the typical feedback control system are given to assist in providing a common vocabulary. Although linear servomechanisms having constant coefficients are considered in the analytical portion of this chapter, the general nomenclature and principles employed can be used to advantage for the case of the more general control problem not having entirely linear performance.

Because of the close interrelation of the feedback principle with the selection of various kinds of control system elements, the effect of feedback in minimizing the changes of gain in a transfer function is developed. Also the effect on feedback control system performance of changes in the feedback gain itself is illustrated.

To strengthen the idea of the functional similarity of seemingly different transfer characteristics of the sort described in the previous chapter, the nature of the three common types of control systems is described. These types are ones in which, after the transient has subsided, the following conditions are obtained:

Type 0. A constant value for the controlled variable requires a constant actuating signal.

Type 1. A constant rate of change of the controlled variable requires a constant actuating signal.

Type 2. A constant acceleration of the controlled variable requires a constant actuating signal.

Although these characteristics are primarily ones that lend themselves to definition in terms of the differential equations of the system, they are also characteristics that adapt themselves fairly easily to identification in terms of the transfer function for a sinusoidal input. In addition, these characteristics lend themselves to identification in terms of their plot in the complex plane. Since the complex plane plot has been shown in Chapter 6 to provide an indication of the system stability, a single complex plane plot can serve to correlate the type of servomechanism and its relative stability.

Additional information is also provided in this chapter to form a basis for selecting the general type of servomechanism that can be used most effectively for a given servomechanism application.

## 8.1 Definition of Feedback Control System Nomenclature and Symbols

The schematic diagram of Figure 8.1–1 shows in literal form the nature of a representative feedback control system. Such a system is one that

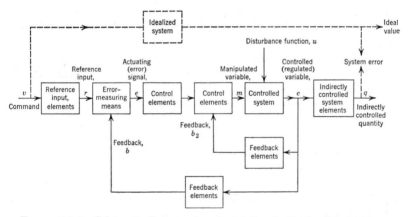

FIGURE 8.1–1. Schematic diagram of representative feedback control system.

might form a complete system by itself or might form a part of a more comprehensive control system. Although some of the control system elements shown in this figure may not be significant in a particular servomechanism or regulator system, they are included for purposes of completeness and are valuable for use with more complicated systems. The boxes shown serve to indicate the physical components that make up the actual equipment.

The dotted lines represent an idealized system whose performance is agreed upon to define the relationship between the ideal value and the command. As such the idealized system is one which exists only as a mathematical formulation, but which nevertheless provides a real basis on which the actual performance of the indirectly controlled quantity can be judged with respect to an ideal value.

The nomenclature used is that recommended by the AIEE Standards Subcommittee on Terminology and Nomenclature of the Feedback Control Committee.[110] This nomenclature has the desirable feature of indicating verbally the function of each variable or element without limiting the interpretation of the control to a particular physical embodiment of feedback control system. The lower-case symbols are used to indicate the values of the corresponding variables when expressed as functions of time. Thus $r(t)$, $e(t)$, and $c(t)$ are shown as $r$, $e$, and $c$. Although some of the symbols shown are identical with ones commonly used for other engineering purposes, the desirability of being able to type these symbols on a standard English typewriter and the restrictions imposed by a 26-letter alphabet make inevitable the duplication of symbols in different fields of engineering. However, this disadvantage is overweighed by the convenience of being able to associate a symbol with the function it represents, regardless of the physical kind of system it may be used in. For the detailed analysis of a particular system in which the various transfer functions are derived, the more customary engineering symbols associated with this field may be used, provided the equivalent appropriate feedback control symbols are indicated on the system diagram representation.

The descriptive terms as used in Figure 8.1–1 have the following significance. The command $v$ is the value that it is desired the control system produce. Because of the presence of reference input elements, the command may differ from the reference input. The *reference input r* is the quantity that is the actual reference signal input to the control system.

The *indirectly controlled quantity q* is the resultant quantity that the controlled system actually produces. Because of the characteristics of the indirectly controlled system elements, the indirectly controlled quantity may differ from the controlled variable. The *controlled variable c* is the output of the controlled system and is used as a basis for comparison with the reference input. The *feedback b* is derived from the controlled variable but may differ from the controlled variable because of the feedback element characteristics. The *actuating signal e* is obtained from an error-measuring means and provides a signal proportional to the difference between the reference input and the feedback. The actuating signal provides an input to the control elements and the controlled system so as to actuate the controlled variable.

The control elements receive the actuating (error) signal, generally at a low energy level, and transmit it at a higher energy level or in a modified physical form. Frequently there is a change in the time relationship as well as the amplitude between the input and the output of signals of a control element. Occasionally additional *feedback* signals, $b_2$, from the controlled variable or from some intermediate variable supply additional inputs to a control element. These feedback signals are generally related to some time function of the controlled variable and are used to improve the accuracy or speed of response of a control element or group of control elements.

The *manipulated variable m* is obtained from the control elements and manipulates the control of the controlled system. The controlled system is generally the major power element of the control system. It may be an element or control means that could be operated manually or independently of any supplemental control system. The output of the controlled system is the controlled variable.

A *disturbance function u* is any unwanted input or upset to the system that affects the value of the controlled variable. Disturbance functions may enter the control system at any one of a number of locations. The control system should act in such a way as to hold to a minimum the effect of any disturbance function on the controlled variable.

The *ideal value*, $I$, is that value of the ultimately controlled variable that would result from an idealized system operating from the same command as the actual system under consideration. The *ultimately controlled* variable is a general term that refers to the indirectly controlled variable, or in the absence of a quantity corresponding to the indirectly controlled variable refers to the controlled variable.

Since the idealized system has been defined as one whose performance is agreed upon to define the relationship between the ideal value and the command, the *system error* is the ideal value minus the value of the ultimately controlled variable. The *system deviation* is the negative of the system error and therefore is the value of the ultimately controlled variable minus the ideal value.

**Block Diagram.** A functional block diagram of a feedback control system is a simplified means of representing the significant variables of the system, the interconnection of these variables, and the dynamic characteristics of the system elements. This type of block diagram presents functional information that tends to stress what is happening in the control system rather than showing by what means this is actually accomplished. As such, the block diagram tends to clarify the physical understanding of the problem and provides a good basis for organizing the problem analysis.   By the orderly use of the AIEE recommended symbols for designating the variables and system elements, the effect of each element on the over-all system performance may be more readily interpreted.

Figure 8.1–2 shows such a block diagram of the representative feedback control system of Figure 8.1–1.   The blocks represent the dynamic characteristics of an element or group of elements.   The arrows shown on the lines connecting the blocks ( ——▸— ) indicate the unidirectional flow of information from one element to the next.   The circular junction points indicate that summing   or differencing

action takes place; a variable having a plus sign at a junction goes through the junction unaltered in sign, a variable having a minus sign at a junction goes through the junction with a sign reversal.

As previously indicated, the lower-case letters ($r$, $c$, $e$, $g$, $h$) are used to designate functions of time.   The corresponding capital letters ($R$, $C$, $E$, $G$, $H$) represent these same quantities when they have been trans-

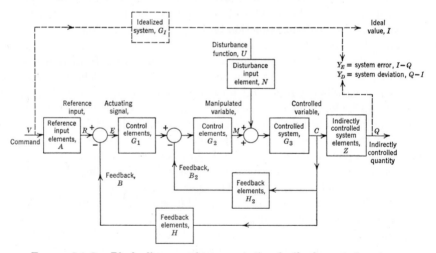

FIGURE 8.1–2.   Block diagram of representative feedback control system.

formed into operational, Laplace transform, or sinusoidally varying quantities.   Thus the symbol $R$ may represent $R(p)$, $R(s)$, or $R(j\omega)$. When there is some necessity for specifying the particular form of representation this can be done by writing the appropriate quantity in the brackets following the symbol.

All the control elements in the forward direction from actuating signal to controlled variable are labeled $(g, G)$. The feedback elements are labeled $(h, H)$; the reference input elements relating the command to reference input are labeled $(a, A)$; the indirectly controlled system elements relating the controlled variable to the indirectly controlled quantity are labeled $(z, Z)$; and the disturbance input elements relating the disturbance function to the control system are labeled $(n, N)$. Literal as well as numerical subscripts may be used to identify the transfer functions should this be desirable. In Figure 8.1–2, it will be noted, all the variables and system elements have been indicated in their transformed form.

When the response of the controlled variable or the indirectly controlled quantity is being determined for disturbance functions located at various positions in the control system, the control elements that originally represented forward or feedback elements respectively may no longer occupy the same relative position. As such one might be tempted to modify the $G$ or $H$ designation for the control elements to make the symbols appropriate for the new relative orientation. By general understanding, control system engineers have generally retained the $G$ or $H$ symbol associated with the original orientation of the control element even though it may no longer play the same forward or feedback role for the disturbance function input.

Frequently the control system being considered is one that has unity feedback, negligible disturbances, and unity value for the reference input and indirectly controlled system elements. This condition is shown in the simplified block diagram of Figure 8.1–3 where the control ele-

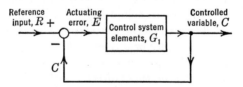

FIGURE 8.1–3. Simplified block diagram of feedback control system with unity feedback and negligible disturbance.

ments and the control system have been grouped together and represented as the controlled system elements. In this figure also the symbols used indicate that the transformed or sinusoidal quantities are represented.

Although the symbols and nomenclature described above are ones which have been recommended by the AIEE Feedback Control Systems Committee's Standards Subcommittee on Terminology and Nomenclature, they have been gaining widespread acceptance by other technical societies and many prominent individuals associated with the automatic control field.    Currently, representatives of the Professional Group on Automatic Control of the Institute of Radio Engineers, the Instruments and Regulators Division of the American Society of Mechanical Engineers, the Feedback Control Systems Committee of the AIEE, and others on the American Standards Association's C-85 Committee on Automatic Control Terminology are working toward agreement on control system standard terms which are essentially those described above.

Some supplemental terms that are frequently used to assist in referring to the portions of a system or to their operation are listed here.

The *input* to a control system or control system element is the signal (or signals) that it receives.

The *output* to a control system or control system element is the signal that it transmits.

A *forward circuit* is the transfer function from input to output of an element or group of elements in the forward direction of signal flow. Thus in Figure 8.1–2 for the condition of a negligible disturbance $U$ the series of elements $G_2$ and $G_3$ constitutes a forward circuit.

A *loop circuit* is a series combination of forward and feedback elements that combine to form a closed loop of control system elements. Again in Figure 8.1–2, with $U$ negligible, the series of elements $G_2$, $G_3$, and $H_2$ forms a loop circuit.    The combined series transfer function $G_2 G_3 H_2$ is the open-loop transfer function of this loop.    The transfer function from $E$ to $C$, including this loop circuit, forms a different forward function for the more comprehensive system.    Sometimes the loop $G_2 G_3 H_2$ is referred to as the *inner loop*, whereas the loop from $E$ to $C$ to $B$ is called the *outer* or *over-all* loop.

An *open-loop control* is one in which the output of the element or group of elements *is not compared* directly with some signal to provide the net input to the element.

A *closed-loop control* is one in which the output of the element or group of elements *is compared* to some other signal *to provide an actuating signal to control the output of the loop.*

## 8.2    Effect of Feedback on Changes in Transfer Function

The use of feedback in control systems permits satisfactory operation with control elements having appreciable variations in gain and dynamic characteristics.    The advantages that result from the use of feedback are readily illustrated in terms of the changes in the ratio between output and input of a servomechanism element as its transfer function changes with and without feedback being used.  Since changes in the feedback transfer function may also occur, the effect of such changes is described in the following.

In the open-loop control system shown in Figure 8.2–1, the controlled variable $C$ is expressed as

$$C = GR \qquad (8.2\text{–}1)$$

It is recalled that the transfer function $G$ may be a function of the frequency of the input and the parameters of the system including the system gain.  It is evident that a variation in any of the parameters with time or with changes in other external factors will affect the controlled

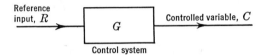

Reference input, $R$      $G$      Controlled variable, $C$

Control system

FIGURE 8.2–1.   Open-loop control system.

variable even if there is no change in the amplitude of the sinusoidal input $R$.  The magnitude of this effect may be determined by differentiating Equation 8.2–1, assuming $R$ to be constant:

$$d[C] = R\,d[G] \qquad (8.2\text{–}2)$$

Dividing Equation 8.2–2 by Equation 8.2–1 gives

$$d[C] = \frac{d[G]}{G}\,C \qquad (8.2\text{–}3)$$

Equation 8.2–3 shows that, for the conditions premised, the change in the controlled variable is directly proportional to the change in the transfer function.  This means that, for precise control, of the order of 1 per cent or better, the variations in the transfer functions cannot exceed the allowable accuracy for the controlled quantity.

Consider now a closed-loop control in which the transfer function of the forward circuit is $G$ and in which the feedback circuit has a transfer function $H$ (see Figure 8.2–2).  The input to the forward circuit is the difference between the reference input signal and the output of the feedback circuit.  Thus

$$C = G(R - HC) \qquad (8.2\text{–}4)$$

Solving for $C$ gives

$$C = \left(\frac{G}{1 + GH}\right) R \qquad (8.2\text{–}5)$$

Assuming a variation in the transfer function $G$ but no variation in the input $R$ or in $H$, one may differentiate as before to find the effect on the controlled variable. This results in the relationship

$$d[C] = \frac{d[G]R}{(1 + GH)^2} \qquad (8.2\text{--}6)$$

Combining Equation 8.2–5 with Equation 8.2–6 gives

$$d[C] = \left(\frac{1}{1 + GH}\right)\frac{d[G]}{G}C \qquad (8.2\text{--}7)$$

Equation 8.2–7 indicates that for the closed-loop system the per cent variation of the controlled variable for a change in the forward transfer

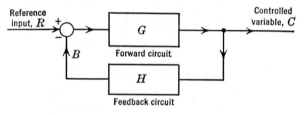

FIGURE 8.2–2.   Closed-loop control system.

function is equal to the per cent change in the transfer function times the factor $1/(1 + GH)$.

Comparing Equations 8.2–3 and 8.2–7, one sees that the change in output for a change in transfer function with and without feedback is

$$d[C]_{\text{with feedback}} = \left(\frac{1}{1 + GH}\right)d[C]_{\text{without feedback}} \qquad (8.2\text{--}8)$$

In many cases where feedback is employed, the term $GH$ may be large for those frequencies where accurate values of $C$ are desired. For this condition Equation 8.2–8 reveals that with feedback the effect of changes of the forward transfer function is greatly reduced from the condition without feedback.

Consider for example the case where direct feedback is employed so that $H$ is equal to 1. With the forward circuit transfer function having a value for $G$ of 100, a change of 10 per cent in this transfer function will result in only a change of $1/101 \times 10\%$ in $C$, or less than 0.1 per cent.

The use of feedback, however, does not permit the same insensitivity of controlled variable changes for changes in the transfer function of the feedback circuit itself. This is demonstrated by differentiating Equation 8.2–5 and allowing only $H$ and $C$ to vary. Thus

$$d[C] = \frac{-G^2 Rd[H]}{(1 + GH)^2} \tag{8.2-9}$$

Using the value of $C$ from Equation 8.2–5 and multiplying and dividing Equation 8.2–9 by $H$, one obtains

$$d[C] = \left(\frac{-GH}{1 + GH}\right)\frac{d[H]}{H} C \tag{8.2-10}$$

Since as was noted previously the term $GH$ may be large compared to 1 for those frequencies where accurate values of $C$ are desired, Equation 8.2–10 reduces to

$$d[C] \cong -\frac{d[H]}{H} C \tag{8.2-11}$$

for this condition.

Equation 8.2–11 shows that a variation in the feedback circuit causes an almost proportional variation in the controlled variable or output. Consequently, the output is more sensitive to variations in the feedback circuit than to variations in the forward circuit. This is a factor of considerable importance in the design of feedback circuits. It will be shown in later chapters that the forward circuit characteristics are frequently determined from such practical considerations as servomechanism power requirements whereas accuracy and stability limitations are the primary influences on the choice of the feedback elements.

## 8.3  Types of Feedback Control Systems

The various types of feedback control systems can be described most effectively for the simple closed-loop direct-feedback system. Figure 8.3–1 shows such a system.

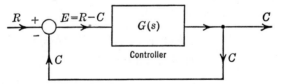

FIGURE 8.3–1.   Simple closed-loop control system with direct feedback.

The controlled variable signal is compared to the reference input signal by means of an error-measuring element. The actuating signal $E$ is

$$E(s) = R(s) - C(s) \tag{8.3-1}$$

The forward transfer function is $G(s)$ so that

$$\frac{C(s)}{E(s)} = G(s) \qquad (8.3\text{--}2)$$

As can be seen from Chapter 7, the transfer function $G(s)$ for power elements such as motors with the associated amplifiers and other stabilizing means as are required for control purposes is of the general form

$$G(s) = \frac{K(1 + a_1 s + a_2 s^2 + \cdots)}{s^n(1 + b_1 s + b_2 s^2 + b_3 s^3 + \cdots)} \qquad (8.3\text{--}3)$$

where        $K$ is the over-all transfer function gain,
   $a_1$, $a_2$, $b_1$, $b_2$, etc., are constant coefficients, and
        $n$ is a power to which the $s$ term in the denominator is raised. It may be 0 or any positive integer and indicates the number of series integrations in the transfer function.

The numerator and the denominator of Equation 8.3-3 can be factored into a series of single or quadratic terms of the form $(1 + Ts)$ or $(1 + 2\zeta Ts + T^2 s^2)$, where the $T$'s are real numbers having the dimensions of time. For a typical case $G(s)$ might appear as

$$G(s) = \frac{K(1 + T_a s)(1 + T_b s)}{s^n(1 + T_1 s)(1 + T_2 s)(1 + T_3 s)} \qquad (8.3\text{--}4)$$

The value of the integer $n$ in Equations 8.3-3 or 8.3-4 *is equal* numerically *to the type* of the system. It indicates the number of series integrating elements in the system. *The type of a system reveals the nature of the controlled variable characteristic as a function of time that results from a constant value of the actuating signal.*
From Equations 8.3-2 and 8.3-4,

$$s^n C(s) = \frac{K(1 + T_a s)(1 + T_b s)E(s)}{(1 + T_1 s)(1 + T_2 s)(1 + T_3 s)} \qquad (8.3\text{--}5)$$

A constant value for the actuating signal means that $E(s) = E_o/s$. Since the steady-state value of the controlled variable is sought, the final value theorem of Equation 4.3-15 can be applied to Equation 8.3-5:

$$\lim_{t \to \infty} [f(t)] = \lim_{s \to 0} [sF(s)] \qquad (4.3\text{--}15)$$

The inverse transform of $s^n C(s)$ is

$$\mathcal{L}^{-1}[s^n C(s)] = \frac{d^n c(t)}{dt^n} \qquad (8.3\text{--}6)$$

This is the time function in Equation 4.3–15 that is to be determined for the steady-state condition.

For the $F(s)$ function of Equation 4.3–15 take the right term of Equation 8.3–5 with $E(s) = E_o/s$.

$$\lim_{s \to 0} \left[ \frac{sK(1 + T_a s)(1 + T_b s)E_o}{(1 + T_1 s)(1 + T_2 s)(1 + T_3 s)s} \right] = KE_o \qquad (8.3\text{--}7)$$

From Equations 4.3–15, 8.3–6, and 8.3–7,

$$\frac{d^n c(t)}{dt^n} = KE_o \qquad (8.3\text{--}8)$$

during the steady state with a constant actuating signal applied.

With $n = 0$, Equation 8.3–8 indicates that a constant value of the controlled variable is obtained for a constant actuating signal. Thus for a type 0 system, a constant actuating signal is needed to produce a constant value of the controlled variable.

For a type 1 system, $n = 1$, and a constant rate of change of controlled variable is produced by a constant actuating signal. With a zero actuating signal, and with zero rate of change of the controlled variable, the controlled variable must be constant and equal to the reference input. For a reference input having a constant rate of change, the type 1 system does require a constant signal.

For a type 2 system, $n = 2$, and the second derivative of the controlled variable is a constant for a constant actuating signal. With a zero actuating signal and a zero second derivative for the controlled variable the rate of the controlled variable is a constant and equal to that of the reference input. For a reference input that has a constant acceleration, the type 2 system does require a constant signal.

Although it might appear that there is no limit to the number of the types of control systems that can be used, actually types 0, 1, and 2 are most commonly employed. This is partially a result of the difficulty in achieving stable operation with the higher numbered types of control systems as will be indicated later in this chapter. In addition, the dynamic errors for the higher numbered types of controls tend to be larger than those for the types 0, 1, and 2, although their steady-state characteristics are desirable.

**Type 0 Servomechanism.**  A constant value of the controlled variable requires a constant actuating signal under steady-state conditions for a type 0 system.  A feedback control system of type 0 is generally referred to as a regulator system.  Such systems are designed primarily to maintain the controlled variable constant at a certain desired value despite disturbance conditions.  They are generally not designed to permit the controlled variable to respond to changes in the reference input with small error signal.

The transfer function for the type 0 feedback control is obtained by setting $n$ equal to zero in the general expression for the transfer function given by Equations 8.3–3 or 8.3–4.  Thus for the type 0 transfer function,

$$G(s) = \frac{C(s)}{E(s)} = \frac{K_P(1 + T_a s)(1 + T_b s)}{(1 + T_1 s)(1 + T_2 s)(1 + T_3 s)} \tag{8.3–9}$$

where $K_P$ is the literal symbol for gain associated with a type 0 system.

When expressed in terms of a sinusoidal input, Equation 8.3–9 becomes

$$G(j\omega) = \frac{C}{E}(j\omega) = \frac{K_P(1 + j\omega T_a)(1 + j\omega T_b)}{(1 + j\omega T_1)(1 + j\omega T_2)(1 + j\omega T_3)} \tag{8.3–10}$$

It will be noted that there is no separate $j\omega$ term in the denominator for this characteristic transfer function for the type 0 servomechanism system.

Figure 8.3–2 shows the sort of complex plane plot that is characteristic of the type 0 servomechanism system.  At $\omega = 0$, $G(j\omega)$ is located

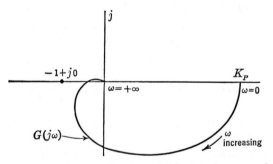

FIGURE 8.3–2.  Representative complex plane plot for type 0 servomechanism system.

along the positive real axis and has a finite value, $K_P$.  With increasing frequency, $G(j\omega)$ generally passes into the fourth, then third quadrants, and, to be stable, passes between $-1$ and 0.  Although the exact shape of the $G(j\omega)$ locus is dependent on the values of the time constants $T_a$, $T_b$, $T_1$, $T_2$, and the others in Equation 8.3–10, the fact that, at $\omega = 0$, $G(j\omega)$ is along the positive real axis means that the stability problem tends to be less severe for this type of control system.

The high degree of stability results from the fact that each $(1 + j\omega T)$ term in the denominator contributes 90° of angular rotation in the clockwise direction while the corresponding term in the numerator produces 90° of angular rotation in the counterclockwise direction. In like fashion the quadratic factors produce 180° angular phase shift. For the condition of instability to be obtained, the system gain must be high. More than two time constants in the denominator must be present, and, in addition, the effect of the time constants in the numerator must not contribute any appreciable angular rotation to the value of $G(j\omega)$ for frequencies in the range where $G(j\omega)$ is near the $-1 + j0$ point.

*Example of Type 0 Servomechanism System.* An example of a type 0 servomechanism system is provided by the speed control of a d-c motor

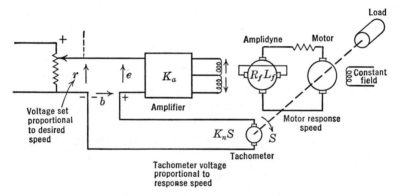

FIGURE 8.3–3.   Speed regulator typical of type 0 servomechanism.

where the reference input $r$ is a voltage proportional to the desired value of speed. The principal feedback signal $b$ is a voltage from a tachometer driven by the motor whose speed is to be controlled. Although the regulating system described here controls the motor speed $S$, similar equations are obtained for other forms of regulators controlling voltage, current, or temperature. Figure 8.3–3 shows the major items of the speed-regulator system.

The error signal

$$e = r - b \qquad (8.3–11)$$

supplies an amplifier that drives the control fields of an amplidyne generator. The amplidyne output voltage is impressed on the d-c drive motor operating with constant field.  The following constants are the parameters of the system:

$K_a$ = net control field amperes per volt actuating error signal,

$K_g$ = no-load amplidyne terminal voltage per net control field current,

$T_f = L_f/R_f$ = time constant of quadrature field of amplidyne, seconds,

$T_m = JR_a/K_T K_e$ = time constant of motor and load, seconds,

$K_e$ = motor volts per radian per second of motor,

$R_a$ = total armature circuit resistance of motor, amplidyne, and leads,

$K_T$ = pound-feet torque from motor per ampere of motor armature current, and

$K_n$ = voltage from tachometer per radian per second of motor.

The transfer function from the actuating error $E(s)$ to the motor speed $S(s)$ can be written as

$$\frac{S(s)}{E(s)} = G(s) = \frac{K_a K_g/K_e}{(1 + T_f s)(1 + T_m s)} \qquad (8.3\text{--}12)$$

From this transfer function it is evident that the system is a type 0 control system and that a constant signal voltage $e$ is required to produce a constant value of the motor speed $S$ under steady-state conditions where $s \to 0$.

The feedback function from motor speed to tachometer feedback voltage is

$$\frac{B(s)}{S(s)} = H(s) = K_n \qquad (8.3\text{--}13)$$

The transfer functions of Equations 8.3–12 and 8.3–13 suggest that the block diagram shown on Figure 8.3–4 represents the regulator of Figure 8.3–3.  This block diagram should be compared with the general closed-loop system shown in Figure 8.2–2.  Combining Equations 8.3–12

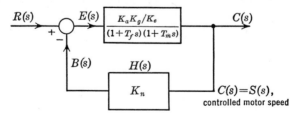

FIGURE 8.3–4.   Block diagram of regulator system of Figure 8.3–3.

and 8.3–13 to obtain the open-loop transfer function $G(s)H(s)$ from which the system stability can be studied,

$$G(s)H(s) = \frac{K_a K_g K_n / K_e}{(1 + T_f s)(1 + T_m s)} \qquad (8.3\text{–}14)$$

From this equation one would observe that instability is no particular problem for this type of control system, provided no additional time constants are present.

**Type 1 Servomechanism.** A constant rate of change of the controlled variable requires a constant actuating signal under steady-state conditions for a type 1 system. A type 1 feedback control system is generally referred to as a servomechanism system. Systems of this type are designed with particular emphasis on the ability of the system to maintain any constant value of the controlled variable with no steady-state error, that is, complete correspondence with the reference input. For reference inputs that change with time at a constant rate, a constant signal is required to produce the same steady-state rate of the controlled variable. For this reason, type 1 systems are sometimes referred to as velocity-type servomechanisms.

For a type 1 feedback control system,

$$G(s) = \frac{C(s)}{E(s)} = \frac{K_V(1 + T_a s)(1 + T_b s)}{s(1 + T_1 s)(1 + T_2 s)(1 + T_3 s)} \qquad (8.3\text{–}15)$$

where $K_V$ has the dimensions of seconds$^{-1}$ and is the literal symbol for gain associated with a type 1 system.

In Table 7.8–1 one notices that the presence of an electric or hydraulic motor will produce the $1/s$ term characteristic of a type 1 system.

Expressed in terms of a sinusoidal input, Equation 8.3–15 becomes

$$G(j\omega) = \frac{C}{E}(j\omega) = \frac{K_V(1 + j\omega T_a)(1 + j\omega T_b)}{j\omega(1 + j\omega T_1)(1 + j\omega T_2)(1 + j\omega T_3)} \qquad (8.3\text{–}16)$$

The $j\omega$ term in the denominator of Equation 8.3–15 is characteristic of the sinusoidal form of the transfer function for a type 1 servomechanism. Shown on Figure 8.3–5 are two representative plots of type 1 transfer functions of the sort indicated by Equation 8.3–16. For each plot as $\omega \to 0$, the plot of $G(j\omega)$ approaches an infinite value along the negative imaginary axis as a result of the single $j\omega$ term. As $\omega$ takes on increasing values, $G(j\omega)$ generally passes into the third, then the second quadrants, passing between $-1$ and $0$ as it crosses the negative real axis to insure stable operation. Although the exact shape of the $G(j\omega)$ locus is dependent on the values of the time constants in Equation 8.3–16, the fact that, as $\omega \to 0$, $G(j\omega)$ approaches $-90°$ as a limit means that this type of system tends to be one that can be made stable without very much trouble. It is, however, more difficult to stabilize than the type 0 servomechanism system.

If the transfer function of the type 1 servomechanism system has only one additional time constant term $(1 + j\omega T_1)$ associated with its denominator, the $G(j\omega)$ function will be limited to the third quadrant of the complex plane, starting at $-90°$ as $\omega \to 0$, ending at $-180°$ as

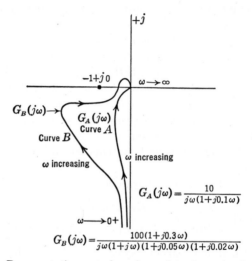

$$G_A(j\omega) = \frac{10}{j\omega(1+j0.1\omega)}$$

$$G_B(j\omega) = \frac{100(1+j0.3\omega)}{j\omega(1+j\omega)(1+j0.05\omega)(1+j0.02\omega)}$$

FIGURE 8.3–5.  Representative complex plane plots for type 1 servomechanism system.

$\omega \to \infty$, and the $-1 + j0$ point cannot be enclosed. Curve $A$ of Figure 8.3–5 shows this sort of condition and indicates no particular instability problem. For the more general transfer function of a type 1 servomechanism system, there is more than one time constant in the denominator as shown by the $G_B(j\omega)$ function of Figure 8.3–5. In this event, the stability problem is considerably increased, and it is necessary either to have a low gain ($K_V$) or to provide other time constant terms in the numerator to insure an adequate measure of stability. Curve $B$ illustrates the use of the latter method for providing stability.

The type 1 servomechanism system, when applied to position control systems, may also be referred to as a "zero displacement-error system." Zero displacement error means that, under steady-state conditions, it is possible for the reference signal to have any desired constant position or displacement and the feedback signal to have the same displacement. Thus the error will be zero, since the controlled variable has the desired value of displacement.  This action of the type 1 servomechanism is to be contrasted with that of the type 0 servomechanism, where an error proportional to the desired value of displacement is required.

*Example of Type 1 Servomechanism System.*  Representative of the type 1 servomechanism is the widely used position control system.  In this type of control it is desired to control the system output position by means of a motor drive so that at all times the controlled variable position is equal to the reference input position.  Figure 8.3–6 is illustrative of such a system.  A voltage $R$ proportional to the reference input

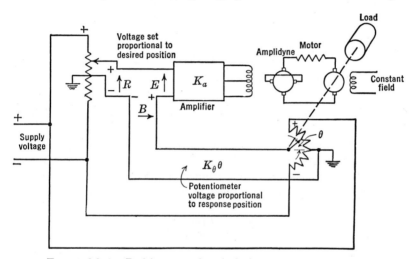

FIGURE 8.3–6.  Position control typical of type 1 servomechanism.

signal is compared to a voltage $B$ obtained from a potentiometer, the slider of which is driven by the system output shaft.  The difference voltage $E$ is amplified and then used to supply the control fields of an amplidyne or other d-c generator.  The generator voltage is impressed on the d-c motor with constant field excitation.  From a comparison of Figures 8.3–3 and 8.3–6, which illustrate examples of type 0 and type 1 servomechanisms, respectively, note that the major items of the two types of systems are comparable, with the exception of the nature of the response signal indicator and the physical quantity that the reference input voltage $R$ represents.

For the system shown in Figure 8.3–6, the parameters are the following:

$K_a$ = net control field amperes per volt error signal,

$K_g$ = no-load amplidyne terminal voltage per net control field current,

$T_f = L_f/R_f$ = time constant of amplidyne quadrature field, seconds,
$T_m = JR_a/K_T K_e$ = time constant of motor and load, seconds,
$K_e$ = motor volts per radian per second of motor,
$R_a$ = total armature circuit resistance of motor, amplidyne, and leads,
$K_T$ = pound-feet torque from motor per ampere of motor armature current, and
$K_\theta$ = voltage from feedback potentiometer per radian of motor.

In terms of $E(s)$, the transform of the actuating signal, the transform of the position of the motor $\theta(s)$ can be written as

$$\theta(s) = \frac{K_a K_g E(s)}{K_e s(1 + T_f s)(1 + T_m s)} \qquad (8.3\text{–}17)$$

from which the transfer function is

$$G(s) = \frac{\theta(s)}{E(s)} = \frac{K_a K_g/K_e}{s(1 + T_f s)(1 + T_m s)} \qquad (8.3\text{–}18)$$

From this equation it is evident that the system is a type 1 servomechanism. Furthermore, it follows that a constant value of actuating error produces a constant rate of change of the controlled variable $\theta$.

The motor position is multiplied by the gain factor $K_\theta$ to form the feedback signal so that

$$H(s) = \frac{B(s)}{\theta(s)} = K_\theta \qquad (8.3\text{–}19)$$

Figure 8.3–7 shows a block diagram representation of the system of Figure 8.3–6 and indicates the forward and feedback transfer function

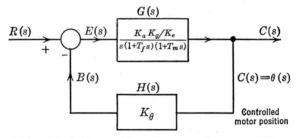

FIGURE 8.3–7. Block diagram of position control system of Figure 8.3–6.

of Equations 8.3–18 and 8.3–19. The open-loop transfer function from which the stability of the system can be judged is

$$G(s)H(s) = \frac{K_a K_g K_\theta}{K_e s(1 + T_f s)(1 + T_m s)} \qquad (8.3\text{–}20)$$

This open-loop transfer function indicates that this system possesses the possibility for instability because of the two time constants in the denominator in addition to the single integrating $s$ term. Stable operation can be obtained by limiting the system gain $K_a K_g K_\theta / K_e$, by using low values for the time constants $T_m$ and $T_f$, or by employing supplemental stabilizing means.

**Type 2 Servomechanism.** A constant acceleration of the controlled variable requires a constant actuating signal under steady-state conditions for a type 2 system. Type 2 feedback control systems are also generally referred to as servomechanism systems. Not only do such systems possess the ability to maintain any constant value of controlled variable with no error, but they also are able to maintain a constant controlled variable speed with no actuating error. For this reason, servomechanisms of type 2 are sometimes referred to as "zero-velocity error" systems, since they may have no error for a constant velocity output. However, for reference inputs that change with time at a constant acceleration, a constant error is required to produce the same steady-state acceleration for the controlled variable.

For a type 2 feedback control system,

$$G(s) = \frac{C(s)}{E(s)} = \frac{K_A(1 + T_a s)(1 + T_b s)}{s^2(1 + T_1 s)(1 + T_2 s)(1 + T_3 s)} \qquad (8.3\text{-}21)$$

where $K_A$ has the dimensions of seconds$^{-2}$ and is the literal symbol for gain associated with a type 2 system. In Table 7.8–1 it will be noted that the transfer function of a galvanometer has the $1/s^2$ characteristic of the type 2 system.

When expressed for a sinusoidal error, Equation 8.3–21 becomes

$$G(j\omega) = \frac{C}{E}(j\omega) = \frac{K_A(1 + j\omega T_a)(1 + j\omega T_b)}{(j\omega)^2(1 + j\omega T_1)(1 + j\omega T_2)(1 + j\omega T_3)} \qquad (8.3\text{-}22)$$

The $(j\omega)^2$ term in the denominator of Equation 8.3–22 is characteristic of the transfer function for the type 2 servomechanism system. Two plots of the characteristics of Equation 8.3–22 on the complex plane are shown on Figure 8.3–8, where for each, as $\omega \to 0$, the plot of $G(j\omega)$ approaches an infinite value along the negative real axis as a result of the $(j\omega)^2$ term. To close the plot of values of $G(j\omega)$ from $\omega = 0+$ to $\omega = 0-$, the complex plane plot can be represented by a circle of infinite radius in which $G(j\omega)$ moves in a counterclockwise direction, as is shown by the dotted lines.

Curve $A$ on Figure 8.3–8 indicates a stable type 2 system; curve $B$ shows a type 2 system that is unstable. The transfer functions for these two curves show that the presence of a single additional time constant in a type 2 control system such as in $G_B(j\omega)$ is sufficient to produce instability.   Stable operation of a type 2 control can be obtained with the inclusion of proper time constant terms in the numerator as is demonstrated by curve $A$ of the $G_A(j\omega)$ function or with the use of other stabilizing means.   Whereas instability is a potential problem in type 0 and type 1 controls, it is an ever-present one with type 2 controllers.

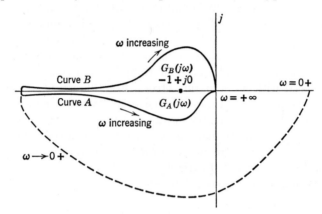

FIGURE 8.3–8.   Representative complex plane plots for type 2 servomechanism systems.

$$G_A(j\omega) = \frac{10(1 + j\omega 2)}{(j\omega)^2(1 + j\omega 0.1)}$$

$$G_B(j\omega) = \frac{10}{j\omega^2(1 + j\omega 0.1)}$$

*Example of Type 2 Servomechanism System.*   A common form in which the type 2 control system is found consists of a position control system in which a pilot motor is used to drive a control element; the position of the control element controls the speed of the main drive motor that supplies power to the load being positioned.   Figure 8.3–9 shows such a system that consists of two motor controls in series.

The error $E$ is amplified in the amplifier which supplies the pilot motor with a voltage proportional to the error.   If the time constant of the pilot motor is neglected, the transfer function from actuating signal to pilot motor position is

$$\frac{M_1(s)}{E(s)} = \frac{K_a}{s} \tag{8.3–23}$$

where $M_1(s)$ = the transform of the position of pilot motor shaft in radians,

$K_a$ = velocity of pilot motor (radians per second) per radian of error, and

$E(s)$ = transform of the error in radians.

The pilot motor shaft has mounted on it a potentiometer brush arm from which a voltage is obtained proportional to the angular displacement $M_1$. This voltage is amplified in the generator and impressed on

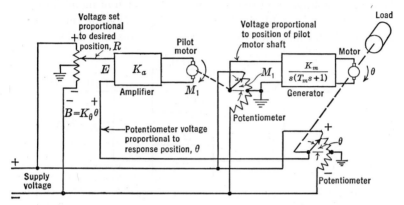

FIGURE 8.3–9.   Position control system typical of type 2 servomechanism.

the main motor. Thus the transfer function from the pilot motor shaft to the main motor position $\theta$ is

$$\frac{\theta(s)}{M_1(s)} = \frac{K_m}{s(T_m s + 1)} \tag{8.3–24}$$

where $T_m$ = time constant of main motor, seconds, and

$K_m$ = velocity of output shaft (radians per second) per radian of $M_1$.

By combining Equations 8.3–23 and 8.3–24, the transfer function of the forward circuit is

$$\frac{\theta(s)}{E(s)} = G(s) = \frac{K_a K_m}{s^2(T_m s + 1)} \tag{8.3–25}$$

The zero-velocity error characteristic of the type 2 servomechanisms is evident from the physical conditions of this example. Since any position of the pilot motor shaft $M_1$ can be maintained with no error signal and since a constant velocity of the main motor is obtained corresponding to the position $M_1$, it is possible for the desired input speed to be duplicated by the load without error. The stability considerations that follow, however, indicate the inherent difficulty present in a system of this type.

The feedback loop consists of a direct feedback proportional to main motor position, namely,

$$\frac{B(s)}{\theta(s)} = H(s) = K_\theta \qquad (8.3\text{-}26)$$

where $K_\theta$ = voltage from potentiometer per radian of main motor.

Figure 8.3–10 is a block diagram representation of the system of Figure 8.3–9 and indicates the forward and feedback transfer functions

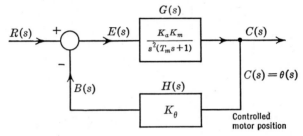

FIGURE 8.3–10.   Block diagram of position control system of Figure 8.3–9.

of Equations 8.3–25 and 8.3–26.   The open-loop transfer function from which the stability of the system can be judged is

$$G(s)H(s) = \frac{B(s)}{E(s)} = \frac{K_a K_m K_\theta}{s^2(T_m s + 1)} \qquad (8.3\text{-}27)$$

This equation indicates that the system is unstable unless additional measures are taken to insure satisfactory operation.   Such measures are discussed later in Chapter 10.

## 8.4   Servomechanism Error Coefficients

By considering the type of a servomechanism as was done in the preceding section, one places emphasis on the ratio of the value of the controlled variable produced by a constant value of actuating error signal. Of comparable or greater importance is a means for relating the value of the reference input and its derivatives to the actuating signal that results from this input.   This relationship is indicated by the *error coefficients of control system* which *are valid for relatively smoothly changing input*, i.e., continuous derivatives, *but do not reflect the signals that exist during transient settling times.*

The error coefficients describe the ratio of actuating signal to reference inputs in terms of the gain and time constants of the system's transfer function.   As such they are particularly valuable in helping to indicate of dynamic actuating signal that will result from the control with a given time function for its reference input.

Combining Equations 8.3–1 and 8.3–2, one can express the ratio of actuating signal to reference input for a control system as

$$\frac{E(s)}{R(s)} = \frac{1}{1 + G(s)} \qquad (8.4\text{–}1)$$

Considering the transfer function $G(s)$ to be of the general form indicated by Equation 8.3–3,

$$G(s) = \frac{K(1 + a_1 s + a_2 s^2 + \cdots)}{s^n(1 + b_1 s + b_2 s^2 + b_3 s^3 + \cdots)} \qquad (8.4\text{–}2)$$

With this expression for $G(s)$, Equation 8.4–1 takes on the form

$$\frac{E(s)}{R(s)} = \frac{s^n(1 + b_1 s + b_2 s^2 + b_3 s^3 + \cdots)}{s^n(1 + b_1 s + b_2 s^2 + b_3 s^3 + \cdots) + K(1 + a_1 s + a_2 s^2 + \cdots)}$$

$$(8.4\text{–}3)$$

Grouping like powers of $s$ in numerator and denominator, Equation 8.4–3 can be expressed as

$$\frac{E(s)}{R(s)} = \frac{B_0 + B_1 s + B_2 s^2 + B_3 s^3 + \cdots}{A_0 + A_1 s + A_2 s^2 + A_3 s^3 + \cdots} \qquad (8.4\text{–}4)$$

where the coefficients $A_0$, $B_0$, $A_1$, $B_1$, etc., are derived from the terms of Equation 8.4–3, the manner of combination depending on the value of $n$, i.e., the type of the system.

Performing the division indicated by Equation 8.4–5, one obtains the relationship

$$\frac{E(s)}{R(s)} = \left(\frac{B_0}{A_0}\right) + \left(B_1 - \frac{A_1 B_0}{A_0}\right)\frac{s}{A_0} + \left[\left(B_2 - \frac{A_2 B_0}{A_0}\right)\right.$$

$$- \frac{A_1}{A_0}\left(B_1 - \frac{A_1 B_0}{A_0}\right)\right]\frac{s^2}{A_0} + \left\{\left[\left(B_3 + \frac{A_3 B_0}{A_0}\right) - \frac{A_2}{A_0}\left(B_1 - \frac{A_1 B_0}{A_0}\right)\right]\right.$$

$$\left. - \frac{A_1}{A_0}\left[\left(B_2 - \frac{A_2 B_0}{A_0}\right) - \frac{A_1}{A_0}\left(B_1 - \frac{A_1 B_0}{A_0}\right)\right]\right\}\frac{s^3}{A_0} + \cdots$$

$$(8.4\text{–}5)$$

Equation 8.4–5 may be written as

$$E(s) = C_0 R(s) + C_1 s R(s) + C_2 s^2 R(s) + C_3 s^3 R(s) + \cdots \qquad (8.4\text{–}6)$$

where the *error coefficients* $C_0$, $C_1$, $C_2$, $C_3$, etc., are substituted for the corresponding grouping of $A$ and $B$ coefficients from Equation 8.4–5.

The ascending power series in $sR(s)$ in Equation 8.4–6 indicates the value of the reference input and its increasing order of derivatives. The error coefficients, $C_0$, $C_1$, $C_2$, $C_3$, etc., indicate the factors which multiply the reference input, its first derivative, its second and higher derivatives, respectively, to produce the over-all expression for the servomechanism or regulator actuating error signal.

Thus, the contribution to the over-all error produced by the acceleration $s^2R(s)$ of the reference input is $C_2s^2R(s)$ where $C_2$ is the error coefficient for the reference input acceleration. The resultant error is the sum of all the contributions to error from the products of the various error coefficients and the corresponding derivatives of reference input.

*Example*

For a type 1 control system with transfer function,

$$G(s) = \frac{K_v(1 + T_as)}{s(1 + T_1s)(1 + T_2s)(1 + T_3s)} \qquad (8.4\text{–}7)$$

find the first four error coefficients. Expanding Equation 8.4–7,

$$G(s) = \frac{K_v(1 + T_as)}{s[1 + (T_1 + T_2 + T_3)s + (T_1T_2 + T_2T_3 + T_3T_1)s^2 + T_1T_2T_3s^3]} \qquad (8.4\text{–}8)$$

Substituting this value of $G$ into Equation 8.4–1, one obtains the following expression for $E(s)/R(s)$

$$\frac{E(s)}{R(s)} = \frac{s + (T_1 + T_2 + T_3)s^2 + (T_1T_2 + T_2T_3 + T_3T_1)s^3 + T_1T_2T_3s^4}{\left\{ \begin{array}{l} K_v + (1 + K_vT_a)s + (T_1 + T_2 + T_3)s^2 \\ \quad + (T_1T_2 + T_2T_3 + T_3T_1)s^3 + T_1T_2T_3s^4 \end{array} \right\}} \qquad (8.4\text{–}9)$$

Comparing terms of Equations 8.4–9 and 8.4–4

$$B_0 = 0$$

$$B_1 = 1$$

$$B_2 = (T_1 + T_2 + T_3)$$

$$B_3 = (T_1T_2 + T_2T_3 + T_3T_1)$$

$$A_0 = K_v \qquad (8.4\text{–}10)$$

$$A_1 = (1 + K_v T_a)$$

$$A_2 = (T_1 + T_2 + T_3)$$

$$A_3 = (T_1 T_2 + T_2 T_3 + T_3 T_1)$$

Substituting these values into Equations 8.4–5 and 8.4–6,

$$C_0 = 0$$

$$C_1 = \frac{1}{K_v}$$

$$C_2 = \frac{1}{K_v}\left[(T_1 + T_2 + T_3) - \left(\frac{1 + K_v T_a}{K_v}\right)\right]$$

$$C_3 = \frac{1}{K_v}\left[(T_1 T_2 + T_2 T_3 + T_3 T_1) - \left(\frac{T_1 + T_2 + T_3}{K_v}\right)\right.$$

$$\left. - \left(\frac{1 + K_v T_a}{K_v}\right)(T_1 + T_2 + T_3) + \left(\frac{1 + K_v T_a}{K_v^2}\right)^2\right]$$

$$(8.4\text{--}11)$$

With

$$K_v = 40 \text{ seconds}^{-1}$$
$$T_a = 1 \text{ second}$$
$$T_1 = 10 \text{ seconds}$$
$$T_2 = 0.0625 \text{ second}$$
$$T_3 = 0.025 \text{ second}$$

then,

$$C_0 = 0 \qquad\qquad (8.4\text{--}12)$$
$$C_1 = +0.025 \text{ second}$$
$$C_2 = +0.226 \text{ second}^2$$
$$C_3 = -0.217 \text{ second}^3$$

As would be expected from a type 1 system, the position error coefficient $C_0 = 0$ and the velocity error coefficient is the reciprocal of the velocity gain constant, $K_v$.

Somewhat of a surprise perhaps are the acceleration error coefficient $C_2$ which is about nine times as great as the velocity error coefficient and the "rate of change of acceleration" error coefficient $C_3$ which is about the same size as the acceleration error coefficient but of the opposite sign. These higher order error coefficients are sometimes responsible for unexpectedly large errors for systems having high velocity gains but also having large time constants and reference inputs with significant accelerations and higher derivatives.

**Comparison of Control System Gain Constants and Control System Error Coefficients.** Before leaving the subject of error coefficients it is of interest to note the relationship between these error coefficients $C_0$, $C_1$, $C_2$ and higher as developed in Equations 8.4–1 through 8.4–6 with the gain constants $K_P$, $K_V$, and $K_A$ for the type 0, 1, and 2 servomechanisms described in Section 8.3. Referring to the general form of the system transfer function presented in Equation 8.4–2, we have the following expressions

Type 0 $\qquad G(s) = \dfrac{K_P(1 + T_a s)(1 + T_b s)}{(1 + T_1 s)(1 + T_2 s)(1 + T_3 s)}$ $\qquad$ (8.4–13)

Type 1 $\qquad G(s) = \dfrac{K_V(1 + T_a s)(1 + T_b s)}{s(1 + T_1 s)(1 + T_2 s)(1 + T_3 s)}$ $\qquad$ (8.4–14)

Type 2 $\qquad G(s) = \dfrac{K_A(1 + T_a s)(1 + T_b s)}{s^2(1 + T_1 s)(1 + T_2 s)(1 + T_3 s)}$ $\qquad$ (8.4–15)

Substituting the value of $G(s)$ from Equation 8.4–13 into Equation 8.4–1, the equation for $E/R(s)$ becomes

Type 0

$$\frac{E(s)}{R(s)} = \frac{(1 + T_1 s)(1 + T_2 s)(1 + T_3 s)}{(1 + T_1 s)(1 + T_2 s)(1 + T_3 s) + K_P(1 + T_a s)(1 + T_b s)}$$

$$(8.4–16)$$

For a constant value of reference input, $R$, the expression for actuating signal, $E$, under steady state conditions reduces to

$$E(s) = \frac{1}{1 + K_P} R(s) \qquad (8.4–17)$$

where the term $\dfrac{1}{1 + K_P}$ is directly comparable to the position error coefficient, $C_0$, of Equation 8.4–6.

With the type 1 transfer function of Equation 8.4–14, the $E/R(s)$ expression is

$$\frac{E(s)}{R(s)} = \frac{s(1 + T_1 s)(1 + T_2 s)(1 + T_3 s)}{s(1 + T_1 s)(1 + T_2 s)(1 + T_3 s) + K_V(1 + T_a s)(1 + T_b s)}$$

$$(8.4–18)$$

With a constant rate of change of reference input, the expression for the actuating signal under steady state conditions is

$$E(s) = \frac{1}{K_V} s R(s) \qquad (8.4–19)$$

Comparing this equation for a type 1 system with Equation 8.4–6, it is noted that $1/K_V$ corresponds to $C_1$, the velocity error coefficient.

In similar fashion for a type 2 system with a constant rate of change of the reference input the actuating signal for steady state operation is

$$E(s) = \frac{1}{K_A} s^2 R(s) \qquad (8.4\text{--}20)$$

Again comparing with Equation 8.4–6, one notes that, for this type 2 system, $1/K_A$ corresponds to the acceleration error coefficient, $C_2$.

Although the above material points out the generally inverse relationship between the gain constants $K_P$, $K_V$, and $K_A$ and error coefficients $C_0$, $C_1$, and $C_2$, it is important to note that it is *the error coefficients that more accurately represent the relationship between the actuating signal and reference input with its derivatives than do the gain constants.* In some of the later material, the terms *effective velocity gain constant* and *effective acceleration gain constant* are used to indicate the reciprocals of the velocity and acceleration error coefficients, $C_1$ and $C_2$, respectively.

# 9

## COMPLEX PLANE REPRESENTATION
## OF FEEDBACK CONTROL SYSTEM PERFORMANCE

### 9.0 Introduction

In Chapter 6 it was mentioned that the complex plane plot of the open-circuit loop gain in a control system could be used to indicate more than the stability of the system. In this chapter close correlation will be shown between the complex plane plot, from which the system stability is determined, and the error response and closed-loop frequency response. The complex plane plot presents a quantitative picture of the system performance accuracy and a qualitative picture of the degree of system stability. It provides a readily interpreted indication of the characteristic methods that are required for improving the system performance.

Although the closed-loop frequency response may be determined easily from the complex plane plot alone, the process can be greatly shortened by use of a plot showing loci of constant values of the ratio of controlled variable to reference input in both magnitude and angle.[31] The characteristics and method of constructing these loci are described in this chapter.

When a control system contains a feedback loop, the means for studying the effects on system performance of varying the direct or feedback transfer functions are not particularly straightforward if the plot of the forward transfer function $G(j\omega)$ is employed. Marcy [53] and others [55] have shown that, if a plot is made of the inverse of the forward transfer function, that is, $1/G(j\omega)$, corresponding to the ratio $E/C$, then not only are simpler loci of the contours of the ratio of constant reference input to controlled variable obtained, but also the effect of the feedback transfer function can be determined from a single vector addition. The significance of the inverse plot and the nature of the loci of constant magnitude and angle are described in this chapter.

## 9.1 Complex Plane Diagram for Feedback Control System with Sinusoidal Input

The steady-state performance of systems with sinusoidal inputs has been described in earlier chapters. After the transients had subsided, all the dependent variables were shown to be operating at the same frequency as the driving function but with different magnitudes and phase angles. Hence a complex plane diagram can be drawn that illustrates for any desired frequency the magnitude and time phase relationship of each of the major variables involved. The relationship among input, output, and error of a simple system in which direct feedback is employed is of particular interest. Such a system has been considered before, as described in Sections 4.4 and 4.8. For example, Figure 9.1–1 shows in block form an elementary control system in which the controlled variable output is compared directly to the input. There

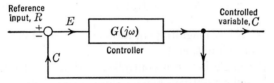

FIGURE 9.1–1.  Block diagram showing an elementary feedback control system.

are two equations describing the system performance with sinusoidal excitation of frequency $\omega$:

$$\frac{C}{E} = G(j\omega) = \left| G(j\omega) \right| e^{j\phi} \tag{9.1-1}$$

where $\left| G(j\omega) \right|$ is the magnitude of $G(j\omega)$ at the frequency $\omega$, and
$\phi$ is the angle of $G(j\omega)$ at the frequency $\omega$ ($\phi$ is positive when measured from $E$ to $C$ in a counterclockwise direction).

$$R - C = E \tag{9.1-2}$$

where $R$ is the reference input that is varying sinusoidally at frequency $\omega$.

Figure 9.1–1 shows that in a physical sense the object of the controller is to reproduce at the output $C$ the reference input signal $R$. However, because of the characteristics of the controller, $C$ differs in magnitude and phase from $R$. This is illustrated in Figure 9.1–2, which shows a complex plane plot relating $R$, $C$, and $E$, with $R$ being chosen as the reference and therefore being located along the real axis. The ratio of output to input can be determined from Equations 9.1–1 and 9.1–2.

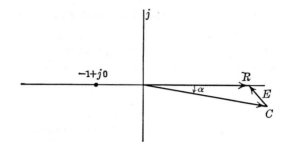

FIGURE 9.1–2. Phase relationships of quantities in Figure 9.1–1. $R$ selected as reference quantity.

This ratio, known as the closed-loop frequency response, can be shown to be

$$\frac{C}{R} = \frac{G(j\omega)}{1 + G(j\omega)} = Me^{j\alpha} \qquad (9.1\text{–}3)$$

where $M = |\,C/R\,|$ = magnitude of ratio of controlled variable to reference input, and

$\alpha$ = the angle between controlled variable and reference input and is positive when measured in a counterclockwise direction from input to output.

Another relationship of interest from the viewpoint of accuracy is the ratio of error to reference input, generally referred to as error response. This is

$$\frac{E}{R} = \frac{1}{1 + G(j\omega)} \qquad (9.1\text{–}4)$$

Since the controller transfer function $G(j\omega)$ is described in terms of the ratio $C/E$, it is convenient to redraw the complex plot in terms of $R/E$, $C/E$, and $E/E$ so that the transfer function appears explicitly. Figure 9.1–3 shows the complex plane plot for the values of $R/E$, $C/E$, and $E/E$ shown on Figure 9.1–2. The ratio $E/E$ is unity so that the reference is now associated with the time when the error is a maximum. Since direct feedback is employed $[H(j\omega) = 1]$, the location of $C/E$, that is, the line $OP$ in Figure 9.1–3, is a point of the plot of $G(j\omega)$ locus necessary for determining system stability.

If now $R/E$ in Figure 9.1–3 is translated parallel to itself one unit to the left, Figure 9.1–4 is obtained, and the quantities $R/E$ and $C/E$ are terminated graphically at the single point $P$. Since $P$ is a point on the locus of the $G(j\omega)$ plot necessary for determining the stability, the ad-

ditional information concerning the controller performance characteristics in terms of $C/R$ and $E/R$ can be obtained graphically from the
same $G(j\omega)$ plot. In Equation 9.1–3 and Figure 9.1–4 $G(j\omega)$ is repre-

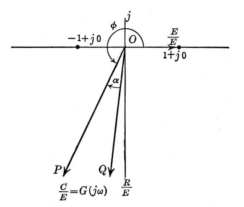

FIGURE 9.1–3.   Figure 9.1–2 modified to show $R/E$, $C/E$, and $E/E$.

sented by the line $OP$, and $1 + G(j\omega)$ is represented by the line $BP$.
Therefore, the ratio of output to input is

$$\frac{C}{R} = \frac{G(j\omega)}{1 + G(j\omega)} = \frac{OP}{BP} = Me^{j\alpha} \qquad (9.1\text{–}5)$$

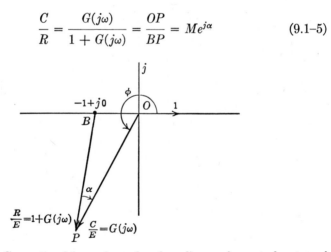

FIGURE 9.1–4.   Conventional form of complex plane diagram for control system of
Figure 9.1–1.

This graphical process yields both magnitude and angle and gives
added usefulness and significance to the complex plane "stability" plot.
In addition, in Equation 9.1–4 and Figure 9.1–4, the ratio of error to

input is indicated graphically by the reciprocal of the line $BP$. That is,

$$\frac{E}{R} = \frac{1}{1 + G(j\omega)} = \frac{1}{BP} \qquad (9.1\text{-}6)$$

In the light of Equation 9.1-6, one is able to obtain a measure of the error response of a servomechanism from the complex plane stability plot. The error to a sinusoidal signal of any desired frequency may be calculated from the reciprocal of the distance from the $-1 + j0$ point to the point on the $G(j\omega)$ locus for the desired frequency. It is evident that the greater the distance from $-1 + j0$ to the point on the $G(j\omega)$ locus, the smaller the error. This characteristic of the transfer function plot for a controller is an item of considerable importance for it provides a simple method for judging the effect on the error of the system produced by changes in the control elements. This subject is amplified further in the next chapter.

## 9.2   Development of Loci of Constant $M$ and $\alpha$

In the previous section it was shown that the ratio of output to input $C/R = Me^{j\alpha}$ for a simple feedback control system operating on a sinusoidal input could be determined from the plot of the system transfer function $G(j\omega)$ on the complex plane. Since, for each point on the complex plane there is a definite value of $M$ and $\alpha$, it is particularly convenient to have a knowledge of the values of $M$ and $\alpha$ throughout the complex plane. This knowledge is acquired by plotting the curves of constant values $M$ and $\alpha$. Hall [31] and others [86] have shown that the loci of points of constant $M$ and $\alpha$ are circles having different centers and radii that are a function of $M$ and $\alpha$. By use of the $M$ and $\alpha$ loci, a feedback control design may be interpreted from the complex plane plot of its transfer function and, in addition to determining its stability, the values of $M$ and $\alpha$ for each frequency may be obtained.

The magnitude of the ratio of output to input of a control system element with direct feedback can be expressed from Equation 9.1-3 as

$$M = \left| \frac{G(j\omega)}{1 + G(j\omega)} \right| \qquad (9.2\text{-}1)$$

Since $G(j\omega)$ is a complex quantity, it may be represented in rectangular form as

$$G(j\omega) = x + jy \qquad (9.2\text{-}2)$$

where $x$ = real part of $G(j\omega)$,
$\quad\;\; y$ = imaginary part of $G(j\omega)$.

Substituting Equation 9.2–2 in Equation 9.2–1 yields

$$M = \left| \frac{x + jy}{1 + x + jy} \right| \tag{9.2-3}$$

$$= \sqrt{\frac{x^2 + y^2}{1 + 2x + x^2 + y^2}}$$

Squared and rearranged, the equation becomes

$$\left[ x - \frac{M^2}{1 - M^2} \right]^2 + y^2 = \left( \frac{M}{1 - M^2} \right)^2 \tag{9.2-4}$$

It can be shown by use of analytic geometry that Equation 9.2–4 is the equation of a circle having a

$$\text{Radius} = + \frac{M}{1 - M^2}$$

and $\tag{9.2-5}$

$$\text{Center at} - \frac{M^2}{M^2 - 1} \text{ on the } x\text{-axis}$$

The loci of constant magnitude of $C/R$ are seen to be a family of circles in the $G(j\omega)$ plane with centers on the real axis, as shown in Figure 9.2–1.

For $M \to \infty$, representing a condition of violent oscillation or resonance, the center of the $M$ circle falls near the point $(-1 + j0)$ and the radius of the circle approaches zero. At $M = 1$, representing the condition where the system output and input are equal in magnitude, the radius is infinite and the locus is a straight line perpendicular to the real axis at $x = -\frac{1}{2}$ as shown. It will be noted that, for all circles of $M > 1$, the center of the $M$ circle lies to the left of $x = -1$ whereas, for all circles of $M < 1$, the center of the $M$ circle lies to the right of $x = 0$, that is, on the positive real axis. As $M \to 0$, the center approaches the origin and the radius approaches zero.

In somewhat similar fashion to that used above it may be shown that the loci of curves of constant $\alpha$ are circles having their centers on the line $x = -1/2$ and passing through the origin and the point $-1 + j0$. The center of the circle for a constant value of $\alpha$ is located at

$$x = -\frac{1}{2}$$

$$\tag{9.2-6}$$

$$y = \frac{1}{2 \tan \alpha}$$

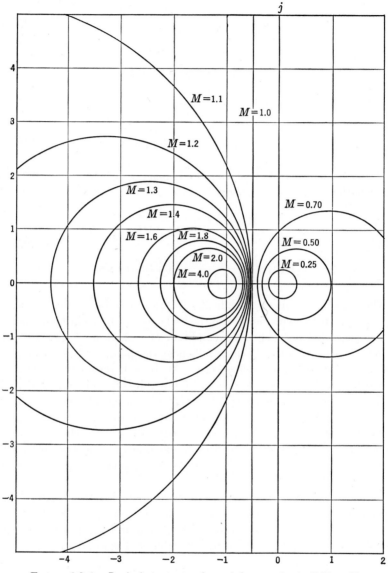

FIGURE 9.2–1.   Loci of constant values of the magnitude $C/R = M$.

Figure 9.2–2 shows a plot of the constant α contours. As in the case of the constant $M$ contours, the constant α contours provide a means for evaluating quantitatively the performance of a servomechanism system as a function of frequency. They are aids that permit the more rapid

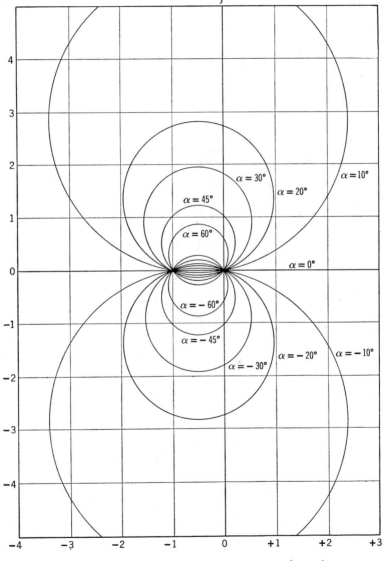

FIGURE. 9.2–2.   Loci of constant values of $\alpha = \underline{/C} - \underline{/R}$.

determination of performance of a servomechanism and hence are a useful tool in system synthesis when the complex plane plot is used.

## 9.3   Closed-Loop Frequency Response and Error Response from Complex Plane Plot

A method frequently used to describe the performance of a feedback control system is to plot the magnitude of the ratio of its output to its input as a function of frequency.[26, 31, 54]   Figure 9.3–1 shows such a closed-loop *frequency response plot* of a typical position control system.   Also

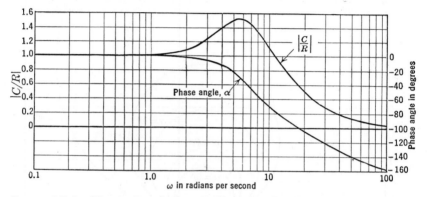

FIGURE 9.3–1.   Magnitude and phase angle of the closed-loop frequency response $C/R$ for a typical position control system.

shown on Figure 9.3–1 is the phase angle $\alpha$ of $C/R$, the frequency response.   Although later chapters will discuss in more detail the nature of the desired characteristics for the frequency response, it is worth noting at this time that the complex plane plot of the transfer function $G(j\omega)$ and the contours of constant $M$ provide all the necessary information for determining the closed-loop frequency response.   The process of drawing up a frequency response plot becomes merely one of replotting the data on a different set of coordinates.

Corresponding to the closed-loop frequency response plot as shown on Figure 9.3–1 is a plot of the magnitude and phase angle of the ratio of $E/R$ as a function of frequency.   Such a plot of $E/R$ is called the error response.   Shown on Figure 9.3–2 is the error response for the same system for which the frequency response was drawn on Figure 9.3–1.   Because of the importance of maintaining the error for a given input to within acceptable limits, the error response is frequently drawn to show the steady-state performance of a servomechanism system.

Two figures of merit that are used to describe the characteristics of the closed-loop frequency response are $M_m$ and $\omega_m$.   $M_m$ is the maximum value of $M = \left| \dfrac{G(j\omega)}{1 + G(j\omega)} \right|$ of the closed-loop control and $\omega_m$ is the fre-

quency at which $M_m$ occurs. Values of $M_m$ in the range $1.1 < M_m < 1.6$ represent good design practice. The speed of response required of the system is intimately related to the value of $\omega_m$, as will be described more

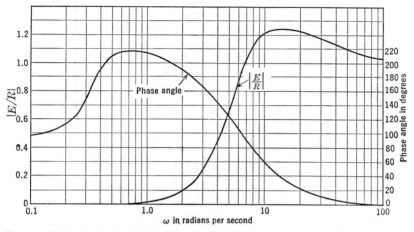

FIGURE 9.3–2.    Magnitude and phase angle of the error response $E/R$ for a typical position control system.

fully in Chapter 14, and no specific values of $\omega_m$ may be assigned for a "good" design. However, for electromechanical systems used for power purposes, values of $\omega_m$ are generally less than 60 radians per second.

The following example illustrates the use of the $M$ and $\alpha$ charts to determine the closed-loop frequency response and the values of $M_m$ and $\omega_m$.

*Example*

The open-loop transfer function of a servomechanism system is

$$G(j\omega) = \frac{3}{j\omega \left( 1 + \dfrac{j\omega}{5} \right) \left( 1 + \dfrac{j\omega}{20} \right)}$$

It is desired to determine the magnitude and angle of the closed-loop frequency response with the aid of the $M$ charts of Figure 9.2–1 and the $\alpha$ charts of Figure 9.2–2. What are the values of $M_m$ and $\omega_m$ for this system?

In Table 9.3–1 are shown the magnitude and angle of $G(j\omega)$ for various values of $\omega$. The values of $\omega$ that are chosen are primarily those that

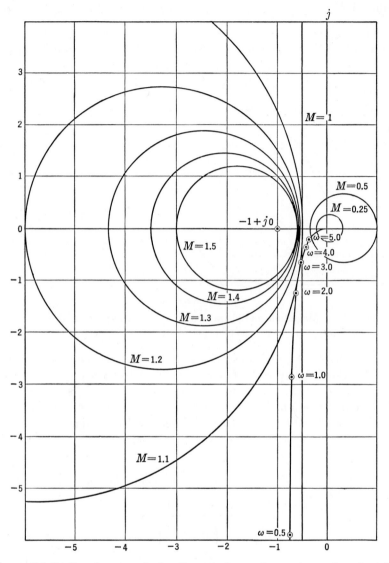

FIGURE 9.3–3. Open-loop transfer function superimposed on contours of constant $M$

$$G(j\omega) = \cfrac{3}{j\omega\left(1 + \cfrac{j\omega}{5}\right)\left(1 + \cfrac{j\omega}{20}\right)}$$

TABLE 9.3–1

Magnitude and Angle of $G(j\omega)$ and $M$ for Various Values of $\omega$

$$G(j\omega) = \frac{3}{j\omega\left(1 + \dfrac{j\omega}{5}\right)\left(1 + \dfrac{j\omega}{20}\right)}$$

| $\omega$ | Magnitude $G(j\omega)$ | Angle $G(j\omega)$ (degrees) | Magnitude $M$ | Angle $\alpha$ (degrees) |
|---|---|---|---|---|
| 0.5 | 5.97 | − 97.1 | 1.01 | − 9.6 |
| 1.0 | 2.94 | −104.2 | 1.03 | − 19.8 |
| 2.0 | 1.39 | −117.5 | 1.08 | − 43.8 |
| 3.0 | 0.85 | −129.5 | 1.06 | − 74.6 |
| 4.0 | 0.57 | −140.0 | 0.86 | −106.6 |
| 5.0 | 0.41 | −149.0 | 0.60 | −130.9 |
| 6.0 | 0.31 | −156.9 | 0.42 | −147.4 |
| 8.0 | 0.18 | −169.8 | 0.23 | −167.5 |
| 10.0 | 0.12 | −180.0 | 0.14 | −180.0 |

yield $G(j\omega)$ values in the third quadrant where the $M$ circles are about 1.0 to 1.4 in magnitude and are spaced rather closely together.

Figure 9.3–3 shows the $G(j\omega)$ transfer function superimposed on the $M$ loci of Figure 9.2–1. These data and those for the corresponding $\alpha$ information are shown in closed-loop frequency response form on Figure 9.3–4, where $M_m$ is shown to be 1.09 and $\omega_m$ is 2.5 radians per second.

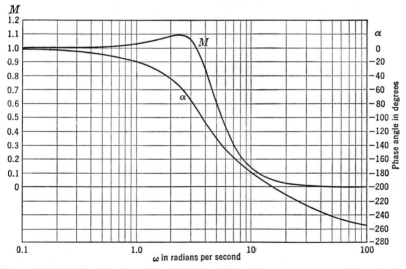

Figure 9.3–4.  Magnitude and angle of closed-loop frequency response for transfer function shown in Figure 9.3–3.

## 9.4   Method for Setting Gain for Specified $M_m$

The loci of constant $M$ and $\alpha$ described in Section 9.2 are useful for determining the value of $M_m$ for a control system for which the $G(j\omega)$ function is known. However, when it is desired to use these $M$ and $\alpha$ curves to establish the gain $K$ associated with $G(j\omega)$ to obtain a specified $M_m$, the obvious process becomes one of cut-and-try. A method has been set forth by Brown and Campbell, Chapter 6, Section 11, that permits one to draw only one curve for the $G(j\omega)$ function and to determine the appropriate value of $K$ with a simplified cut-and-try process. This Brown and Campbell method is based upon the following facts.

The radius of the $M$ circle and the distance from the origin (0,0) to the center of a given $M$ circle are both a function of $M$ alone. Referring to Figure 9.4–1, where $p$ is the point of tangency from the origin to the

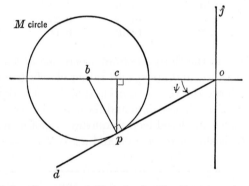

FIGURE 9.4–1.   Geometry of $M$ circles for the direct transfer function.

$M$ circle, one observes that the ratio of $bp$ to $ob$ is a constant for a given $M$. The ratio $bp/ob = \sin\psi$ is defined solely in terms of $M$ by means of Equations 9.2–5. Thus,

$$\sin\psi = \frac{1}{M} \qquad (9.4\text{–}1)$$

The perpendicular from $op$ to the line $ob$ is $pc$. Again, using Equations 9.2–5, the ratio of the lengths $oc$ to $ob$ is that of 1 to $M^2/M^2-1$. Hence, $c$ represents the location of the $-1 + j0$ point to the same scale for which $bp$ represents the length $M/M^2-1$.

For a given $G(j\omega)$ function to have a maximum $M$ value of $M_m$, it must also be tangent to the $M$ circle having a value of $M_m$.

By using these facts, the following procedure can be formulated:

1. Draw the locus of the $G(j\omega)$ function on the complex plane with the value of $K$ set equal to 1. (9.4–2)

2. With the value of $M_m$ specified, determine the angle $\psi$ from the relationship,                                                                                                  (9.4–3)

$$\psi = \sin^{-1}\left(\frac{1}{M_m}\right)$$

3. Using the angle $\psi$ determined from 2, draw the line $od$ on the complex plane as shown in Figure 9.4–1.                                          (9.4–4)

4. By cut-and-try, draw the circle that has its center on the negative real axis and its tangent to both the $G(j\omega)$ locus and to the line $od$ at some point $p$ as shown in Figure 9.4–2.                                          (9.4–5)

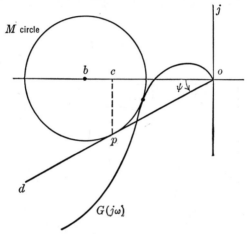

FIGURE 9.4–2.    Use of $M$ circle for determining gain for specified $M_m$.

5. Draw a perpendicular $pc$ from the point of tangency $p$ to the negative real axis. Multiply the values of $oc$ and $G(j\omega)$ by the value $K$ such that $K$ times $oc$ is equal to 1.0.                                          (9.4–6)

The value of $K$ thus determined is the gain associated with $G(j\omega)$ that will yield the specified value of $M_m$. Knowing the proper net gain $K$, one may then change by $K$ the scale of the plot used in the preceding steps and use the same data to obtain the over-all closed-loop response data. As an alternate method, one may replot the $G(j\omega)$ function with the proper $K$ included and thereby obtain the conventional open-loop transfer function, plotted to a more convenient scale. The process of determining the amount by which the open-loop gain must be changed to obtain a desired $M_m$ is illustrated in the following example.

*Example*

For the servomechanism system described in Section 9.3, it is desired that the maximum value of the frequency response be 1.4. Determine the amount the gain must be changed to obtain this value of $M_m$.  At what value of frequency does $\omega_m$ occur?

Figure 9.4–3 is a complex plane plot of the frequency-dependent portion of $G(j\omega)$, namely,

$$G'(j\omega) = \frac{1}{j\omega\left(1 + \dfrac{j\omega}{5}\right)\left(1 + \dfrac{j\omega}{20}\right)}$$

For $M_m = 1.4$, the angle $\psi$ is

$$\psi = \sin^{-1}\left(\frac{1}{1.4}\right) = 45.6°$$

The center of the circle tangent to the $\sin^{-1}(1/1.4)$ line and to $G'(j\omega)$ is found to be located at $-0.42$.  The perpendicular from the point of

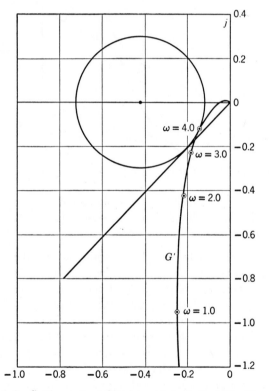

FIGURE 9.4–3.  Setting gain of $G'(j\omega)$ to obtain desired $M_m$ (direct plot).

$$G'(j\omega) = \frac{1}{j\omega\left(1 + \dfrac{j\omega}{5}\right)\left(1 + \dfrac{j\omega}{20}\right)}$$

tangency to the $\sin^{-1}(1/1.4)$ line to the negative real axis is located at
$-0.20$. It is necessary to scale up the plot of $G'(j\omega)$ by $1/0.2 = 5.0$ to
cause the perpendicular to be located at $-1 + j0$.

This means that the net gain for the transfer function $G'(j\omega)$ must be
5 for $M_m = 1.4$. Since the original gain of $G(j\omega)$ was 3, the change in
gain will be $5.0/3 = 1.67$. The frequency $\omega_m$ is equal to 4.0, which is
obtained from Figure 9.4–3 at the point of tangency of $G'(j\omega)$ with the
$M = 1.4$ circle.

## 9.5 Inverse Complex Plane Plot

Although the use of the complex plane plot of the transfer function
$C/E = G(j\omega)$ occurred earliest in the development of servomechanism
study, there are certain inherent drawbacks to the use of this method
for many feedback control systems. This is particularly true for those
systems in which the controlled variable is not compared directly to the
input or ones in which there are internal feedback loops present. In addition, the loci of the constant $M$ and $\alpha$ circles described in Section 9.2
for use with the complex plane plot of the transfer function are not particularly simple to locate or to remember. As a result, Whitely,[55]
Marcy,[53] and others have recommended the use of a complex plot of the
inverse transfer function, namely, $E/C = 1/G(j\omega)$ to obtain the necessary quantitative information on system performance. In addition to
the usefulness of the inverse complex plane plot for quantitative purposes, the conditions for determining the system stability can also be
interpreted in terms of the inverse complex plane plot. Although the
use of the inverse transfer function plot has been somewhat limited because of the introduction of the attenuation concept to the analysis of
servomechanisms, described later in Chapter 11, nevertheless the inverse plot presents some advantages when complex plane plots are employed. In particular, the inverse complex plane plot for determining
the system closed-loop frequency response involves the use of *concentric*
circles about the $-1 + j0$ point for obtaining the $1/M$ value.

**Inverse Plot for General Feedback Control System.** Consider the
general feedback control system shown in Figure 9.5–1. The following
relationships may be written in terms of the direct transfer functions:

$$\frac{C}{M_1} = G(j\omega) \tag{9.5-1}$$

$$\frac{B}{C} = H(j\omega) \tag{9.5-2}$$

and

$$R - B = M_1 \tag{9.5-3}$$

Combining these three equations gives the familiar expression for the ratio of output to input, namely,

$$\frac{C}{R} = \frac{G(j\omega)}{1 + G(j\omega)H(j\omega)} \qquad (9.5\text{--}4)$$

The inverse of Equation 9.5–4 shows the ratio of input to output to be

$$\frac{R}{C} = \frac{1}{G(j\omega)} + H(j\omega) \qquad (9.5\text{--}5)$$

in which the forward and feedback transfer functions appear as separate terms. Since the resultant $R/C$ ratio is obtained from the sum of sepa-

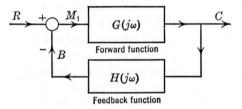

FIGURE 9.5–1.   Feedback control system not having direct feedback.

rate functions of $G(j\omega)$ and $H(j\omega)$, the effect of changes in either one on changes in $R/C$ may be readily appraised.

When the forward function of the controller is established, $G(j\omega)$ is known; therefore the inverse function $1/G(j\omega)$ is likewise known and may be plotted on the complex plane. The proper selection of the feedback transfer function $H(j\omega)$ may now be made by considering the requirements of stability and accuracy.

In Equations 9.5–1 and 9.5–3 it will be noted that $M_1$, the net input to the forward function, is not the error of the system since the quantity $B$ that is compared to $R$ is not in general equal to $C$. However, by starting with the basic definition that

$$R - C = E \qquad (9.5\text{--}6)$$

the expression for the ratio of error to input is found to be

$$\frac{E}{R} = \frac{\dfrac{1}{G(j\omega)} + H(j\omega) - 1}{\dfrac{1}{G(j\omega)} + H(j\omega)} \qquad (9.5\text{--}7)$$

In the inverse form Equation 9.5-7 can be written as

$$\frac{R}{E} = \frac{\dfrac{1}{G(j\omega)} + H(j\omega)}{\dfrac{1}{G(j\omega)} + H(j\omega) - 1} \tag{9.5-8}$$

Since the complex quantity $1/G(j\omega) + H(j\omega)$ in Equation 9.5-8 is identical with the expression for $R/C$ given in Equation 9.5-5, it is evident that the complex plot that shows $1/G(j\omega)$ and $H(j\omega)$ may be utilized to advantage to demonstrate in graphical fashion the vector corresponding to $R/E$. Figure 9.5-2 shows the various vectors of interest for determining $R/C$ and $R/E$ for a particular value of frequency.

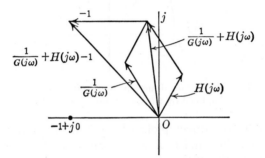

FIGURE 9.5-2.  Inverse transfer function representation of various functions of feedback control system without direct feedback.

**Inverse Transfer Function Plot for Systems with Direct Feedback.** The preceding development has been general in nature and has not emphasized sufficiently the important case where direct feedback is employed and $H(j\omega)$ is 1.  Considering now a system where this condition is obtained, Equations 9.5-5 and 9.5-8 become

$$\frac{R}{C} = \frac{1}{G(j\omega)} + 1 \tag{9.5-9}$$

and

$$\frac{R}{E} = \frac{\dfrac{1}{G(j\omega)} + 1}{\dfrac{1}{G(j\omega)}} \tag{9.5-10}$$

Figure 9.5-3 shows the inverse transfer function $1/G(j\omega)$ represented by $OP$ and the $R/C$ ratio that is equal to $1/G(j\omega) + 1$ and is represented by $BP$. Hence the magnitude of the ratio of reference input to controlled variable for a control system having an inverse transfer function represented by a definite point on the complex plane for a given frequency is equal to the distance from $-1 + j0$ to the point represented by $1/G(j\omega)$. Equation 9.5–10, giving the ratio of reference input to error, shows that this ratio may be obtained graphically by taking the ratio of $BP$ to $OP$. Hence the $R/E$ ratio appears graphically as the ratio of two lines from the inverse plot whereas the $R/C$ ratio is represented simply as one line. This condition is reversed from

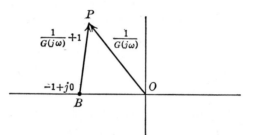

FIGURE 9.5–3. Inverse transfer function representation of Figure 9.4–2 when simplified by the use of direct feedback.

that obtained in the direct plots where $E/R$ was represented graphically by a single line and $C/R$ was obtained as the ratio of two lines as described in Section 9.1.

The complex plane stability criterion for an inverse transfer function plot of a system in which direct feedback is employed and which has a stable forward transfer function may be stated simply as follows:

1. Plot $1/G(j\omega)$ in the complex plane for values of $\omega$ from $-\infty$ to $+\infty$.                                                                      (9.5–11)

2. If the $-1 + j0$ point is not enclosed, the system is stable; if the $-1 + j0$ point is completely enclosed, the system is unstable.

(9.5–12)

Figure 9.5–4 shows the inverse plot of a stable system. Contrasted with this is the unstable system shown in Figure 9.5–5. Note for both cases that the criteria of encirclement can be obtained by plotting the function only in the region from $\omega = 0$ to $\omega = +\infty$.

It is also of interest to note that, even though the criteria of stability for both the direct and inverse plots are the same, the curves themselves appear different. This difference occurs because in closing the inverse plot between $+\infty$ and $-\infty$ the return trace must be made in the clockwise direction. This plot is to be contrasted with the direct plot in which

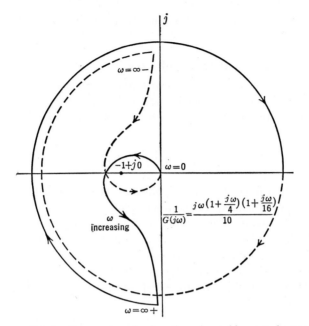

FIGURE 9.5–4.   Inverse transfer function of a stable control system.

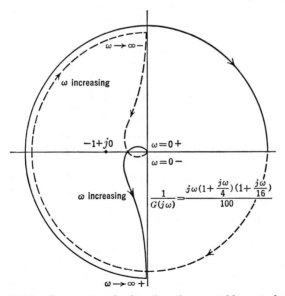

FIGURE 9.5–5.   Inverse transfer function of an unstable control system.

the closure $\omega = 0+$ to $\omega = 0-$ must be made in the counterclockwise direction.

## 9.6 Loci of Constant $1/M$ and $-\alpha$

In Section 9.5 it has been shown that the inverse plot of the direct transfer function indicates as a single line the ratio of $R/C$. The loci of constant system performance can be expressed in terms of

$$\frac{R}{C} = \frac{1}{G(j\omega)} + 1 = \frac{1}{M} e^{-j\alpha} \qquad (9.6\text{-}1)$$

where $M$ and $\alpha$ have the same significance they had in Equation 9.1–3, where they were defined for the direct plot.

Since $R/C$ is merely the distance from the $-1 + j0$ point to any point on the complex plane, the loci of constant $1/M$ are once again circles, this time having a *common center* at $-1 + j0$. The radii of the circles are equal to $1/M$. The loci of the points of constant angle $\alpha$ are merely straight lines radiating from the $-1 + j0$ point. Figure 9.6–1 shows the

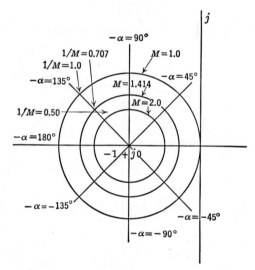

FIGURE 9.6–1. Loci of constant $1/M$ and $-\alpha$ for use with $[1/G(j\omega)]$ plots.

family of circles of $1/M$ and the straight lines of constant $-\alpha$ for use with the inverse transfer function plots. Since the ratio of controlled variable to reference input is generally the design objective sought, the value of $M$ corresponding to the $1/M$ locus plotted is also indicated on each circle.

A method similar to that outlined in Section 9.4 for setting the gain for a specified $M_m$ may be used in conjunction with the inverse transfer function plot as pointed out by Brown and Campbell. Figure 9.6–2 shows the angle $\psi$ which is formed at the origin between the line tangent

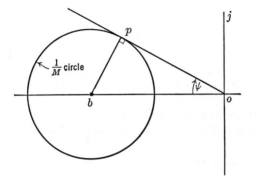

FIGURE 9.6–2.  Geometry of $1/M$ circles for the inverse transfer function.

to a $1/M$ circle and the line passing through the $1/M$ circle center. As in the case of the direct transfer function,

$$\sin \psi = \frac{1}{M} \tag{9.6–2}$$

This means that to the scale on the complex plane for which the $1/M$ circle is drawn, the point $b$ is $-1 + j0$.

The procedure for selecting the proper gain consists of plotting the inverse transfer function $1/G'(j\omega)$ in which $G'(j\omega)$ is the same as $G(j\omega)$ but having a gain of 1. The angle $\psi = \sin^{-1}(1/M_m)$ is then determined and plotted as on Figure 9.6–3. A circle is then located that has its

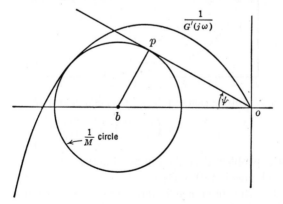

FIGURE 9.6–3.  Use of $1/M$ circle for determining gain for specified $M_m$.

center on the negative real axis and is tangent to both the $1/G'(j\omega)$ function and the $\psi = \sin^{-1}(1/M_m)$ line. The distance $ob$ from the origin to the center of the $1/M_m$ circle is equal to 1 for the proper scale of $1/G(j\omega)$. Hence the correct net gain $K$ for $G(j\omega)$ is determined from the relationship

$$ob\, \frac{1}{K} = 1$$

or

$$K = ob$$

That is, the proper gain for $G(j\omega)$ is directly equal to the center of the $1/M_m$ circle in Figure 9.6–3.

The net change in gain required of the open-loop transfer function $G(j\omega)$ is given by dividing $K$ by the original gain of the open-loop transfer function.

Figure 9.6–4 shows the $1/G'(j\omega)$ curve and the $\sin \psi = 1/M$ line associated with using the above process in determining the proper gain

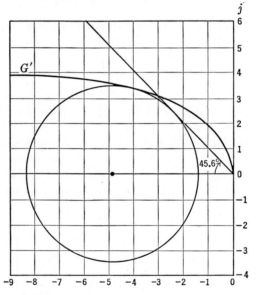

FIGURE 9.6–4. Setting gain of $1/G'(j\omega)$ to obtain desired $M_m$ (inverse plot).

$$\frac{1}{G'(j\omega)} = j\omega \left(1 + \frac{j\omega}{5}\right)\left(1 + \frac{j\omega}{20}\right)$$

setting for the problem described in Section 9.4. In this case $K = 4.83$, and the gain change is 1.61. These values differ slightly from that found in Section 9.4; the difference is indicative of the accuracy obtainable in graphical methods of this type.

## 9.7   Comparative Usefulness of Direct and Inverse Plots

Both the direct and inverse plots have their field of usefulness as well as their followers.  Fortunately the conversion of data from one form to the other is relatively simple so that the choice of the use of one plot does not rule out the possibility of interpreting data in both forms.

Since much of the literature and many of the reports on servomechanism design and performance are expressed in terms of the direct plot, use of this form permits ready comparison with previous work.  Furthermore, if changes in the transfer function of the system are to be accomplished largely by the use of control elements in series with the main transfer function, then use of the direct plot is more time saving.  When complex multiple-loop systems are being analyzed in which there are series as well as feedback elements, in general, the majority of elements are connected in series so that use of the direct plot is most convenient.

However, when the problem of design consists of determining the proper feedback characteristic to produce a desired system performance, the inverse plot may be used to advantage.  Since the effect of the feedback transfer function may be determined by a single vector addition, the synthesis of an adequate characteristic is greatly facilitated.  In view of the fact that the low frequency portion of the inverse plot is presented near the origin instead of near infinity, the performance of the system in this important region of operation is somewhat more easily determined from the inverse plot.  However, since the information is concentrated in a small area, sufficient accuracy is not always obtainable.

# 10

## DESIGN USE OF COMPLEX PLANE PLOT
## TO IMPROVE SYSTEM PERFORMANCE

### 10.0 Introduction

Determination of the system stability and the quantitative performance of a servomechanism or regulator system does not represent the full field of usefulness of the complex plane plot. Study and understanding of the complex plane plot are valuable also because they guide the designer to improvements in his system design as well as indicate means for the synthesis and design of systems.[31, 86] Although this chapter discusses synthesis from the complex plane viewpoint, it will be shown in later chapters that a more direct approach is made possible by the use of the attenuation-versus-frequency concept.[62]

Two different means are available to the designer for improving system performance, namely, (1) the use of series (cascade) stabilization and (2) the use of feedback (parallel) stabilization. The term stabilization indicates that provision has been made to permit stable control system operation with the system gain satisfactory for the maintenance of low errors when the system is operated on low-frequency signal inputs. In many cases, either or both methods of stabilization noted above may be used to advantage, and it is largely a question of practical considerations as to which will determine the selection of one method over the other or the amount of each that should be used.

It is, of course, understood that servomechanisms and controllers will be required to operate on various types of inputs and that satisfactory transient performance is of great importance. Nevertheless, the use of the complex plane plot is such a valuable aid to the synthesis of systems with proper performance characteristics [86] that only the steady-state performance of the controller with sinusoidal inputs will be considered in this chapter. Experimental and analytical studies have indicated that an intimate relationship exists between the steady-state sinusoidal response of a system and its transient response. In Chapter 14 a summary of some of the salient features in the relationships of the system response for these two conditions is presented. The correlation of transient and steady-state performance is such as to justify the use of steady-state sinusoidal approach for the major portion of the system design.

In using series means of stabilization, the designer may employ two basically different types of networks that may be used individually or jointly. They are (1) phase lag networks and (2) phase lead networks. The characteristics of each of these types of series networks are discussed in this chapter, and examples are presented illustrating each method.

When feedback means are employed for stabilization, varying amounts of system stabilization are achieved, depending on whether the feedback is essentially, (1) direct feedback or (2) feedback through a frequency-sensitive network. These two types of feedback are described and illustrations of each are presented in Section 10.2. In addition, regenerative feedback is also described.

In Section 10.3 the series and the feedback methods of stabilization are compared briefly as to their effectiveness. In this comparison some of the factors influencing the choice of one or the other stabilizing method are indicated.

## 10.1   Series Network Approach to System Design

In Chapters 7 and 8 it has been shown that many servomechanisms and regulators are composed essentially of a number of control elements connected in series, the output of one being used as the input to the next. If the loading between control elements is small, it has been shown in Section 7.3 that the resultant transfer function is equal to the product of the individual transfer functions and the resultant value may be determined with comparative ease. Such practical considerations as horsepower rating, weight, size, and reliability determine the characteristics of the controlled system.[73, 75, 89, 93]   Therefore this part of the resultant transfer function is relatively fixed.

The remaining portion of the the resultant transfer function must be selected so that adequate stability and accuracy can be obtained. By use of the complex plane loci of constant $M$ and $\alpha$, plots can be made of the *transfer function for the known elements* as well as an *acceptable transfer function for the resultant system*. The difference between these two in magnitude and phase angle at each frequency may be determined. It is this difference that must be supplied by the series network. Hence the general stabilization requirements are established fairly readily, and the process of obtaining the necessary series stabilizing characteristics becomes one of designing suitable networks. Although performance requirements for the stabilizing networks may be determined directly, the limits to the performance obtainable from physically realizable networks make it difficult to achieve exactly the desired stabilization characteristics. Since the desired stabilization needs are stringent only over a comparatively small frequency range, it is usually possible to design networks the performance of which approximates the desired characteristics of gain and phase angle over the important range of frequencies. Fortunately, from practical considerations it is frequently quite easy to

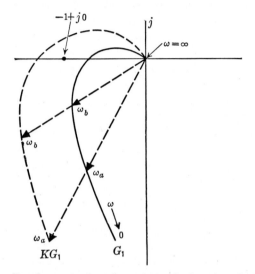

FIGURE 10.1-1.   Sketch on complex plane of transfer functions for low gain $G_1$ and higher gain $KG_1$ servomechanism systems.

insert in series with the main power elements the amplifiers and frequency-sensitive elements to produce the required transfer functions for stabilization.[84]

Before the characteristics of phase lag and phase lead networks for purposes of stabilization are discussed in detail, a broad delineation will be made between the fields of usefulness for the two types. In servomechanism systems such as the types 0 and 1 described in Chapter 8, system stability can be obtained if the gain of the system is reduced sufficiently. *Phase lag networks* may be used to *reduce* the *system gain* as a function of frequency such that at low frequencies a high system gain consistent with the accuracy requirements can be used, whereas at high frequencies a low system gain is produced consistent with the stability requirements. The decrease in gain may be accomplished without appreciable phase shift over broad ranges of frequency. Figure 10.1–1 shows a type 1 system capable of stable operation with a low gain and therefore low accuracy, as shown by the solid curve of $G_1$. The dotted curve of $KG_1$ shows the same system with its gain higher by $K$ but not capable of stable operation. It is evident that the ability of the phase lag network to decrease its gain as a function of frequency might be used to advantage in stabilizing a system of the sort shown in Figure 10.1–1. The design considerations involved in selecting the proper phase lag network for such an application are described later in this section.

In Chapter 8 it was shown that for servomechanisms of type 2 or higher the systems are inherently unstable so that no amount of decrease in gain will produce satisfactory stable operation. To avoid encircling the $-1 + j0$ point, the transfer function of such a system must be advanced in phase, that is, the phase angle of the transfer function must be shifted counterclockwise in the region of frequencies in the vicinity of the $-1 + j0$ point. The transfer function of a type 2 system that is definitely unstable is shown by the solid line in Figure 10.1–2. The dot-

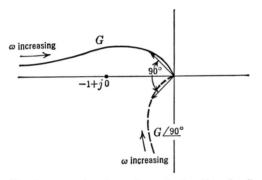

FIGURE 10.1–2. Sketch on complex plane of transfer functions for $G$ and $G$ advanced in phase by 90°.

ted line on the same figure shows the transfer function loci that would be obtained *if* the phase of the transfer function could be advanced by a definite amount such as 90°, for all frequencies. Although phase lead networks have the ability to advance the phase of a sinusoidal signal somewhat in the manner of the preceding illustration, this ability tends to be limited to a certain range of frequencies. In addition, the *phase lead* is accompanied by an *increase in the amplitude of the output* signal as a function of frequency over this frequency range. The application of phase lead networks to servomechanisms of the 0 and 1 types may also be employed to advantage when the procedure of advancing the phase of a transfer function locus can be used to produce stability or otherwise improve performance. The application of the phase lead network to both type 1 and type 2 servomechanisms is illustrated later in this section.

**Use of Phase Lag Networks.**  A phase lag network is one in which the phase angle of the output lags that of the input and the magnitude of the output decreases with increasing frequency.  An electrical network of the type that has this property is shown in Figure 10.1–3.  The transfer function of this network is

$$\frac{E_o}{E_{in}} = \frac{R_2C_2s + 1}{(R_1 + R_2)C_2s + 1} = \frac{T_2s + 1}{T_1s + 1} \qquad (10.1–1)$$

where $T_2 = R_2C_2$, and
$$T_1 = (R_1 + R_2)C_2.$$

With a sinusoidal input voltage, $s = j\omega$, the magnitude and phase of the denominator increase more rapidly with increasing frequency than

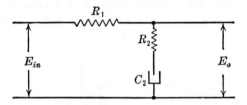

FIGURE 10.1–3.   Representative phase lag network.

$$\frac{E_o}{E_{in}} = \frac{T_2s + 1}{T_1s + 1}$$

$$T_2 = R_2C_2$$

$$T_1 = (R_1 + R_2)C_2$$

does the numerator for low frequencies.  Finally at high frequencies this ratio becomes a constant, $R_2/(R_1 + R_2) = T_2/T_1$.  The complex plane plot for this network as a function of frequency is shown in Figure 10.1–4, where it can be seen that the output voltage $E_o$ lags in phase angle the input $E_{in}$ for all values of frequency except $\omega = 0$ and $\omega = \infty$. It will be noted that the magnitude of $E_o/E_{in}$ decreases from 1 at $\omega = 0$ to the value $E_o/E_{in} = R_2/(R_1 + R_2)$ at $\omega = \infty$.

Actually the range of frequencies at which $E_o/E_{in}$ departs from either 1 or $R_2/(R_1 + R_2)$ is comparatively small so that the transition in gain takes place over a somewhat limited region of the frequency spectrum. Proper choice of the value of $R_2C_2 = T_2$ is influenced by the conflicting requirements that the ratio of $E_o/E_{in}$ should be maintained large up to fairly high frequencies, but at those frequencies where it is desired that $E_o/E_{in} \cong R_2/(R_1 + R_2)$ the phase shift should be low.  Proper choice of the value of $R_2/(R_1 + R_2)$ is determined by the magnitude that is desired for the ratio of $E_o/E_{in}$ at $\omega = \infty$.

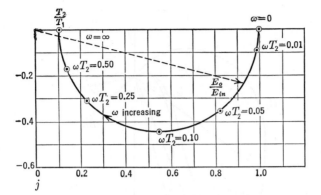

FIGURE 10.1-4. $E_o/E_{in}$ as a function of frequency for phase lag network of Figure 10.1-3.

$$\frac{E_o}{E_{in}} = \frac{1 + j\omega T_2}{1 + j\omega T_1}$$

$$\frac{T_2}{T_1} = 0.1$$

*Example*

The block diagram of a type 1 control system having a transfer function of the sort shown in Figure 10.1-1 is shown by the solid blocks in Figure 10.1-5. The dotted blocks in this figure show the additional

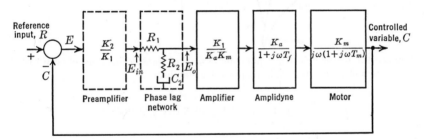

FIGURE 10.1-5. Type 1 control system, using a series phase lag network for stabilization.

$$\frac{T_2}{T_1} = \frac{R_2}{R_1 + R_2} = \frac{K_1}{K_2}$$

amplifier and phase lag network which would be necessary to provide an improved accuracy at low frequencies as well as an adequate measure of stability.

On Figure 10.1-6 is shown a sketch on the complex plane to an approximate scale of the transfer functions for various portions of the system shown in Figure 10.1-5. In Figure 10.1-7 some of the transfer functions on the complex plane are plotted to proper scale with the actual

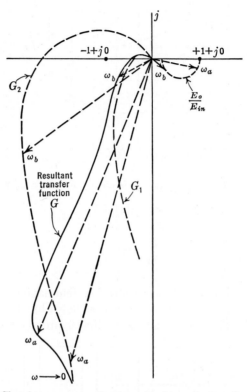

FIGURE 10.1–6.  Sketch to an approximate scale of transfer functions of type 1 control system of Figure 10.1–5, using phase lag stabilization.

$$G = \frac{40(1 + j4\omega)}{j\omega(1 + j80\omega)(1 + j0.25\omega)(1 + j0.0625\omega)}$$

$$G_1 = \frac{2}{j\omega(1 + j0.25\omega)(1 + j0.0625\omega)}$$

$$G_2 = \frac{40}{j\omega(1 + j0.25\omega)(1 + j0.0625\omega)}$$

$$\frac{E_o}{E_{in}} = \frac{(1 + j4\omega)}{(1 + j80\omega)}$$

$$\frac{K_2}{K_1} = 20$$

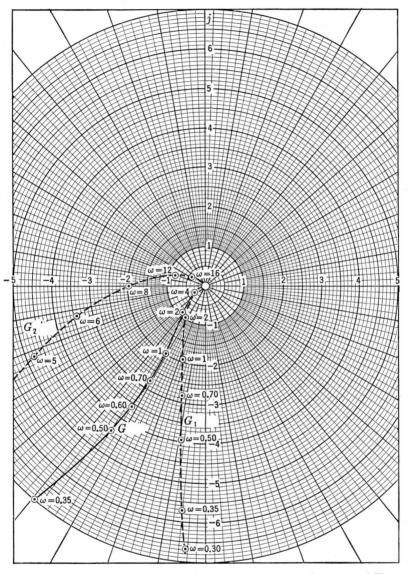

FIGURE 10.1–7.   Actual transfer functions for type 1 control system of Figure
10.1–5, using series phase lag stabilization.

frequencies indicated. The reasons for the choice of the parameters for the preamplifier and the phase lag networks are made more apparent when reference is made to these figures.

The preamplifier gain, $K_2/K_1$ (Figure 10.1–5) has been selected so as to make the net system gain $K_2$ at low frequencies, that is, $\omega \to 0$. The resistance ratio $R_2/(R_1 + R_2) = K_1/K_2$ of the phase lag network has been chosen so that the net gain of the preamplifier and phase lag network is 1 for high frequencies, that is, $\omega \to \infty$. The time constant $T_2 = R_2 C_2 = 4$ has been chosen so that at the frequency $\omega = 2.5$ radians per second corresponding to $\omega T_2 = 10$ the additional phase lag introduced by the phase lag network is about 6°. At this frequency $G_1$ has a magnitude slightly less than 1, and the phase shift is such that an additional phase lag of six to ten degrees may be tolerated.

The resultant open-loop transfer function of the system expressed as a function of frequency is

$$\frac{C}{E} = G = \frac{K_2(j\omega T_2 + 1)}{j\omega(j\omega T_f + 1)(j\omega T_m + 1)\left(j\omega \dfrac{K_2 T_2}{K_1} + 1\right)} \qquad (10.1\text{--}2)$$

Figure 10.1–6 is a sketch of this transfer function to an approximate scale for purposes of illustration. The resultant transfer function of Equation 10.1–2 for the values of the parameters indicated is shown by the solid curve. Dotted lines are also shown indicating:

The original transfer function with gain $K_1$:

$$G_1 = \frac{K_1}{j\omega(j\omega T_f + 1)(j\omega T_m + 1)} \qquad (10.1\text{--}3)$$

The original transfer function with a preamplifier of gain $K_2/K_1$ added:

$$G_2 = \frac{K_2}{j\omega(j\omega T_f + 1)(j\omega T_m + 1)} \qquad (10.1\text{--}4)$$

The phase lag network:

$$\frac{E_o}{E_{in}} = \frac{(j\omega T_2 + 1)}{\left(j\omega T_2 \dfrac{K_2}{K_1} + 1\right)} \qquad (10.1\text{--}5)$$

Figure 10.1–6 shows that for low values of $\omega$, $E_o/E_{in} = 1$ so that $G$ is essentially the same as $G_2$. At a higher frequency such as $\omega_a$, $E_o/E_{in}$

has a magnitude slightly less than 1 and a small lagging angle; the point on the $G$ locus corresponding to $\omega_a$ is somewhat reduced in amplitude and has a greater lagging angle than the point for $\omega_a$ on $G_2$ in which there is no series stabilization. As the frequency is increased still further to $\omega_b$, $E_o/E_{in}$ of the phase lag network is very nearly equal to $K_1/K_2$ and is still slightly lagging. The $\omega_b$ point on the curve of $G_2$ is appropriately modified as shown on the resultant curve of $G$. For higher values of $\omega$, $E_o/E_{in}$ is equal to $K_1/K_2$, and $G$ becomes coincident with $G_1$. The system shown in Figure 10.1–5, therefore, has the desired characteristics of high amplification at low values of $\omega$, and an amplification of less than 1, at 180° phase shift.

Figure 10.1–6 was drawn to a scale to accentuate the performance characteristics of the phase lag network. To obtain a proper perspective of the action of the phase lag network, however, refer to Figure 10.1–7, in which the transfer functions $G$, $G_1$, and $G_2$ are drawn to their proper scale. It is evident that only a portion of the curves of Figure 10.1–6 appear here. Also the low-frequency region of operation is at frequencies lower than $\omega = 0.35$ radian per second as is shown on the $G$ plot.

Although the preceding illustration utilized one particular form of phase lag network, other phase lag networks such as those described for mechanical or hydraulic elements might have been employed. Likewise other electrical phase lag networks might be used to advantage. It is also apparent that the gain attributed to the preamplifier might be obtained in the original amplifier by the addition of another stage of amplification or some other means for increasing the gain for a constant signal.

It is interesting to note that the phase lag network permits the system to operate with a higher gain at low frequency and then reduces the amplification in the region of frequencies where the transfer function plot crosses the negative real axis. To accomplish this, the network is designed so that the additional phase lag introduced in the region of frequencies where the resultant transfer function plot crosses the negative real axis is not great. However, at the frequency where the new transfer function does cross the negative real axis its magnitude is less than the value for the original transfer function. This slight phase shift, introduced by the phase lag network, is in general undesirable since it tends to make for system instability rather than for stability. The effectiveness of a phase lag network is therefore due not to the phase shift, but to the decrease in the system gain in the proper region of frequencies.

It is shown in the following section that phase *lead* networks may be used to provide series stabilization for certain systems. In these instances, the phase shift of the phase lead network has a favorable effect from a stability point of view, although the magnitude amplification of this network may be undesirable.

**Use of Phase Lead Networks.**[64] A phase lead network is one in which the phase angle of the output leads that of the input and the magnitude of the output increases as the frequency of the sinusoidal input excitation increases. An electrical network of the type that has this property is shown in Figure 10.1–8. The transfer function of this network is

$$\frac{E_o}{E_{in}} = \frac{R_2}{R_1 + R_2}\left[\frac{R_1C_1s + 1}{\dfrac{R_2}{R_1 + R_2}R_1C_1s + 1}\right] = \frac{T_2}{T_1}\left[\frac{T_1s + 1}{T_2s + 1}\right] \quad (10.1\text{–}6)$$

where $T_1 = R_1C_1$,

$$T_2 = \frac{R_2R_1C_1}{R_1 + R_2} = \frac{R_2T_1}{R_1 + R_2}.$$

With a sinusoidal input voltage of low frequency, the phase angle of the numerator tends to increase more rapidly with increasing frequency

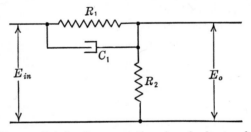

FIGURE 10.1–8.    Representative phase lead network.

$$\frac{E_o}{E_{in}} = \frac{T_2}{T_1}\left[\frac{T_1s + 1}{T_2s + 1}\right]$$

$$T_1 = R_1C_1$$

$$T_2 = \frac{R_2R_1C_1}{R_1 + R_2}$$

than the phase angle of the denominator, and the net phase shift of $E_o/E_{in}$ is positive. However, as the frequency is increased further, the numerator and the denominator both approach $90°$ phase shift so that the phase shift difference is again reduced to zero.

Figure 10.1–9 shows a complex plane plot of Equation 10.1–6 for frequencies of $\omega = 0$ to $\omega = \infty$. From this it can be seen that the output voltage $E_o$ leads the input voltage $E_{in}$ for all values of frequency except

$\omega = 0$ and $\omega = \infty$.  The magnitude of $E_o/E_{in}$ increases with frequency from a value of

$$\frac{E_o}{E_{in}} = \frac{R_2}{R_1 + R_2} = 0.1 \text{ at } \omega = 0 \qquad (10.1\text{-}7)$$

to

$$\frac{E_o}{E_{in}} = 1.0 \text{ at } \omega = \infty \qquad (10.1\text{-}8)$$

As was the case for the phase lag network, the range of values of frequencies in which $E_o/E_{in}$ departs from either $R_2/(R_1 + R_2)$ or 1 is comparatively small so that only over a limited region of frequencies is the

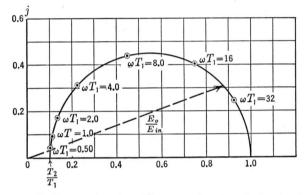

FIGURE 10.1–9.  $E_o/E_{in}$ as a function of frequency for phase lead network of Figure 10.1–8.

$$\frac{E_o}{E_{in}} = \frac{T_2}{T_1}\left[\frac{1 + j\omega T_1}{1 + j\omega T_2}\right]$$

phase lead characteristic appreciable.  Proper choice of $T_1 = R_1 C_1$ is determined by the range of frequencies in which it is desirable for the phase lead to be appreciable.  Proper choice of the $R_2/(R_1 + R_2) = T_2/T_1$ ratio is determined by the maximum value of the phase shift desired.  The greater phase shift required, the smaller is the $R_2/(R_1 + R_2)$ ratio needed.

The phase lead type network may be used to advantage in providing stability for both type 1 and type 2 systems as shown in the following illustrations.

*Type 1 System.*  Consider a type 1 system having initially a transfer function represented by the solid blocks shown in Figure 10.1–10.  The characteristics of this system are identical with those shown in Figure 10.1–5.  In this case stabilization is to be achieved by the addition of a preamplifier and phase lead network such as is shown by the dotted blocks of Figure 10.1–10. The phase lead network has a transfer function given by Equation 10.1–6, where the time constant $R_1C_1 = T_1 = 0.25$ second has been chosen so as to be equal to $T_m$, which is the largest time constant of the system. The ratio $R_2/(R_1 + R_2) = T_2/T_1$ is chosen to be small, of the order of 0.10 to 0.05, so as to allow the maximum phase lead obtainable to be appreciable. Because there is a decrease in the forward gain at low frequencies caused by the $R_2/(R_1 + R_2)$ term of the

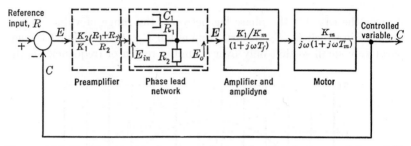

FIGURE 10.1–10. Type 1 control system, using a series phase lead network for stabilization.

$$\frac{E_o}{E_{in}} = \frac{R_2}{R_1 + R_2}\left[\frac{1 + j\omega T_1}{1 + j\omega \dfrac{R_2}{R_1 + R_2} T_1}\right]$$

phase lead network, additional d-c gain in the amount of $(R_1 + R_2)/R_2$ has been provided in the preamplifier to compensate for this loss in forward gain.

In addition to the gain $(R_1 + R_2)/R_2$, which merely compensates for the loss in gain due to the lead network, the preamplifier must provide an additional gain in the amount $K_2/K_1$ in order to increase the system gain at the lower frequency range. The resultant preamplifier gain required, therefore, is $\dfrac{K_2}{K_1}\dfrac{(R_1 + R_2)}{R_2}$, as noted in Figure 10.1–10.

The resultant transfer function of the system is

$$\frac{C}{E} = G = \frac{K_2(1 + j\omega T_1)}{j\omega(1 + j\omega T_m)(1 + j\omega T_f)\left(1 + j\omega \dfrac{R_2 T_1}{R_1 + R_2}\right)} \qquad (10.1\text{–}9)$$

Since $T_1$ has been chosen to be equal to $T_m$, Equation 10.1–9 can be simplified to

$$\frac{C}{E} = G = \frac{K_2}{j\omega(1 + j\omega T_f)\left(1 + j\omega \dfrac{R_2}{R_1 + R_2} T_m\right)} \qquad (10.1\text{–}10)$$

By the original premise, $T_f < T_m$. In addition, $\dfrac{R_2}{R_1 + R_2} T_m$ is made much less than $T_m$. Hence the system shown by solid blocks in Figure 10.1–10 for which the transfer function was

$$\frac{C}{E'} = G_1 = \frac{K_1}{j\omega(1 + j\omega T_m)(1 + j\omega T_f)} \qquad (10.1\text{–}11)$$

has been modified by the use of the preamplifier and phase lead network to produce a system in which the dominant time constant $T_m$ has been reduced by a factor of $R_2/(R_1 + R_2) = T_2/T_1$.

If the preamplifier and phase lead networks are combined, the transfer function between $E$ and $E'$ is

$$\frac{E'}{E} = \frac{K_2(1 + j\omega T_1)}{K_1 \left(1 + j\omega \dfrac{R_2 T_1}{R_1 + R_2}\right)} \qquad (10.1\text{–}12)$$

Figure 10.1–11 is a sketch of this $E'/E$ transfer function to an approximate scale. The resultant transfer function of Equation 10.1–10 for the values of the parameters indicated is shown by the solid curve. Dotted lines are also shown indicating: $G_1$, the original transfer function of Equation 10.1–11, $E'/E$, the transfer function of the stabilizing network, and $G_2$, showing the original system with merely an increase in gain of $K_2/K_1$. For low values of $\omega$, $E'/E = K_2/K_1$ so that the resultant transfer function $G$ is essentially the same as $G_2$. At a higher frequency such as $\omega_a$, $E'/E$ has a magnitude slightly greater than $K_2/K_1$ and a small leading angle so that the point on the $G$ locus corresponding to $\omega_a$ is somewhat increased in amplitude and has a lesser lagging angle than the point for $\omega_a$ on the $G_2$ curve. For a still higher frequency $\omega_b$, the $E'/E$ ratio is further increased in phase and amplitude so that the phase angle and magnitude of $G$ is therefore increased from the corresponding $\omega_b$ point on $G_2$ to the position shown. At very high frequencies the phase shift of $E'/E$ again approaches 0, although the gain of $E'/E$ is now $\dfrac{K_2}{K_1} \dfrac{(R_1 + R_2)}{R_2}$. Despite the large contribution of $E'/E$ to the system gain at these high frequencies, the general level of the amplitude of the transfer function is so low as to fail to indicate adequately on the complex plane plot the difference between $G_2$ and $G$.

Figure 10.1–12 shows to an exact scale the transfer functions for the resultant system of Figure 10.1–10, $G$ (solid line) and the transfer func-

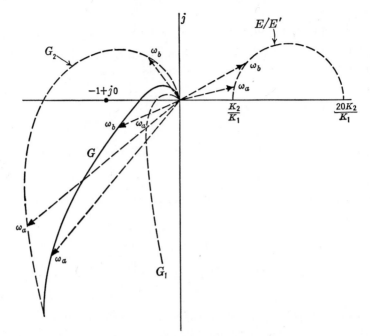

FIGURE 10.1–11.  Sketch to an approximate scale of transfer functions of type 1 control system of Figure 10.1–10, using phase lead stabilization.

$$G = \frac{40}{j\omega(1 + j0.0625\omega)(1 + j0.0125\omega)}$$

$$G_1 = \frac{2}{j\omega(1 + j0.25\omega)(1 + j0.0625\omega)}$$

$$G_2 = \frac{40}{j\omega(1 + j0.25\omega)(1 + j0.0625\omega)}$$

$$\frac{E'}{E} = \frac{K_2(1 + j0.25\omega)}{K_1(1 + j0.0125\omega)}$$

$$\frac{(R_1 + R_2)}{R_2} = 20$$

tion $G_2$ representing the high gain system without stabilization (dotted line).  Also shown by dotted line on Figure 10.1–12 is the transfer function $C/E = G_1$, which is similar to $G_2$ but has a lower gain so as to make it identical with the original type 1 system of the previous example. These plots fail to show so graphically the characteristics illustrated in Figure 10.1–11, but they are an accurate representation of the complex plane plots of actual systems.

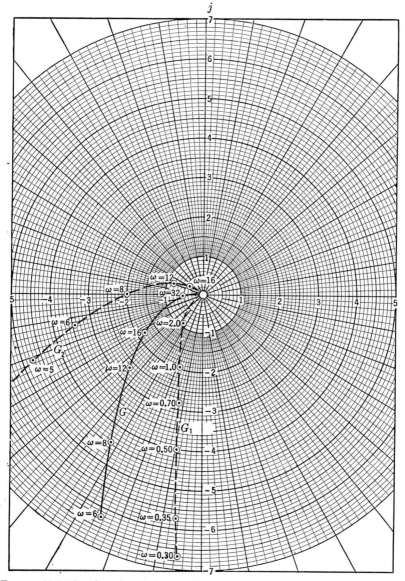

FIGURE 10.1–12. Actual transfer functions for type 1 control system of Figure 10.1–10, using series phase lead stabilization.

$$G = \frac{40}{j\omega(1 + j0.0125\omega)(1 + j0.0625\omega)}$$

$$G_1 = \frac{2}{j\omega(1 + j0.25\omega)(1 + j0.0625\omega)}$$

$$G_2 = \frac{40}{j\omega(1 + j0.25\omega)(1 + j0.0625\omega)}$$

From Figures 10.1–11 and 10.1–12 it appears that the system shown in Figure 10.1–10 has the desired characteristics of high gain at low frequencies and a gain of less than unity at 180° phase shift.  It is evident that the phase lead network employed is not the only one that might be used to advantage nor is the use of a separate preamplifier to obtain the required added gain imperative.  Reference to Figures 10.1–11 and 10.1–12 reveals that by the use of the phase lead method of stabilization the frequency at which the complex plane plot of the resultant transfer function $G$ crosses the negative real axis is higher than the corresponding value of frequency that would have been obtained by merely reducing the system gain to obtain stability.  The control system that results when series phase lead stabilization is employed will tend to have a higher gain at the higher frequencies than would be obtainable by using phase lag stabilizing methods with the same basic power elements.

*Type 2 System.*  Although for type 1 systems a choice exists as to whether phase lead or phase lag methods of series stabilization may be employed, for a type 2 system such as is shown in the solid blocks of Figure 10.1–13 only phase lead methods of series stabilization can be

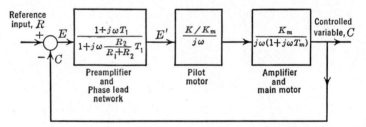

Figure 10.1–13.  Type 2 servomechanism system, using phase lead series stabilization.

used to produce satisfactory results.  The transfer function of this portion of the system is found to be

$$\frac{C}{E'} = G' = \frac{K}{(j\omega)^2(1 + j\omega T_m)} \tag{10.1–13}$$

The preamplifier and phase lead networks shown combined in the dotted block have been selected so that the net gain of the combination is unity at $\omega = 0$, the preamplifier gain being equal to the loss in gain of the phase lead network with a d-c signal.  The transfer function from $E$ to $E'$ is therefore

$$\frac{E'}{E} = \frac{1 + j\omega T_1}{1 + j\omega \dfrac{R_2 T_1}{R_1 + R_2}} \tag{10.1–14}$$

The lead network time constant, $R_1C_1 = T_1$ has been chosen to be considerably greater than $T_m$, the time constant of the motor. As in the previous example for the type 1 servomechanism, the $R_2/(R_1 + R_2)$ ratio should be chosen to be 0.1 or less to insure ample phase lead from the phase lead network.

The resultant transfer function of the complete system in Figure 10.1–13 is

$$G = \frac{K(1 + j\omega T_1)}{(j\omega)^2 \left(1 + j\omega \dfrac{R_2T_1}{R_1 + R_2}\right)(1 + j\omega T_m)} \qquad (10.1\text{–}15)$$

which is shown to an approximate scale on the complex plane by the solid curve of Figure 10.1–14. Shown also, by dotted lines, are the un-

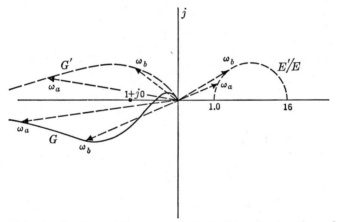

FIGURE 10.1–14. Sketch to an approximate scale of transfer functions of type 2 control system of Figure 10.1–13, using phase lead stabilization.

$$G = \frac{0.25(1 + j4\omega)}{(j\omega)^2(1 + j0.25\omega)^2}$$

$$G' = \frac{0.25}{(j\omega)^2(1 + j0.25\omega)}$$

$$\frac{E'}{E} = \frac{(1 + j4\omega)}{(1 + j0.25\omega)}$$

stabilized system $C/E'$ of Equation 10.1–13 and the stabilizing network $E'/E$ of Equation 10.1–14. For low values of $\omega$, $E'/E = 1$ so that $G$ is essentially the same as $G'$; a slight difference in phase angle separates the two. At a higher frequency such as $\omega_a$, $E'/E$ has a magnitude that is slightly greater than 1 and a small leading angle so that the point on the $G$ locus corresponding to $\omega_a$ is somewhat increased in amplitude and

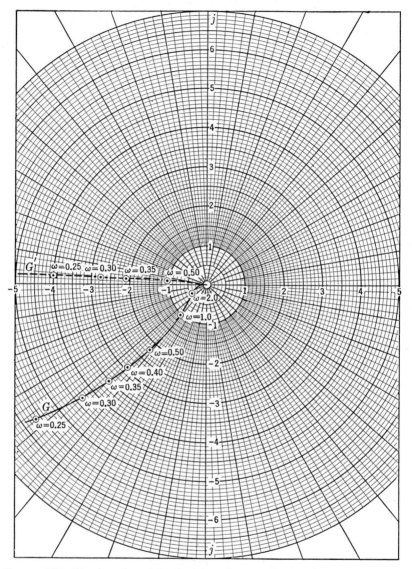

FIGURE 10.1–15.  Actual transfer functions for type 2 control system of Figure 10.1–13, using series phase lead stabilization.

$$G = \frac{0.25(1 + j4\omega)}{(j\omega)^2(1 + j0.25\omega)^2}$$

$$G' = \frac{0.25}{(j\omega)^2(1 + j0.25\omega)}$$

has a smaller lagging angle than the point for $\omega_a$ on the $G'$ curve. For a still higher frequency $\omega_b$, the $E'/E$ ratio is still further increased in phase and amplitude so that the phase angle and magnitude of $G$ is therefore increased from the corresponding $G'$ point to the position shown. At still higher frequencies the amplitude of $E'/E$ approaches $(R_1 + R_2)/R_2$, and the phase shift is zero. The resultant transfer function, however, has a net amplitude of less than 1 at that frequency where the negative real axis is crossed. Therefore satisfactory system operation has been obtained as far as stability is concerned. Since the gain at low frequencies has not been altered, high-accuracy performance can be insured for low-frequency sinusoidal inputs. Figure 10.1–15 shows to actual scale the complex plane plot of the transfer functions for the stabilized $G$ and the unstabilized $G'$ type 2 control system of Figure 10.1–13 with the values of system parameters noted.

The comments on the use of other phase lead networks made about the type 1 system using phase lead series stabilization apply with equal validity here in connection with the type 2 system.

**Use of Lead-Lag Series Networks.** Not only may the principles of stabilization described for the use of phase lead and phase lag networks

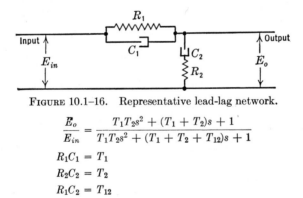

FIGURE 10.1–16.   Representative lead-lag network.

$$\frac{E_o}{E_{in}} = \frac{T_1 T_2 s^2 + (T_1 + T_2)s + 1}{T_1 T_2 s^2 + (T_1 + T_2 + T_{12})s + 1}$$

$$R_1 C_1 = T_1$$
$$R_2 C_2 = T_2$$
$$R_1 C_2 = T_{12}$$

be employed separately, but they may also be used jointly in a single network. This is accomplished by proper choice of network parameters such that the network performs its function as a lag network at the lower portion of the frequency range, and over a higher portion of the frequency range it acts as a lead network. Such a network is shown in Figure 10.1–16.

The transfer function for this network is

$$\frac{E_o}{E_{in}} = \frac{T_1 T_2 s^2 + (T_1 + T_2)s + 1}{T_1 T_2 s^2 + (T_1 + T_2 + T_{12})s + 1} \qquad (10.1\text{–}16)$$

where $T_1$, $T_2$, and $T_{12}$ have the values noted in Figure 10.1–16. The frequency characteristic for the $E_o/E_{in}$ ratio of this network, as shown on the complex plane plot of Figure 10.1–17, is a circle with its center on the positive real axis. At $\omega = 0$ and $\omega = \infty$ the output is equal to the input in phase and magnitude.

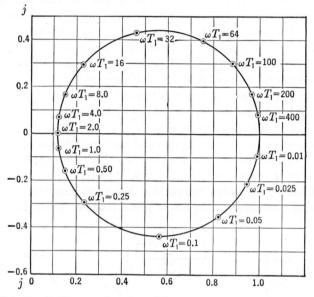

FIGURE 10.1–17. $E_o/E_{in}$ as a function of frequency for lead-lag network of Figure 10.1–16.

$$\frac{E_o}{E_{in}} = \frac{(j\omega T_1 + 1)(j0.25\omega T_1 + 1)}{(j10\omega T_1 + 1)(j0.025\omega T_1 + 1)}$$

$$T_2 = 0.25T_1 \qquad T_{12} = 9.0T_1$$

It is worthy of note that with sinusoidal excitation and

$$T_1 T_2 \omega^2 = 1 \qquad\qquad (10.1\text{–}17)$$

the ratio of $E_o/E_{in}$ of Equation 10.1–16 also has zero phase angle as shown by the value of $\omega T_1 = 2$ in Figure 10.1–17. For this frequency the magnitude of the $E_o/E_{in}$ ratio is

$$\frac{E_o}{E_{in}} = \frac{T_1 + T_2}{T_1 + T_2 + T_{12}} \qquad\qquad (10.1\text{–}18)$$

which is its minimum value. Knowing at what frequency it is desirable to obtain the minimum $E_o/E_{in}$ ratio of Equation 10.1–18, one is able to calculate the value of the $T_1 T_2$ product by means of Equation 10.1–17.

Further consideration of Equation 10.1–16 reveals that, to obtain large values of phase lead and phase lag, it is necessary for the minimum value of $E_o/E_{in}$ from Equation 10.1–17 to be small, so that $T_{12}$ should be appreciably greater than $T_1 + T_2$. From this it follows that $R_1$ should be greater than $R_2$ and $C_2$ should be greater than $C_1$. In many cases it will be desirable for $T_1$ not to be equal to $T_2$. A further discussion of the proper choice of network parameters is taken up in Chapters 12 and 13.

By use of the lead-lag network the system gain for low-frequency signals may be increased because of the lag portion of the network, and the system frequency response may be maintained up to higher frequencies because of the lead portion of the network. For these reasons the lead-lag network is most desirable and is frequently used in applications employing series stabilization.

*Example*

Figure 10.1–18 is a block diagram in which the solid blocks represent the type 1 system previously considered and the dotted block represents additional series gain as well as a lead-lag network for stabilization purposes.

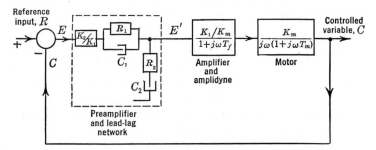

FIGURE 10.1–18.   Type 1 control system, using series lead-lag network for stabilization.

$$\frac{E'}{E} = \frac{K_2}{K_1} \frac{(1 + j\omega T_1)(1 + j\omega T_2)}{[1 + j\omega(T_1 + T_2 + T_{12}) + (j\omega)^2 T_1 T_2]}$$

The transfer function of the preamplifier and lead-lag network is given by the equation

$$\frac{E'}{E} = \frac{K_2}{K_1} \frac{(1 + j\omega T_1)(1 + j\omega T_2)}{[1 + j\omega(T_1 + T_2 + T_{12}) + (j\omega)^2 T_1 T_2]} \qquad (10.1\text{–}19)$$

The transfer function of the original system is

$$G_1 = \frac{K_1}{j\omega(1 + j\omega T_m)(1 + j\omega T_f)} \qquad (10.1\text{–}20)$$

whereas

$$G_2 = \frac{K_2}{j\omega(1 + j\omega T_m)(1 + j\omega T_f)} \qquad (10.1\text{--}21)$$

is the transfer function of the original system with the gain raised from $K_1$ to $K_2$.

By selecting $T_2$ of Equation 10.1–19 to be equal to $T_m$, the largest time constant, by having $T_1$ to be four times $T_2$, and by having the minimum value of $E_o/E_{in}$ from Equation 10.1–18 to be of the order of 0.1, suitable values for the various time constants and network parameters for the $E'/E$ equation can be obtained. To permit the system to operate with the same or somewhat increased gain in that region of frequencies where $E_o/E_{in}$ is a minimum, it is necessary that the value of $K_2/K_1$ of Equation 10.1–19 be such that

$$\frac{K_2}{K_1}\left(\frac{T_1 + T_2}{T_1 + T_2 + T_{12}}\right)$$

is 1 or somewhat greater.

If the parameters are selected for Equation 10.1–19 in the fashion described above, the net transfer function from $E$ to $C$ in Figure 10.1–18, as obtained by combining Equations 10.1–19 and 10.1–20, is

$$\frac{C}{E} = G = \frac{K_2(1 + j4\omega T_m)}{j\omega(1 + j\omega T_f)[1 + j\omega(5T_m + T_{12}) + (j\omega)^2 4T_m^2]} \qquad (10.1\text{--}22)$$

Reference to Figure 10.1–19, in which the transfer functions on the complex plane are shown to an approximate scale, shows that at low frequencies such as $\omega_a$ the resultant system $G$ shown by the solid curve has a similar accuracy to the high gain system of $G_2$. In the region of frequencies between $\omega_a$ and $\omega_m$ the phase lag portion of the series network is effective in reducing gain and increasing phase shift. At $\omega_m$ the resultant system has the same phase angle as the lower gain system $G_1$, although the magnitude is greater because

$$\frac{K_2}{K_1}\frac{(T_1 + T_2)}{(T_1 + T_2 + T_{12})} = 2$$

For frequencies higher than $\omega_m$, such as $\omega_b$, the phase lead portion of the series network is effective and the phase of $G_1$ is advanced and the amplitude is increased to make up the resultant $G$ function. Figure 10.1–20 shows to actual scale on the complex plane the three transfer function curves $G$, $G_1$, and $G_2$ of Figure 10.1–19.

Although the choice of parameters for the preamplifier and lead-lag network may not yield the optimum $M_m$ and further refinements in

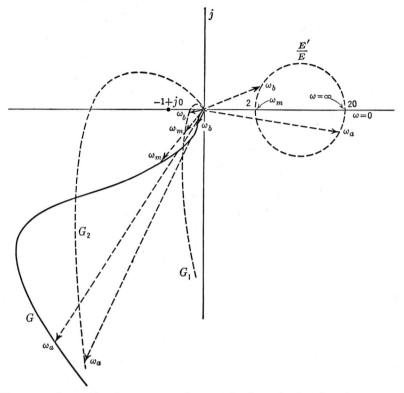

FIGURE 10.1–19.   Sketch to an approximate scale of transfer function of type 1 control system of Figure 10.1–18, using lead-lag stabilization methods.

$$G = \frac{40(1 + j\omega)}{j\omega(1 + j10\omega)(1 + j0.0625\omega)(1 + j0.025\omega)}$$

$$G_1 = \frac{2}{j\omega(1 + j0.25\omega)(1 + j0.0625\omega)}$$

$$G_2 = \frac{40}{j\omega(1 + j0.25\omega)(1 + j0.0625\omega)}$$

$$\frac{E'}{E} = 20\frac{(1 + j\omega)(1 + j0.25\omega)}{(1 + j10\omega)(1 + j0.025\omega)}$$

design may be made based on the determination of the closed-loop frequency response, nevertheless the values chosen do result in a satisfactory system operation with considerable improvement in system performance.  The attenuation methods outlined in Chapter 12 provide a somewhat more direct method of system synthesis than that indicated here, although the method used here is satisfactory.

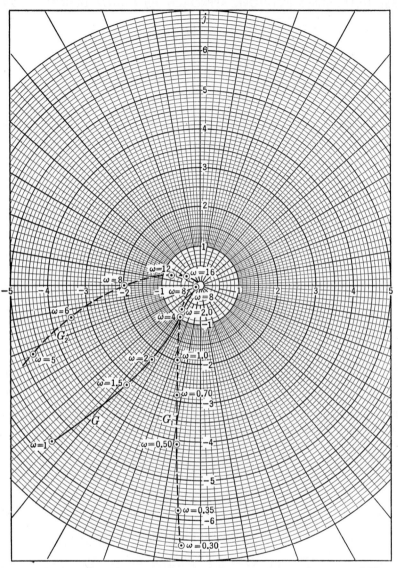

FIGURE 10.1–20. Actual transfer functions for type 1 control system of Figure 10.1–19, using a series lead-lag network.

$$G = \frac{40(1 + j\omega)}{j\omega(1 + j10\omega)(1 + j0.0625\omega)(1 + j0.025\omega)}$$

$$G_1 = \frac{2}{j\omega(1 + j0.25\omega)(1 + j0.0625\omega)}$$

$$G_2 = \frac{40}{j\omega(1 + j0.25\omega)(1 + j0.0625\omega)}$$

## 10.2  Feedback Methods for Use in System Design

Successful as series methods of stabilization appear to be, there are certain inherent limitations to the use of series means for stabilization that may be imposed on the controller by changes of the system parameters either within the control system or outside it. In addition, other requirements such as the size, weight, and cost of large capacitors or other elements that may be required for obtaining the necessary series stabilizing means may prove disproportionate to the corresponding values that would be required with the use of stabilizing means employing feedback.

A mathematical approach to the subject of feedback has been presented in Section 8.2. Not only may this feedback principle be applied to whole servomechanism loops as is done when the controlled variable is fed back and compared to the reference input, but the feedback principle may also be employed to advantage when used on an individual control element or group of elements. Some of the advantages which are realized from use of feedback are:

1. A faster time of response can be obtained from a given element, that is, less phase shift.

2. The performance of the element can be made more dependent on the characteristics of the feedback element than on the characteristic of the original element itself.

In general, the advantages of feedback in improving stability are obtained at the expense of loss of amplification over a range of frequencies so that inherently high gain elements are desirable for use when feedback is employed.

Frequency-sensitive networks of the type of the phase lead, phase lag, and combinations thereof as previously mentioned for use in series stabilized systems are also used extensively in feedback loops. However, the effect of such networks on the performance of the closed loop with high gain tends to be the inverse of their effect when used as series elements.

**Direct Feedback.** The simplest type of feedback that can be employed is the direct feedback of the output to the input of a control element or group of elements, as shown in Figure 10.2–1. $I$ represents the input signal, $O$ the output signal, and $M_1 = I - O$ the net signal to the control element. The transfer function of the element itself is $G_1$. From these definitions it follows that the ratio of output to input is

$$\frac{O}{I} = \frac{G_1}{1 + G_2} \tag{10.2–1}$$

a familiar expression that has previously been obtained for over-all control systems. If the amplitude of the transfer function is large, that is, $G_1 \gg 1$, in the region of frequencies of interest, the $O/I$ ratio is approximately equal to unity. The control element using direct feedback produces an output equal to the input in magnitude but presumably at a higher power level or in a different form of energy from the input.

Direct feedback is frequently used to convert an element from a type 1 or "velocity" type element to a type 0 or "position" type element. An example of this sort of application of the feedback principle is the use of

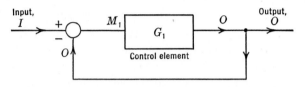

FIGURE 10.2–1.  Direct feedback for a control element.

the output position feedback of the piston position for a hydraulic valve-piston combination. The transfer function of the valve-piston control element with an additional time constant (see Section 7.6) is

$$\frac{O}{M_1} = G_1 = \frac{K_1}{j\omega(j\omega T_v + 1)} \qquad (10.2\text{–}2)$$

Using this expression for $G_1$ in Equation 10.2–1 gives

$$\frac{O}{I} = G = \frac{K_1}{j\omega(j\omega T_v + 1) + K_1} \qquad (10.2\text{–}3)$$

For the condition where $\omega \to 0$, the $O/I$ ratio of Equation 10.2–3 reduces to

$$\frac{O}{I} = 1 \qquad (10.2\text{–}4)$$

If the transfer function from $I$ to $O$ is considered as that of a single control element, it is evident from Equation 10.2–4 that this element is of type 0, a constant value of input being required to produce a constant value of output.

The complex plane plots of the valve piston control element with and without feedback are shown in Figure 10.2–2. Without feedback the element has a constant velocity at $\omega = 0$. At low values of $\omega$, the phase shift is slightly more negative than $-90°$, and as $\omega$ increases the phase shift changes to $-180°$ as shown. The phase shift at any frequency is greater than for the element with feedback; therefore the use of the element without feedback in a complete servomechanism system would tend to produce a less stable system than if direct feedback were used.

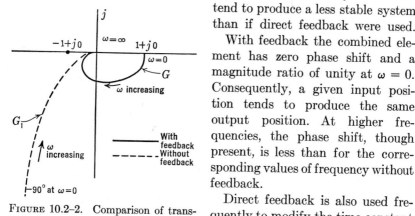

With feedback the combined element has zero phase shift and a magnitude ratio of unity at $\omega = 0$. Consequently, a given input position tends to produce the same output position. At higher frequencies, the phase shift, though present, is less than for the corresponding values of frequency without feedback.

Direct feedback is also used frequently to modify the time constant of a control element. An example of the use of direct feedback was described in Section 3.8. To illustrate this point by means of the complex diagram, consider the transfer function of a series resistance-inductance combination. Referring to Figure 10.2–1, let

$$\frac{O}{M_1} = G_1 = \frac{K_a}{(j\omega T_f + 1)} \tag{10.2–5}$$

where $K_a$ = amplifier gain, amperes/volt,

$T_f = L_f/R_f$, time constant in seconds for $RL$ element, and

$O$ = current in inductance, amperes,

$M_1$ = actuating error in volts.

If direct feedback of a voltage proportional to the current in the inductance is used, the resultant transfer function is

$$\frac{O}{I} = \frac{K_a}{j\omega T_f + 1 + K_a} = \frac{K_a}{1 + K_a}\left[\frac{1}{j\omega \dfrac{T_f}{1 + K_a} + 1}\right] \tag{10.2–6}$$

From this equation it may be seen that the time constant $T_f$ has been reduced to $1/(1 + K_a)$ of its original value and that the gain of the amplifier has been decreased by the same ratio. Figure 10.2–3 shows a comparison of the complex plane plots of Equations 10.2–5 and 10.2–6.

FIGURE 10.2–2. Comparison of transfer function of type 1 element with and without direct feedback.

Since the additional gain can be obtained by suitable amplifier means without a corresponding change in the time constant, a net improvement in the performance of the control element can be realized.

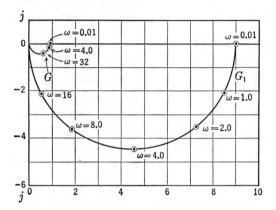

FIGURE 10.2–3.   Use of direct feedback to reduce time constant of a single time constant element.

$$G = \frac{K_a}{1 + K_a}\left[\frac{1}{1 + \dfrac{j\omega T_f}{1 + K_a}}\right]$$

$$G_1 = \frac{K_a}{1 + j\omega T_f}$$

$$K_a = 9.0$$

$$T_f = 0.25$$

**Feedback through Frequency-Sensitive Elements.**   The marked loss in gain at low frequencies caused by the use of direct feedback as illustrated in the previous section may be avoided without severely limiting some of the desirable features of feedback.   This may be accomplished by feeding back a suitable function of the output rather than the output itself.   In general, the function of the output being fed back is dependent in magnitude and phase upon the frequency of the output; for this reason the output is said to be fed back through a "frequency-sensitive" element.   Typical of such frequency-sensitive elements are tachometers or other rate or acceleration-sensitive devices that may be fed back directly or through suitable stabilizing means.   By these means the net input to the controlled system tends to be a function of the rate and acceleration of the output or the controlled variable as well as of the actuating error.

In Section 8.2 the general relationships existing in a control element with feedback were developed. These are listed below for control system elements as shown in Figure 10.2–4.

$$O = G_1 M_1 \tag{10.2-7}$$

$$B = HO \tag{10.2-8}$$

$$I - B = M_1 \tag{10.2-9}$$

If these three equations are combined, the over-all expression relating output to input is

$$\frac{O}{I} = \frac{G_1}{1 + G_1 H} \tag{10.2-10}$$

It will be noted that Equation 10.2–10 differs from Equation 10.2–1 for the case of direct feedback by the presence of the feedback transfer

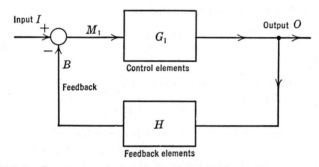

FIGURE 10.2–4. Control element with feedback through frequency-sensitive element.

function $H$ in the denominator multiplying the transfer function of the original control element. However, Equation 10.2–10 reduces to the case of $O/I$ for direct feedback (Equation 10.2–1) when $H = 1$.

The nature of the resultant $O/I$ transfer function that results for various values of $H$ can be determined from study of Equation 10.2–10. For example, if $H$ is exceedingly small so that $G_1 H \ll 1$, the denominator of Equation 10.2–10 approaches unity. Thus

$$\frac{O}{I} \cong G_1 \tag{10.2-11}$$

For this condition, the control element with feedback retains essentially the transfer conditions of the original control element without feedback. According to Figure 10.2–4, this means that the frequency-sensitive feedback network prevents the output from being fed back and influencing the net signal $M_1$. This condition is frequently obtained at very low frequencies where $H$ is made small, $G_1$ is high, and the $O/I$ characteristic has a high gain.

Again at very high frequencies, where $G_1$ approaches zero as $\omega$ approaches $\infty$, the product $G_1H$, however, approaches zero despite the fact that $H$ may not be small. That is, the output signal in Figure 10.2–4 is so small there is no appreciable signal appearing at $B$ to alter the input signal $I$. Hence, for this condition, the ratio of $O/I$ is again given by Equation 10.2–11.

For an intermediate region of frequencies it is desirable that the loop gain function $G_1H$ be much greater than 1. For this condition Equation 10.2–10 may be written as

$$\frac{O}{I} = \frac{1}{H}\left[\frac{G_1H}{1 + G_1H}\right]$$    (10.2–12)

from which $O/I$ may be approximated as

$$\frac{O}{I} = \frac{1}{H}$$    (10.2–13)

Thus for the region of frequencies in which

$$G_1H \gg 1$$    (10.2–14)

the resultant transfer function for $O/I$ is dependent almost entirely on the characteristics of the feedback network, Equation 10.2–13, and is independent of the characteristics of the control element itself. This means that undesirable resonance magnitudes or large phase shifts of control elements may be minimized in certain frequency ranges or perhaps eliminated completely by proper choice of the feedback element.

It should be noted that the combined control element and feedback network described above need not comprise a complete servomechanism or regulator by itself. The modified control element can, however, be made to possess a markedly improved transfer characteristic so that, when used as part of a feedback control, the resultant system has its performance greatly improved.

Summarizing, then, to obtain the desirable type of performance described above, the feedback network must be such that

$$G_1H \ll 1 \text{ at low frequencies}$$    (10.2–15)

so that

$$\frac{O}{I} \cong G_1$$

and

$$G_1 H \gg 1 \text{ at intermediate frequencies}$$

so that

$$\frac{O}{I} \cong \frac{1}{H} \qquad (10.2\text{-}16)$$

Consider now the significance of Equations 10.2–15 and 10.2–16 from the point of view of the complex plane diagram.   Figure 10.2–5 shows by the solid line the transfer function of a motor-type element for which

$$G_1 = \frac{K}{j\omega(1 + j\omega T_m)(1 + j\omega T_f)} \qquad (10.2\text{-}17)$$

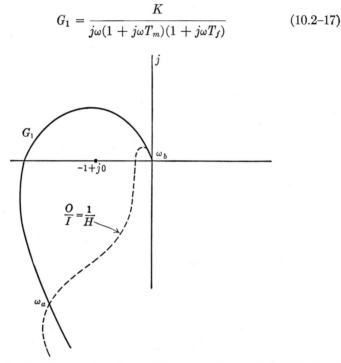

FIGURE 10.2–5.   Transfer function of unmodified motor element $G_1$ (solid line) and acceptable form for transfer function $O/I$ (dotted line).

It is apparent from this figure that it would be desirable to reduce the phase angle of this transfer function in the region where the $-1 + j0$ point is encircled.   The dotted curve on Figure 10.2–5 shows an acceptable form for the resultant $O/I$ function.   If feedback methods are employed to obtain the desired resultant characteristic, it is evident from Equation 10.2–16 that $1/H$ should have a form that can be roughly approximated by $1/j\omega$ over a frequency range $\omega_a < \omega < \omega_b$.   This is true since the magnitude of the $G_1$ function decreases from being much greater than 1 at $\omega_a$ to a value less than 1 at $\omega_b$.  Interpreted in this light, then, a part of the criterion for the selection of $H$ is that

$$H = K_H j\omega$$

for the frequency range where $G_1 > 1$ to where $G_1 < 1$.

The complex plane plots of $H = 10j\omega$ and $1/H = 1/10j\omega$ shown on Figure 10.2–6 illustrate an ideal feedback transfer function of the type

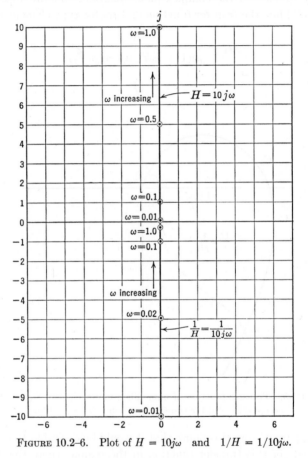

FIGURE 10.2–6.  Plot of $H = 10j\omega$  and  $1/H = 1/10j\omega$.

described above.  At low frequencies $H$ is small so that $G_1H$ tends to be small compared to 1.  At higher frequencies $H$ is large so that $G_1H$ tends to be larger than 1; furthermore $1/H$ has the $1/j\omega$ characteristic desired for $O/I$ at these higher frequencies.  Since the value of $G_1H/(1 + G_1H)$ in Equation 10.2–12 is seldom identically 1, there is some contribution of this quantity toward modifying $1/H$ of the feedback element alone.

Hence the dotted $1/H$ function of Figure 10.2–5 is actually more representative than the idealized $1/H$ function shown in Figure 10.2–6.

As shown in Figure 10.2–5, for frequencies less than $\omega_a$, the $G_1$ function should have sufficiently high gain to be relatively unaffected by its large phase shift characteristics. Hence at these low frequencies the feedback element is not required to decrease the phase shift of $O/I$ from the value of the original element $G_1$, and the feedback function $H = j\omega$ is not required to be effective. For very high values of frequency $\omega > \omega_b$, the gain of $G_1$ is so low that the phase shift is no longer of importance; hence the feedback requirements again are not so critical and the unmodified value of $O/I = G_1$ may be adequate.

**Basis for Determining Characteristics for Feedback Elements.** It has been shown in Equation 10.2–15 that, to avoid sacrificing gain at low

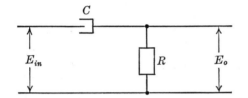

FIGURE 10.2–7.   Single $RC$ network useful as feedback element.

$$RC = T$$

$$\frac{E_o}{E_{in}} = \frac{j\omega T}{1 + j\omega T}$$

frequencies, it is desirable that the loop gain around forward and feedback elements should be low at low frequencies, $G_1H \ll 1$ as $\omega \to 0$. It was also shown that this desirable condition could be approached by feeding back a quantity proportional to the rate of change, that is, the derivative, of the output quantity since at low frequencies the derivative of the output is small and approaches zero as $\omega$ approaches zero. For a control element having a mechanical output, this rate of change of output may be obtained by such means as a tachometer voltage, a spring-dashpot arrangement, or an electrical voltage proportional to the output velocity. For a system having an electrical output, stabilizing transformers whose secondary voltage is proportional to the rate of change of the output current or voltage may be used to advantage.

Although the use of quantities proportional to output rate may be desirable as a basic feedback signal, it is frequently advantageous to utilize further means to provide a more marked change in the amplitude of $G_1H$ as a function of frequency. This can be done by inserting in series with the feedback signal a "high pass" network somewhat similar

to the phase lead network described in Section 10.1.   It will be recalled
that the characteristics of these networks were a reduced output at low
frequencies and full output at higher frequencies, hence the term high
pass.   An electrical network of this general type, shown in Figure 10.2–7,
is commonly known as the single $RC$ feedback network.

The transfer function for this network is

$$\frac{E_o}{E_{in}} = \frac{Ts}{1 + Ts} = \frac{j\omega T}{1 + j\omega T} \qquad (10.2\text{–}18)$$

a plot of which is shown in Figure 10.2–8.   From this figure it can be

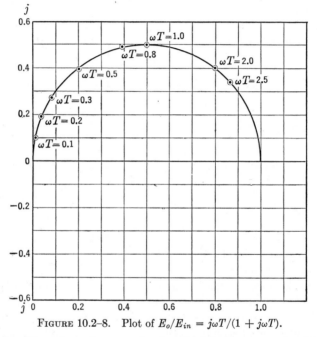

FIGURE 10.2–8.   Plot of $E_o/E_{in} = j\omega T/(1 + j\omega T)$.

seen that, although an increase in signal with frequency is obtained at
low frequencies, after $\omega T$ is greater than 2 there is comparatively little
change in amplitude.

Another type of high-pass network is shown in Figure 10.2–9, and is
frequently referred to as the double $RC$ feedback network.   The transfer
function for this network is

$$\frac{E_o}{E_{in}} = \frac{T_1 T_2 s^2}{T_1 T_2 s^2 + (T_1 + T_2 + T_{21})s + 1}$$

$$= \frac{-\omega^2 T_1 T_2}{(1 - \omega^2 T_1 T_2) + j\omega(T_1 + T_2 + T_{21})} \qquad (10.2\text{–}19)$$

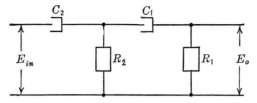

FIGURE 10.2–9.   Double $RC$ network useful as feedback element.

$$\frac{E_o}{E_{in}} = \frac{T_1 T_2 s^2}{T_1 T_2 s^2 + (T_1 + T_2 + T_{21})s + 1}$$

$$R_1 C_1 = T_1$$

$$R_2 C_2 = T_2$$

$$R_2 C_1 = T_{21}$$

and is plotted in the complex plane in Figure 10.2–10.   It will be noted that at low frequencies $E_o/E_{in}$ increases as $\omega^2$.   However, for values of

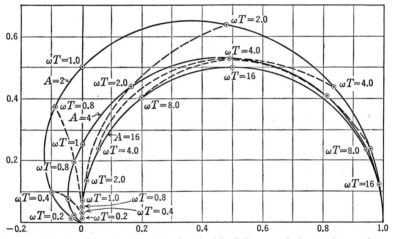

FIGURE 10.2–10.   Transfer function for double $RC$ network for various values of network parameters ($A$).   $A = (T_1 + T_2 + T_{21})/\sqrt{T_1 T_2}$.

$$\frac{E_o}{E_{in}} = \frac{-\omega^2 T^2}{(1 - \omega^2 T^2) + jA\omega T}$$

frequency where $\left| \omega^2 T_1 T_2 - 1 \right| > \left| \omega(T_1 + T_2 + T_{21}) \right|$, $E_o/E_{in}$ approaches unity in magnitude and is comparatively unaffected by a further increase in $\omega$.

This double $RC$ network has a more effective reduction of signal at low frequencies than the single $RC$ network; hence it is used to provide a more rapid change in amplitude with frequency from the condition where $G_1 H \ll 1$ to where $G_1 H \gg 1$.   Occasionally even additional $RC$ stages are employed to provide a more rapid increase in the transmission of the feedback signal as the frequency changes.

As used in many feedback applications, the single or double $RC$ feedback networks are placed in series with an' output tachometer or rate signal so as to insure a low feedback gain at low frequencies. The $RC$ network parameters are chosen so that at the frequency range where high feedback is desired, $\omega_a < \omega < \omega_b$ in Figure 10.2–5, there is essentially full transmission through these feedback networks. This means that the feedback function has become the rate feedback that, as has been previously indicated, produces an almost ideal characteristic in this frequency range. The effect of changing the feedback gain is to control the range of the frequencies for which $G_1H$ is greater than 1. For increased values of feedback gain $H$, $O/I$ is equal to $1/H$ for a greater range of frequencies but, since $H$ is larger, the magnitude of $O/I$ is reduced. Conversely, decreasing $H$ means that $O/I$ is equal to $1/H$ for a more limited range of frequencies and is equal to $G_1$ over a greater portion of the frequency range.

*Example*

As an illustration of the use of a single $RC$ feedback network with tachometer feedback, consider the d-c Ward-Leonard type control pictured by the solid blocks of Figure 10.2–11 and the tachometer and $RC$ feedback elements shown by the dotted blocks.

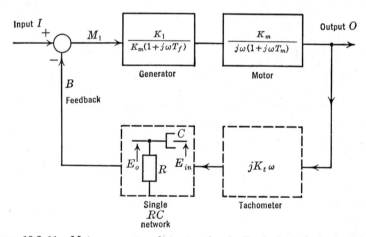

FIGURE 10.2–11.  Motor-generator element, using feedback through single $RC$ network.

Use of the feedback principle is described here merely as a means of modifying the characteristics of a group of control elements. However, it will be apparent that the improved motor generator transfer function characteristic obtained is one that readily adapts itself to use with direct feedback from $O$ to $I$ to produce an improved closed-loop feedback control system.   Thus the resultant transfer function from $I$ to $O$ will be found suitable for the $G$ function from actuating error to controlled variable, $C/E$, for a feedback control system with direct feedback.   Figure 10.2–12 illustrates the inclusion of the $O$ to $I$ transfer function in such a control system.

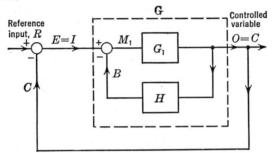

FIGURE 10.2–12.   Motor generator element, using feedback through single $RC$ network as part of a more complete feedback control system.

Reference to Figure 10.2–11 for the motor-tachometer loop shows that the transfer functions for the various portions of the loop are:

Forward circuit:

$$\frac{O}{M_1} = G_1 = \frac{K_1}{j\omega(1 + j\omega T_m)(1 + j\omega T_f)} \tag{10.2–20}$$

where $K_1$ = radians per second of $O$ per volt of $M_1$.

Feedback circuit:

$$\frac{B}{O} = H = \frac{(j\omega)^2 K_h}{1 + j\omega T} \tag{10.2–21}$$

where $K_t$ = volts per radian per second of $O$,
  $T$ = $RC$ in seconds, and
  $K_h$ = $K_t T$ volts per radian.

The combined loop function $G_1H$, as obtained from Equations 10.2–20 and 10.2–21, is

$$G_1H = \frac{B}{M_1} = \frac{j\omega K_1 K_h}{(1 + j\omega T_m)(1 + j\omega T_f)(1 + j\omega T)} \tag{10.2–22}$$

It will be noticed in Equation 10.2–22 that the desired condition that $G_1H \to 0$ as $\omega \to 0$ is realized by virtue of the presence of the $RC$ network that contributes the $j\omega T/(1 + j\omega T)$ term.  Using only tachometer feedback is not enough, for the presence of the motor with its $1/j\omega$ characteristic in the main control element cancels the $j\omega$ term produced by the tachometer.  Without the $RC$ network, the value of $B/M_1$ would not approach zero as $\omega \to 0$.

The choice of the feedback network parameters and the feedback tachometer gain can be determined in the following fashion.  At some frequency, $\omega_a$, it is no longer essential that the low-frequency gain $O/I = G_1$ be maintained.  Hence at $\omega_a$, $G_1H$ from Equation 10.2–22 can be set equal to 1.  Since $\omega_a$ should be at a frequency where $\omega_a T_m$, $\omega_a T_f$, $\omega_a T$ are all less than 1, the magnitude of $G_1H$ reduces to

$$\omega_a K_1 K_h = 1 \tag{10.2–23}$$

from which

$$K_h = \frac{1}{\omega_a K_1} \tag{10.2–24}$$

The $O/I$ function for frequencies higher than $\omega_a$ now becomes approximately equal to

$$\frac{O}{I} = \frac{1}{H} = \frac{1 + j\omega T}{(j\omega)^2 K_h} \tag{10.2–25}$$

Since it is desired for stability reasons that $1/H = 1/\omega$ when the magnitude of $1/H$ is approximately 1, $\omega T$ must be greater than 1 for this condition.  Therefore, let $\omega T = 4$ and approximate the magnitude of $1 + j\omega T$ by $\omega T$.  Hence Equation 10.2–25 becomes in magnitude

$$1 = \frac{4}{\omega^2 K_h} \tag{10.2–26}$$

or

$$\omega = \sqrt{\frac{4}{K_h}} = \sqrt{4\omega_a K_1} \tag{10.2–27}$$

when $\dfrac{1}{H} = 1$.

Since $\omega T$ has been chosen as 4 and $\omega$ is equal to $\sqrt{4\omega_a K_1}$, $T$ is given by the expression

$$T = \frac{4}{\omega} = \sqrt{\frac{4}{\omega_a K_1}} = \sqrt{4K_h} \tag{10.2–28}$$

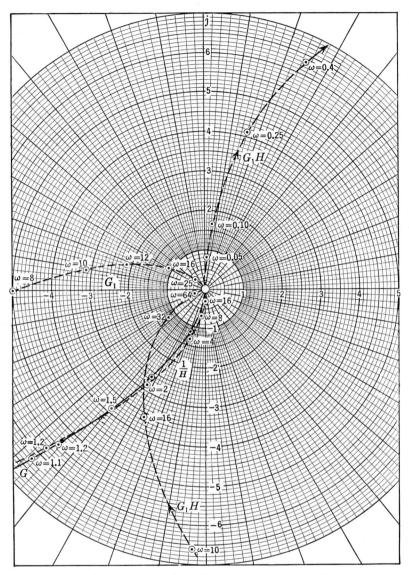

FIGURE 10.2–13. Actual complex plane plots of transfer functions for motor generator element, using feedback through single $RC$ network of Figure 10.2–11.

$$G_1 = \frac{100}{j\omega(1 + j0.25\omega)(1 + j0.0625\omega)}$$

$$H = \frac{0.167(j\omega)^2}{(1 + j0.8\omega)}$$

$$G = \frac{1}{H}\left[\frac{G_1H}{1 + G_1H}\right]$$

309

Using the following values of $K_1$ and $\omega_a$,

$$K_1 = 100$$

$$\omega_a = 0.06$$

The feedback gain and time constant become

$$K_h = \tfrac{1}{6} = 0.167$$

and

$$T = \sqrt{4K_h} = \sqrt{0.667} \cong 0.8 \text{ second}$$

Shown in Figure 10.2–13 are the complex plane plots in the vicinity of the $-1 + j0$ point for $G_1$, $G_1H$, $1/H$ and the resultant transfer function $O/I = G$. The system constants that have been used are those indicated above. For the range of frequencies shown, the complex plane plot of $O/I$ can be seen to follow closely the $1/H$ curve, deviating from this curve only as the frequency is increased and $O/I$ becomes more nearly equal to $G_1$. Although not shown on this figure, the condition of high gain has been met at frequencies below 0.06 radian per second as evidenced by the velocity coefficient of 100 for $O/I$. As can be seen from Figure 10.2–13 in the range of frequencies near the $-1 + j0$ point, an adequate measure of stability has been met by the use of tachometer and network feedback shown.

The method described above for determining the parameters for the feedback tachometer and network is similar to that described in Chapters 12 and 13, where the attenuation-frequency concepts are employed. Although the inverse transfer function plot might be employed to advantage in determining the required characteristics for the feedback circuit, it is considered more worth while to present the above method of determining the feedback parameters. This method is along the lines of the complex plane counterpart of the method later used for describing the attenuation-frequency method of synthesis. Since other examples of selection of feedback circuit parameters will be illustrated in later chapters, no further examples of typical systems will be given at this time.

**Regenerative Feedback.** The preceding material in this section has emphasized a "degenerative" type of feedback as may be seen by reference to Figures 10.2–1 and 10.2–4. With degenerative feedback, the feedback signal is opposite in sign to the input signal so that the net signal $M_1$ tends to subtract from the input. The response of a control element using degenerative feedback was found to have reduced gain over a portion of the frequency range and to have a faster time of response.

Contrasted with degenerative feedback is "regenerative feedback," [86] in which the output is fed back with a positive sign as is shown in Figure 10.2–14. For this case the ratio of output to input is

$$\frac{O}{I} = \frac{G_1}{1 - G_1 H} \tag{10.2-29}$$

Because of the negative $(-)$ sign in the denominator of Equation 10.2–29 the possibility exists of the denominator becoming zero and the value of $O/I$ becoming infinite. The condition of an infinite output for a finite

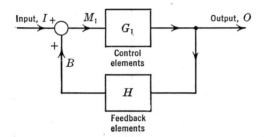

FIGURE 10.2–14.   Control elements with regenerative feedback.

input indicates physically a possible condition of instability if sufficiently high gain is achieved around the $G_1 H$ loop and if other stabilizing means are not employed.

To illustrate some of the different kinds of resultant transfer functions that might result for various control and feedback elements, consider the following two examples.

*Example 1. Direct Feedback around a Single Time Constant*

$$G_1 = \frac{K}{1 + j\omega T}$$

$$H = H, \text{ a numeric}$$

Placing these values in Equation 10.2–29 gives

$$\frac{O}{I} = \frac{K}{1 - KH + j\omega T} = \frac{\dfrac{K}{1 - KH}}{1 + \dfrac{j\omega T}{1 - KH}} \tag{10.2-30}$$

The gain of the transfer function is increased by a factor $1/(1 - KH)$ while the time constant is likewise increased by the same amount.   If

$1 - KH$ were made exactly equal to zero, Equation 10.2–30 could be written as

$$\frac{O}{I} = \frac{K}{j\omega T} \qquad (10.2\text{–}31)$$

which indicates a perfect integrating element. However, small changes in the value of $K$ or $H$ may result in the characteristic of $O/I$ changing markedly, even to the extent of having the sign of $O/I$ at $\omega = 0$ be changed from $+$ to $-$. Figure 10.2–15 shows a number of forms that the $O/I$ function can have for various values of $KH$ greater and less

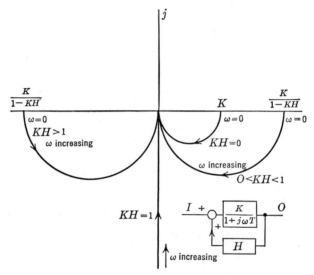

FIGURE 10.2–15.  $K/(1 - KH + j\omega T)$ for various values of $KH$ greater and less than 1.

than 1. Although apparently this characteristic is one that might be objectionable from system stability considerations, actually it can be used effectively in practical systems.

*Example 2.  Single RC Feedback around a Linear Amplifier*

$$G_1 = K$$

$$H = \frac{H_1 j\omega T}{1 + j\omega T}$$

Placing these values into Equation 10.2–29 gives

$$\frac{O}{I} = \frac{K(1 + j\omega T)}{1 + (1 - KH_1)j\omega T} \qquad (10.2\text{–}32)$$

The derivative or lead effect present in the feedback element has been introduced directly into the resultant transfer function to obtain a proportional plus lead effect. By so selecting the value of the gain $KH_1$ that $(1 - KH_1)$ is equal to zero, the denominator can be made equal to 1. However, a further increase in the combined gain $KH_1$ will result in the denominator having a "negative" time constant corresponding to a potential condition of unstable operation. In order to obtain an ap-

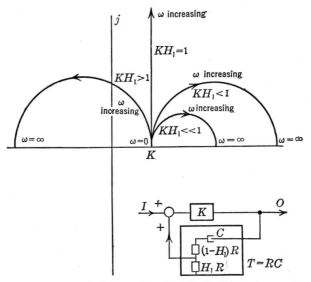

FIGURE 10.2–16. $K(1 + j\omega T)/[1 + (1 - KH_1)j\omega T]$ for various values of $KH_1$ greater and less than 1.

preciable lead action from this amplifier network combination, $(1 - KH_1)$ must be made small, that is, of the order of 0.1. Changes in the amplifier gain $K$ of the order of 10 to 20 per cent will change adequate derivative action either into slight derivative action with a decrease in gain or into unstable operation with an increase in gain. Figure 10.2–16 shows the various complex plane plots that $O/I$ may have dependent upon whether $KH$ is greater or less than 1. Practically, system operation with $KH$ approximately equal or greater than 1 is objectionable in that high-frequency oscillations may result.

## 10.3 Comparison of Relative Merits of Series and Feedback Methods of System Stabilization

Both series and feedback methods of stabilization are employed extensively and to good advantage in servomechanisms. Frequently both methods appear in a well-designed system as will be illustrated in later chapters where other representative designs are described. At this time, however, it is worth while to indicate some of the advantages and disadvantages of the two types of stabilization.

**Series Stabilization.** Regarding series stabilization, in many cases light inexpensive resistance capacitance networks may be incorporated with amplifier stages to provide the necessary stability for the system. By proper design the apparent time constants of the system may be changed to produce a higher performance system than without stabilization.

Contrasted with the advantages cited above, effective series stabilization may be limited by changes in the gain or time constants of the other series control elements. As indicated in Section 8.2, the full effect of changes in the transfer function of any element in the series of control elements will show up directly as a change in the over-all transfer function. Hence closer manufacturing tolerances and more expensive materials may be required to insure uniform and constant characteristics for the major power components. Otherwise instability for increases in gain or high errors for a decrease in gain may result.

Occasionally when phase lag $RC$ networks are employed to obtain series stabilization, larger, heavier capacitors are required than would be needed if feedback stabilizing means were used. Generally, when series phase lead networks are employed, increased open-loop system gain is maintained up to higher frequencies than would be the case if the system used feedback stabilization. Because the loop gain is maintained to higher frequencies, additional amplifier gain may be required at these higher frequencies. With such amplifiers, extraneous, erratic, high-frequency noise signals in the input tend to be accentuated by phase lead networks so that later amplifier stages may be overloaded by these undesired signals.

**Feedback Stabilization.** As shown in Section 8.2 changes in the transfer function of control elements having feedback around them is reduced by a factor of $1/(1 + GH)$ so that much broader tolerances may be placed on the individual control components when a large amount of feedback is employed. As was shown in Equation 10.2–15, no loss of gain at low frequencies need result when feedback is used through suitable frequency-sensitive elements. Equation 10.2–16 illustrated the fact that over an important range of frequencies the performance characteristics of a group of control system elements can be made dependent primarily on the transfer function of the feedback element rather than that of the control element. Since the feedback element may be selected for its accuracy and stability rather than for its power, torque, and other characteristics, more satisfactory system performance can be obtained.

By use of feedback the magnitude of the effective time constants of control elements may be changed and certain resonances may be eliminated from the resultant transfer function.

Unfortunately the means for obtaining feedback signals frequently involve costly or bulky equipment such as tachometers or stabilizing transformers that must be located at or near the output while the signal may be required at the amplifier some distance away. Occasionally rather expensive means are required to obtain a feedback signal at the proper voltage and/or impedance level to minimize loading or coupling effects on the input signal. For small servomotor applications, the size of a tachometer to obtain the output velocity signal may be comparable to the drive motor itself.

In general a high gain is required of systems employing feedback to allow for the loss of gain for those frequencies where feedback is effective. However, since high gain is required for any high-performance system, this is not entirely a function of the use of feedback.

Further advantages and disadvantages of the use of series and feedback stabilization methods will be apparent from the examples described in the chapters that follow.

# 11

## ATTENUATION CONCEPTS FOR USE
## IN FEEDBACK CONTROL SYSTEM DESIGN

### 11.0  Introduction

The preceding chapters have illustrated a method of studying servo-mechanism and regulator behavior from the point of view of the Nyquist stability criterion and the associated complex plane diagrams. This method yields very satisfactory results when properly applied. There are, however, definite limitations to the ease and speed with which the necessary calculations can be performed.

From the standpoint of *analysis* of systems, the complex plane method is quite straightforward; from the standpoint of *synthesis*, however, this method is likely to involve much "cut and try" because the quantitative effect of changes in the parameters is not so readily apparent. Also, the use of the linear scale of amplitudes for representing the control element transfer functions on the complex plane tends to limit the range of frequencies covered to those in the vicinity of the $-1 + j0$ point.

In addition, the necessity of measuring the phase angle as well as the magnitude of the controlled variable to error signal ratio imposes definite practical limitations to the comparison of test and calculated results using the complex plane representation. Although amplitudes of low-frequency oscillations of the order of 0 to 20 cycles per second can be accurately measured, the accurate measurement of phase angles in the region of frequencies from 2 to 20 cycles per second is not so easily performed. Even though equipment and techniques [63, 67] have been developed recently that yield satisfactory results, no simple single piece of equipment seems to fit the needs for accurately determining phase shift over the desired range of low frequencies.

It is evident, therefore, that a method of analysis and synthesis is desired that gives the correct results inherent in the complex plane approach but presents a more direct method for obtaining these results. The outstanding work of H. W. Bode [14, 43] in relating the phase and amplitude characteristics of networks operating with sinusoidal excitation has provided a method of analysis that can be employed in servomechanism and regulator design to circumvent some of the difficulties involved in using the complex plane diagram for determining system performance. The theoretical background of the Bode and the complex plane methods is quite similar; the two methods differ mainly in the manner of presentation of information and in some of the limitations that apply to their use.

In this chapter are presented some of the concepts whereby the Nyquist stability criterion is interpreted in the light of the Bode theorems. Next two of the more important of Bode's theorems relating attenuation and phase shift are discussed. Primary emphasis is placed on the nature of their usefulness in practical servomechanism design. One of the virtues of the attenuation concept is the simplicity with which approximate results of satisfactory accuracy may be obtained. The mechanics of determining the attenuation and phase characteristics for the transfer functions of various kinds of control elements is presented both for the approximate and the exact methods of representation. Finally a development is given for the equations of the contours of $M$ and $\alpha$ for the $C/R$ ratio in terms of the amplitude and phase angle of the open-loop transfer function $C/E$ when expressed in terms of decibels and phase margin. These contours, first drawn up by N. B. Nichols,[62] are most useful in design work and are used extensively.

## 11.1 Correlation of the Nyquist Stability Criterion with Bode's Attenuation Theorems

It is the purpose of this section to illustrate the more common form of the Nyquist stability criterion and to indicate how Bode's network theorems provide the basic information necessary to simplify greatly the work of a designer in obtaining a stable system. To this end only systems for which the abbreviated form of the Nyquist stability criterion apply are considered, that is, the systems are ones that are stable when the control system loop is open. It is also assumed that a direct comparison is made of the controlled variable with the reference input. For this case the following equations are used to describe the system:

$$\frac{C}{E} = G = |G| \underline{/\phi} \tag{11.1-1}$$

and

$$R - C = E \tag{11.1-2}$$

where the symbols have the same significance as they did in Section 9.1, Equations 9.1–1 and 9.1–2. Figure 9.1–4 illustrating these various vectors for some frequency $\omega$ is redrawn in Figure 11.1–1. In addition, to the other angles previously considered, Figure 11.1–1 also shows the angle, $\gamma$.  This angle, called the *phase margin*, is found convenient to use in the attenuation frequency concept.

Recalling that the *phase angle $\phi$ is positive when measured counterclockwise from zero*, and considering the *phase margin $\gamma$ as positive when measured counterclockwise from 180°*, one sees that the relationship between phase angle and phase margin is

$$\gamma = 180 + \phi \qquad (11.1\text{–}3)$$

The significance of the term phase margin becomes apparent when one considers the various transfer functions shown on Figures 11.1–2 and

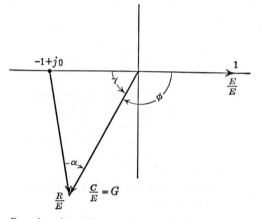

FIGURE 11.1–1.  Complex plane diagram of quantities in elementary control system.

11.1–3.  The same frequency-varying function is illustrated for each of the three transfer functions on each figure; however, different values of gain are used for each case with the gain increasing from $K_a$ to $K_c$. Also shown on the two figures are the unit circle, that is, circle of radius = 1, and the values of the phase angle $\phi$ for each transfer function at the unit circle.  When the abbreviated form of the Nyquist criterion is applied to these transfer functions, it is evident that the $K_a G_1$ and the $K_a G_2$ functions represent stable systems.  At the unit circle the phase angle $\phi_a$ for these cases is less negative than $-180°$ so that the phase margin $\gamma$ for these stable systems is positive.

The systems represented by $K_b G_1$ and $K_b G_2$ are on the borderline of stability and $\phi_b = 180°$; hence the phase margin $\gamma = 0$.  The systems represented by $K_c G_1$ and $K_c G_2$ are unstable systems, $\phi_c$ is more negative than $-180°$, and the phase margin $\gamma$ is negative.  From these illustrative examples the following generalization may be made for systems for which the abbreviated form of the Nyquist criterion applies.

*Systems having positive phase margin when their transfer function crosses the unit circle are stable, whereas systems with negative phase margin when their transfer function crosses the unit circle are unstable.*

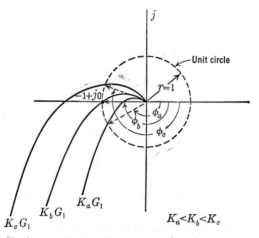

FIGURE 11.1–2. Similar transfer functions on complex plane, showing significance of phase margin at unit circle.

Although this stability criterion appears to be somewhat limited by the numerous restrictions placed upon it, it is valid for the majority of control problems and serves to point out a useful short cut to determining

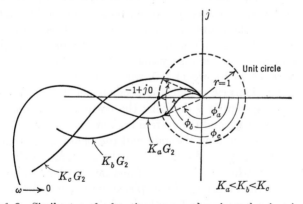

FIGURE 11.1–3. Similar transfer functions on complex plane, showing significance of phase margin at unit circle.

the stability of a feedback control system. The short cut is established from the fact that the stability of a system can be determined from its phase margin at unit gain. Bode's theorems show that the *phase angle* of a system *is related* to the *attenuation or gain characteristics* of the system *as a function of frequency.*  Hence the phase margin, which is related to the phase angle by Equation 11.1–3, as well as the amplitude of the transfer function is established by the attenuation characteristic of $C/E$ alone.

In particular the first of the Bode theorems described in Section 11.2, which follows, shows that the phase angle at any desired frequency is dependent on the rate of change of gain with frequency, where the rate of change of gain at the desired frequency has the major influence on the value of the phase angle at that frequency.  Thus it is possible to establish another approximate means for determining the stability of a system, namely, *if the rate of change of gain of a system with frequency exceeds a certain value in that range of frequencies where the gain is one;* that is, where the transfer function crosses the unit circle, *the system is unstable.*  Conversely, if the rate of change of gain with frequency is less than this value in the range of frequencies where the gain is unity, the system is stable.

It should be emphasized that these statements in no way contradict the Nyquist criterion, but rather they endeavor to replace the more complete Nyquist criterion with an approximate criterion suitable for most design purposes.

To illustrate the principles set forth above, Figures 11.1–4 and 11.1–5 are drawn showing the attenuation and phase margin for transfer functions of a stable and unstable system, respectively.  In Figure 11.1–4, which represents a stable system, the attenuation rate is low (20 decibels per decade) at $\omega_c$, where the gain of the system is 1, that is, 0 decibels. It will be noted that the phase margin curve, which is also plotted, is positive at 0 decibels, the necessary condition for stability for this simple system.  However, in Figure 11.1–5, which illustrates an unstable system, the attenuation rate is high (60 decibels per decade) at $\omega_c$, where the gain of the system is 0 decibels; the corresponding phase margin curve is negative at $\omega_c$, and the system is shown to be unstable.  All the information for determining the gain and the phase margin, and therefore the stability, may be obtained from the attenuation characteristic alone.  However, when the transfer function can be expressed in an analytical form, the attenuation and phase margin may be found more directly from the conventional methods of determining the amplitude and angle of a complex number.

From the analytical point of view, the amount of calculations to determine the stability of a system has not been altered appreciably by the introduction of these new stability criteria.  However, the work of the system designer in synthesizing a stable control has been greatly reduced

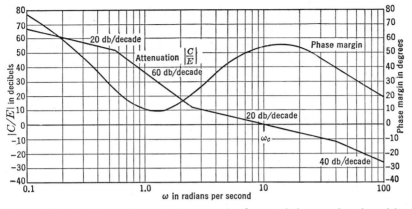

FIGURE 11.1-4. Attenuation and phase margin characteristics as a function of frequency for a stable system.

$$\frac{C}{E} = \frac{200(1 + j0.4\omega)^2}{j\omega(1 + j1.789\omega)^2(1 + j0.025\omega)}$$

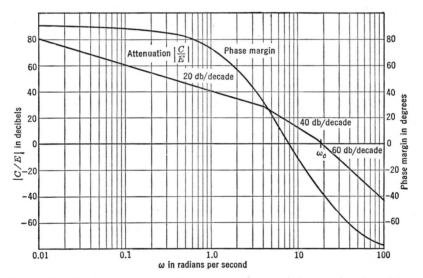

FIGURE 11.1-5. Attenuation and phase margin characteristics as a function of frequency for an unstable system.

$$\frac{C}{E} = \frac{100}{j\omega(1 + j0.25\omega)(1 + j0.0625\omega)}$$

by the change. His job is now well defined. *He may design the open-loop characteristic so as to have any gain that is desired, provided that the gain is much higher or lower than unity. In the range of frequencies near unity gain, he must design the open-loop characteristic so that its rate of change of gain with frequency is less than a prescribed amount.* Hence the requirements of stability tend to manifest themselves primarily over a limited range of frequencies. The designer is thus able to consider the stability aspect of a system only over a limited range of frequencies rather than throughout the whole frequency spectrum from $0 < \omega < \infty$, as was apparently the case for the Nyquist criterion. It should again be emphasized, however, that the Nyquist and the Routh stability methods are more complete and exact and should be applied in any case of doubt.

### 11.2 Two of Bode's Theorems

Since the phase shift and attenuation characteristics of servomechanisms and regulators determine their stability as well as their performance, it is important that a clear picture be obtained of the relationship between these characteristics. The preceding chapters have served to point out that control system performance requirements demand that a high loop gain be obtained for low-frequency signals to be transmitted accurately. It has also been shown in the preceding section and elsewhere that for the higher frequency signals, where the transfer function is in the vicinity of the $-1 + j0$ point, the phase angle must be such that a positive phase margin is obtained for stable operation. Using only the complex plane approach to control system design, one is soon convinced that the two conditions of high accuracy and adequate stability are closely intermingled, but the exact relationship is not clear or in usable form.

Bode's theorems show these relationships definitely and in a quantitative fashion. They indicate that, if the attenuation characteristic of a system is chosen arbitrarily, the phase shift characteristic of the system is defined; conversely, if the phase shift characteristic of the system is selected arbitrarily, the corresponding attenuation characteristic is fixed. It is possible, however, to select somewhat independently the attenuation characteristic in one portion of the frequency spectrum and the phase shift characteristic in another portion. This means that a compromise between high gain and adequate stability can be made although not without a sacrifice in the control of the phase shift and attenuation characteristics for those frequencies where these characteristics are not specifically selected. Although the gain at low frequencies and the stability of a system are not entirely independent, they may be made fairly so.

Two of the more important of Bode's network theorems can be stated as follows:

1. The phase shift of a network or system at any desired frequency can be determined from the slope of its attenuation-versus-frequency characteristic over the range of frequencies from $-\infty$ to $+\infty$. The slope of the attenuation-frequency characteristic at the desired frequency is weighted most heavily, and the attentuation-frequency slope at frequencies further removed from the desired frequency has a lesser importance.

2. The attenuation characteristic in one portion of the frequency spectrum and the phase characteristic in the remainder of the frequency spectrum may be chosen independently; in doing so, the phase characteristic in the first range of frequencies and the attenuation characteristic in the second range of frequencies are definitely fixed.

Before elaborating on these theorems, it is worth while to note that as originally developed they are limited to a type of electrical network known as the "minimum phase" type.[43] A minimum phase network is one that has the minimum phase shift possible for the number of energy storage elements in the network. Contrasted with the minimum phase network is the "non-minimum phase" network. Such non-minimum phase networks are ones that do not have the minimum phase shift possible for the attenuation characteristic represented by it. Networks of this type often have transfer functions containing negative terms in both the numerator and the denominator, and as such the networks may be unstable. Examples of such networks are provided by the regenerative feedback systems discussed in Section 10.2 and described by Equations 10.2–30 and 10.2–32. Each of these equations represents a non-minimum phase network when the loop gain $KH$ is greater than 1. The equations then become

$$\frac{O}{I} = -\frac{K}{KH-1}\left(\frac{1}{1 - \dfrac{j\omega T}{KH-1}}\right) \qquad (11.2-1)$$

and

$$\frac{O}{I} = \frac{K(1 + j\omega T)}{1 - (KH - 1)j\omega T} \qquad (11.2-2)$$

Other examples of non-minimum phase elements are the missile control systems described in Sections 6.5 and 7.7.

The restriction of the use of Bode's theorems to minimum phase networks has limited significance in the study of servomechanisms, although it is worth while to realize the nature of the limitations that are implied.

The theorems are limited to use with linear systems containing fixed, lumped parameters. As such, the theorems do not apply to conditions on a transmission line or to other systems where field equations describe the performance. However, such distributed parameter systems can sometimes be handled satisfactorily with the aid of their lumped parameter "equivalents." The theorems do not apply to unstable systems that have roots with positive real parts. Although systems with non-linear coefficients cannot be handled directly by these theorems, the method may be applied to a system that is linear for small oscillations. These limitations present a negligible restriction to the use of the *concepts* of these theorems as employed with servomechanisms for which the transfer functions are known.

Formal mathematical statement of these Bode theorems follows.

**Theorem 1** [14]

$$B(\omega_d) = \frac{\pi}{2} \left| \frac{dA}{du} \right|_0 + \frac{1}{\pi} \int_{-\infty}^{+\infty} \left[ \left| \frac{dA}{du} \right| - \left| \frac{dA}{du} \right|_0 \right] \ln \coth \left| \frac{u}{2} \right| du$$

$$(11.2\text{–}3)$$

where $B(\omega_d)$ is the phase shift of the network in radians at the desired frequency $\omega_d$, and

$A$ is the attenuation in nepers where 1 neper $= \ln |e|$.

An additional interpretation of the terms $A$ and $B$ is given by the fact that, when the usual transfer function is written in the exponential form,

$$G = e^{-(A+jB)} \qquad (11.2\text{–}4)$$

then $A$ is the attenuation in nepers,

$B$ is the phase shift in radians,

$u$ is a numeric that is the logarithm of the ratio of the actual frequency $\omega$ to the frequency $\omega_d$ at which the phase shift is sought. Thus

$$u = \ln \frac{\omega}{\omega_d} \qquad (11.2\text{–}5)$$

$\left( \dfrac{dA}{du} \right)$ is the slope of the attenuation logarithm-frequency

curve in nepers per unit change in $u$, that is, a change in frequency of the ratio of 2.718:1. For practical purposes it is convenient to measure the slope in decibels per decade; the rate of change of 1 neper per unit change of $u$ being equal to 20 decibels per decade or approximately 6 decibels per octave. The slope $(dA/du)_0$ is the attenuation-frequency slope at the reference point $\omega_d$, such that $u = 0$.

$\ln \coth \left| \dfrac{u}{2} \right|$ is the weighting function shown in Figure 11.2–1. This function determines the contribution that an attenuation-frequency slope at a frequency $\omega$ has on the phase shift contribution at $\omega_d$.

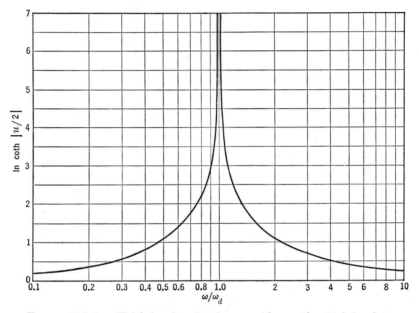

FIGURE 11.2–1.   Weighting function for use with equation 11.2–3, where $u = \ln \omega/\omega_d$.

Although the use of this theorem for numerical calculations is seldom required, since the attenuation and phase may be calculated from the expression for the transfer function, the form of the equation is such as to provide a valuable physical interpretation of the phase shift-attenuation relationship. The first term of Equation 11.2–3 is phase shift contribution of the attenuation-frequency slope at the reference frequency. This yields $\pi/2$ radians or $90°$ phase shift for each neper per unit of $u$, that is, 20 decibels per decade. The second term of Equation 11.2–3 is proportional to the integral of the product of the difference of the attenuation-frequency slope at any frequency, as compared to its value at the reference frequency, and the symmetrical weighting function $\ln \coth | u/2 |$.

Since the product has a zero value at $u = 0$ and at large values of $u$, the value of the integral will be small if the slope $dA/du$ is constant over a broad range of frequencies about $\omega_d$. Under this condition, the phase shift is determined largely by the first term of Equation 11.2–3. From this point of view it appears that, for the phase shift to be less negative than $-180°$ at frequencies in the vicinity of the $-1 + j0$ point, the attenuation slope should be less than 2 nepers per unit of $u$ or less than 40 decibels per decade over a fairly broad range of frequencies. More detailed quantitative criteria pertaining to the necessary attenuation conditions for a desirable servomechanism are discussed later in this chapter.

**Theorem 2.**[43]

$$\int_0^{\omega_0} \frac{A\, d\omega}{\sqrt{\omega_0^2 - \omega^2}(\omega^2 - \omega_d^2)} + \int_{\omega_0}^{\infty} \frac{B\, d\omega}{\sqrt{\omega^2 - \omega_0^2}(\omega^2 - \omega_d^2)}$$

$$= \frac{\pi}{2} \frac{B(\omega_d)}{\omega_d \sqrt{\omega_0^2 - \omega_d^2}} \quad \text{(for } \omega_d < \omega_0\text{)}$$

$$= -\frac{\pi}{2} \frac{A(\omega_d)}{\omega_d \sqrt{\omega_d^2 - \omega_0^2}} \quad \text{(for } \omega_d > \omega_0\text{)} \quad (11.2\text{–}6)$$

where $\omega_0$ is the frequency in radians per second above which the phase characteristic is specified and below which the attenuation characteristic is specified. $\omega_d$ is the frequency at which it is desired to determine the phase shift or attenuation, depending on which is not known.

The interdependence of phase shift and attenuation over the entire frequency spectrum is emphasized by this theorem. Although it is possible to define one of these quantities in one part of the spectrum, the effect of the other quantity in the remainder of the spectrum is also reflected back into the first range of frequencies. Thus the integration with respect to frequency is performed over the entire range of frequencies from zero to infinity.

The process outlined above permits one to determine the over-all performance of a feedback control system. For example, it is used where it is desired to establish the attenuation characteristic for good accuracy at low frequencies and the phase characteristic for that region of frequencies where stability considerations require fairly definite phase characteristics. As such, Equation 11.2–6 could provide a good check of the limiting performance obtainable.

It should be emphasized again that, although servomechanism analysis and synthesis have been benefited greatly by the Bode theorems relating phase shift and attenuation, the limitations applied on the theorems do not restrict the use of the attenuation phase shift concept for feedback control design. *The actual theorems relating phase shift and attenuation are seldom used directly for numerical calculations.* Although complete servomechanism systems will probably be of the minimum phase type, individual network components making up the system need not be thus limited.

## 11.3 Mechanics of Drawing Attenuation Diagrams for Transfer Functions

The use of the attenuation-frequency diagrams for representing control element transfer functions is greatly facilitated by taking advantage of certain simplifying approximations.[62] This makes it possible to represent approximately the exact attenuation plots, which are smooth curves, by straight lines that can be easily constructed. The resultant straight lines generally differ from the actual attenuation characteristic by only a comparatively few decibels. It is the purpose of this section to describe these simplifying approximations for use with transfer functions that have either real or complex roots and to indicate the magnitude of the errors involved in using them. In addition some of the basic factors involved in determining the phase shift characteristic as a function of frequency are described. These various methods are then illustrated for a number of representative transfer functions.

**Single Time Constant.** In the preceding chapters where the expressions for the transfer function of different types of control elements were developed, one common form of equation was for an element having a single time constant, $T$. This equation was shown to be

$$\frac{E_o}{E_{in}} = \frac{1}{1 + j\omega T} = \frac{1}{1 + j\dfrac{\omega}{\omega_0}} \qquad (11.3\text{--}1)$$

where $\omega_0 = 1/T$.

In Figure 11.3–1 the exact value of $E_o/E_{in}$ in Equation 11.3–1 as a function of the frequency ratio $\omega/\omega_0$ is shown by the solid line. The dotted line in the same figure represents an approximate value of $E_o/E_{in}$ of Equation 11.3–1, which is frequently used to describe this same attenuation characteristic. The nature of the approximation indicated may be described in two different ways although the result is the same from each.

From a graphical consideration, *the approximate characteristic is obtained by drawing the asymptotes to the straight-line portions of the actual* *characteristic. The intersection of the two straight lines thus drawn occurs at that frequency for which $\omega T = 1$ or $\omega/\omega_0 = 1$.*

Although this method is useful for determining the time constant of a transfer function for which experimental data alone are known, this definition does not lead to any saving of time when an analytical expression for the transfer function is known. When the equation for the

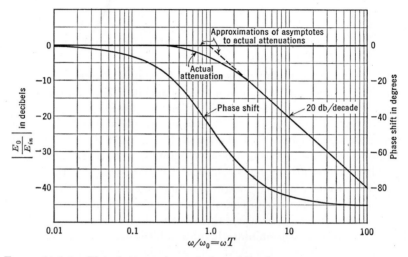

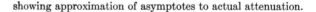

FIGURE 11.3–1. Plot of attenuation and phase shift of

$$\frac{E_o}{E_{in}} = \frac{1}{1 + j\omega T} = \frac{1}{1 + \dfrac{j\omega}{\omega_0}}$$

$$T = 1$$

showing approximation of asymptotes to actual attenuation.

transfer function is known, the approximate characteristic may be readily determined by the following relationships. For frequencies for which $\omega T = \omega/\omega_0 \leq 1$, the magnitude of $E_o/E_{in}$ from Equation 11.3–1 is

$$\left|\frac{E_o}{E_{in}}\right| \cong 1 \tag{11.3–2}$$

whereas for frequencies for which $\omega T = \omega/\omega_0 \geq 1$, the magnitude of $E_o/E_{in}$ from Equation 11.3–1 is

$$\left|\frac{E_o}{E_{in}}\right| \cong \frac{1}{\omega T} = \frac{\omega_0}{\omega} \tag{11.3–3}$$

Table 11.3–1 shows a comparison of the actual $E_o/E_{in}$ with the value given by the approximation. It is apparent that, for values of $\omega T$ far removed from $\omega T = 1$, the approximation is very good.

TABLE 11.3–1

COMPARISON OF $\dfrac{E_o}{E_{in}} = \dfrac{1}{1 + j\omega T}$ TO STRAIGHT-LINE APPROXIMATIONS

| $\omega T = \dfrac{\omega}{\omega_0}$ | Actual Value of $\dfrac{1}{1 + j\omega T}$ | | Approximate Value of $\dfrac{1}{1 + j\omega T}$ | | Error in Decibels |
|---|---|---|---|---|---|
| | Numeric | Decibels | Numeric | Decibels | |
| 0.01 | $1.000 / -0.6°$ | 0 | 1.0 | 0 | 0 |
| 0.04 | $1.000 / -2.3°$ | 0 | 1.0 | 0 | 0 |
| 0.10 | $0.999 / -5.7°$ | $-0.04$ | 1.0 | 0 | $+0.04$ |
| 0.40 | $0.928 / -21.8°$ | $-0.65$ | 1.0 | 0 | $+0.65$ |
| 1.0 | $0.707 / -45°$ | $-3.01$ | 1.0 | 0 | $+3.01$ |
| 4.0 | $0.242 / -76°$ | $-12.32$ | 0.25 | $-12$ | $+0.32$ |
| 10.0 | $0.0995 / -84.3°$ | $-20.04$ | 0.10 | $-20$ | $+0.04$ |
| 40.0 | $0.025 / -88.6°$ | $-32.0$ | 0.025 | $-32$ | 0 |
| 100 | $0.010 / -89.4°$ | $-40.0$ | 0.010 | $-40$ | 0 |

At $\omega T = 1$, the approximation is in greatest error, and this amounts to only 3 decibels. When plotted against frequency to the semi-log scales, the error characteristic of the actual value $|E_o/E_{in}|$ in decibels minus the value of $|E_o/E_{in}|$ from the approximate expression is found to be symmetrical as shown in Figure 11.3–2. When it is necessary to obtain exact values for the attenuation of a single time constant transfer function, the straight line approximations of Equations 11.3–2 and 11.3–3 may be modified by the error functions described in Figure 11.3–2. The validity of this method may be verified by reference to Figure 11.3–1, where the exact and the approximate attenuation characteristics for Equation 11.3–1 are compared.

At frequencies for which $\omega \ll 1/T$, $|E_o/E_{in}| = 1$ from Equation 11.3–2, and there is no change of attenuation with frequency. At frequencies for which $\omega \gg 1/T$, $|E_o/E_{in}| = 1/\omega T$ from Equation 11.3–3, and the attenuation change with frequency is constant as indicated by the uniform slope of the dotted curve on Figure 11.3–1. The attenuation-frequency characteristic slope associated with the amplitude expression, $1/\omega T$, is

$$20 \log_{10} \frac{\omega_2 T}{\omega_1 T}$$

Thus for a 2 to 1 change in $\omega$, that is, one octave, the change in attenuation is 6.02 decibels; for a 10 to 1 change in $\omega$, the attenuation is 20 deci-

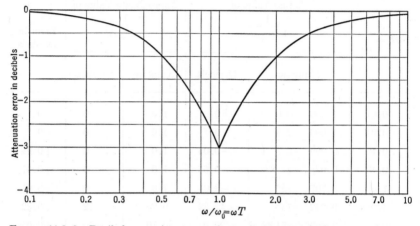

FIGURE 11.3–2.  Decibel correction term to be applied to straight-line approximation to $E_o/E_{in}$ as a function of the frequency ratio $\omega/\omega_0$ in the vicinity of 1.

$$\frac{E_o}{E_{in}} = \frac{1}{1 + j\omega T} = \frac{1}{1 + j\dfrac{\omega}{\omega_0}}$$

Note: For $\dfrac{E_o}{E_{in}} = \dfrac{1 + j\omega T}{1} = 1 + j\dfrac{\omega}{\omega_0}$ the attenuation correction term has same magnitude but opposite sign to that shown on curve.

bels. Therefore the *attenuation rate for the $1/\omega T$ characteristic* is referred to as *6 decibels per octave or 20 decibels per decade*.

The attenuation rate of 6 decibels per octave or 20 decibels per decade, characteristic of a single time constant transfer function for $\omega \gg 1/T$, also applies to other elements for which the amplitude is inversely proportional to frequency. Thus an ideal type 1 control system, for example, also has this same limiting slope.

Figure 11.3–1 shows that an abrupt change in the attenuation frequency slope of 20 decibels per decade takes place at the frequency $\omega = \omega_0 = 1/T$. Hence, by observing where the abrupt 20 decibels per decade change in attenuation slope occurs, one can readily determine the value of the time constant $T$ should its value not be otherwise stated.   Thus

$$T = \frac{1}{\omega_0}$$

where $\omega_0$ is the frequency in radians per second at which the break occurs, and $T$ is the value in seconds of the time constant to be determined.

Also shown in Figure 11.3–1 is a plot of the phase shift associated with the ratio of $E_o/E_{in}$ from Equation 11.3–1.   This phase shift curve as plotted on the semi-log paper is symmetrical about the frequency $\omega_0 = 1/T$; the value of phase shift $\phi$ is $-45°$ at this frequency.   Verification of the symmetry of the phase shift curve about the value $\phi = -45°$ can be illustrated from a consideration of the $1 + j\omega T$ in the denominator of Equation 11.3–1.   Since there is no phase shift associated with the numerator of Equation 11.3–1, one can consider only phase shift of the denominator alone.   It will be shown that the phase shift $\phi_a$, associated with a value of $\omega_a T < 1$, is equal to a phase shift $90 - \phi_a$ at the value of $1/\omega_a T$.

By definition, $\omega_a T$ and $1/\omega_a T$ are symmetrically placed with respect to 1 on the semi-log plot since the product $\omega_a T/\omega_a T = 1$.   The phase shift of the denominator of Equation 11.3–1 is

$$\tan \phi_a = \omega_a T \qquad\qquad (11.3\text{–}4)$$

Taking the reciprocal of Equation 11.3–4, one obtains

$$\frac{1}{\omega_a T} = \frac{1}{\tan \phi_a} = \cot \phi_a = \tan (90 - \phi_a) \qquad (11.3\text{–}5)$$

The amount by which the angle $\phi_a$ is less than $45°$ is equal to the amount by which the angle $90 - \phi_a$ is greater than $45°$; hence the phase shift of $\omega_a T$ and $1/\omega_a T$ is symmetrically placed at about $45°$ as $\omega_a T$ and $1/\omega_a T$ are placed about $\omega T = 1$.   Since the values of phase shift used in the calculations and plots are obtained directly from the actual transfer functions, they are not subject to any approximations.

For a transfer function $E_o/E_{in} = 1 + j\omega T$, the straight-line approximations corresponding to Equations 11.3–2 and 11.3–3 are

$$\frac{E_o}{E_{in}} \cong 1$$

for frequencies for which $\omega T \leq 1$, and

$$\frac{E_o}{E_{in}} \cong \omega T$$

$$(11.3\text{–}6)$$

for frequencies for which $\omega T \geq 1$.

As noted on Figure 11.3–1, the decibel correction term to be applied to the straight-line approximations noted above has the same magnitude but the opposite sign to that shown on this figure. The phase shift plot for $1 + j\omega T$ is merely the negative of that for $1/(1 + j\omega T)$ and has the same symmetrical properties as a function of frequency with respect to the value of $45°$ at $\omega T = 1$.

*Example of Attenuation Diagram for a Product of Single Time Constants*

Although the over-all transfer function of a series of control elements is frequently represented as $G$, it is often possible to express the $G$ function as a fraction with the numerator and denominator each composed of a number of factors of the form $(1 + j\omega T)$. Since the process of taking logarithms involves only the addition of product terms, the effect of a gain factor $K$ amounts to the addition of a constant term. Therefore, consider as an example a transfer function for which

$$G = \frac{(1 + j\omega T_2)}{(1 + j\omega T_1)(1 + j\omega T_3)}$$

The exact magnitude of $G$ in decibels at any frequency $\omega$ is

$$20 \log_{10} \frac{(1 + j\omega T_2)}{(1 + j\omega T_1)(1 + j\omega T_3)} = +20 \log_{10} | 1 + j\omega T_2 |$$
$$-20 \log_{10} | 1 + j\omega T_1 |$$
$$-20 \log_{10} | 1 + j\omega T_3 |$$

where a term $| 1 + j\omega T |$ represents the magnitude $\sqrt{1 + (\omega T)^2}$. Thus the attenuation contribution of each time constant term can be determined by a direct addition or subtraction of its value in decibels, depending on whether the time constant appears in the numerator or the denominator.

If the approximations regarding magnitudes indicated by Equations 11.3–2 and 11.3–3 are employed for this transfer function, then

$$| 1 + j\omega T_1 | = 1 \text{ for } \omega T_1 < 1$$
$$| 1 + j\omega T_2 | = 1 \text{ for } \omega T_2 < 1$$
$$| 1 + j\omega T_3 | = 1 \text{ for } \omega T_3 < 1$$

and

$$| 1 + j\omega T_1 | = \omega T_1 \text{ for } \omega T_1 > 1$$
$$| 1 + j\omega T_2 | = \omega T_2 \text{ for } \omega T_2 > 1$$
$$| 1 + j\omega T_3 | = \omega T_3 \text{ for } \omega T_3 > 1$$

In Figure 11.3–3 a plot of the approximate gain versus frequency characteristic is shown for each of the terms of the $G$ function indicated above when $T_1 > T_2 > T_3$. Also shown is the resultant decibel versus frequency plot of the whole $G$ term. It will be noted that the value of frequency at which each break in the attenuation curve occurs is obtained

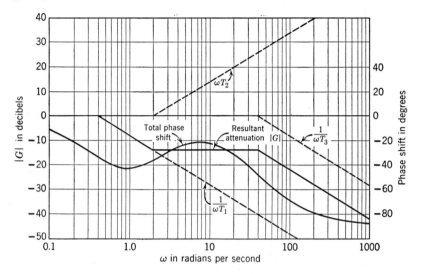

FIGURE 11.3–3. Approximate gain and exact phase shift versus frequency for

$$G = \frac{(1 + j\omega T_2)}{(1 + j\omega T_1)(1 + j\omega T_3)}$$

showing gain for each component as well as resultant gain.

$$T_1 = 2.5 \text{ seconds}$$
$$T_2 = 0.5 \text{ second}$$
$$T_3 = 0.025 \text{ second}$$

from a knowledge of the time constant associated with the break. Thus $\omega = \omega_1 = 1/T_1$ is the first break downward caused by the $(1 + j\omega T_1)$ term in the denominator, and $\omega = \omega_2 = 1/T_2$ is a break upward caused by the $(1 + j\omega T_2)$ term in the numerator. Finally at $\omega = \omega_3 = 1/T_3$ the last downward break occurs as a result of the $(1 + j\omega T_3)$ term in the denominator. Depending on the relative values of $T_1$, $T_2$, and $T_3$, the breaks in the attenuation curve may occur at frequencies such that the resultant curve may appear somewhat different from that shown in Figure 11.3–3. Yet the methods of construction outlined above are valid and can be employed.

*In the text and sketches that follow the approximations to the attenuation curves will generally be used unless it is specifically stated to the contrary.*

The phase shift $\phi$ for the transfer function is given by the phase angle of $G$. Thus, for the transfer function being considered,

$$\phi = + \tan^{-1} \omega T_2 - \tan^{-1} \omega T_1 - \tan^{-1} \omega T_3$$

which is the result obtained by adding the phase angles associated with the time constants in the numerator and subtracting the phase angles associated with the time constants in the denominator. Also shown in Figure 11.3–3 is the resultant phase shift curve for the transfer function considered.

The relationship between the time constant $T$ and the frequency $\omega_0$ at which the breaks occur, that is, $T = 1/\omega_0$, makes it possible to rewrite the above equation for phase shift entirely in terms of frequencies. Thus

$$\phi = + \tan^{-1} \frac{\omega}{\omega_2} - \tan^{-1} \frac{\omega}{\omega_1} - \tan^{-1} \frac{\omega}{\omega_3}$$

To determine the phase shift at some frequency, such as $\omega = 20$, it is necessary merely to substitute $\omega = 20$ in the equation for $\phi$ and to evaluate the angles indicated. For example,

$$+ \tan^{-1} \frac{20}{2} = \qquad\qquad +84.3°$$

$$- \tan^{-1} \frac{20}{0.4} = - 88.9°$$

$$- \tan^{-1} \frac{20}{40} = - 26.5°$$

$$\overline{-115.4°} \qquad \overline{+84.3°}$$

Total phase shift $= -31.1°$ at $\omega = 20$ radians per second

Since the phase shift contribution of each $1 + j\omega T$ term at any frequency $\omega$ is merely the arc tangent of the ratio of $\omega$ to the frequency at which the break occurs in the plot of $1 + j\omega T$, it is possible to prepare a scale in which the phase shift angles corresponding to appropriate values of the $\omega/\omega_0$ ratio are indicated. Such a scale, shown in Figure 11.3–4, is of considerable help in simplifying the numerical work involved in determining the phase shift associated with a given attenuation characteristic. Use can be made of a scale of this type in either of two ways.

First, if the $\omega/\omega_0 = 1$ index is placed on a break in the characteristic and the scale is used as shown in Figure 11.3–4, the phase shift produced by this break at any other frequency, $\omega_a$, can be read directly off the phase scale at the value of frequency $\omega_a$. Thus, at $\omega/\omega_0 = 10$, the phase

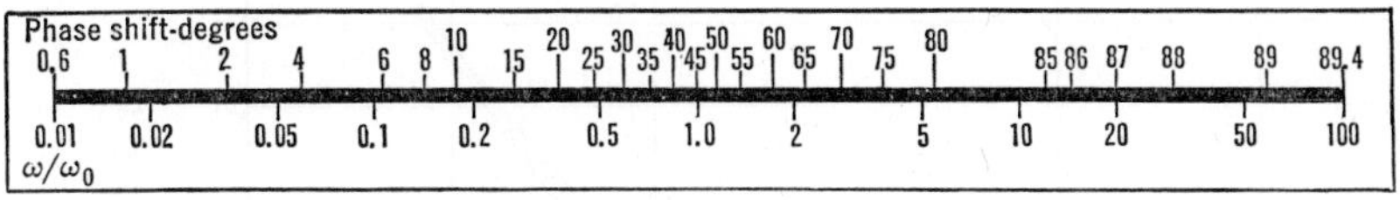

FIGURE 11.3–4

shift contributed by the time constant break at $\omega/\omega_0 = 1$ is 84.3°. In this way the phase shift contribution of a particular time constant can be determined at a number of different frequencies.

If, on the other hand, the $\omega/\omega_0 = 1$ index is placed at the frequency at which the resultant phase shift is sought and the scale is turned end for end, as shown in Figure 11.3–5, the phase shift in degrees produced at this frequency by each break in the attenuation diagram can be read off the phase shift scale at the frequency at which each break occurs.

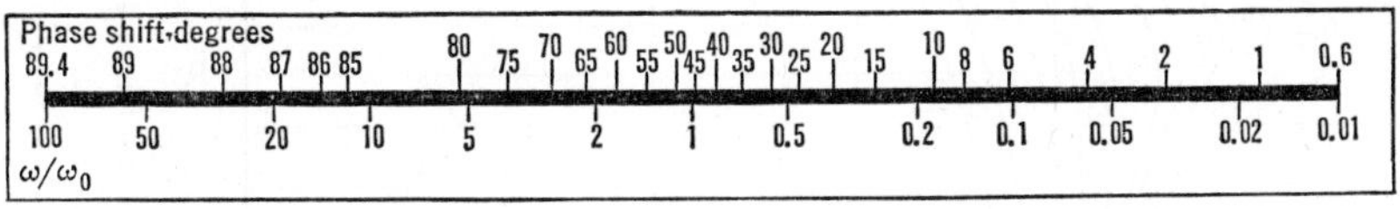

FIGURE 11.3–5

Thus a break located at the frequency $\omega/\omega_0 = 10$ on the scale, as shown in Figure 11.3–5, produces a phase shift of 84.3° at $\omega/\omega_0 = 1$ on the scale. This follows from the symmetrical relationship of the phase shift curve with respect to the break at $\omega/\omega_0 = 1$, which was previously noted.

This and other short-cut methods are used extensively where detailed numerical design work is required. Lucite templates marked off with scales as those shown on Figures 11.3–4 and 11.3–5 and also drawn with such other information as the straight line slopes corresponding to 20 db/decade, 40 db/decade, and 60 db/decade have been prepared for detailed design use. Also used occasionally are templates of the quadratic response functions shown on Figures 11.3–6 and 11.3–7.

**Complex Roots or Time Constants.** Although many transfer functions can be factored into terms having real roots such as were considered in the preceding section, certain types of control elements, such as hydraulic motors where compressibility of the oil in the pipes is appreciable or some steering problems where the viscous damping is small, give rise to transfer functions in which the factors are complex numbers repre-

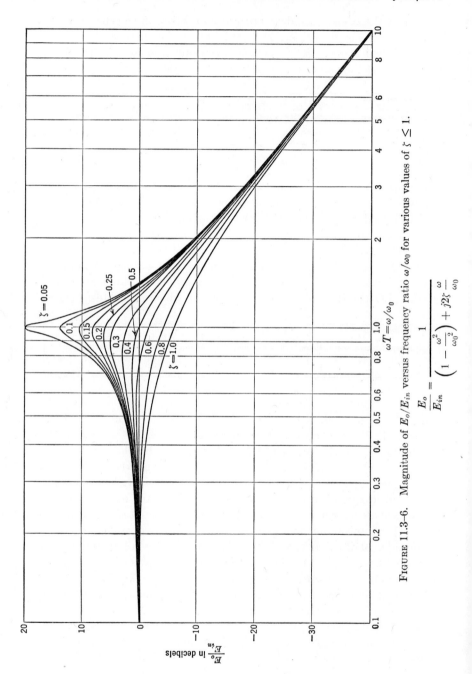

FIGURE 11.3-6.    Magnitude of $E_o/E_{in}$ versus frequency ratio $\omega/\omega_0$ for various values of $\zeta \le 1$.

$$\frac{E_o}{E_{in}} = \cfrac{1}{\left(1 - \cfrac{\omega^2}{\omega_0^2}\right) + j2\zeta \cfrac{\omega}{\omega_0}}$$

senting complex roots.  In a fashion similar to that employed for real time constants, straight-line approximations to the attenuation curves can be used that are asymptotic to the straight-line portion of the actual transfer functions at frequencies much lower and much higher than those at which resonance occurs.  These straight lines have slopes of 0 decibels per decade and $-40$ decibels per decade, respectively.  In the vicinity of resonance the deviation of the straight-line approximation from the actual curves may be appreciable, depending on the degree of damping, and it is necessary to resort to correction curves that show the deviation between the approximate and actual attenuation.

To illustrate more clearly the nature of the approximation involved, consider a transfer function that may or may not be factorable into real time constants.

$$\frac{E_o}{E_{in}} = \frac{1}{T^2(j\omega)^2 + 2\zeta T(j\omega) + 1} = \frac{1}{\left(j\,\dfrac{\omega}{\omega_0}\right)^2 + 2\zeta j\,\dfrac{\omega}{\omega_0} + 1} \qquad (11.3\text{-}7)$$

where $T = 1/\omega_0$.

If the real and the imaginary components are separated, Equation 11.3–7 becomes

$$\frac{E_o}{E_{in}} = \frac{1}{\left(1 - \dfrac{\omega^2}{\omega_0^2}\right) + j2\zeta\,\dfrac{\omega}{\omega_0}} \qquad (11.3\text{-}8)$$

Plots of the attenuation and phase shift of Equation 11.3–7 are shown in Figures 11.3–6 and 11.3–7, respectively, for various values of $\zeta \leq 1$. For values of $\zeta > 1$, the denominator of Equation 11.3–7 can be expressed as the product of two real time constants, and the graphical representation may be handled in the manner indicated in the preceding section.  The phase shift curves, shown in Figure 11.3–7, appear symmetrical about $\omega/\omega_0 = 1$.  It will be noted that the asymptotes to the attenuation curves of Figure 11.3–6 have 0 decibels per decade and $-40$ decibels per decade slope at frequencies lower and higher than $\omega = \omega_0$, respectively.  Hence the same sort of first-order approximation to the attenuation characteristic can be made by having an abrupt break of 0 decibels per decade to $-40$ decibels per decade at $\omega_0 = 1/T$.  The errors in the attenuation characteristic that are produced by making this approximation are shown in Figure 11.3–8 as a function of the frequency ratio $\omega/\omega_0$, where $\omega_0$ is the frequency at the break.

It is worthy of note in passing that, when it is desired to determine the transfer function corresponding to a simple quadratic such as described

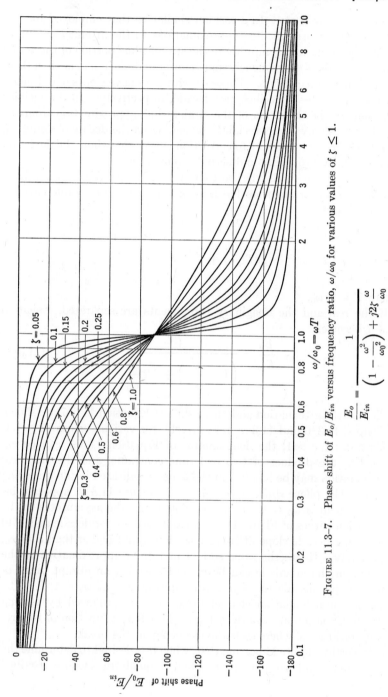

FIGURE 11.3-7.   Phase shift of $E_o/E_{in}$ versus frequency ratio, $\omega/\omega_0$ for various values of $\zeta \leq 1$.

$$\frac{E_o}{E_{in}} = \frac{1}{\left(1 - \dfrac{\omega^2}{\omega_0^2}\right) + j2\zeta\dfrac{\omega}{\omega_0}}$$

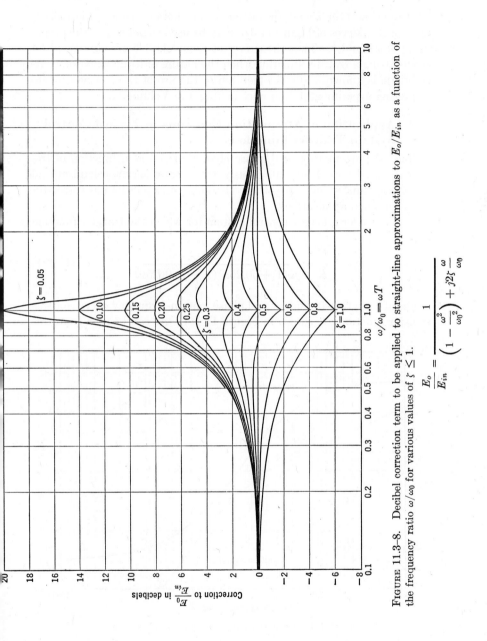

FIGURE 11.3–8. Decibel correction term to be applied to straight-line approximations to $E_o/E_{in}$ as a function of the frequency ratio $\omega/\omega_0$ for various values of $\zeta \leq 1$.

$$\frac{E_o}{E_{in}} = \frac{1}{\left(1 - \frac{\omega^2}{\omega_0^2}\right) + j2\zeta\,\frac{\omega}{\omega_0}}$$

by Equation 11.3–7 and the attenuation characteristic in decibels is known, the curves of Figure 11.3–6 may be used to determine the proper value of $\omega T$ and $\zeta$. Thus the curves of Figure 11.3–6 are also useful for curve-fitting a transfer function when the nature of its attenuation characteristic is known. Further mention of the use of these curves for interpreting experimental data may be found in Volume II.

### 11.4   Application of Attenuation Diagrams to Typical Control System Transfer Functions

Since the attenuation and phase characteristics as a function of frequency can be used advantageously to describe servomechanism and regulator transfer functions, these characteristics will be illustrated for a few common applications.

First consider a type 1 control system for which the transfer function is

$$\frac{C}{E} = \frac{4}{j\omega(1 + j0.25\omega)(1 + j0.0625\omega)} \tag{11.4–1}$$

The attenuation-frequency and phase margin-frequency curves for this transfer function are shown in Figure 11.4–1. As can be seen from this

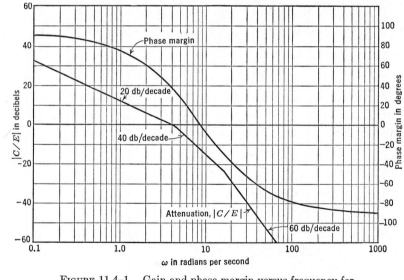

FIGURE 11.4–1.   Gain and phase margin versus frequency for

$$\frac{C}{E} = \frac{4}{j\omega(1 + j0.25\omega)(1 + j0.0625\omega)}.$$

figure, the attenuation is 0 decibels in the vicinity of $\omega = 4$ radians per second, at which frequency the phase shift is less negative than $-180°$. Hence a positive phase margin exists and the system is stable. It will be noted that associated with the $j\omega$ term in the denominator is a uniform slope of $-20$ decibels per decade and a $-90°$ phase shift at low frequencies. This may be considered to be characteristic of the integrating action of a type 1 control system.

Occasionally it is desirable to indicate how much change in gain would cause a stable system to have unity gain at phase crossover, i.e., where the phase angle of the open-loop ratio is 180°. The term *Gain Margin* used for this purpose is defined as *the amount by which the magnitude of the open-loop ratio of a stable system is different from unity at phase crossover*. It is conveniently expressed in decibels. For example, in Figure 11.4–1, the phase crossover occurs at $\omega = 8.5$ radians per second and the gain margin is approximately 12 decibels.

Comparable to the use of Gain Margin is the use of the term *Phase Margin* which has been defined to mean *the angle by which the phase of the open-loop ratio of a stable system differs from 180° at gain crossover;* i.e., when the magnitude of the open-loop ratio is unity (0 decibels). Thus, the phase margin, as has been described in Section 11.1, at 0 db is equal to the *Phase Margin*. On Figure 11.4–1 this is approximately $18°$ at $\omega = 4$ radians per second.

**Velocity Gain Constant Obtainable from Attenuation Diagram.** The importance of the velocity gain constant, $K_V$, in effecting the system accuracy makes it highly advantageous for one to be able to obtain this value from the attenuation diagram. For type 1 systems this information can be obtained directly from the attenuation-frequency diagram at $\omega = 1$ radian per second or by extending the initial 20 decibels per decade slope until the extension intersects the line of 0-decibel gain. Reference to Equation 11.4–1 above and to Figure 11.4–1, for which the approximations of Equations 11.3–2 and 11.3–3 are employed, shows that the value of $C/E$ at $\omega = 1$ is equal to 12 decibels, the velocity gain constant for this system. Since for this transfer function the time constants do not become effective in reducing the system gain from that of an ideal type 1 control until somewhat higher frequencies of the order of $\omega = 2$ to 4 radians per second, the value of $C/E$ at $\omega = 1$ is equal to the velocity gain constant. It is also evident that, if the time constants in the denominator are ignored, the frequency at which the initial slope intersects the 0-decibel line will be equal to the velocity gain constant.

*The velocity gain constant can be determined directly* from the attenuation diagram *only* in the case *when all the time constants are less than unity.* If any time constants exceed 1, one must draw on the attenuation-frequency diagram a continuation of the initial 20 decibels per decade slope at low frequencies, which ignores the presence of these larger time constants. Figure 11.4-2 illustrates such a system for which the transfer function is

$$\frac{C}{E} = \frac{100(1 + j1.25\omega)^2}{j\omega(1 + j5\omega)^2(1 + j0.02\omega)(1 + j0.005\omega)} \qquad (11.4\text{-}2)$$

The solid line on this figure is the approximate attenuation-frequency curve that is used. The dotted line with a slope of $-20$ decibels per decade is the continuation of the initial slope that is used to determine

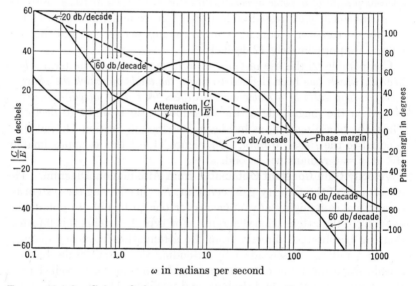

$\omega$ in radians per second

FIGURE 11.4-2.   Gain and phase margin versus frequency for

$$\frac{C}{E} = \frac{100(1 + j1.25\omega)^2}{j\omega(1 + j5\omega)^2(1 + j0.02\omega)(1 + j0.005\omega)}$$

illustrating extrapolation of initial slope to obtain velocity gain constant.

the velocity gain constant at $\omega = 1$ or to intersect the line of 0-decibel gain. Note that this dotted line is merely an extension of the initial slope of the attenuation curve that was started at a frequency of $\omega = 0.1$ and that its intersection with the 0-decibel line gives the velocity constant. This initial slope is determined by the exponent of the $j\omega$ term in the denominator of the transfer function and is $-20$ decibels per decade for a type 1 system. It will be noted from Figure 11.4-2 that the velocity gain constant is 40 decibels, whereas the decibel gain at $\omega = 1$ radian per second is only 16 decibels.   This serves to emphasize the fact that the velocity gain constant may have a somewhat limited significance when signals other than those of constant velocity are considered.   ·

**Acceleration Gain Constant Obtainable from Attenuation Diagram.** For a type 2 control in which the transfer function contains a $(j\omega)^2$ term in the denominator, the acceleration gain constant, $K_A$, may be obtained at $\omega = 1$ in similar fashion.   In this case the initial slope, that is, the slope at lower values of frequency than those at which the largest time constant becomes effective, is $-40$ decibels per decade.   As in the determination of the velocity gain constant, it may be necessary to extend the initial slope to $\omega = 1$ radian per second if any time constant greater than unity is present.   Figure 11.4–3 illustrates a transfer function for

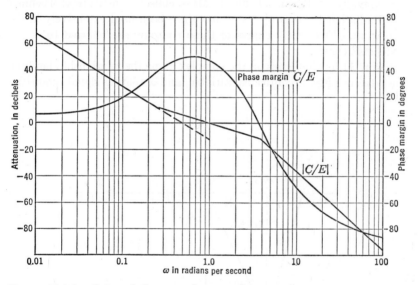

FIGURE 11.4–3.   Gain and phase margin versus frequency for

$$\frac{C}{E} = \frac{0.25(1 + j4\omega)}{(j\omega)^2(1 + j0.25\omega)^2}$$

illustrating extrapolation of initial slope to obtain acceleration gain constant.

which the acceleration gain constant is 0.25, although the actual value of $C/E$ at $\omega = 1$ is 1.   It should be noted that the intersection of the initial 40 decibels per decade slope with the line of 0-decibel gain does not indicate the value of the acceleration gain constant coefficient except when $K_A = 1$.

## 11.5   Contours of Constant $M$ and $\alpha$ Loci

In Chapter 9 it was indicated that knowledge of the ratio of the output to the input amplitude $M$ and phase angle $\alpha$ for any value of a transfer function $C/E = G$ was of great help in determining quantitatively the desirability of the transfer function in question. The nature of the constant contours of $M$ and $\alpha$ in the complex plane is described in Equations 9.2–5 and 9.2–6. The attenuation-frequency and phase shift-frequency plots described in the previous sections present the same magnitude and phase angle information about a transfer function as is shown on a complex plane plot. It is evident that contours of constant $M$ and $\alpha$ for a closed-loop system having an attenuation of $|C/E|$ in decibels and the phase shift (or phase margin) of $C/E$ in degrees are therefore uniquely defined and can be drawn up in chart form. This was first done by N. B. Nichols at the Massachusetts Institute of Technology Radiation Laboratory [62] and has since been used extensively in design work. Frequently charts of these contours are referred to as the "Nichols" charts.

Figure 11.5–1 indicates on the complex plane the relationship between the reference input, controlled variable, and actuating signal quantities

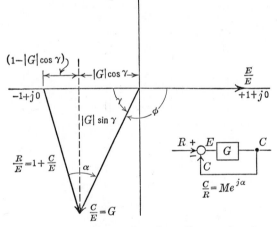

FIGURE 11.5–1.   Components of complex plane diagram for elementary control system.

involved. From Equation 9.1–3 the equation defining $M$ and $\alpha$ is found to be

$$Me^{j\alpha} = \frac{C}{R} = \frac{G}{1 + G} \qquad (11.5\text{–}1)$$

where $C/E = G$.

As illustrated in Figure 11.5–1,

$$\frac{C}{E} = |G| e^{j(\pi+\gamma)} \qquad (11.5\text{–}2)$$

Substituting Equation 11.5–2 in Equation 11.5–1 gives

$$\frac{C}{R} = \frac{|G| e^{j\gamma}}{|G| e^{j\gamma} - 1} = \frac{1}{1 - \dfrac{e^{-j\gamma}}{|G|}} \qquad (11.5\text{–}3)$$

which is also equal to

$$\frac{C}{R} = \frac{1}{1 - \dfrac{1}{|G|} \cos\gamma + j\dfrac{\sin\gamma}{|G|}} \qquad (11.5\text{–}4)$$

Expressing the $C/R$ ratio of Equation 11.5–4 as a magnitude and an angle and comparing terms with the $M$ and $\alpha$ of Equation 11.5–1 gives

$$M = \frac{1}{\sqrt{1 - \dfrac{2\cos\gamma}{|G|} + \dfrac{1}{|G|^2}}} \qquad (11.5\text{–}5)$$

and

$$\alpha = \tan^{-1}\frac{-\sin\gamma}{|G| - \cos\gamma} \qquad (11.5\text{–}6)$$

Plots of $M$ and $\alpha$ from Equations 11.5–5 and 11.5–6 are presented in three different forms in Figures 11.5–2, 11.5–3, and 11.5–4 so as to emphasize different aspects of this relationship. Figure 11.5–2 shows the $M$-$\alpha$ contours for values of $\gamma$ from 0 to $\pm180°$. It serves to indicate the symmetry of the $M$ contours about the phase margin $\gamma = 0$ line as well as the negative relationship between values of $\alpha$ for the same $|G|$ but with equal magnitude and opposite signs for the value of $\gamma$.

Figure 11.5–3 is a somewhat expanded version of the region of phase margin $0 < \gamma < 180°$, which presents more detailed data on $M$ and $\alpha$ for use in design studies. Contours of $M$ are labeled both in decibels and in direct numerical values. Figure 11.5–4 is drawn for use with single-loop systems where it is desired to know the amplification rather exactly in the region from $+20$ decibels to $-6$ decibels and for phase margins of 0 to $+90°$. Depending on the use for which the values of $M$ and $\alpha$ are desired, one or the other of the three figures will be most valuable.

Two common methods of using the data presented on these $M$ and $\alpha$ contours are listed on p. 350.

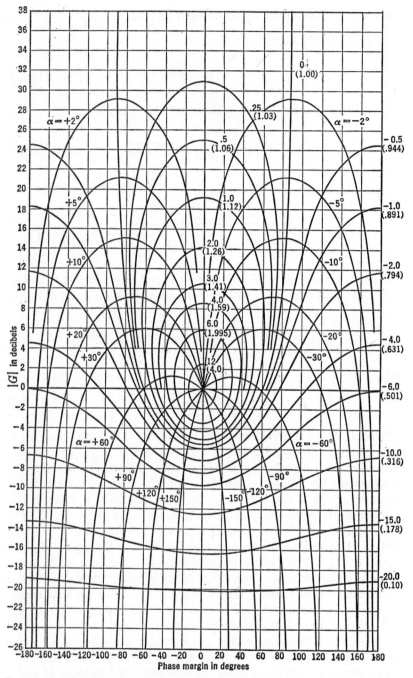

FIGURE 11.5-2. Contours of $M$ and $\alpha$ for values of $\pm 180°$ of phase margin as a function of $|G|$ in decibels. $M$ labeled in decibels and as a numeric (  ).

346

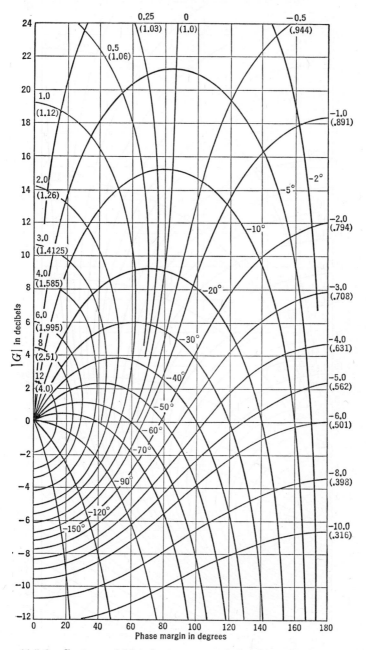

FIGURE 11.5-3. Contours of $M$ and $\alpha$ to an expanded scale covering 0 to $+180°$ of phase margin $M$ labeled in decibels and as a numeric ( ).

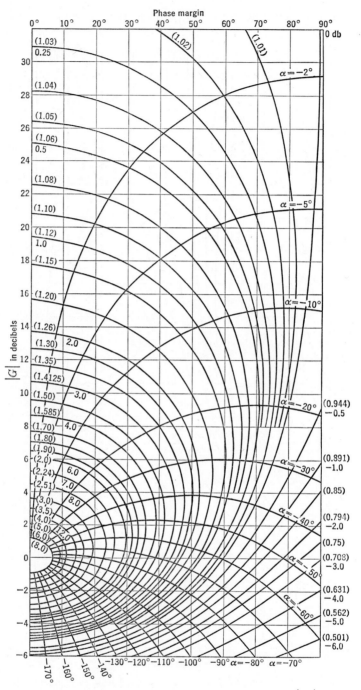

Phase margin

FIGURE 11.5–4. Detailed contours of $M$ and $\alpha$ in the region of $|G|$ +32 to −6 decibels and phase margin 0 to +90°. $M$ labeled in decibels and as a numeric ( ).

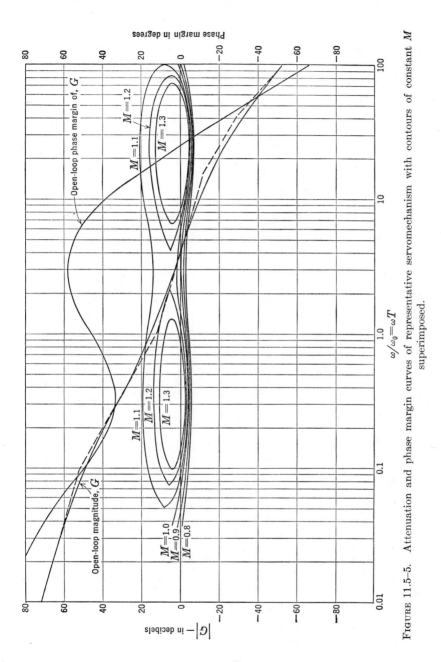

FIGURE 11.5-5.    Attenuation and phase margin curves of representative servomechanism with contours of constant $M$ superimposed.

1. Drawing the constant $M$ contours corresponding to the actual values of gain and phase margin for the system transfer function on the attenuation-frequency diagrams.

2. Drawing a separate plot of the frequency response from the values of $M$ corresponding to the $|G|$ and phase margin of the system transfer function.

These are illustrated by Figures 11.5–5 and 11.5–6, respectively, which are drawn for a system having for the idealized transfer function,

$$G = \frac{C}{E} = \frac{K_1(1 + T_2s)}{s(1 + T_1s)(1 + T_3s)(1 + T_4s)}$$

The intersections of the $M$ contours and the attenuation curve in Figure 11.5–5 for the representative servomechanism system indicate the values of frequency at which the corresponding values of $M$ are obtained. From these intersections one may readily draw the more conventional frequency response curve shown in Figure 11.5–6.

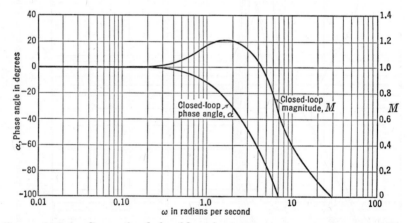

FIGURE 11.5–6.  Conventional closed-loop frequency response curve corresponding to servomechanism attenuation and phase margin characteristic described in Figure 11.5–5.

From the point of view of aiding with detailed design, the $M$ contours of Figure 11.5–4 contain much useful information. Study of these loci will provide design objectives that can serve to shorten the work of synthesizing a system with satisfactory performance. Rule-of-thumb relationships, such as the following, can readily be obtained.

1. To limit the maximum value of $M$ to 1.4, it is necessary that the phase margin be not less than 40° near 0 decibels.

2. A greater phase margin is required for values of $|G|$ somewhat larger than 0 decibels than is required for the same value of $M$ at values of $|G|$ less than 0 decibels.

3. For $|G|$ greater than $+16$ decibels or less than $-5$ decibels, the maximum value of $M$ is 1.2 for any value of phase margin.

4. Since the value of $G$ in Equation 11.5–1 might represent any complex quantity, as well as $C/E$, the $M$ and $\alpha$ contours showing loci of constant magnitude and angle for the ratio $G/(1 + G)$ can be shown to be particularly useful in conjunction with multiple- as well as single-loop systems.

## 11.6 Conclusion

The attenuation and phase margin characteristics of a system that have been presented as a function of frequency (Figures 11.4–1 to 11.4–3) contain the same information as was indicated previously on the complex plane plot. As such, this information can be used to describe the performance of the control, that is, its stability and its accuracy. In the sense of the simplified Nyquist stability criterion, systems having a positive phase margin at unity gain, 0 decibels, are stable. Systems having a negative phase margin at 0 decibel gain are unstable. With the use of the Nichols charts (Figures 11.5–2, 11.5–3, 11.5–4) the system performance for sinusoidal reference inputs can be determined.

However, the attenuation frequency concepts are more than an alternative method of presenting the complex plane information. They offer a shorthand method of attenuation and phase shift representation that is a very convenient and useful method of describing system performance. Also, through the Bode theorems, a better understanding of the potentialities of network and system performance as a function of frequency can be obtained.

# 12

## APPLICATION OF ATTENUATION-PHASE DIAGRAMS
## TO FEEDBACK CONTROL DESIGN PROBLEMS

### 12.0 Introduction

The preceding chapter has shown how the general attenuation and phase angle versus frequency characteristics for networks pointed out by Bode can be used to advantage to describe the performance of control elements. Work at the Bell Laboratories,[28, 43, 46, 56] the Massachusetts Institute of Technology Radiation Laboratories,[62] and elsewhere,[86, 125] has served to develop and extend to a high degree the usefulness of this to feedback control design problems.

It is now worth while to investigate in detail such representative control system designs as those discussed in Chapter 10 from the complex plane point of view. In this way the effectiveness and clarity of the attenuation-frequency approach to design will be revealed, and the salient features of the various methods of providing control system stabilization can be considered from the attenuation-frequency point of view. The significance and reasons for selection of some of the stabilizing networks used in Chapter 10 will be more evident when the attenuation diagrams are drawn in terms of the performance of physically realizable networks rather than in terms of a "desired" network response. One can use the attenuation-frequency approach to describe the performance of servomechanisms and regulating systems using series elements for stabilization as well as to describe the performance of control systems using feedback methods of stabilization. Although the use of the straight-line attenuation diagrams may introduce larger errors for feedback than for series stabilization, with the aid of the Nichols charts, one can eliminate completely the error for either method of stabilization, provided correction terms are applied to the straight-line approximations.

From a study of the attenuation-phase characteristics of a number of representative feedback control systems, it is possible to acquire an understanding of the effects produced by stabilizing networks comparable to that obtained from long periods of experience with control system design problems.  Furthermore, from a grasp of the methods of determining the performance of simple control systems, the techniques utilized in designing and synthesizing the more complicated multi-loop systems discussed in later chapters are made more evident.

## 12.1   Examples of Series Stabilization Methods

In Section 10.1 the use of series networks for stabilizing purposes was described from the complex plane point of view.  The same lag and lead networks will now be considered from the attenuation-frequency viewpoint, and the illustrative examples will also be presented on the attenuation diagrams.  Whereas the complex plane presentation permitted the open-loop system performance to be represented over only a comparatively small portion of the frequency range, a range of three or four decades of frequency and gain variations of 10,000 to 1, and greater, may now be clearly displayed.

**Phase Lag Networks.**  The representative phase lag network shown in Figure 10.1–3 was found to have the transfer function

$$\frac{E_o}{E_{in}} = \frac{R_2 C_2 s + 1}{(R_1 + R_2)C_2 s + 1} = \frac{T_2 s + 1}{T_1 s + 1} \qquad (12.1\text{–}1)$$

where $T_1 = (R_1 + R_2)C_2$ and
   $T_2 = R_2 C_2$.

Figure 12.1–1 shows a plot of this equation on the attenuation-frequency diagram with $s = j\omega$.  The interrelationship of the decreasing attenuation characteristic with that of a lagging phase angle is evident.  The proper choice for the values of the time constants $T_1$ and $T_2$ for a given system can be made quite readily from a consideration of the phase angle versus frequency characteristics in the range of frequencies near $\omega_1$ and $\omega_2$ and the nature of the system without the phase lag network.

Consider now the control system shown in Figure 10.1–5 wherein a phase lag network is used for providing stable system operation with higher gain in the low-frequency range.  The initial system, consisting of amplifier, amplidyne, and motor, was described in Equation 10.1–3 as having the transfer function

$$G_1 = \frac{K_1}{j\omega(1 + j\omega T_f)(1 + j\omega T_m)} \qquad (12.1\text{–}2)$$

The attenuation and phase margin of this transfer function are shown in Figure 12.1–2 by dotted lines.

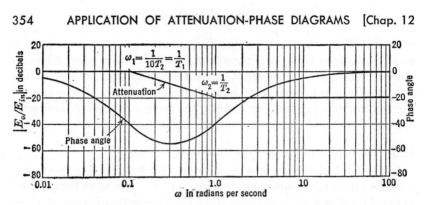

FIGURE 12.1–1. Attenuation and phase characteristics as a function of frequency for phase lag network.

$$\frac{E_o}{E_{in}} = \frac{1 + j\omega T_2}{1 + j\omega T_1}$$

$$T_2 = 1.0$$

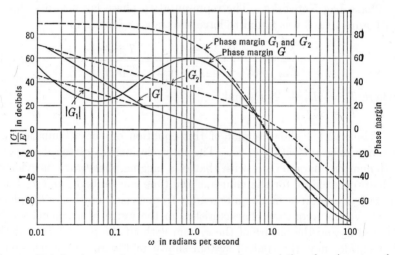

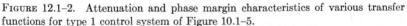

FIGURE 12.1–2. Attenuation and phase margin characteristics of various transfer functions for type 1 control system of Figure 10.1–5.

$$G = \frac{40(1 + j4\omega)}{j\omega(1 + j80\omega)(1 + j0.25\omega)(1 + j0.0625\omega)}$$

$$G_1 = \frac{2}{j\omega(1 + j0.25\omega)(1 + j0.0625\omega)}$$

$$G_2 = \frac{40}{j\omega(1 + j0.25\omega)(1 + j0.0625\omega)}$$

By increasing the through gain an amount $K_2/K_1$ by means of a pre-amplifier or additional amplifier gain, the transfer function

$$G_2 = \frac{K_2}{K_1} G_1 = \frac{K_2}{j\omega(1 + j\omega T_f)(1 + j\omega T_m)} \qquad (12.1\text{-}3)$$

is obtained. As shown by the upper dotted line in Figure 12.1–2, this has the effect of causing the transfer function to have a phase shift in excess of 180° when $G_2$ equals 0 decibels.

By the addition of the series phase lag network the resultant transfer function of the system becomes

$$G = \frac{K_2(1 + j\omega T_2)}{j\omega(1 + j\omega T_f)(1 + j\omega T_m)\left(1 + j\omega \dfrac{K_2}{K_1} T_2\right)} \qquad (12.1\text{-}4)$$

for which the attenuation and phase characteristics are shown by the solid curves in Figure 12.1–2. The phase lag network has reduced the gain of the resultant transfer function from $G_2$ for frequencies higher than $\omega = K_1/K_2 T_2 = 0.0125$ radian per second. Furthermore, for frequencies greater than $\omega = 1/T_2 = 0.25$ radian per second, the resultant transfer function is nearly equal to $G_1$. Although the phase lag network reduces the gain from $G_2$ for these higher frequencies, it is no longer effective in producing appreciable additional phase lag. Hence a satisfactory phase margin in the frequency range where $|C/E|$ is 0 decibels has been obtained at the expense of utilizing the additional gain $K_2/K_1$ only in the limited range of frequencies below $\omega = K_1/K_2 T$.

**Phase Lead Networks.** The representative phase lead network of Figure 10.1–8 with the transfer function

$$\frac{E_o}{E_{in}} = \frac{R_2}{R_1 + R_2}\left[\frac{R_1 C_1 s + 1}{\dfrac{R_2}{R_1 + R_2} R_1 C_1 s + 1}\right] = \frac{T_2}{T_1}\frac{(1 + j\omega T_1)}{(1 + j\omega T_2)}$$

where $T_1 = R_1 C_1$ and $\qquad\qquad\qquad\qquad\qquad\qquad\qquad (12.1\text{-}5)$

$$T_2 = \left[\frac{R_2}{R_1 + R_2}\right] R_1 C_1,$$

is shown on the attenuation-frequency plot of Figure 12.1–3. As can be seen from this figure, there is a leading phase angle associated with the increasing gain characteristic. Since the major effect of the leading phase angle is centered between $\omega = 1/T_1$ and $1/T_2$, one is readily able to determine a suitable choice of values for these time constants $T_1$ and $T_2$. Consideration of the attenuation and phase versus frequency characteristics for the systems described in Figures 10.1–10 and 10.1–13 will illustrate this point further.

*Type 1 System.* The original system of Figure 10.1–10 has the transfer function

$$\frac{C}{E'} = G_1 = \frac{K_1}{j\omega(1 + j\omega T_f)(1 + j\omega T_m)} \tag{12.1–6}$$

for which the attenuation and phase characteristics are shown as a func-

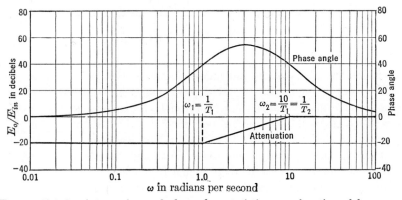

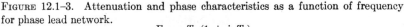

FIGURE 12.1–3. Attenuation and phase characteristics as a function of frequency for phase lead network.

$$\frac{E_o}{E_{in}} = \frac{T_2\,(1 + j\omega T_1)}{T_1\,(1 + j\omega T_2)}$$

$$T_1 = 1$$

tion of frequency by the dotted lines in Figure 12.1–4. The resultant system of Figure 10.1–10, including the phase lead network, has the transfer function indicated by Equation 10.1–10, namely,

$$\frac{C}{E} = G = \frac{K_2}{j\omega(1 + j\omega T_f)\left(1 + j\omega\,\dfrac{R_2 T_m}{R_1 + R_2}\right)} \tag{12.1–7}$$

the characteristics for which are shown by the solid lines in Figure 12.1–4. As can be seen from this figure, the increased gain between $G$ and $G_2$ as a function of frequency from $\omega = 1/T_m = 4$ to $\omega = (R_1 + R_2)/R_2 T_m = 80$ represents the contribution of the phase lead net-

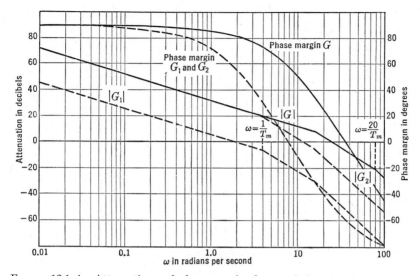

FIGURE 12.1–4. Attenuation and phase margin characteristics of various transfer functions for type 1 control system of Figure 10.1–10.

$$G = \frac{40}{j\omega(1 + j0.0625\omega)(1 + j0.0125\omega)}$$

$$G_1 = \frac{2}{j\omega(1 + j0.25\omega)(1 + j0.0625\omega)}$$

$$G_2 = \frac{40}{j\omega(1 + j0.25\omega)(1 + j0.0625\omega)}$$

work.  To be able to realize this gain, an added gain of $(R_1 + R_2)/R_2 = 20$ was required in addition to the increase in gain of $K_2/K_1$ over the initial $G_1$ system.  However, this amplification $K_2(R_1 + R_2)/K_1R_2$ was not available to increase the gain of $C/E'$ at frequencies lower than $\omega = 1/T_m$ since the attenuation of the phase lead network was equal to $R_2/(R_1 + R_2)$ at these frequencies.  Although full advantage could not be taken of the additional system gain, stable operation of an otherwise unstable system has been obtained.

*Type 2 System.*  Figure 10.1–13 shows the block diagram of a type 2 system in which the transfer function of the original system is

$$\frac{C}{E'} = G' = \frac{K}{(j\omega)^2(1 + j\omega T_m)} \tag{12.1–8}$$

The attenuation-phase characteristics of Equation 12.1–8 are indicated by the dotted lines in Figure 12.1–5.  By the addition of the phase lead

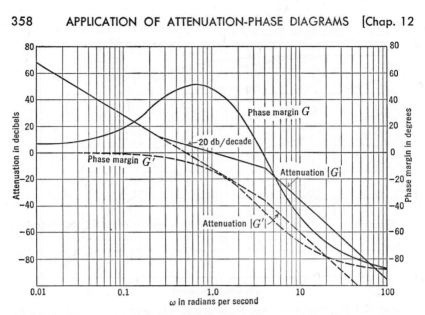

FIGURE 12.1–5. Attenuation and phase margin characteristics of transfer functions for type 2 control system of Figure 10.1–13.

$$G' = \frac{0.25}{(j\omega)^2(1 + j0.25\omega)}$$

$$G = \frac{0.25(1 + j4\omega)}{(j\omega)^2(1 + j0.25\omega)^2}$$

network of Equation 10.1–14, in which the effect of additional gain $(R_1 + R_2)/R_2 = 16$ has been included, the resultant open-loop transfer function becomes

$$\frac{C}{E} = G = \frac{K(1 + j\omega T_1)}{(j\omega)^2 \left(1 + j\omega \dfrac{R_2 T_1}{R_1 + R_2}\right)(1 + j\omega T_m)} \qquad (12.1\text{–}9)$$

The solid attenuation and phase characteristics in Figure 12.1–5 represent this transfer function of Equation 12.1–9 for the values of parameters indicated. As can be seen from Figure 12.1–5, the time constants of the phase lead network have been chosen so as to decrease the slope of the attenuation characteristic to 20 decibels per decade for a couple of octaves above and below the frequency at which the open-loop gain is 0 decibels. In this way the phase angle of the resultant transfer function has been made less negative, and an adequate phase margin of more than 40° has been obtained.

**Lead-Lag Networks.** The transfer function of the general lead-lag network shown in Figure 10.1–16 is

$$\frac{E_o}{E_{in}} = \frac{(T_1 s + 1)(T_2 s + 1)}{T_1 T_2 s^2 + (T_1 + T_2 + T_{12})s + 1} \qquad (12.1\text{--}10)$$

The characteristics of attenuation and phase as a function of frequency for Equation 12.1–10 are shown in Figure 12.1–6. As can be seen, the characteristics previously described for lead and lag networks

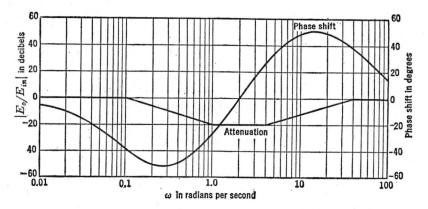

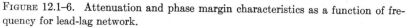

FIGURE 12.1–6. Attenuation and phase margin characteristics as a function of frequency for lead-lag network.

$$\frac{E_o}{E_{in}} = \frac{(1 + j\omega T_1)(1 + j0.25\omega T_1)}{(1 + j10\omega T_1)(1 + j0.025\omega T_1)}$$

$$T_1 = 1$$

separately are combined in the one lead-lag network. The comments made in Section 10.1 on the reasons for selecting the proper values of the resistor and capacitor components for such a network are still valid; however, the attenuation-frequency approach appears to provide a broader picture of the effects produced by the use of the various elements. In Volume II the matter of proper choice of network elements is discussed at considerable length.

The use of a lead-lag network for improving system performance has been illustrated by the system shown in Figure 10.1–18. In Figure 12.1–7 the attenuation and phase characteristics of the original system, $G_1$, are shown by dotted lines. Also shown by dotted lines is this system with its gain increased by the ratio of $K_2/K_1$, $G_2$. The resultant system

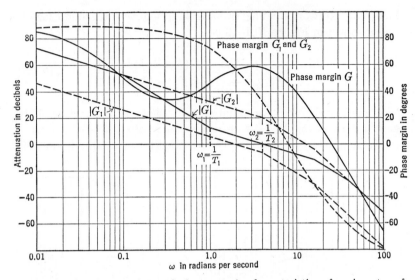

Figure 12.1–7. Attenuation and phase margin characteristics of various transfer functions for type 1 control system of Figure 10.1–18.

$$G = \frac{40(1 + j\omega)}{j\omega(1 + j10\omega)(1 + j0.0625\omega)(1 + j0.025\omega)}$$

$$G_1 = \frac{2}{j\omega(1 + j0.25\omega)(1 + j0.0625\omega)}$$

$$G_2 = \frac{40}{j\omega(1 + j0.25\omega)(1 + j0.0625\omega)}$$

characteristics are shown in Figure 12.1–7 by the solid lines. The transfer function of the original system is

$$\frac{C}{E'} = G_1 = \frac{K_1}{j\omega(1 + j\omega T_f)(1 + j\omega T_m)} \qquad (12.1\text{–}11)$$

The transfer function of the resultant system is

$$\frac{C}{E} = G = \frac{K_2(1 + j\omega T_1)}{j\omega(1 + j\omega T_3)(1 + j\omega T_f)(1 + j\omega T_4)} \qquad (12.1\text{–}12)$$

where $T_2$, the smaller time constant in the numerator of the lead-lag network, has been made equal to $T_m$, the motor time constant.

Since the d-c gain of the lead-lag network is unity as can be seen from Figure 12.1–6, the gain that must be added to the system is indicated directly by the ratio of $K_2/K_1 = 20$. Although the lag portion of the network has increased the phase shift of the open-loop characteristic for frequencies below $\omega = 1/T_1 = 1$ radian per second, the phase lead characteristic becomes effective at frequencies in excess of $\omega = 1/T_m = 1/T_2 = 4$ radians per second so that the net phase margin is positive in the range of frequencies adjacent to the point where the open-loop transfer function goes through 0 decibels.

Since the performance of the system is not at all affected by the method used to analyze it, the results of the complex plane and attenuation-frequency methods of representation must be identical. It is in ease of system synthesis and speed of analysis that the two methods differ.

Because of the intimate relationship that exists between phase angle and attenuation it is possible to establish quantitatively the characteristics of a suitable stabilizing network with reference largely to the attenuation characteristics, which are essentially straight lines. Although additional calculations that take into account the phase angles and the exact attenuation characteristic are required to determine the actual closed-loop performance, the changes in the stabilizing networks that result from these calculations tend to be minor.

## 12.2   Examples of Feedback Stabilization Methods

In the preceding section the attenuation-frequency characteristics of servomechanisms employing series methods of providing stabilization were presented. In series stabilization the effect of the stabilizing network multiplies the initial transfer function of the system so that the magnitude of the resultant transfer function can be obtained from the sum of values of the various terms expressed in logarithm form, that is, in decibels. Likewise the phase angles of the transfer functions of the initial system and the stabilizing network are added directly to obtain the phase angle of the resultant transfer function.

Unfortunately this simple process may not be applied directly to the systems using feedback stabilization. For the general case using feedback stabilization such as that shown in Figure 10.2–4, the combined transfer function for the control and feedback elements was shown by Equation 10.2–10 to be

$$\frac{O}{I} = \frac{G_1}{1 + G_1 H} \tag{12.2-1}$$

where $G_1$ is the transfer function of the forward control element, $H$ is the transfer function of the feedback element, and $O$ and $I$ are the output and input, respectively.

In Equation 10.2–12 it was indicated that a more convenient form for Equation 12.2–1 is

$$\frac{O}{I} = \frac{1}{H}\left[\frac{G_1H}{1 + G_1H}\right] \tag{12.2-2}$$

which is in the form of a product of two terms. It will be recalled that the term $G_1H$ is itself a product of terms of the form $(1 + j\omega T_a)/(1 + j\omega T_b)$, for which the *magnitude* in decibels can be approximated by straight lines of constant slope 1, $\omega T_a$, $1/\omega T_b$, or $T_a/T_b$ when plotted versus frequency to a log scale. Therefore it appears that the term $1 + G_1H$ may also be handled in a similar approximate fashion, thus:

$$1 + G_1H = 1 \text{ for } 1 > G_1H \tag{12.2-3}$$

and

$$1 + G_1H = G_1H \text{ for } 1 < G_1H \tag{12.2-4}$$

These approximations, previously mentioned in connection with the complex plane representation, are used most extensively in attenuation-frequency plots.

Substituting the approximations of Equations 12.2–3 and 12.2–4 in Equation 12.2–2, the magnitude of $O/I$ takes on two different, but continuous values, which can be represented by approximate straight lines on attenuation-frequency plots. Thus

$$\frac{O}{I} = G_1 \text{ for } 1 > G_1H \tag{12.2-5}$$

and

$$\frac{O}{I} = \frac{1}{H} \text{ for } 1 < G_1H$$

It should be recognized at the outset that this is an *approximation* that *is not always valid*, and is particularly subject to error at those frequencies where $G_1H$ is about equal to 1. However, the amount by which the approximation is in error can be calculated, and this correction can be applied to the approximate value. The resultant corrected value is exact. The method of determining the magnitude and angle of the correction term is explained in Section 12.5. Since the approximate method frequently yields results that are satisfactory, it is worth while to present in some detail the mechanics of the various steps in obtaining the approximate solution.

**Attenuation-Frequency Characteristic for Direct Feedback.** In Section 10.2 the use of direct feedback was described with the aid of the complex plane diagram. Utilizing the approximations listed in the preceding sections, one may also indicate on the attenuation-frequency di-

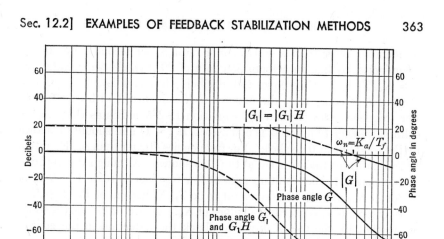

FIGURE 12.2–1.  Attenuation and phase shift characteristics, showing use of direct feedback to reduce time constant of a single time constant element.

$$H = 1$$

$$G_1 = \frac{K_a}{1 + j\omega T_f}$$

$$G = \frac{K_a}{1 + K_a}\left[\frac{1}{1 + j\omega\,\dfrac{T_f}{1 + K_a}}\right]$$

$$K_a = 9.0$$
$$T_f = 0.25$$

agram the change in control element characteristics brought about by direct feedback.  As in Equations 10.2–5 and 10.2–6, let

$$G_1 = \frac{K_a}{1 + j\omega T_f} \tag{12.2–6}$$

and, for direct feedback,

$$H = 1 \tag{12.2–7}$$

The resultant transfer function is exactly

$$G = \frac{O}{I} = \frac{\dfrac{K_a}{1 + j\omega T_f}}{1 + \dfrac{K_a}{1 + j\omega T_f}} = \left(\frac{K_a}{1 + K_a}\right)\left(\frac{1}{1 + \dfrac{j\omega T_f}{1 + K_a}}\right) \tag{12.2–8}$$

Figure 12.2–1 shows the straight-line approximation to the equations for $G_1$, $G_1H$, and $G$.  The dotted line representing $G_1$ has a gain of $K_a$ for frequencies lower than $\omega = 1/T_f = 4$ radians per second. For higher frequencies, $G_1$ has an attenuation rate of 20 decibels per decade. At $\omega = K_a/T_f = \omega_n$, $G_1$ is equal to 0 decibels, that is, unity.

Since $H$ is equal to 1, the plot for $G_1H$ is identical with that for $G_1$. For frequencies lower than $\omega_n$, Equation 12.2–5 indicates that the resultant transfer function $G$ is equal to $1/H$ ($= 1$) and should be shown by the solid line at 0 decibels. For frequencies greater than $\omega_n$, Equation 12.2–5 indicates that $G$ is equal to $G_1$ as shown. Although the approximations indicate the resultant gain at low frequencies to be 1 instead of $K_a/(1 + K_a)$ and the time constant to be $T_f/K_a$ instead of $T_f/(1 + K_a)$, these errors are small for large values of $K_a$. Figure 12.2–1 serves to indicate that by the use of direct feedback the reduction in the control element time constant is obtained at the expense of a loss of gain.

**Attenuation-Frequency Characteristic with Feedback through Frequency-Sensitive Element.** The type of system that will be used to illustrate the application of the attenuation-frequency approach to the representation of a feedback system using a frequency-sensitive element is shown in Figure 10.2–11. Briefly, the control element is a motor-type control having two time constants for which the transfer function is

$$G_1 = \frac{O}{M_1} = \frac{K_1}{j\omega(1 + j\omega T_f)(1 + j\omega T_m)} \qquad (12.2–9)$$

The feedback element, consisting of tachometer feedback through a single $RC$ network of time constant $T$, has the transfer function

$$H = \frac{B}{O} = \frac{K_t T(j\omega)^2}{(1 + j\omega T)} = \frac{K_h(j\omega)^2}{(1 + j\omega T)} \qquad (12.2–10)$$

The resultant transfer function $G$ from Equation 12.2–2 is

$$G = \frac{O}{I} = \frac{1}{H}\left[\frac{G_1 H}{1 + G_1 H}\right] \qquad (12.2–11)$$

Below is a list of figures and the transfer functions for which the attenuation-frequency diagrams are represented:

Figure 12.2–2    $G_1$

Figure 12.2–3    $H$, solid line

$\dfrac{1}{H}$, dotted line

Figure 12.2–4    $G_1 H$

Figure 12.2–5    $G = \dfrac{G_1}{1 + G_1 H}$, solid line

$G_1$, dotted line

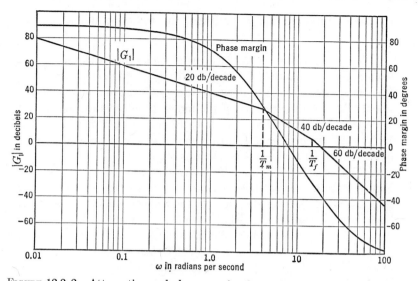

FIGURE 12.2–2. Attenuation and phase margin of transfer function of forward element, $G_1$ of Figure 10.2–11.

$$G_1 = \frac{100}{j\omega(1 + j0.25\omega)(1 + j0.0625\omega)}$$

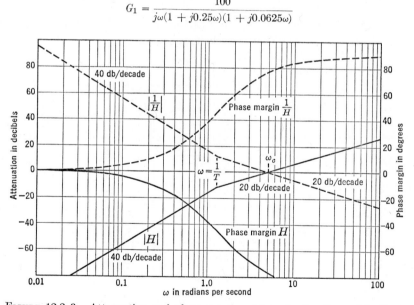

FIGURE 12.2–3 Attenuation and phase margin of transfer functions of feedback element $H$ and its reciprocal $1/H$ of Figure 10.2–11.

$$H = \frac{0.167(j\omega)^2}{(1 + j0.8\omega)}$$

$$T = 0.8$$

In these figures, in the order listed, the following items of interest should be noted:

1. The gain of the control element alone as shown in Figure 12.2–2 is sufficiently high that $G_1$ is attenuating at 60 decibels per decade when this curve crosses 0 decibels at $\omega = 19$ radians per second. At $\omega = 1/T_m = 4$ the presence of the motor time constant increases the slope from 20 decibels per decade to 40 decibels per decade. At $\omega = 1/T_f = 16$ the field time constant increases the slope again, and the final slope of 60 decibels per decade is obtained.

2. The transfer function of the feedback network $H$, shown in Figure 12.2–3, crosses the 0-decibel line at the frequency $\omega_c$ with a slope of 20 decibels per decade. $T$, the time constant of the $RC$ feedback filter, determines at what frequency the initial 40 decibels per decade slope of the feedback function changes to the 20 decibels per decade slope that continues on through 0 decibels to much higher frequencies. Note that the inverse function $1/H$ is the mirror image of $H$ about the 0-decibel axis.

3. Figure 12.2–4 shows the attenuation diagram around the motor-tachometer loop, $G_1H$, indicating that this loop gain is 0 decibels at $\omega_h$ and $\omega_n$. This indicates that at $\omega_h$ the positive value of decibel gain for $G_1$ is equal in magnitude to the negative decibel gain of $H$. At fre-

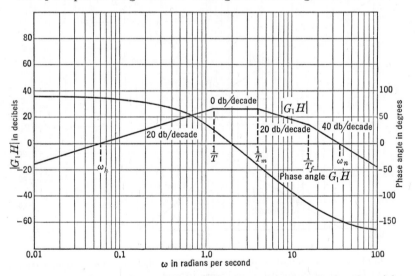

FIGURE 12.2–4. Attenuation and phase shift of open-loop transfer function of forward and feedback elements, $G_1H$, from Figures 12.2–2 and 12.2–3.

$$G_1H = \frac{16.7(j\omega)}{(1 + j0.8\omega)(1 + j0.25\omega)(1 + j0.0625\omega)}$$

quencies lower than $\omega_h$, $G_1H < 1$. For the region of frequencies between $\omega_h$ and $\omega_n$, $G_1H > 1$. Hence it is in the region of frequencies from $\omega_h$ to $\omega_n$ that $O/I$ has the approximate value of $1/H$. It should be noted that all the time constants, $T$, $T_m$ and $T_f$, influence the range of frequency from $\omega_h$ to $\omega_n$. The added attenuation of the motor control element at higher frequencies caused by $T_m$ and $T_f$ reduces the signal being impressed on the feedback filter. For $\omega > \omega_n$, $G_1H$ falls below 0 decibels, indicating that the signal being fed back is less than the input signal $I$, so that the approximate expression for $O/I$ reverts to $G_1$.

When in the process of synthesizing the characteristics of the feedback network, the values of $K_h$ and $T$ may not be known although the general shape of the straight-line representation for $H$ may be available. As described above, the time constant $T$ may be calculated directly from the frequency at the break or breaks in the $H$ or $1/H$ function. To determine $K_h$, it will be noted that at $\omega_h$, $G_1H = 1$.

Taking advantage of the fact that $(1 + j\omega T_m)$, $(1 + j\omega T_f)$ and $(1 + j\omega T)$ are approximately one at $\omega_h$, one can write

$$\frac{K_1}{\omega_h} K_h \omega_h^2 = 1 \qquad (12.2\text{–}12)$$

from which

$$K_h = \frac{1}{K_1 \omega_h} \qquad (12.2\text{–}13)$$

In this way the value of the feedback gain $K_h$ necessary for proper system stabilization can be readily determined. Recalling from Equation 12.2–10 that $K_h = K_t T$, the tachometer gain $K_t$ is found from $K_h/T$.

4. The resultant transfer function of the system has the following dominant breaks in the straight lines:

(a) At frequencies lower than $\omega_h$, $|G_1H| < 1$ and $O/I$ is equal to $G_1$.

(b) From $\omega_h$ to $\omega_n$ during which frequencies $|G_1H| > 1$, $O/I$ is equal to $1/H$.

(c) At $\omega = 1/T$ there is a break that is determined by the time constant of the feedback filter. The 20 decibels per decade slope through 0 decibels at $\omega_c$ is produced by the velocity feedback through the feedback element that is no longer attenuated by the $RC$ network.

(d) For frequencies above $\omega_n$, the resultant curve reverts to the original $G_1$ curve since the motor control element is unable to follow well enough to produce a feedback signal that will alter the net input from $I$, the input without feedback.

It should be noted that the motor and field time constants $T_m$ and $T_f$ do not appear directly in the resultant $O/I$; their major effect is to influence the cut-off frequency $\omega_n$, after which $O/I$ reverts to $G_1$. Hence the feedback is sometimes said to "have eliminated the time constants of the motor."

Reference to Figure 12.2–5 and comparison of the dotted curve for the system without feedback and the solid curve for the system with feedback show that the feedback has served to reduce the system gain in the region from $\omega_h$ to $\omega_n$ but has provided the proper attenuation slope, and consequently phase shift, to insure stable system operation.

The phase margin characteristic shown in Figure 12.2–5 has been determined from the phase shift of an equivalent minimum phase system composed entirely of series elements having the straight-line attenuation-frequency characteristic of Figure 12.2–5. Thus, for purposes of calculating the phase margin, it is assumed that

$$\frac{O}{I} \cong \frac{100(1 + j0.8\omega)}{j\omega(1 + j16.67\omega)(1 + j0.0278\omega)^2} \qquad (12.2\text{–}14)$$

The principles illustrated in this sample problem may be utilized with different forms of the transfer functions for the control and feedback elements. Two stages of the $RC$ filter are frequently used to produce a 60-decibel-per-decade slope in the frequency range of $\omega_h$ to $1/T$. In this way $\omega_h$ is not required to occur at as low a frequency, and higher gains corresponding to $G_1$ can be maintained out to a higher frequency for $\omega_h$.

An additional item that should be considered is the stability of the motor-tachometer loop, that is, the $G_1H$ loop, for which the attenuation curve is shown in Figure 12.2–4. Since this is a closed loop the possibility for self-sustained oscillations within this loop exist. For a system to be highly stable the phase shift for the frequencies $\omega_h$ and $\omega_n$, at which 0 decibel gain for this closed loop is obtained, should be such as to produce positive phase margin. It should be noted, however, that resonance of this closed loop that occurs at low frequencies such as $\omega_h$ is usually found at high values of gain for the over-all system loop. Figure 12.2–5 shows this. Thus the effect of additional gain or phase shift at these frequencies may not be objectionable. In fact, advantage is sometimes taken of a resonance condition in the vicinity of $\omega_h$ to obtain additional open-loop gain. Such a resonance condition may be produced by positive slopes of the $G_1H$ characteristic of 40, to 60, or even 80 decibels per decade in this region.

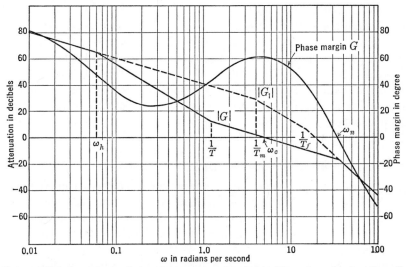

FIGURE 12.2–5.  Attenuation and phase margin of closed-loop transfer function, $G$, and attenuation of forward element alone, $G_1$, of Figures 12.2–2 through 12.2–4.

$$G_1 = \frac{100}{j\omega(1 + j0.25\omega)(1 + j0.0625\omega)}$$

$$G = \frac{1}{H}\frac{G_1 H}{(1 + G_1 H)}$$

$$H = \frac{0.167(j\omega)^2}{(1 + j0.8\omega)}$$

However, the attenuation and phase margin of the over-all system loop in the vicinity of $\omega_n$ is frequently quite critical.  Hence closed-loop resonances in this region of frequencies should be carefully investigated. From an attenuation-frequency point of view it is desirable that the slope of the $GH$ function at $\omega_n$ be 20 to 40 decibels per decade.  Although means may be available for permitting stable operation of the over-all system when the inner loop is unstable at $\omega_n$, undesirable high-frequency oscillations may exist in the inner loop that may limit the life of, or otherwise damage, the equipment.  Frequently an accelerometer or a similar signal proportional to the rate of change of velocity is employed to achieve inner loop stability.

The straight-line attenuation method of feedback system analysis described in this section, although approximate, is generally adequate for the preliminary stage of design.  Before the system design is complete, however, the exact attenuation and phase-margin curves should be drawn.  This is especially true where the frequency response is desired of a closed-loop system for which the $O/I$ here considered is the open-loop characteristic $C/E$. Refer to Figure 10.2–12 as an example of such a system. In many cases an error of but 2 or 3 decibels in the attenuation curve can cause a relatively large error in the closed-loop frequency response curve. This is readily evident from Figure 11.5–4, showing the closed-loop $M$ characteristics corresponding to decibels and phase margin for the open-loop characteristics. Section 12.5 describes two methods whereby the straight-line approximations may be refined to obtain the exact attenuation and phase characteristics.

### 12.3    Attenuation-Frequency Diagram Nomenclature

Certain terms have developed in the servomechanism art in conjunction with the use of the attenuation and phase margin representations of servomechanism performance. Two of these terms used to describe the servomechanism characteristics are *equalization* [28] and *conditional stability*.

**Equalization.**    Equalization is a term that has reference to the attenuation rate of a servomechanism for frequencies less than the frequency at which 0 decibels is obtained. The term *totally equalized* has been used to describe a servomechanism in which stabilizing means are employed to produce an attenuation slope of 20 decibels per decade from very low frequencies up to frequencies beyond that at which 0-decibel gain is obtained. This term has resulted from the fact that an ideal motor has a characteristic attenuation rate of 20 decibels per decade and that a good measure of stability is available from such a characteristic.

Figure 12.1–4 shows that, for this system, $G$ is very nearly totally equalized. The initial 20 decibels per decade slope has been maintained by phase lead networks up to a frequency of almost 16 radians per second whereas 0 decibels occurs at about 25 radians per second.

A *partially equalized* system is one in which the ideal motor characteristic of 20 decibels per decade slope is only partially attained although adequate phase margin at 0 decibels is obtained to provide stable operation. Referring to the attenuation frequency diagrams for systems using phase lag, lag-lead, or feedback means of stabilization (see Figures 12.1–2, 12.1–7, and 12.2–5), one notes that in many cases the attenuation rate of a servomechanism is increased above 20 decibels per decade at frequencies lower than that at which 0 decibels occurs. However, for reasons of stability, the attenuation is altered to 20 decibels per decade for the range of frequencies in the vicinity of 0 decibels. A servomechanism having the general attenuation characteristic described above, namely, having an attenuation rate in excess of 20 decibels per decade for frequencies lower than that at which 0 decibels occurs, but nevertheless having satisfactory stable operation, is said to be *partially equalized*.

Frequently the attenuation diagram of a partially equalized system takes the following general form. The transfer function is allowed to attenuate at a rate of greater than 20 decibels per decade until the gain falls to a value of about 12 to 18 decibels. Then a stabilizing means is used to decrease the attenuation rate to 20 decibels per decade until the frequency is reached at which the open-loop gain is about −12 decibels. After this the attenuation rate may revert to the value it had without "equalizing" or stabilizing means, provided adequate phase margin is maintained for stable operation and the performance is satisfactory otherwise.

By the use of partially equalized transfer functions, lower gain requirements are placed on the amplifiers compensating for the loss in gain brought about by the series or feedback stabilizing means. Furthermore, by attenuating the transfer function more rapidly, the closed-loop frequency response is made to attenuate at a lower frequency and an improvement may be attained in the ability of the system to reject unwanted signals of higher frequencies.

**Conditional Stability.** The term conditional stability is used to describe a partially equalized system in which a negative value of phase margin occurs at a frequency lower than that at which the open-loop transfer function passes through 0 decibels. Conditional stability means that, if the over-all gain of a system is reduced sufficiently, the system can be made to be unstable. Conversely, an *unconditionally* stable system is one in which no amount of decrease in over-all system gain would produce instability. The servomechanisms described in Figures 12.1–2, 12.1–4, 12.1–7, and 12.2–5 all have positive phase margins for frequencies lower than those at which 0-decibel gain occurs. However, Figure 6.5–3a shows a complex plane representation of a conditionally stable system. As higher performance is required of a servomechanism system, the designer is forced more in the direction of conditionally stable systems. Examples in later chapters will serve to illustrate conditionally stable systems. In general, position controls using tachometer feedback through a double *RC* network are conditionally stable servomechanisms.

The possibility of instability arising due to a decrease in the over-all loop gain that exists for conditionally stable systems places more rigorous limitations on the dependability of the gain characteristics of amplifiers and other elements that directly influence this loop gain of the system. Means that can be taken to insure stable gain characteristics for amplifiers are discussed in Volume II.

## 12.4    Application of Nichols Charts to Obtain Closed-Loop Performance

In Sections 12.1 and 12.2 the open-loop transfer functions in terms of their attenuation and phase margin as a function of frequency are shown for systems using series and feedback stabilizing means.   In each case it was possible to obtain a system that had adequate phase margin at 0 decibels for stable operation and had generally suitable values for the

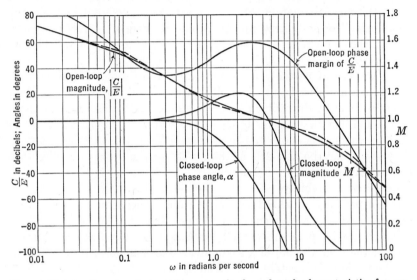

FIGURE 12.4–1.   Open- and closed-loop magnitude and angle characteristics for control system described in Figure 12.1–7.   $M$ and $\alpha$ are obtained from actual open-loop curves.

$C/E$ ratio at low frequencies.   However, to determine the over-all performance of these systems in a more quantitative fashion, it is necessary to obtain the closed-loop frequency response corresponding to these open-loop characteristics.   By means of the Nichols charts shown in Figures 11.5–3 and 11.5–4, the closed-loop characteristic can be determined directly from the values of $|C/E|$ in decibels and the phase margin at each frequency without having to resort to the algebra of complex numbers.[62]

Figures 12.4–1 and 12.4–2 show the phase margin, the open-loop magnitude $|C/E|$, the closed loop $C/R$ ratio $(M)$, and the angle $\alpha$ of $C/R$ for the servomechanism systems described in Figures 12.1–7 and 12.2–5. The values of $M$ and $\alpha$ are based upon the actual value of $|C/E|$ as shown by the open-loop magnitude characteristics as contrasted with the straight-line approximations to the attenuation characteristics. As can be seen in Figures 12.4–1 and 12.4–2, the closed-loop magnitude characteristics shown have comparatively low values for the maximum of $M$, of the order of 1.2, and as such have quite acceptable characteristics in this respect. It will be noted that the frequency at which the maximum $M$ occurs is less than half the frequency at which the open-loop attenuation characteristic is 0 decibels. A more detailed discussion

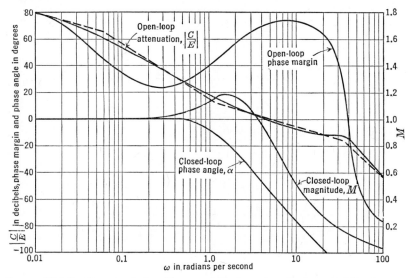

FIGURE 12.4–2. Open- and closed-loop magnitude and angle characteristics for control system described in Figure 12.2–5. $M$ and $\alpha$ are obtained from actual open-loop curves.

of the relationship between open- and closed-loop characteristics of control systems is presented in Chapter 14.

As an aid to understanding better the effect of changes in the over-all system gain, the control system designer frequently transfers a number of the contours of constant $M$ from the Nichols chart to the open-loop attenuation-phase margin diagram. Such contours are shown in Figure 12.4–3 for the servomechanism system previously considered in Section 12.1 and for which the frequency response is shown in Figure 12.4–1. The intersection of the $M$ contours and the attenuation-frequency plots indicates the value of frequency at which the corresponding value of $M$ is obtained. Since the value of $M$ is a function of both $|\,C/E\,|$ and the phase margin, the contours of $M$ on the attenuation-frequency diagrams will differ from system to system. Hence they must be drawn for each open-loop transfer function.

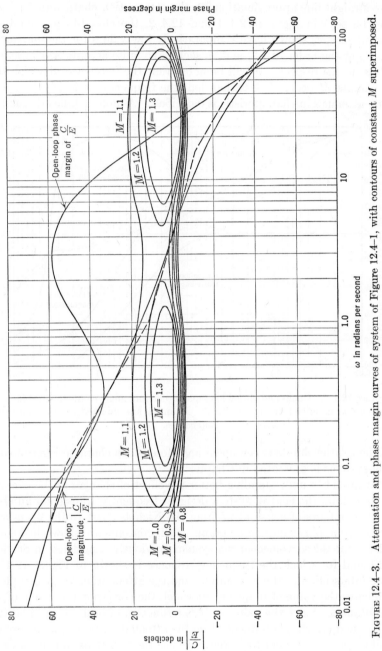

FIGURE 12.4–3. Attenuation and phase margin curves of system of Figure 12.4–1, with contours of constant $M$ superimposed.

The effect of changes in the over-all gain of the system can be determined directly from Figure 12.4–3. Since changing the gain of the system does not change the phase margin, the contours of constant $M$ remain fixed with respect to the 0-decibel gain line. However, gain changes do move the plot of open-loop magnitude $C/E$ up or down with respect to 0-decibel gain. Such a shift in $C/E$ causes it to intersect the $M$ contours at different values of $M$, which correspond to changing the closed-loop frequency response.

Because of the nature of the partially equalized system shown in Figure 12.4–3 it appears that a reduction of gain will cause an increase in the maximum $M$, a $M_m$ of 1.3 occurring at $\omega = 1.2$ radians per second for a 6-decibel decrease in loop gain. The effect of an increase in open-loop gain is also to increase the maximum $M$. With an increase in gain of 8 decibels, the maximum $M$ occurs at $\omega = 9$ radians per second and has a value of 1.3.

## 12.5   More Exact Feedback Control System Representation of Attenuation, Phase Margin Characteristics

To present more clearly the underlying ideas of the use of the attenuation-frequency diagrams, the straight-line approximations to the exact attenuation characteristics have been employed for the most part in the preceding sections of this chapter. This practice is also employed generally by control system designers in the preliminary stages of design as a convenience in obtaining the significant time constants and gains required for a design. However, before a design is complete, it is usually essential that a more exact representation of the attenuation and phase margin characteristics be made. The failure of the straight-line approximations to reveal certain objectionable resonances makes this especially necessary.

**System Composed of Series Elements.**  For control elements arranged in a series fashion, the procedure outlined in Chapter 11 for refining the straight-line attenuation plots yields the exact values of phase angles and also permits one to determine the magnitude of the correction to the straight-line attenuation characteristics. Section 11.3 describes the correction as a function of the ratio of the actual frequency to the frequency at the break for a simple time constant control element. Also, in that section the corresponding decibel correction as a function of the same frequency ratio for complex time constants is shown. These modifications in the attenuation characteristic are simple and may be performed directly to the straight-line attenuation characteristics previously described. This procedure is illustrated below as a part of the process employed when feedback stabilizing means are used.

**System with Feedback Stabilization.** The exact expression for the open-loop transfer function that employs feedback stabilization has been shown to be

$$\frac{C}{E} = \frac{1}{H}\left[\frac{G_1 H}{1 + G_1 H}\right] = G \qquad (12.5\text{-}1)$$

If the term in brackets is considered, it appears that this has the same *form* as the expression for which the Nichols charts were developed, namely

$$\frac{C/E}{1 + C/E} \qquad (12.5\text{-}2)$$

Hence, if the magnitude of $G_1 H$ in decibels and the corresponding phase margin of $G_1 H$ are determined, the exact magnitude and phase of $G_1 H/(1 + G_1 H)$ can be evaluated. Since, in the straight-line approximation method of determining system performance, the $G_1 H$ function is determined, the necessary data can be readily obtained. However, care must be taken to express $G_1 H$ in the proper angular measure of *phase margin*, which is the angle coordinate of the Nichols charts. The $M$ and $\alpha$ contours shown in Figure 11.5–3 are presented in a form that is frequently found convenient for the range of values of $G_1 H$ likely to be encountered.

Since the magnitude and phase angle of $1/H$ can also be evaluated on the basis of its being a series element by itself, the resultant value of $C/E$ in decibels and phase angle or phase margin can be obtained exactly. By utilizing the Nichols charts again to calculate the closed-loop frequency response $C/R$, from the $C/E$ data, the desired performance of a feedback control system employing feedback stabilization may be obtained.

Although the form of Equation 12.5–1 is particularly convenient for determining the value of $C/E$ in the region of frequencies where $C/E \cong 1/H$, for the remaining frequencies where $C/E \cong G_1$, the expression

$$\frac{C}{E} = G_1\left[\frac{1}{1 + G_1 H}\right] \qquad (12.5\text{-}3)$$

$$= G_1\left[\frac{1/G_1 H}{1 + (1/G_1 H)}\right] = G \qquad (12.5\text{-}4)$$

may be employed to greater advantage. For these frequencies, the bracketed term will contribute a small correction term, and the function $1/G_1 H$ may be evaluated from the reciprocal of the value of $G_1 H$ previously determined. Again the Nichols charts of Figure 11.5–3 can be employed to obtain the magnitude and phase angle of the bracketed term, with $1/G_1H$ being used to provide the magnitude and *phase margin* for entering the chart.

*Example*

To illustrate the method of representing exactly the attenuation and phase characteristics of a servomechanism using the straight-line approximations as a starting point, the attenuation and phase characteristics of the feedback system described in Section 12.2 are redrawn on Figures 12.5–1 through 12.5–8, using the methods outlined above.

Below is a list of figures and the transfer functions for which the attenuation and phase characteristics are shown:

$$\text{Figure 12.5–1} \quad G_1H$$

$$\text{Figure 12.5–2} \quad \frac{G_1H}{1 + G_1H}$$

$$\text{Figure 12.5–3} \quad \frac{1}{H}$$

$$\text{Figure 12.5–4} \quad \frac{1}{H}\left[\frac{G_1H}{1 + G_1H}\right]$$

$$\text{Figure 12.5–5} \quad \frac{1}{G_1H}$$

$$\text{Figure 12.5–6} \quad \frac{\dfrac{1}{G_1H}}{1 + \dfrac{1}{G_1H}}$$

$$\text{Figure 12.5–7} \quad G_1$$

$$\text{Figure 12.5–8} \quad G_1\left[\frac{\dfrac{1}{G_1H}}{1 + \dfrac{1}{G_1H}}\right]$$

Figures 12.5–1 through 12.5–4 illustrate the various steps in obtaining the $C/E$ transfer function in the form of Equation 12.5–1. Reference to Figure 12.5–1, in which $G_1H$ is considered as merely a series arrangement of elements, shows that the exact attenuation shown by the solid line differs only slightly from the approximate value shown by the dotted lines.

Figure 12.5-2 shows how nearly the magnitude of $G_1H/(1 + G_1H)$ is equal to 0 decibels over the range of frequencies from $\omega_h$ to $\omega_n$, where the approximate solution assumes the value to be exactly 0 decibels.

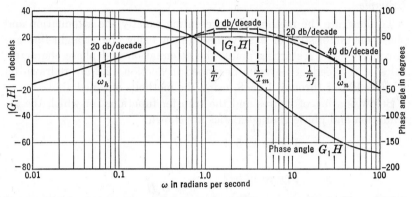

FIGURE 12.5-1.    Attenuation and phase angle of $G_1H$ corresponding to Figure 12.2-4.

$$G_1H = \frac{16.7(j\omega)}{(1 + j0.8\omega)(1 + j0.25\omega)(1 + j0.0625\omega)}$$

Figure 12.5-3, showing $1/H$, indicates that for this series of elements the exact attenuation characteristic differs from the approximate one by only the correction factor mentioned in Section 11.3.

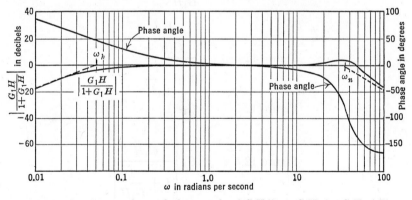

FIGURE 12.5-2.    Attenuation and phase angle of $G_1H/(1 + G_1H)$ for $G_1H$ of Figure 12.5-1.

The resultant open-loop transfer function shown in Figure 12.5-4 should be compared with $O/I$, the straight-line approximation for this same transfer function, as shown in Figure 12.2-5. Although the two figures at first glance appear to be somewhat dissimilar, a more careful check of the two attenuation characteristics indicates the differences to be small and of the order of the magnitudes shown by the difference of

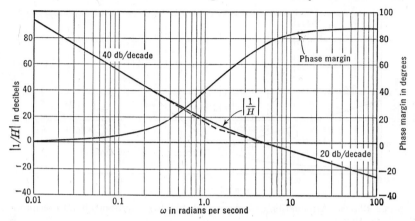

FIGURE 12.5–3. Attenuation and phase margin of $1/H$ corresponding to Figure 12.2–3.

$$\frac{1}{H} = \frac{1 + j0.8\omega}{0.167(j\omega)^2}$$

$G_1H/(1 + G_1H)$ in Figure 12.5–2 from 0 decibels over the general range of frequencies from $\omega_h$ to $\omega_n$. Figures 12.5–2 and 12.5–3 show that, for frequencies lower than $\omega_h$ and higher than $\omega_n$, $1/H$ and $G_1H/(1 + G_1H)$

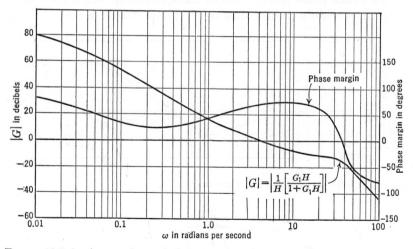

FIGURE 12.5–4. Attenuation and phase margin of closed-loop transfer function, $G$, corresponding to Figure 12.2–5.

both have appreciable magnitudes in decibels so that the product of the two as shown on Figure 12.5-4 differs from each of them. Hence in these ranges of frequencies both terms must be determined accurately.

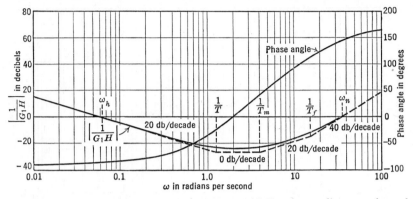

FIGURE 12.5-5. Attenuation and phase angle of $1/G_1H$ corresponding to reciprocal of Figure 12.2-4.

$$\frac{1}{G_1H} = \frac{(1 + j0.8\omega)(1 + j0.25\omega)(1 + j0.0625\omega)}{16.7(j\omega)}$$

Comparing the exact phase margin of $G$ in Figure 12.5-4 with the approximate value shown in Figure 12.2-5 obtained from the equivalent series element system shows that appreciable differences exist in the frequency range adjacent to $\omega_n$. For frequencies slightly lower than $\omega_n$, the actual phase margin exceeds the approximate value whereas for frequencies slightly greater than $\omega_n$ the phase margin is lower. These

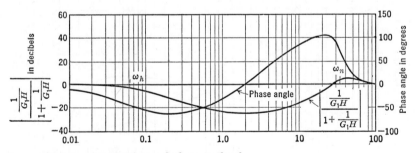

FIGURE 12.5-6. Attenuation and phase angle of

$$\frac{\dfrac{1}{G_1H}}{1 + \dfrac{1}{G_1H}}$$

for $1/G_1H$ of Figure 12.5-5.

differences in phase margin occur in the vicinity of frequencies where the amplitude resonance occurs and have the same sort of characteristics as noted for a control element having a pair of complex factors with a

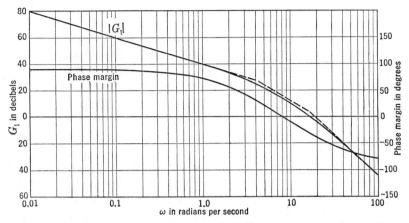

FIGURE 12.5–7. Attenuation and phase margin of $G_1$ corresponding to Figure 12.2–2

$$G_1 = \frac{100}{j\omega(1 + j0.25\omega)(1 + j0.0625\omega)}$$

damping ratio less than 0.7 (see Section 11.3). Since the approximate phase margin curve is less than the actual phase margin, the error involved in using the approximate values provides a margin of safety.

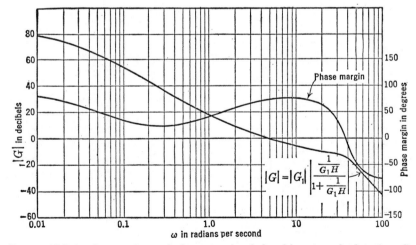

FIGURE 12.5–8. Attenuation and phase margin of closed-loop transfer function, $G$, corresponding to Figures 12.2–5 and 12.5–4.

Figures 12.5–5 through 12.5–8 illustrate the various steps in obtaining the $C/E$ transfer function in the form of Equation 12.5–4. Figure 12.5–6, in which the exact attenuation characteristic of $\dfrac{1/G_1H}{1 + 1/G_1H}$ is given, shows that for frequencies below $\omega_h$ and above $\omega_n$ the attenuation characteristic differs from 0 decibels by a comparatively few decibels. Hence over these ranges of frequencies the attenuation characteristics of $G_1$ shown in Figure 12.5–7 are very nearly those of the resultant transfer function shown in Figure 12.5–8. However, in the range of frequencies from $\omega_h$ to $\omega_n$, which is of greater concern from the system performance point of view, it is necessary to obtain accurately the attenuation characteristics of both $G_1$ and $\dfrac{1/G_1H}{1 + 1/G_1H}$.

The figures above serve to illustrate that either of the two methods described above for obtaining the exact attenuation-phase characteristics can be used to advantage. The choice of which method should be used will depend somewhat on the range of frequencies over which more accurate attenuation figures are required and the degree of accuracy that is sought.

# 13

## APPLICATION OF ROOT LOCUS
## TO FEEDBACK CONTROL DESIGN PROBLEMS

### 13.0 Introduction

In many feedback control systems the requirements may be expressed most directly in terms of transient performance. In these cases use of the root locus approach to system design is effective in enabling the designer to visualize the effect of parameter changes on system performance. The root locus method provides another way of arriving at stabilizing methods for improving system performance that emphasizes the time response of the control system rather than its frequency response. To provide a uniform basis for judging the various design methods, the cases considered in Chapters 10 and 12 will be studied again from the root locus method. In addition, this chapter will consider a number of aids in drawing the root locus more readily and in interpreting the significance of the root locus plots once drawn. An introduction will be made to some of the aids to system synthesis using the root locus method.

### 13.1 Significance of Location of Roots in Complex Plane

Since the root locus method of analysis and synthesis presents the closed-loop control system performance in terms of the location of these roots in the complex plane, it is important for one to understand the implications of the root location as expressed in such performance terms as decrement factor, decay rate, and natural frequency. Where possible it is also desirable to relate these transient performance criteria to the corresponding frequency response terms.[118] Although this cannot be done readily in general, the performance terms for a simple second order system can be set down and much useful information can be derived. As a further aid in appreciating the significance of the closed-loop pole and zero locations, the values of these terms will be related to the position, velocity, and acceleration error coefficients.

**Interpretation of Root Location.** As a background for interpreting the significance of the root location, it will be desirable to refer back to some of the examples of simple oscillatory circuits and systems described in Chapter 3.

Consider the case shown on Figure 13.1–1 where a closed-loop pole is located at

$$s = -\alpha + j\beta \tag{13.1-1}$$

The transient term corresponding to this pole is of the form

$$A e^{(-\alpha + j\beta)t} \tag{13.1-2}$$

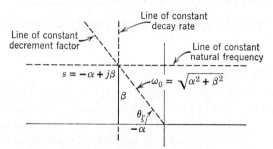

FIGURE 13.1–1.    Lines of constant decrement factor, constant decay rate, and natural frequency passing through pole at $s = -\alpha + j\beta$.

From this it will be noted that $\alpha$ is the exponential decrement rate and $\beta$ is the natural frequency for this term.    The value of the exponential decrement rate establishes the time required for a transient disturbance to decay and is dependent only on the magnitude of $-\alpha$.    Thus all closed-loop poles located on a given vertical line will decay at the same time rate.    Hence the lines of constant decay rates are vertical lines parallel to the imaginary axis; the greater the distance to the left of the axis the more rapid the decay.

The value of the natural frequency of system establishes its sinusoidal oscillation frequency for any disturbance and is dependent only on $\beta$. Thus, all closed-loop poles located on a given horizontal line will have the same frequency of oscillation.    Lines of constant natural frequency are horizontal lines parallel to the real axis; the greater the distance from the real axis the higher the frequency of oscillation.

Another term that is of significance in connection with the location of the closed-loop poles in the complex plane is the decrement factor, $\zeta$, which is defined as the

$$\zeta = \frac{\text{actual damping rate}}{\text{undamped natural frequency}} \tag{13.1-3}$$

where $\omega_0$, the undamped natural frequency, is,

$$\omega_0 = \sqrt{\alpha^2 + \beta^2}$$

The physical significance of $\zeta$ is that it expresses the decrement rate per cycle and is therefore a per unit type quantity.

As shown on Figure 13.1–1, lines of constant $\zeta$ are described graphically by the angle, $\theta_\zeta$,

$$\theta_\zeta = \cos^{-1} \frac{-\alpha}{\omega_0} = \tan^{-1} \frac{\beta}{-\alpha} \qquad (13.1\text{--}4)$$

Radial lines through the origin are lines of constant decrement factor, high decrement factors being located near the negative real axis and low decrement factors being located near the imaginary axis.

In connection with these three sets of loci corresponding to constant decay rate, constant frequency of oscillation, and constant decrement factor, it is of interest to note that specifications stated in terms of these quantities may not be consistent throughout the complex plane. Referring to Figure 13.1–2, one notes that the shaded area denotes all the

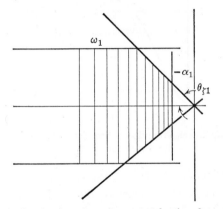

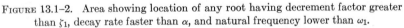

FIGURE 13.1–2.  Area showing location of any root having decrement factor greater than $\zeta_1$, decay rate faster than $\alpha$, and natural frequency lower than $\omega_1$.

possible root locations of systems having a decay rate greater than $-\alpha_1$, an oscillation frequency less than $\omega_1$, and a decrement factor greater than $\zeta_1$. By placing all the specified restraints on the root locus plot, one is able to tell at a glance whether particular root locations meet the overall system requirements.

*Overshoot Time to Reach Peak, and Settling Time Expressed in Terms of Root Location.* Since the root locus results provide the values of decay rate, $\alpha$, decrement factor, $\zeta$, and undamped natural frequency, $\omega_0$, it is worthwhile to determine the relationships between these parameters and such system performance criteria for a step input as peak overshoot, time to reach the peak, and the settling time. To establish an indication of the order of magnitude of these relationships, they will be evaluated for the case of a second-order system for which the step response, as given by Equation 3.8–10, is

$$c(t) = C_0 \left( 1 - \frac{e^{-\zeta \omega_0 t}}{\sqrt{1 - \zeta^2}} \sin \left[ \sqrt{1 - \zeta^2} \omega_0 t + \phi \right] \right), \quad (13.1\text{–}5)$$

where $\phi = \tan^{-1} \dfrac{\sqrt{1 - \zeta^2}}{\zeta}$.

Figure 13.1–3 shows the time response of this second-order system and indicates the performance terms of interest.

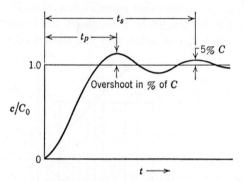

FIGURE 13.1–3.  Response as a function of time for an oscillating second-order system for a step-function input.

To find $t_p$, the time necessary for the controlled variable to reach its maximum overshoot, it is necessary to differentiate Equation 13.1–5 and set the derivative equal to zero.

$$\frac{dc(t)}{dt} = \frac{-C_0 e^{-\zeta \omega_0 t}}{\sqrt{1 - \zeta^2}} \left( -\zeta \omega_0 \sin \left[ \sqrt{1 - \zeta^2} \omega_0 t + \phi \right] \right.$$

$$\left. + \sqrt{1 - \zeta^2} \, \omega_0 \cos \left[ \sqrt{1 - \zeta^2} \omega_0 t + \phi \right] \right) = 0 \quad (13.1\text{–}6)$$

from which,

$$\sin \sqrt{1 - \zeta^2} \omega_0 t = 0 \quad (13.1\text{–}7)$$

and

$$\sqrt{1 - \zeta^2} \omega_0 t_p = \pi \quad (13.1\text{–}8)$$

Solving for $t_p$,

$$t_p = \frac{\pi}{\sqrt{1 - \zeta^2} \omega_0} = \frac{\pi}{\beta} \quad (13.1\text{–}9)$$

From this equation it appears that the time for the system to reach its peak is dependent only on the oscillation frequency.

Substituting the value of $t_p$ from Equation 13.1–9 for $t$ in Equation 13.1–5, one obtains the value for the controlled variable at its greatest overshoot.

$$\frac{c}{C_0}(t_p) = e^{-\frac{\zeta\pi}{\sqrt{1-\zeta^2}}} \qquad (13.1\text{–}10)$$

The settling time, $t_s$, is arbitrarily chosen to be the time at which the magnitude of the controlled variable stays below 5% of its initial value. Considering only the exponentially decaying term

$$e^{-\zeta\omega_0 t_s} = 0.05 \qquad (13.1\text{–}11)$$

for which

$$\zeta\omega_0 t_s = 3.0 \qquad (13.1\text{–}12)$$

and

$$t_s = \frac{3.0}{\zeta\omega_0} \qquad (13.1\text{–}13)$$

The number of oscillations $N$ for the system to settle is obtained from the ratio

$$N = \frac{t_s}{t_0} = \frac{t_s}{1/f_0} = t_s f_0 = \frac{t_s\sqrt{1-\zeta^2}\,\omega_0}{2\pi} \qquad (13.1\text{–}14)$$

Substituting $t_s$ from Equation 13.1–13

$$N = \frac{1.5\sqrt{1-\zeta^2}}{\pi\zeta}$$

Table 13.1–1 gives the values of maximum overshoot and number of

TABLE 13.1–1

| Decrement Factor, $\zeta$ | Maximum Overshoot in % of Initial Step | Number of Oscillations to Settle to 5% |
|---|---|---|
| 0 | 1.00 | ∞ |
| 0.1 | 0.730 | 4.76 |
| 0.2 | 0.527 | 2.34 |
| 0.4 | 0.254 | 1.09 |
| 0.5 | 0.166 | 0.82 |
| 0.6 | 0.0955 | 0.64 |
| 0.707 | 0.042 | 0.48 |
| 0.8 | 0.016 | 0.36 |
| 1.0 | 0.0 | 0.0 |

oscillations for the response to settle to 5% of its initial value as a function of the decrement factor.

*Bandwidth in Terms of Root Location.* In Section 11.3 were plotted the attenuation and phase characteristics of a second-order position control system as a function of the undamped natural frequency $\omega_0$ for various values of damping factor. From Equation 11.3–8 the equation for the magnitude of the closed loop transfer function can be expressed as

$$\frac{C}{R}(\omega) = \frac{1}{\left\{\left[1 - \left(\frac{\omega}{\omega_0}\right)^2\right]^2 + 4\zeta^2 \frac{\omega^2}{\omega_0^2}\right\}^{1/2}} \qquad (13.1\text{–}15)$$

The bandwidth of such a closed-loop control is defined as the maximum frequency at which the closed-loop gain is 3 decibels below the gain value for zero frequency. Thus, at the bandwidth frequency $\omega = \omega_b$, $C/R(\omega)$ is equal to $-3$ db. Substituting this into Equation 13.1–15.

$$-3 = 40 \log \omega_0 - 10 \log \left[(\omega_0{}^2 - \omega_b{}^2)^2 + 4\zeta^2\omega_b{}^2\omega_0{}^2\right] \quad (13.1\text{–}16)$$

Solving this equation for $\omega_b$ in terms of $\omega_0$ and $| C/R(\omega) |$, the following relationship is obtained

$$\omega_b = \omega_0 \sqrt{1 - 2\zeta^2 + \sqrt{2 - 4\zeta^2 + 4\zeta^4}} \qquad (13.1\text{–}17)$$

Table 13.1–2 shows the ratio of bandwidth to undamped natural fre-

TABLE 13.1–2

ATIO OF BAND WIDTH $\omega_b$ TO UNDAMPED NATURAL FREQUENCY $\omega_0$ AS A FUNCTION OF DAMPING FACTOR, $\zeta$

| $\zeta$ | $\omega_b/\omega_n$ |
|---|---|
| 0 | 1.55 |
| 0.1 | 1.54 |
| 0.2 | 1.51 |
| 0.3 | 1.45 |
| 0.4 | 1.39 |
| 0.5 | 1.27 |
| 0.6 | 1.13 |
| 0.707 | 1.0 |
| 0.8 | 0.90 |
| 0.9 | 0.74 |

quency as a function of damping factor $\zeta$ for a second-order system.

Although the relationships presented in tables 13.1–1 and 13.1–2 describing control system performance in terms of $\zeta$ and the undamped or natural frequencies are applicable directly for only second-order control systems, they are useful in establishing a rough order of magnitude for other systems as well when more exact computations are not warranted. More exact relationships for systems having higher order characteristic equations can be derived using methods described in Section 13.5.

**Position, Velocity and Acceleration Error Coefficients Expressed in Terms of Closed-Loop Characteristic Poles and Zeros.**   Although the closed-loop pole and zero locations have a direct bearing on the transient response characteristic of a control system, it is also possible and desirable to relate the closed-loop poles and zeros to the position, velocity, and acceleration error coefficients.   Since frequently control system performance characteristics are expressed in terms of these error coefficients as well as the desired transient response, being able to express these coefficients in terms of the pole and zero values enables the designer to place additional restraints on the pole and zero locations with the accompanying increase in information pertaining to the system performance.

As shown in Section 8.4 the expression for the position, velocity, and acceleration errors can be written in a series as a ratio of the actuating signal to reference input.   Thus

$$\frac{E}{R}(s) = C_0 + C_1 s + C_2 s^2 + \cdots \qquad (13.1\text{--}18)$$

where $C_0$, $C_1$, and $C_2$ are respectively the position, velocity, and acceleration error coefficients of Equation 8.4–6.

Since $C(s) = R(s) - E(s)$, Equation 13.1–18 can be written in terms of $C/R(s)$ as

$$\frac{C}{R}(s) = 1 - C_0 - C_1 s - C_2 s^2 - \cdots \qquad (13.1\text{--}19)$$

$C/R(s)$ can also be written in terms of its closed-loop poles and zeros as the ratio

$$\frac{C}{R}(s) = \frac{K(s + z_1)(s + z_2)(s + z_3) \cdots (s + z_m)}{(s + p_1)(s + p_2)(s + p_3) \cdots (s + p_n)} \qquad (13.1\text{--}20)$$

Expanding Equation 13.1–20 in a polynomial in ascending powers of $s$

$$\frac{C}{R}(s) = \frac{a_0 + a_1 s + a_2 s^2 + a_3 s^3 + \cdots a_m s^m}{b_0 + b_1 s + b_2 s^2 + b_3 s^3 + \cdots b_n s^n} \qquad (13.1\text{--}21)$$

where $a_0 = K$ (product of all the $z$'s, $m$ at a time),

$$= K z_1 z_2 z_3 \cdots z_m,$$

$a_1 = K \Sigma$ (products of all the $z$'s, $(m - 1)$ at a time),

$$= K(z_1 z_2 z_3 \cdots z_{m-1} + z_1 z_2 z_3 \cdots z_{m-2} z_m + \cdots),$$

$$a_1 = \sum_1^m \frac{a_0}{z_i},$$

$a_2 = K \Sigma$ (products of all the $z$'s, $(m - 2)$ at a time),

$$a_2 = K(z_1 z_2 z_3 \cdots z_{m-2} + z_1 z_2 z_3 \cdots z_{m-3} z_m + \cdots),$$

$$a_2 = \frac{1}{2} \sum_{1, i \neq j}^m \frac{a_0}{z_i z_j},$$

$b_0 =$ product of all the $p$'s, $n$ at a time,

$$b_0 = p_1 p_2 p_3 \cdots p_n,$$

$b_1 = \Sigma$ (products of all the $p$'s, $(n - 1)$ at a time),

$$= \Sigma (p_1 p_2 p_3 \cdots p_{n-1} + p_1 p_2 p_3 \cdots p_{n-2} p_n + \cdots),$$

$$b_1 = \sum_1^n \frac{b_0}{p_i},$$

$b_2 = \Sigma$ (products of all the $p$'s, $(n - 2)$ at a time),

$$= \Sigma (p_1 p_2 p_3 \cdots p_{n-2} + p_1 p_2 p_3 \cdots p_{n-3} p_n + \cdots),$$

$$b_2 = \frac{1}{2} \sum_{1, i \neq j}^n \frac{b_0}{p_i p_j}.$$

Dividing out the expression for $C/R(s)$ of Equation 13.1–21 in an increasing series in $s$,

$$\frac{C}{R}(s) = \frac{a_0}{b_0} + \left( a_1 - \frac{a_0 b_1}{b_0} \right) \frac{s}{b_0}$$

$$+ \left[ a_2 - \frac{a_0}{b_0} b_2 - \frac{b_1}{b_0} \left( a_1 - \frac{a_0 b_1}{b_0} \right) \right] \frac{s^2}{b_0} + \cdots \quad (13.1\text{–}22)$$

Comparing coefficients of the corresponding terms of Equations 13.1–19 and 13.1–22, one obtains the following error coefficients.

*Position Error Coefficient, $C_0$*

$$1 - C_0 = \frac{a_0}{b_0}$$

and

$$C_0 = 1 - \frac{a_0}{b_0} \quad (13.1\text{–}23)$$

Note for systems having zero position error, i.e., infinite position gain, $a_0/b_0 = 1$.

*Velocity Error Coefficient, $C_1$.* In evaluating the velocity and acceleration error coefficients, it will be assumed that the position error coefficient is zero so that $a_0/b_0 = 1$.

$$C_1 = \left(\frac{a_0}{b_0} b_1 - a_1\right)\frac{1}{b_0} \qquad (13.1\text{--}24)$$

$$C_1 = (b_1 - a_1)\frac{1}{b_0} = \sum_1^n \left(\frac{1}{p_i}\right) - \sum_1^m \left(\frac{1}{z_i}\right)$$

Since the poles, $p_i$, and the zeros, $z_i$, occur in conjugate pairs, only the real portions remain.  From this expression for $C_1$, it is evident that the smaller values of $p_i$ and $z_i$ are the ones that have the dominant effect and that additional poles and zeros of large magnitudes do not change the effect of the smaller poles and zeros, appreciably.

*Acceleration Error Coefficient, $C_2$*

$$-C_2 = \frac{1}{b_0}\left[-\frac{b_1}{b_0}(a_1 - b_1) + a_2 - b_2\right]$$

$$+C_2 = -C_1\left[\sum_1^n \frac{1}{p_i}\right] + \frac{1}{2}\left[\sum_1^n \left(\frac{1}{p_i p_j}\right) - \sum_1^m \left(\frac{1}{z_i z_j}\right)\right] \qquad (13.1\text{--}25)$$

Again as in the case of the velocity error coefficient, it is the smaller values of the poles and zeros which have the most dominant effect.  The expressions for $C_2$ and $C_1$ indicate that it is possible to exert some measure of control of one error coefficient without affecting the other in similar fashion although they are both influenced by the same general parameters.

*Example 1*

For a control system having no zeros and three real poles, it is desired that a velocity error coefficient of 0.01 second be obtained.  What are three values of closed loop poles that will produce the desired performance?

$$C_1 = \frac{1}{p_1} + \frac{1}{p_2} + \frac{1}{p_3}$$

Selecting $p_1$ to be 150, i.e., larger than 100, and $p_2 = p_3/2$

$$\frac{1}{100} = \frac{1}{150} + \frac{2}{p_3} + \frac{1}{p_3}$$

$$3p_3 = 2p_3 + 600 + 300$$

$$p_3 = 900$$

$$p_2 = 450$$

*Example 2*

What are the velocity and acceleration error coefficients for a control system for which the poles are $-10$, $-20 \pm j30$ and the zero is $-9$?

$$C_1 = \frac{1}{10} + \frac{1}{20 + j30} + \frac{1}{20 - j30} - \frac{1}{9}$$

$$= \frac{\left\{ \begin{array}{c} 9(20 + j30)(20 - j30) + 90(20 - j30) \\ + 90(20 + j30) - 10(20^2 + 30^2) \end{array} \right\}}{90 \times (20^2 + 30^2)}$$

$$= \frac{9(1300) + 1800 + 1800 - 10(1300)}{90(1300)}$$

$C_1 = 0.0197$, corresponding to an effective velocity gain constant of 50.8

$$C_2 = \frac{1}{50.8}\left(\frac{15{,}300}{90 \times 1300}\right)$$

$$+ \frac{1}{2}\left[\frac{1}{10(20 + j30)} + \frac{1}{10(20 - j30)} + \frac{1}{(20^2 + 30^2)}\right]$$

$$= -0.00258 + \frac{1}{2}\left[\frac{20 - j30 + 20 + j30 + 10}{10(1300)}\right]$$

$C_2 = 0.00384 - 0.00258 = 0.00126$

$C_2 = 0.00126$, corresponding to an effective acceleration gain constant of 795

Equation 13.1–24 serves an additional useful function in that it indicates whether or not the poles and zeros selected yield a positive velocity error coefficient corresponding to the conventional type 1 servo.

The position, velocity, and acceleration error coefficient expressions of Equations 13.1–23, 13.1–24, and 13.1–25, respectively, provide a close tie between the values of actuating signal for slowly changing forms of the reference input and the locations of the system's closed-loop poles and zeros. As such they serve to place limiting-value restraints on the poles and zeros which might otherwise be selected on the basis of transient response and stability considerations alone. The control system design process described in Section 13.6 is a more direct synthesis procedure by virtue of the knowledge one has of the relationships between the pole-zero configurations, the error coefficients, and the form of the transient response.

## 13.2  Examples of Series Stabilization Methods

Having related the location of the closed-loop system roots to the system performance, it is now appropriate to look at the specific root locus plots for examples of the various control system stabilization methods previously studied in Chapters 10 and 12, respectively. In this section will be considered the series stabilization cases. The terms lead, lag, and lead-lag used to define series stabilization networks as viewed from complex-plane and attenuation frequency methods of analysis have quite different connotations when used with the root locus method. For example, the effect of a lead term is to introduce an open-loop zero in the complex plane, whereas the effect of a lag term is to introduce an open-loop pole in the complex plane. The following examples will provide a basis for understanding specific system performance from the root locus plots.

**Phase Lag Networks.** The transfer function of the representative phase lag network shown in Figure 10.1–3 can be expressed most conveniently for plotting the root locus by the form

$$\frac{E_o}{E_{in}} = \frac{T_2}{T_1} \frac{(s + 1/T_2)}{(s + 1/T_1)} \qquad (13.2\text{–}1)$$

where $T_1 = (R_1 + R_2)C_2$ and $T_2 = R_2C_2$.

Since for an effective lag network $(R_1 + R_2)$ is considerably larger than $R_2$, i.e., $T_2/T_1 < 1$, the presence of the constant term in Equation 13.2–1 reflects the fact that, at values of $s$ large compared with $1/T_1$ and $1/T_2$, the gain of the transfer function is reduced by the $T_2/T_1$ ratio. Further, the value of the pole produced by $1/T_1$ is considerably smaller than the value of the zero produced by $1/T_2$.

Figure 13.2–1 shows the location of the pole and zero associated with a simple phase lag network and indicates that for systems having low decay rates and low natural frequencies the presence of the pole, $1/T_1$, near the origin will contribute additional negative phase angle toward making $-180°$ in Equation 6.6–3 over what would be the case if the phase lag network were not present. For values of $s$ remote from $-1/T_1$ and $-1/T_2$ the angular effect of each tends to nullify the other. Because of this tendency for the effect of the pole and zero of the phase lag network to have a cancelling effect at regions remote from them, the phase lag characteristic may appear like a dipole and can be used effectively to decrease the velocity error coefficient of a system, see Equation 13.1–24.

Consider now the control system shown in Figure 10.1–5 wherein a phase lag network is used for providing stable system operation despite the use of higher gain in the low frequency range. The amplifier, amplidyne, and motor system without the phase lag network has the transfer

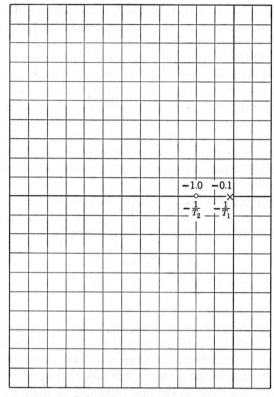

FIGURE 13.2–1.   Pole and zero location for phase lag network

$$\frac{E_o}{E_{in}} = \frac{T_2}{T_1} \frac{(s + 1/T_2)}{(s + 1/T_1)}$$

Shown for $T_1 = 10$, $T_2 = 1$

function,

$$G_1(s) = \frac{K_1}{s(T_f s + 1)(T_m s + 1)} = \frac{K_1}{T_f T_m s(s + 1/T_f)(s + 1/T_m)}$$

$$(13.2\text{–}2)$$

for which the root locus plot is shown in Figure 13.2–2. With the nominal gain of 2 the system is shown to be stable and have its lowest decay rate 1.7 seconds$^{-1}$, a natural frequency of oscillation of 2.2 radians per second, and a decrement factor of 0.61.

By increasing the through gain an amount $K_2/K_1 = 20$, the transfer function

$$G_2 = \frac{K_2}{K_1} G_1 = \frac{K_2}{T_f T_m s(s + 1/T_f)(s + 1/T_m)} \qquad (13.2\text{–}3)$$

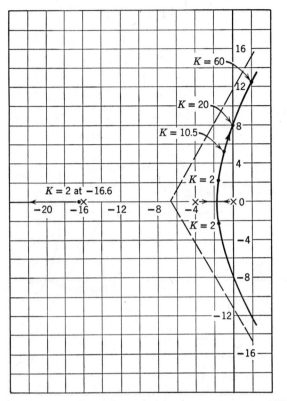

FIGURE 13.2–2.   Root locus plot of resultant type 1 control system of Figure 10.1–5.

$$G_1 = \frac{2}{s(s/4 + 1)(s/16 + 1)} = \frac{64K}{s(s + 4)(s + 16)}$$

is obtained. As can be seen from Figure 13.2–2, the system is now unstable $(K = 40)$.

By the addition of the series phase lag network, shown on Figures 10.1–5 and 10.1–6 the resultant transfer function of the system becomes

$$G = \frac{K_2 T_2(s + 1/T_2)}{T_f T_m T_1 s(s + 1/T_f)(s + 1/T_m)(s + 1/T_1)} \qquad (13.2\text{--}4)$$

for which the root locus plot is as shown on Figure 13.2–3. The presence of the phase lag network and the increase in gain to $K = 40$ has altered the root locus characteristic shown on Figure 13.2–2 in the following respects:

1. An additional branch has been produced that has resulted in an additional closed-loop pole at $s = -0.286$, slightly more negative in

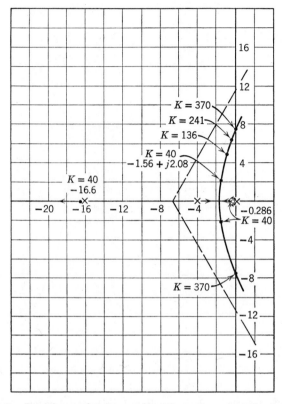

FIGURE 13.2–3.  Root locus plot for resultant type 1 servomechanism of Figures 10.1–6 and 12.1–2 using phase-lag stabilization.

$$G_1 = \frac{3.2 \times 40 \, (s + 1/4)}{s(s + 4)(s + 16)(s + 1/80)}$$

magnitude to the open-loop zero at $s = -\frac{1}{4}$. The effect of this is to produce an additional, slowly decaying root.

2. The dominant pair of complex poles remains approximately the same decreasing in decay rate and increasing in frequency slightly despite the marked increased value of gain.  Likewise, the large negative closed loop pole near $s = -16.6$ is just about the same.

3. The directions of the asymptotes to the root locus are the same as previously and their intersection with the real axis is essentially unaltered.  The frequency at which the root locus crosses the real axis is reduced slightly from 8.0 to 7.7 radians per second.

The presence of the lag network has permitted a marked increase in the static gain, $K_2$, of the system with a number of the transient response characteristics being relatively unchanged but with the addition of a slowly decaying pole near the location of the open-loop zero. The increase in static gain possible is about the same as the ratio of the pole to the zero of the lag network.

**Phase Lead Networks.** The representative phase lead network of Figure 10.1–8 with the transfer function

$$\frac{E_o}{E_{in}} = \frac{s + 1/T_1}{s + 1/T_2} \tag{13.2–5}$$

where $T_1 = R_1 C_1$ and

$$T_2 = \frac{(R_2)}{(R_1 + R_2)} R_1 C_1$$

is shown by its pole and zero on the complex plane on Figure 13.2–4.

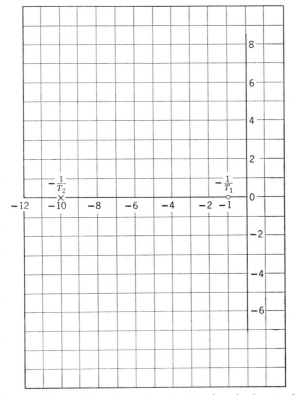

FIGURE 13.2–4.   Pole and zero location for phase lead network.

$$\frac{E_o}{E_{in}} = \frac{s + 1/T_1}{s + 1/T_2}$$

Shown for $T_1 = 1$, $T_2 = 0.1$.

The effect of the open-loop zero being closer to the origin than the open-loop pole is to reduce the angular rotation of the total $G(s)H(s)$ function of Equation 6.6–3 in the region in the vicinity of the origin. However, in this region the gain of the phase lead network is also reduced.

At large values of $s$, Equation 13.2–5 shows that the transfer function contributes neither phase nor magnitude change to the $E_o/E_{in}$ ratio.

*Type 1 System.* The original control system of Figure 10.1–10 has the transfer function

$$\frac{C}{E'} = G' = \frac{K_1}{T_f T_m s(s + 1/T_f)(s + 1/T_m)} \qquad (13.2–6)$$

for which the root locus is as shown on Figure 13.2–2. The resultant system of Figure 10.1–10, including the phase lead network, has the transfer function indicated by Equation 10.1–10, namely,

$$\frac{C}{E} = G = \frac{K_2}{T_f \times \dfrac{R_2 T_m}{R_1 + R_2} s(s + 1/T_f)\left(s + \dfrac{R_1 + R_2}{R_2 T_m}\right)} \qquad (13.2–7)$$

for which the root locus is shown on Figure 13.2–5. The open-loop zero

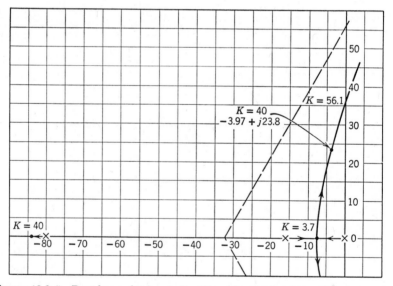

Figure 13.2–5. Root locus plot for resultant type 1 control system of Figure 10.1–10.

of the phase lead network was so chosen that the pole caused by the motor time constant has been canceled. In its place, however, there appears the pole of the phase lead network at a considerably greater negative value.

Referring to Figure 13.2–5 and comparing the closed loop-poles with those of the system without the phase lead network, Figure 13.2–2, one notes the following:

1. With a gain of 40, the original system is unstable, whereas the system with the phase lead added is able to operate stably with a decay rate of 3.97 seconds$^{-1}$, a natural frequency of 23.8, and a decrement factor of 0.165.

2. The slowly decaying pole that was present when phase lag stabilization was used is not present with the phase lead network. With phase lead the response decays more rapidly; it is more oscillatory during the process.

3. Although the same slope is obtained for the asymptotes to the root locus as was obtained with phase lag stabilization, the intersection of the asymptotes with the real axis is at a larger negative value, namely, $-32$ instead of $-6.67$. Likewise the intersection of the imaginary axis is increased from 7.7 for phase lag to 35.8 for phase lead stabilization.

*Type 2 System.* The type 2 system, shown in block diagram form in Figure 10.1–13, has the transfer function

$$\frac{C}{E'} = G' = \frac{K}{T_m s^2 (s + 1/T_m)} \qquad (13.2\text{–}8)$$

The root locus plot is sketched on Figure 13.2–6 and shows that with the two poles located at zero, the system is unstable for all values of gain. The use of a lead network having a zero between the origin and the pole $-1/T_m$ is necessary to reshape the root locus in the vicinity of the origin.

The addition of the preamplifier and phase lead network described in Figures 10.1–13 and 10.1–15 causes the resultant system to have the transfer function given by Equation 10.1–15.

$$G = \frac{KT_1(s + 1/T_1)}{\dfrac{R_2 T_1 T_m s^2}{(R_1 + R_2)} \left[ s + \left( \dfrac{R_1 + R_2}{R_2 T_1} \right) \right] \left[ s + \dfrac{1}{T_m} \right]} \qquad (13.2\text{–}9)$$

The root locus plot of this equation is shown on Figure 13.2–7 and indicates that the system is stable with the gain of 0.25. However, for increased gains in excess of 1.75 the system can be made unstable.

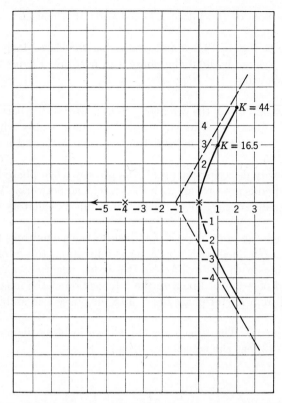

FIGURE 13.2-6.   Root locus for original type 2 control system of Figure 10.1-15.

$$G' = \frac{1/4}{s^2(s/4 + 1)} = \frac{4K}{s^2(s + 4)}$$

The presence of the zero at $-\frac{1}{4}$ introduced by the phase lead network has an effect tending to cancel out one of the poles at the origin and causing the locus to start into the second and third quadrants at low gains rather than into the first and fourth as was the case without the lead network.   The locus is able to pass to the left of the zero and produce more rapid decrement rates for the oscillatory terms, although the presence of this zero in the open loop characteristic does produce a slowly decaying closed loop pole at $-0.35$.

Although the effect of changes in the system gain for a given set of time constants are directly apparent from the root locus plot, the quantitative effect of changing the time constants as well as gains is less obvious.

**Lead-lag Networks.**   The transfer function of the general lead-lag

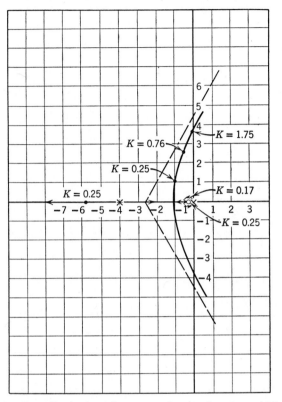

FIGURE 13.2-7.   Root locus of resultant type 2 control system of Figure 10.1–15.

$$G = \frac{0.25\,(4s+1)}{s^2(s/4+1)^2} = \frac{64K(s+1/4)}{s^2(s+4)^2}$$

network shown on Figure 10.1–16 can be written as

$$\frac{E_o}{E_{in}} = \frac{(s+1/T_1)(s+1/T_2)}{s^2 + (1/T_1 + 1/T_2 + T_{12}/T_1T_2)s + 1/T_1T_2} \qquad (13.2\text{--}10)$$

To perform the desired lead-lag function, the pole-zero orientations are a combination of the ones described for the phase lag and phase lead networks separately as is shown in Figure 13.2–8.

Use is made of the small pole-zero combination of the phase lag network to permit an improvement in the velocity error coefficient, while the larger zero-pole combination of the phase lead network enhances the system performance at the region of larger gains and speedier responses.

Use of a lead-lag network has been described for the system shown in Figures 10.1–18 and 12.1–7.

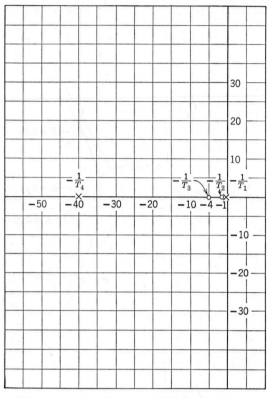

Figure 13.2–8.  Pole and zero location for lead lag network.

$$\frac{E_o}{E_{in}} = \frac{(T_2s + 1)(T_3s + 1)}{(T_1s + 1)(T_4s + 1)} = \frac{(s + 1)(s + 4)}{(s + 1/10)(s + 40)}$$

Shown for $T_1 = 10.0$, $T_2 = 1$
$T_3 = 1/4$, $T_4 = 1/40$

The transfer function of the original system is given by Equation 13.2–2 as

$$G_1 = \frac{K_1}{T_f T_m s(s + 1/T_f)(s + 1/T_m)} \qquad (13.2\text{--}11)$$

The transfer function of the resultant system with the gain increased and the lead-lag network added is

$$G = \frac{K_2 T_1(s + 1/T_1)}{T_f T_3 T_4 s(s + 1/T_f)(s + 1/T_3)(s + 1/T_4)} \qquad (13.2\text{--}12)$$

where $T_2$, the smaller time constant in the numerator, was equal to $T_m$ so that this zero and pole combination cancel.

Figure 13.2–2 has shown the pole configuration of the original system and Figures 13.2–9a and 13.2–9b show an approximate and the actual

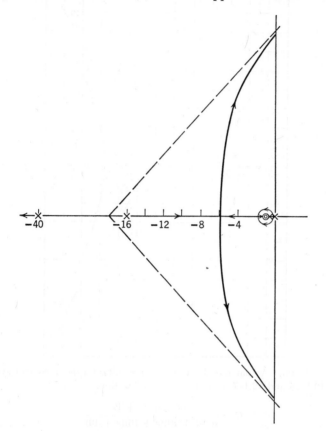

FIGURE 13.2–9(a).   Approximate root locus plot for resultant type 1 control system of Figures 10.1–18 and 12.1–7 using lead-lag stabilization.

$$G = \frac{40 \times 64 \,(s + 1)}{s(s + 1/10)(s + 16)(s + 40)}$$

pole-zero configurations of the resultant system when the lead-lag network and appropriate gain increase have been made.   Comparing the two root loci, it will be noted that the lag characteristic shows up as the pole at $-\frac{1}{10}$ and the zero at $-1$.   Since the lead characteristic has been chosen to have a zero at $-4$, it cancels the pole originally there while the added pole now appears at $-40$.   In effect the pole at $-4$ has been replaced by one at $-40$ so that the critical frequency at which zero damping exists has been raised from $\omega = 8$ on Figure 13.2–2 to $\omega = 24.2$

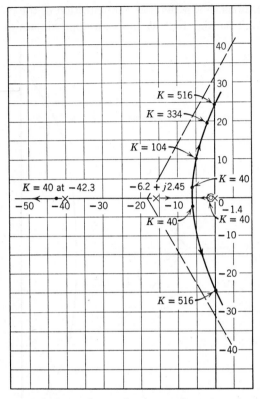

FIGURE 13.2–9(b).  Actual root locus plot for resultant type 1 control system of Figures 10.1–18 and 12.1–7 using lead-lag stabilization.

$$G = \frac{40 \times 64 \, (s + 1)}{s(s + 1/10)(s + 16)(s + 40)}$$

on Figure 13.2–9b.  The corresponding gain for this condition has been raised from $K = 20$ to $K = 516$.  This permits the higher operating gain of $K = 40$ to be utilized.  Again the presence of the open-loop zero near to the origin results in a slowly decaying closed-loop pole at $-1.4$.

The use of the root locus presentation of the performance of the system provides a means for determining its transient response characteristics and how they change with system gain.  As such it provides a means for rounding out one's understanding of the over-all system's performance.  As described later in this section it can also be employed effectively as a basis for synthesizing systems with desired performance characteristics.  Its application is particularly straightforward for series methods of stabilization.

## 13.3   Examples of Feedback Stabilization Methods

As was noted in the attenuation-frequency approach to systems analysis, the presence of feedback requires a departure from the method of treatment used for series elements.

Consideration of the basic equations involved leads one to an understanding of methods for handling the case of feedback. Thus, for the general case of feedback shown on Figure 13.3–1,

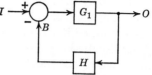

$$\frac{0}{I} = \frac{G_1}{1 + G_1 H} \qquad (13.3\text{–}1)$$

for $G_1 = \dfrac{G_N}{G_D}$ and $H = \dfrac{H_N}{H_D}$.

FIGURE 13.3–1.   Control element with feedback.

$$\frac{0}{I} = \frac{G_N}{G_D\left(1 + \dfrac{G_N H_N}{G_D H_D}\right)} = \frac{G_N H_D}{G_D H_D + G_N H_N} \qquad (13.3\text{–}2)$$

From Equation 13.3–2 it is apparent that the zeros of the resultant expression are equal to $G_N$, the zeros of the forward element, and $H_D$, the poles of the feedback element. The poles of the resultant expression are obtained by setting $G_D H_D + G_N H_N = 0$, or

$$\frac{G_N H_N}{G_D H_D} = -1 \qquad (13.3\text{–}3)$$

Referring to Equation 6.6–3, one notices that this is the form of the expression for obtaining the root locus. Thus the closed-loop poles determined from the root locus establish the poles of the resultant element with feedback. The closed-loop zeros are determined from inspection of the forward element's zeros and the feedback element's poles.

In similar fashion to the methods employed when the attenuation frequency analyses are used, the general block diagram of a control element with feedback as shown in Figure 13.3–1 can be redrawn as if unity feedback existed but with an additional series element shown, Figure 13.3–2.

Thus,

$$\frac{0}{I} = \frac{G_1}{1 + G_1 H} = \frac{1}{H}\left[\frac{G_1 H}{1 + G_1 H}\right] \qquad (13.3\text{–}4)$$

To determine the root locus of $0/I$, one employs the following steps as indicated by Equations 13.3–2, 13.3–3, and 13.3–4.

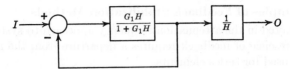

FIGURE 13.3–2. Block diagram equivalent of control element with feedback of Figure 13.3–1.

(1) Apply the root locus method to the open loop gain function, $G_1H$, to obtain the poles of $G_1H/(1 + G_1H)$. This is the procedure that has been followed in the preceding examples.

(2) Next, the zeros of $G_1H/(1 + G_1H)$ must be determined. These are equal to the zeros of $G_1H$ alone as is evident from consideration of the $G_1H/(1 + G_1H)$ expression.

(3) Finally, the zeros and poles of $1/H$ are obtained directly from the poles and zeros of the known $H$ function.

Since the effect of changing the gains within the feedback loop is to change the resultant time constants, i.e., poles and/or zeros, it is necessary to establish a value or perhaps a series of values of loop gain for which the resultant poles and zeros of the loop with feedback are determined. With the poles and zeros of $0/I$ established, this control element with the effect of the feedback around it exactly represented may be included with the remaining elements in the system.

**Root Locus for Direct Feedback.** For direct feedback, $H = 1$ so the process of obtaining the resultant root locus for a control element with feedback is relatively simple. Consider the example cited in Section 10.2 where direct feedback is used to reduce the time constant of a control element. From Figure 10.2–1,

$$G_1 = \frac{K_a}{(T_f s + 1)} = \frac{K_a}{T_f(s + 1/T_f)}$$

$$(13.3–5)$$

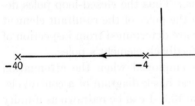

FIGURE 13.3–3. Root locus of simple control element with direct feedback.

$$G_1 = \frac{K_a}{T_f(s + 1/T_f)}$$

$$K_a = 9; \qquad T_f = \frac{1}{4}$$

With only one pole the root locus starts at $s = -1/T_f$ and proceeds towards $-\infty$ along the negative real axis. For $K_a = 9$, and $T_f = \frac{1}{4}$, the value of $s_a$ for the root locus is

$$\frac{9}{\frac{1}{4}(s_a + 4)} = -1 \quad (13.3–6)$$

from which $s_a = -40$ as shown on Figure 13.3–3.

Thus, the time constant has been reduced from $\frac{1}{4}$ to $1/s_a = \frac{1}{40}$ second.

To establish what is the resultant gain of the element with feedback, it is necessary to return to the original equation for $0/I$

$$\frac{0}{I} = \frac{G_1}{1 + G_1} = \frac{K_a}{T_f(s + 1)\left(1 + \dfrac{K_a}{T_f s + 1}\right)} = \frac{K_a/(1 + K_a)}{1 + \dfrac{T_f s}{1 + K_a}} \quad (13.3\text{-}7)$$

where the gain is shown to be $K_a/(1 + K_a)$.

*Root-Locus Characteristic with Feedback Through Frequency-Sensitive Element.* The system shown in Figure 10.2–11 and considered from an attenuation frequency point of view in Figures 12.2–2 through 12.2–5 will now be studied by the root locus method. As shown on Figure 13.3–4, the motor control element, having two time constants, has the transfer function

$$G_1 = \frac{K_1}{s(T_f s + 1)(T_m s + 1)} \quad (13.3\text{-}8)$$

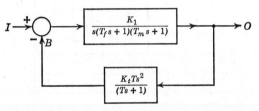

Figure 13.3–4.  Block diagram of motor generator with tachometer feedback through lead network as in Figure 10.2–11.

The feedback element, consisting of a tachometer feedingback through a single $RC$ network of time constant, $T$, has the transfer function

$$H = \frac{K_t T s^2}{(Ts + 1)} = \frac{K_t s^2}{(s + 1/T)} \quad (13.3\text{-}9)$$

The resultant $GH$ function is therefore

$$G_1 H = \frac{K_1 K_t s}{T_f T_m (s + 1/T_f)(s + 1/T_m)(s + 1/T)} \quad (13.3\text{-}10)$$

A root locus plot of this function is shown on Figure 13.3–5. With this plot and the values of the gains $K_1$ and $K_t$ assigned, $s_1$, $s_2$, and $s_3$, the resultant values for the poles are found by Equation 13.3–10 to be

$$s_1 = -0.069, \text{ and } s_2 \text{ and } s_3 = -10.6 \pm j32.3$$

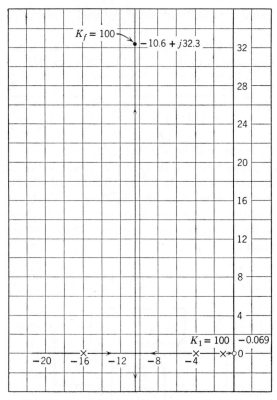

FIGURE 13.3–5.   Root locus of $G_1(s)H(s)$ loop for data of Figure 10.2–13.

$$G_1(s) = \frac{100}{s(s/4 + 1)(s/16 + 1)}$$

$$H(s) = \frac{0.167s^2}{(0.8s + 1)}$$

See also Equation 13.3–10.

Note that moderate changes in the gains $K_1$ or $K_t$ will cause the oscillatory roots along the $-10.6$ line to have a higher or lower frequency varying in the same direction as $K_1K_t$ gain product.

To find the gain associated with $G_1H/(1 + G_1H)$, one substitutes in the value of $G_1H$ from Equation 13.3–10 and obtains the equation

$$\frac{G_1H}{1 + G_1H} = \frac{K_1K_tTs}{(T_ms + 1)(T_fs + 1)(Ts + 1) + K_1K_ts} \quad (13.3\text{–}11)$$

from which the gain term is $K_1K_tT$. Thus, in factored form the equation for $G_1H/(1 + G_1H)$ can be written as

$$\frac{G_1H}{1 + G_1H} = \frac{K_1K_tTs}{\frac{1}{80}(s + 0.069)(s + 10.6 - j32.3)(s + 10.6 + j32.3)}$$

$$(13.3\text{-}12)$$

where it will be noted that the term $\frac{1}{80}$ represents the reciprocal of the constant term of the product of the three factors $(s + 0.069)(s + 10.6 - j32.3)$ $(s + 10.6 + j32.3)$.

Using the expression for $\frac{0}{I}\left( = \frac{1}{H}\left[\frac{G_1H}{1 + G_1H}\right]\right)$ from Equation 13.3–4 and the values of $H$ and $G_1H/(1 + G_1H)$ from Equations 13.3–9 and 13.3–12 respectively,

$$\frac{0}{I} = \frac{64K_1(s + 1.25)}{s(s + 0.069)(s + 10.6 - j32.3)(s + 10.6 + j32.3)} \quad (13.3\text{-}13)$$

Figure 13.3–6 shows the root locus plot using $0/I$ from Equation 13.3–13 for presenting the equivalent series transfer function. From this plot it appears that for $K_1 = 100$ as is the case, the two complex poles have an oscillation frequency of $\omega = 31.6$ radians per second and have a relatively low damping ratio ($\zeta = 0.312$). The two other poles are $-1.85$ and $-4.2$.

Comparing these results with the attenuation-frequency plot on Figure 12.2–5, it will be noticed that the relatively high frequency oscillation occurs at the frequency of the closing of the inner loop approximately 30 radians per second, while the open-loop attenuation crossover occurs at a lower frequency of 5 radians per second. The decrement times for both the oscillatory roots and the two other roots are about similar. The presence of a zero having a still lower decrement rate helps decrease the velocity error coefficient for the system as can be determined from Equation 13.1–24.

This study of the root locus characteristics has made apparent some of the difficulties that appear during transient conditions that were not so evident from the approximate attenuation frequency diagrams. As such it has proved a valuable aid to an increased knowledge of the overall system performance.

The preceding analysis by the root locus method of a system employing frequency sensitive feedback has served to illustrate the techniques whereby the root locus of such a system may be determined. The procedure involves first the determination of the poles of the inner loop, then its zeroes, and finally its over-all characteristic. After this the inner loop is replaced by its series equivalent and the remainder of the loop is handled along with this series equivalent representation. The procedure is exact throughout and no approximations are required.

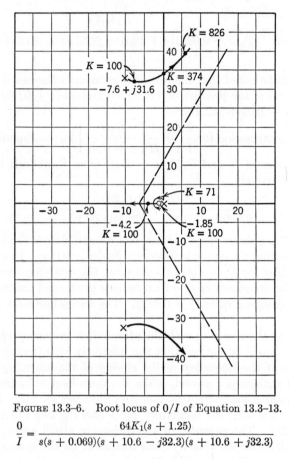

FIGURE 13.3–6.   Root locus of $0/I$ of Equation 13.3–13.

$$\frac{0}{I} = \frac{64K_1(s + 1.25)}{s(s + 0.069)(s + 10.6 - j32.3)(s + 10.6 + j32.3)}$$

## 13.4   Aids for Establishing the Root Locus

The two preceding sections have pointed up the desirability of being able to determine the root locus plots to increase one's understanding of a system's transient performance.   In Section 6.6 was outlined the basic rules that are helpful for drawing the general shape of the root locus.

It is worthwhile now to examine further some additional aids for establishing this locus with sufficient accuracy for engineering purposes.

The three different ways which will be presented here included graphical techniques as set forth by Evans,[120] use of charts relating pole-zero location and root locus as for example those published by Yeh,[121] and numerical calculations such as those described by Donahue.[134]   Although other methods have been advocated, such as those using electrostatic field analogies and phase angle loci plots,[128] the use of these supplemental methods may not be warranted unless considerable detailed design work must be performed.

**Graphical Aids.** The basic rules for sketching the general shape of the root locus set forth in Section 6.6 are helpful for obtaining an approximate root locus plot. These rules establish the number of branches, the limiting values of the locus at $K = 0$ and $\infty$, the direction and number of asymptotes as well as their intersection with the real axis, and the direction with which the locus leaves each root and pole. The problem now remains of establishing, as precisely as is required, the exact location of the locus in those regions of practical interest, namely, at those values of gain removed from 0 or $\infty$.

Graphically this amounts to a cut-and-try procedure in which the approximate values of the locus are obtained by the initial sketches made as described above. A particular point $s$ is chosen and the net angle at that point is determined from the angles measured from the zeros and poles to this point. If this angle is not 180°, an adjacent point is chosen and the net angle is again calculated. By means of interpolation or extrapolation, it should be possible with the two values of angle obtained to establish the location of $s$ for the 180° angle condition to be met. Figure 13.4–1 shows the process for a point in Figure 13.2–9.

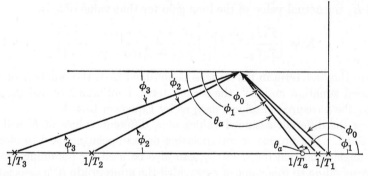

FIGURE 13.4–1. Angular relationships involved in determining the net angle for $G(s)H(s)$ for a point in the $s$ plane.

$$G(s)H(s) = \frac{KT_a(s + 1/T_a)}{T_1T_2T_3s(s + 1/T_1)(s + 1/T_2)(s + 1/T_3)}$$

The equation to be solved is that given by Equation 6.6–3, namely,

$$G(s)H(s) = |\,1\,|\,\underline{/180°\,q} \qquad (13.4\text{–}1)$$

where $q$ is any odd integer i.e., $\pm1$, $\pm3$, $\pm5$, and $G(s)H(s)$ is expressed in the form

$$G(s)H(s) = \frac{K(T_as + 1)(T_bs + 1)\,\cdots}{s^n(T_1s + 1)(T_2s + 1)\,\cdots} \qquad (13.4\text{–}2)$$

Since all the factors of $G(s)H(s)$ have $s$ in them, the angles and vector lengths can be measured from the $s$ point. The vectors $(s - s_x)$ on the root locus plot have their tails located at the poles and zeros and their arrows located at the $s$ point chosen. Thus by locating a protractor on the $s$ point, with its origin horizontal to the left and its angles increasing counterclockwise, one can measure and add together the angles associated with the factors of the denominator, $\phi_0$, $\phi_1$, and $\phi_2$, then measure and subtract the angle associated with the factors of the numerator, $\theta_a$ and $\theta_b$. The length of the vectors on the root locus plot from $s$ to each of the poles and zeros can be measured directly to provide $K''$ the necessary magnitude information to satisfy the magnitude requirement in Equation 13.4–1. Thus, for the $G(s)H(s)$ of Equation 13.4–2,

$$K'' = \frac{\left| (s - s_a)(s - s_b) \cdots \right|}{\left| s^n \right| \left| (s - s_1)(s - s_2) \cdots \right|} \tag{13.4–3}$$

However, the literal expression for the magnitude of $G(s)H(s)$ from Equation 13.4–2 can be written as

$$G(s)H(s) = \frac{KT_aT_b}{T_1T_2} = K'' \tag{13.4–4}$$

and $K$, the actual value of the loop gain for that value of $s$, is

$$K = \left\{ \frac{T_1T_2 \cdots}{T_aT_b \cdots} \right\} \left\{ \frac{\left| (s - s_a)(s - s_b) \cdots \right|}{\left| s^n \right| \left| (s - s_1)(s - s_2) \cdots \right|} \right\} \tag{13.4–5}$$

where the first term in parenthesis is obtained from the numbers of the original equation and $K''$, the second term, is obtained by calculation using the measured graphical data as by Equation 13.4–3.

For the different assumed values of $s$, different values of $K$ will be obtained. The process of interpolating or extrapolating used to obtain the angle condition for $s$, $180° q$, can also be used for obtaining the $K$ corresponding to this value of $s$ provided the appropriate $K''$s associated with these $s$'s are used.

Although the preceding description of the graphical method has shown the poles and zeros all to be real, the method is also directly applicable to complex values of poles and zeros. The magnitudes and angles of the distances from any pole or zero to the assumed value of $s$ is alone of importance.

The graphical processes of measuring the angles of the numerator and denominator, then adding or subtracting as required, and of measuring the lengths of the vectors and multiplying or dividing as indicated can be appreciably shortened with the use of the "Spirule." [120] This device, obtainable from the Spirule Company, 9728 El Venado, Whittier, California, and shown on Figure 13.4–2, consists of an arm and disk held

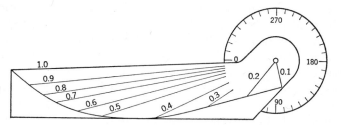

FIGURE 13.4–2.  Spirule.

together with a light friction fit by a special eyelet that also serves as a pivot point.  The pivot point is placed at a trial $s$ point and the disk is initially aligned.  The arm is then rotated with respect to the disk through each of the vector angles to obtain their resultant sum as a direct reading on the disk.

A logarithmic spiral curve on the arm permits the logarithm of the length from the trial points to the poles and zeros to be obtained as an angle.  Hence the addition of these angles corresponds to the addition of logarithms and the resultant angle is proportional to the magnitude $K''$ described previously in Equation 13.4–3.  High speed and acceptable engineering accuracy can be obtained by one who is familiar with the use of the Spirule.

*Use of Charts for Establishing Root Locus.*  As was noted in connection with the attenuation-frequency method of control system design and analysis, the relative magnitudes of the various time constants and gain terms in the numerator and denominator of the transfer function give rise to certain characteristic attenuation curves from which much information can be inferred about the system's stability and performance.  In similar fashion, Yeh has analyzed the nature of the root locus that results from a number of different orientations of the pole-zero configurations for systems having up to four poles and up to two zeros.  In many instances Yeh has developed analytical expressions describing the equations for the root locus in terms of the parameters of the transfer function.

In this section, root loci have been plotted in a general form, as shown on Figures 13.4–3 through Figure 13.4–10, and a good understanding of the nature of the root locus plot of a new system can be obtained by comparing its pole-zero $(p, z)$ configuration with that of the corresponding pole-zero $(p, z)$ configuration of these charts.  Although detailed graphical and/or numerical work will probably be required for more complex systems, in some instances the approximate root locus plot may be made almost by inspection.

The following examples from Yeh [121] show not only how the roots may vary along a locus when the gain is changed but also how the entire root locus is reshaped when one of the control system time constants is altered relative to the rest. The systems considered are ones for which the number of poles $p$ is equal to or greater than the number of zeros $z$. The number of poles and zeros are indicated by $(p, z)$ where the number of poles precedes the number of zeros. It should be noted that, although the pole of smallest value may not be indicated as being at the origin corresponding to the presence of an integrator, there is no discontinuity as the origin is reached. The same general shape locus is retained where a small real value for the pole is used as when its value is zero. Of course, the values of the error coefficients are appreciably affected by this difference, however.

A thorough familiarity with the basic shapes of the root loci is valuable in the design of control systems. Systematic studies of the movement of the root loci with changes in pole and root orientation as well as with gain will greatly facilitate the design problem.

**Systems Having First-Order Poles—Types (1, 0) and (1, 1).**  Root loci of first-order systems, shown in Figure 13.4–3, lie entirely along the real

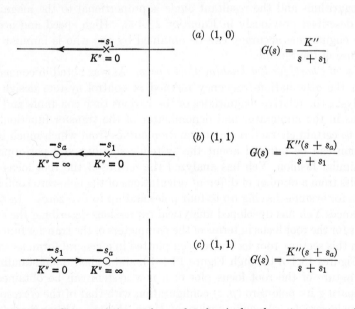

FIGURE 13.4–3.  Characteristic root locus plots for single pole systems, $a$-type $(1, 0)$, and $b$–$c$ type $(1, 1)$.

negative axis.  The type (1, 0), indicated by the $a$ curve, represents the case of a single pole and shows the effect of increasing gain to be the increase of the value of the pole.  This case was discussed in Section 13.3, and a faster dynamic response was shown for increasing values of gain.

The type (1, 1) systems shown by the $b$ and $c$ curves represent the single-phase lag and the single-phase lead network cases, respectively, described in Section 13.2.  The values of the root locus move from that of the pole for low values of gain to the zero for high values of gain having a negative real value throughout.  Depending on whether the pole or the zero is initially greater, the root locus will move to the left or the right with increasing gain.

**Systems Having Second-Order Poles—Types (2, 0), (2, 1).**  The root loci of type (2, 0) second-order systems are shown in Figure 13.4–4.

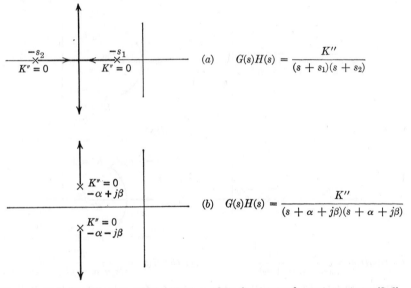

$$(a)\qquad G(s)H(s) = \frac{K''}{(s + s_1)(s + s_2)}$$

$$(b)\qquad G(s)H(s) = \frac{K''}{(s + \alpha + j\beta)(s + \alpha + j\beta)}$$

FIGURE 13.4–4.  Characteristic root locus plots for two pole systems type (2, 0).

When the two poles are real, the root locus consists of the real axis connecting the two poles and the locus of the perpendicular bisector of the line between the two poles, curve $a$.  Increasing the gain causes the real roots to come closer to each other until at critical damping the roots are equal.

Further increase in gain causes the roots to separate with an increasing natural frequency and a lower damping ratio.  For a (2, 0) system with the poles initially under-damped, the root locus lies on the line connecting them, curve $b$, and an increase in gain causes the roots to separate further.

Figure 13.4–5 shows six possible configurations of root loci for a type (2, 1) transfer function. These curves show the circular nature of a portion of the root locus for the two pole system in which the zero is the

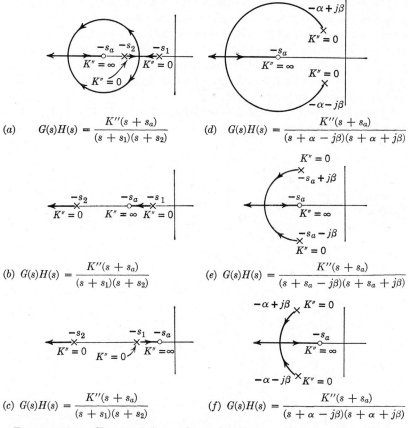

$$(a) \quad G(s)H(s) = \frac{K''(s + s_a)}{(s + s_1)(s + s_2)}$$

$$(b) \quad G(s)H(s) = \frac{K''(s + s_a)}{(s + s_1)(s + s_2)}$$

$$(c) \quad G(s)H(s) = \frac{K''(s + s_a)}{(s + s_1)(s + s_2)}$$

$$(d) \quad G(s)H(s) = \frac{K''(s + s_a)}{(s + \alpha - j\beta)(s + \alpha + j\beta)}$$

$$(e) \quad G(s)H(s) = \frac{K''(s + s_a)}{(s + s_a - j\beta)(s + s_a + j\beta)}$$

$$(f) \quad G(s)H(s) = \frac{K''(s + s_a)}{(s + \alpha - j\beta)(s + \alpha + j\beta)}$$

FIGURE 13.4–5. Characteristic root locus plots for two pole systems type (2, 1).

center of the circle and the radius passes through the two poles when they are complex. When the poles and zeros lie along the real axis and alternate, curve b, the circular part of the locus does not exist and the system will not oscillate.

**Systems Having Third-Order Poles—Types (3, 0), (3, 1) and (3, 2).** Since systems having third and higher order poles characterize many of the control systems encountered in practice, it is worthwhile to consider a number of pole-zero arrangements to illustrate some of the forms that the root locus plots may take.

For the type $(3, 0)$ system, Yeh shows the root locus to consist of a hyperbola (or its degenerate forms) and the real axis as shown in Figure 13.4–6. With three real roots as in curve $a$, the root locus starts out along the real axis. The two smaller roots after becoming equal depart from the real axis and take on complex values and finally approach the $\pm 60°$ asymptote indicated by the rules of Section 6.6. Curves $b$, $c$, and $d$ also show the hyperbolic nature of the root locus when two of the open-loop poles are complex. In these cases too, the locus plots approach

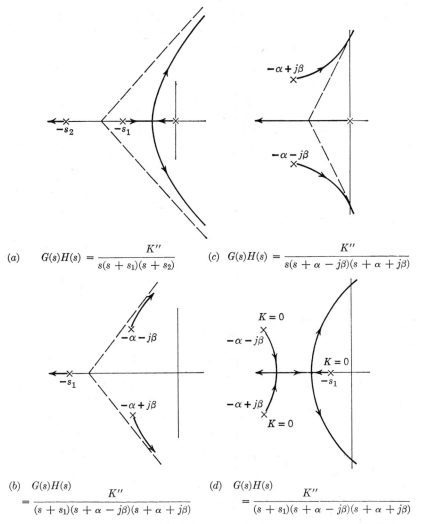

$(a)\quad G(s)H(s) = \dfrac{K''}{s(s + s_1)(s + s_2)}$

$(c)\quad G(s)H(s) = \dfrac{K''}{s(s + \alpha - j\beta)(s + \alpha + j\beta)}$

$(b)\quad G(s)H(s)$
$\quad = \dfrac{K''}{(s + s_1)(s + \alpha - j\beta)(s + \alpha + j\beta)}$

$(d)\quad G(s)H(s)$
$\quad = \dfrac{K''}{(s + s_1)(s + \alpha - j\beta)(s + \alpha + j\beta)}$

FIGURE 13.4–6.   Characteristic root locus plots for three pole systems, type $(3, 0)$.

hyperbolically the asymptotes, but their initial values are complex corresponding to the open-loop poles. As one can see by comparing curves $c$ and $d$, the nature of the root locus in the intermediate range of gains may differ considerably for the same general orientation of open-loop poles depending on the actual values of the parameters. In each case, however, the same asymptotic conditions of $\pm 60°$ and $\pm 180°$ are approached.

Figure 13.4–7 shows the characteristic root locus for the type (3, 1)

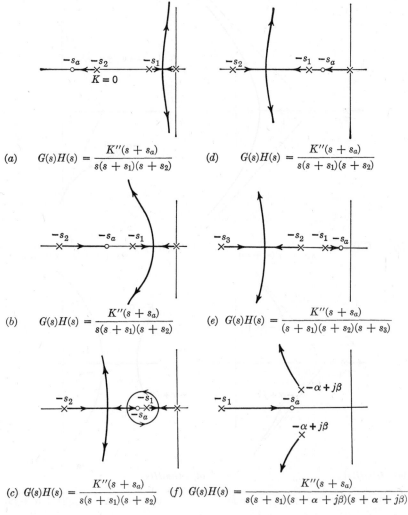

(a)   $G(s)H(s) = \dfrac{K''(s + s_a)}{s(s + s_1)(s + s_2)}$

(b)   $G(s)H(s) = \dfrac{K''(s + s_a)}{s(s + s_1)(s + s_2)}$

(c)   $G(s)H(s) = \dfrac{K''(s + s_a)}{s(s + s_1)(s + s_2)}$

(d)   $G(s)H(s) = \dfrac{K''(s + s_a)}{s(s + s_1)(s + s_2)}$

(e)   $G(s)H(s) = \dfrac{K''(s + s_a)}{(s + s_1)(s + s_2)(s + s_3)}$

(f)   $G(s)H(s) = \dfrac{K''(s + s_a)}{s(s + s_1)(s + \alpha + j\beta)(s + \alpha + j\beta)}$

FIGURE 13.4–7.   Characteristic root locus for three pole systems type (3, 1).

system with a number of relative orientations of the zero with respect to the poles. The progression of curves from $a$ to $e$ is generally from having the zero located at large negative real values and proceeding to the right toward smaller negative real values. Since the directions of the asymptotes for the (3, 1) systems are $\pm \dfrac{180°}{3 - 1} = \pm 90°$, in each case the root loci end up perpendicular to the real axis for increasing values of $s$ and $K$. For these systems, increasing the gain produces oscillations of higher frequency. The location of these asymptotes is at the sum of the poles minus the value of the zero divided by two, (3 − 1). Hence as the zero takes on smaller negative values, the location of the asymptote moves to the left corresponding to more negative values. For those cases where all the poles and the zero are on the axis, the formula for the point at which the root locus leaves the real axis is given by rule 5 of Section 6.6.

Although a detailed discussion of the shape of each of the curves is not warranted, the following brief remarks are appropriate. In curve $a$, since the zero and the neighboring poles are so nearly equal in value and are so far removed from the two other zeros, the root locus in the vicinity of the two small poles is approximately the same as it would be without the added pole and zero. In curve $b$, the zero and the middle pole tend to cancel one another so that after leaving the real axis, the root locus takes on a form somewhat similar to what would be the case if only the pole at the origin and the large negative pole were present.

Curve $c$ with its circular portion at small values of $s$ takes on near the origin a shape similar to the (2, 1) system of curve $a$ of Figure 13.4–5. At larger negative values of $s$, the zero and one pole tend to cancel one another, and the curve behaves like a (2, 0) system. In curves $d$ and $e$, the zero and the pole at or near the origin have only a minor effect on the remaining portion of the root locus which appears similar to what would be the case if only the two larger negative poles were present. In curve $f$ the two complex poles having small negative real values combine with the remaining pole and zero to produce a characteristic similar to that for curve $b$ at higher values of gain. Increasing the gain produces a system in which the oscillatory terms decay more rapidly and the oscillation frequency increases.

The characteristic root locus plots for a three pole (3, 2) system as shown in Figure 13.4–8 are ones for which the asymptote is at $\pm 180°$, i.e., along the negative real axis. Depending on the relative orientation of the open-loop poles and zeros, the root locus may be a two-loop or a one-loop curve. If the open-loop poles and zeros are alternated along

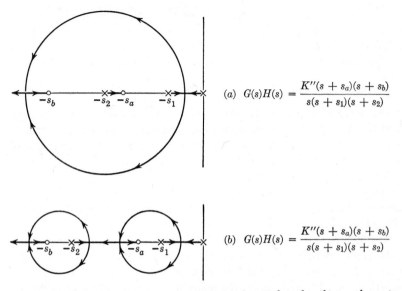

$$(a) \quad G(s)H(s) = \frac{K''(s + s_a)(s + s_b)}{s(s + s_1)(s + s_2)}$$

$$(b) \quad G(s)H(s) = \frac{K''(s + s_a)(s + s_b)}{s(s + s_1)(s + s_2)}$$

FIGURE 13.4–8 (a and b).   Characteristic root locus plots for three pole systems type (3, 2).

the real axis, the root locus consists only of the real axis, and the system is non-oscillatory.

Referring to curve a, where the zero -$s_a$ and the pole -$s_2$ are of approximately the same magnitude, the root locus appears somewhat similar to a type (2, 1) system consisting of 0, −$s_1$, and −$s_b$.  Curve b appears similar to a composite of two (2, 1) systems, one made up of 0, −$s_1$, and −$s_a$; the other consisting of −$s_2$, −$s_b$, and an equivalent pole from 0, −$s_1$, and −$s_a$.

Curve c again appears to be a composite of two simpler systems.  The outer curve has a characteristic somewhat similar to what would be obtained if −$s_a$, −$s_1$, and −$s_2$ were replaced by an equivalent pole, and this pole along with the pole at the origin and the zero -$s_b$ made up a simpler (2, 1) system.  The shape of the inner curve does not appear to develop directly from a consideration of equivalent simpler pole, zero configurations.

Curve d is shown for two sets of pole conditions: one with real poles −$s_1$ and −$s_2$; the other with complex poles (−$\alpha \pm j\beta$) as shown.  When the pole at the origin has a zero nearby, the remaining two poles −$s_1$ and −$s_2$ and the zero at −$s_b$ tend to produce a characteristic like an equivalent (2, 1) system.  See curve a, Figure 13.4–5.  With the complex poles (−$\alpha \pm j\beta$) instead of −$s_1$ and −$s_2$, the equivalent (2, 1) system appears similar to curve d of Figure 13.4–5.

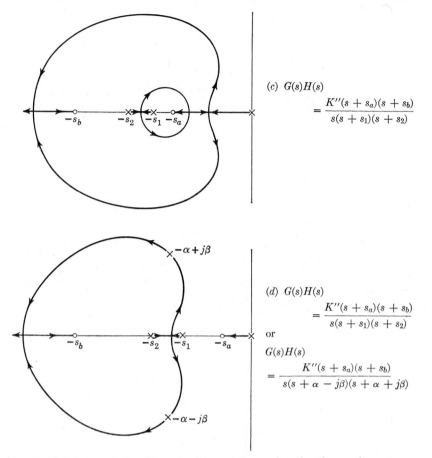

(c)  $G(s)H(s)$

$$= \frac{K''(s + s_a)(s + s_b)}{s(s + s_1)(s + s_2)}$$

(d)  $G(s)H(s)$

$$= \frac{K''(s + s_a)(s + s_b)}{s(s + s_1)(s + s_2)}$$

or

$G(s)H(s)$

$$= \frac{K''(s + s_a)(s + s_b)}{s(s + \alpha - j\beta)(s + \alpha + j\beta)}$$

FIGURE 13.4–8 (c and d).  Characteristic root locus plots for three pole systems type (3, 2).

**Systems Having Fourth-Order Poles—Types (4, 0) and (4, 1).**  Root locus plots for type (4, 0) systems are shown on Figure 13.4–9.  Characteristic of this system are the asymptotes at $\pm \dfrac{180}{4 - 0} = \pm 45°$ and at $\pm \dfrac{180 \times 3}{4 - 0} = \pm 135°$.  The location of the intersection of the asymptotes on the real axis can be calculated readily by rule 8 of Section 6.6 so that the dotted lines showing the asymptotes may be easily located.

On curve $a$ all the poles are real, and for low gains all the poles of the root locus are on the negative real axis.  As the gain is increased, complex roots of low and high decrement rates are obtained after which the system becomes unstable as the gain is further increased.

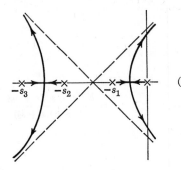

(a)    $G(s)H(s) = \dfrac{K''}{s(s + s_1)(s + s_2)(s + s_3)}$

(b)

$$G(s)H(s) = \dfrac{K''}{s(s + \alpha + j\beta)(s + \alpha - j\beta)(s + s_3)}$$

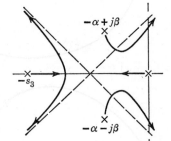

(c)  $G(s)H(s) =$

$$\dfrac{K''}{(s+\alpha-j\beta)(s+\alpha+j\beta)(s+s_3)(s+s_4)}$$

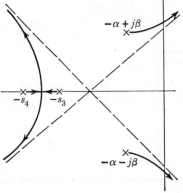

(d)  $G(s)H(s) =$

$$\dfrac{K''}{s(s + s_1)(s + \alpha - j\beta)(s + \alpha + j\beta)}$$

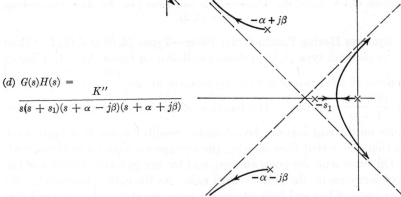

FIGURE 13.4–9.  Characteristic root locus plots for four pole systems types (4, 0).

Curves $b$, $c$, and $d$ show the root locus for (4, 0) systems having two real and two complex poles. Curve $b$ shows the condition where the complex pair of poles lies between the two real poles, while curves $c$ and $d$ are for the cases where the two real poles are more negative and less negative, respectively, than the complex pair.

On Figure 13.4–10 are shown two curves for (4, 1) systems. Characteristic of these systems are asymptotes at $\pm \dfrac{180}{4-1} = \pm 60°$ and $\pm \dfrac{180 \times 3}{4-1} = \pm 180°$. The intersections of these asymptotes can be determined by direct calculation and the dotted lines showing the asymptotes are indicated on the curves. Curve $a$ shows the case of four real poles, while curve $b$ shows the case of two real and two complex roles.

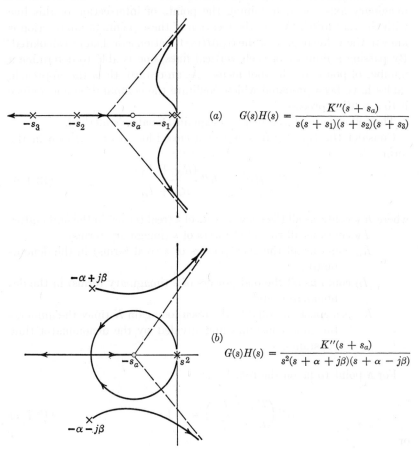

$$(a) \quad G(s)H(s) = \frac{K''(s + s_a)}{s(s + s_1)(s + s_2)(s + s_3)}$$

$$(b) \quad G(s)H(s) = \frac{K''(s + s_a)}{s^2(s + \alpha + j\beta)(s + \alpha - j\beta)}$$

FIGURE 13.4–10.  Characteristic root locus plots for four pole systems types (4, 1).

Although the numerous root locus curves shown on Figures 13.4–3 through 13.4–10 do not describe all possible shapes likely to be encountered, they do provide an orderly basis for judging the form of root locus likely to be obtained with a number of the more common pole-zero configurations. As such they are a valuable aid in sketching an approximate root locus plot quickly.

**Numerical Calculations.** System performance may require the determination of the values of roots to greater accuracy than can readily be obtained by graphical means. Further, it is desirable to have a method of locating roots that provides a direct solution when roots do exist in an area. Such a direct computational method which lends itself to simple slide-rule usage has been devised by Robert Donahue.[134]

The method is based upon passing a vertical line on or parallel to the imaginary axis and determining the points of intersection of this line with the root locus. When the location of these points of intersection is known, the value of gain of the $G(s)H(s)$ function can then be calculated. By passing a number of such vertical lines, one is able to determine a number of points on the root locus. As an outgrowth of this approach, tables have been prepared which facilitate the computation and reduce it to a routine process.

The following material helps to explain Donahue's method.

Consider the transfer function of a closed-loop to be written in the form

$$G(s)H(s) = K'' \frac{(R_N + I_N)}{R_D + I_D} \qquad (13.4\text{–}6)$$

where $R_N$ contains all the even powers of $s$ (real terms) in the numerator,

$I_N$ contains all the odd powers of $s$ (imaginary terms),

$R_D$ contains all the even powers of $s$ (real terms) in the denominator,

$I_D$ contains all the odd powers of $s$ (imaginary terms) in the denominator, and

$K''$ is a constant equal to the open-loop gain $K$ times the numerator time constants and divided by the denominator time constants.

For a point to lie on the root locus,

$$K'' \left( \frac{R_N + I_N}{R_D + I_D} \right) = -1 \qquad (13.4\text{–}7)$$

or

$$K'' R_N + K'' I_N = -R_D - I_D \qquad (13.4\text{–}8)$$

Equating the even terms in $s$, and equating the odd terms in $s$,

$$-K'' = \frac{R_D}{R_N} \qquad (13.4\text{--}9)$$

$$-K'' = \frac{I_D}{I_N} \qquad (13.4\text{--}10)$$

and combining these two equations

$$R_D I_N = R_N I_D \qquad (13.4\text{--}11)$$

Equation 13.4–11 provides the necessary relationship to calculate the value of $s$ at the root locus crossing of the $j\omega$ axis and Equation 13.4–9 or 13.4–10 then provides the solution for $K''$ at the corresponding crossing.

*Example 1*

$$G(s)H(s) = \frac{K(T_a s + 1)}{s(T_1 s + 1)(T_2 s + 1)(T_3 s + 1)} \qquad (13.4\text{--}12)$$

Taking for this case the numerical values from Figure 13.2–3,

$$G(s)H(s) = \frac{40(4s + 1)}{s(80s + 1)(s/4 + 1)(s/16 + 1)} \qquad (13.4\text{--}13)$$

$$= \frac{40 \times 4(s + \frac{1}{4})}{80 \times \frac{1}{4} \times \frac{1}{16}s(s + \frac{1}{80})(s + 4)(s + 16)} \qquad (13.4\text{--}14)$$

$$G(s)H(s) = \frac{40 \times 3.2(s + 0.25)}{s^4 + 20.01s^3 + 64.25s^2 + 0.8s} \qquad (13.4\text{--}15)$$

For this equation

$$R_N = 0.25 \qquad\qquad R_D = s^4 + 64.25s^2 \qquad (13.4\text{--}16)$$

$$I_N = s \qquad\qquad I_D = 20.01s^3 + 0.8s$$

$$K'' = K \times 3.2$$

Substituting these values into Equation 13.4–11

$$(s^4 + 64.25s^2)s = \tfrac{1}{4}(20.01s^2 + 0.8)s$$

or

$$s^4 + 59.25s^2 - 0.2 = 0$$

with $s = j\omega$,

$$\omega^4 - 59.25\omega^2 - 0.2 = 0$$

or

i.e.,
$$\omega^2 = 59.25, \ -0.0$$
$$\omega = \pm 7.7 \qquad (13.4\text{--}17)$$

To find $K''$, substitute the values of $\omega$ into the values of either $I_D$ and $I_N$ and use Equation 13.4–9, or into the values of $R_D$ and $R_N$ and use Equation 13.4–10.  Thus

$$-K'' = -20.01 \times 59.25 + 0.8 = -1184 \qquad (13.4\text{--}18)$$

Referring to Equation 13.4–15, one notes that the term corresponding to $K''$ of Equation 13.4–6 is $40 \times 3.2$, where 40 is the actual gain of the system and 3.2 is derived from the time constant terms.  Therefore, $K$, the value of system gain corresponding to a $K''$ of 1184, is

$$K = \frac{1184}{3.2} = 370 \qquad (13.4\text{--}19)$$

This value of $K$ corresponds to 370/40, (roughly 9.2) times the present gain of the system.

Figure 13.2–3 is the root locus plot for this system and shows the intersection of the root locus plot with the $j$ axis to be at $\omega = 7.7$ and $K = 370$ as calculated above.

To be able to obtain the intersection of the root locus with any particular vertical line parallel to the $j$ axis, the substitution

$$s = \lambda + \sigma \qquad (13.4\text{--}20)$$

is made where $\lambda$ is a new variable replacing $s$ and $\sigma$ is a real number corresponding to a shift in the location of the axis parallel to the $j\omega$ axis. *Plus (+) values of $\sigma$ shift the intersection with the root locus to the right of the origin, and negative values of $\sigma$ shift the intersection with the root locus to the left.*

Since the substitution of Equation 13.4–20, means that

$$s^2 = \lambda^2 + 2\sigma\lambda + \sigma^2, \qquad (13.4\text{--}21)$$

$$s^3 = \lambda^3 + 3\sigma\lambda^2 + 3\sigma^2\lambda + \sigma^3, \text{ etc.}$$

a transfer function of the form

$$G(s) = \frac{K''(s + h_0)}{s^4 + r_3 s^3 + r_2 s^2 + r_1 s + r_0} \qquad (13.4\text{--}22)$$

becomes altered to

$$G(s) = \frac{K''(\lambda + b_0)}{\lambda^4 + a_3\lambda^3 + a_2\lambda^2 + a_1\lambda + a_0} \qquad (13.4\text{--}23)$$

where

$$b_0 = h_0 + \sigma \tag{13.4-24}$$

$$a_0 = \quad r_0 + r_1\sigma + r_2\sigma^2 + r_3\sigma^3 + \sigma^4$$

$$a_1 = + r_1 + 2r_2\sigma + 3r_3\sigma^2 + 4\sigma^3$$

$$a_2 = + r_2 + 3r_3\sigma + 6\sigma^2$$

$$a_3 = + r_3 + 4\sigma$$

Donahue [134] has provided two sets of charts to facilitate the numerical process involved in the solution of the general equation such as 13.4–6. The first set of charts, table 13.4–1, relates the $r$ and $h$ coefficients of the transfer function in the form of Equation 13.4–22 to the $a$ and $b$ coefficients of Equation 13.4–23 in the fashion shown in Equation 13.4–24. It is evident that the same form applies for the relationships between the $a$'s and the $r$'s as between the $b$'s and the $h$'s.

The procedure is essentially that employed in Equations 13.4–6 to 13.4–18, but the advantage of table 13.4–2 is that the values of $\omega^2$ and $-K''$ are expressed directly as formulae so that the intermediate arithmetic steps have been eliminated. The column labeled $(p, z)$ to the left indicates by the $p$ the order of the polynomial in the denominator and by $z$ the order of the polynomial in the numerator.

*Example 2*

For
$$G(s)H(s) = \frac{40 \times 3.2(s + \frac{1}{4})}{s^4 + 20.01s^3 + 64.25s^2 + 0.8s} \tag{13.4-25}$$

as given by Equation 13.4–15, determine the intersection of the root locus with the line $-1$

$$\sigma = -1 \tag{13.4-26}$$

$$a_0 = 0.8(-1) + 64.25 - 20.01 + 1 = +44.44 \tag{13.4-27}$$

$$a_1 = 0.8 + 2(64.25)(-1) + 3(20.01) - 4 = -71.67$$

$$a_2 = + 64.25 - 3(20.01) + 6 = +10.22$$

$$a_3 = + 20.01 - 4 = +16.01$$

$$b_0 = 0.25 - 1 = -0.75$$

$$K'' = 3.2K$$

From $(p, z) = (4, 1)$ of table 13.4–2

$$\omega^2 = \tfrac{1}{2}[(a_2 - b_0a_3) \pm \sqrt{(b_0a_3 - a_2)^2 + 4(b_0a_1 - a_0)}]$$

$$\omega^2 = \tfrac{1}{2}[22.23 \pm 23.05]$$

$$\omega^2 = 22.64 \text{ and } (-0.82) \tag{13.4-28}$$

## TABLE 13.4-1

*Expression for a's (or b's) in Equations of the form*

$$a_0 + a_1\lambda + a_2\lambda^2 + a_3\lambda^3 + a_4\lambda^4 + \cdots a_n\lambda^n$$

or

$$(b_0 + b_1\lambda + b_2\lambda^2 + b_3\lambda^3 + b_4\lambda^4 + \cdots b_n\lambda^n)$$

*In Terms of r's (or h's) in Equations of the form*

$$r_0 + r_1 s + r_2 s^2 + r_3 s^3 + r_4 s^4 + \cdots r_n s^n$$

or

$$(h_0 + h_1 s + h_2 s^2 + h_3 s^3 + h_4 s^4 + \cdots h_n s^n)$$

when $s = \lambda + \sigma$

where $\lambda$ is a new variable, and $\sigma$ is a constant.

*Order of Polynomial*

| | $a_0$ | $a_1$ | $a_2$ |
|---|---|---|---|
| 1. | $r_0 + \sigma$ | — | — |
| 2. | $r_0 + r_1\sigma + \sigma^2$ | $r_1 + 2\sigma$ | — |
| 3. | $r_0 + r_1\sigma + r_2\sigma^2 + \sigma^3$ | $r_1 + 2r_2\sigma + 3\sigma^2$ | $r_2 + 3\sigma$ |
| 4. | $r_0 + r_1\sigma + r_2\sigma^2 + r_3\sigma^3 + \sigma^4$ | $r_1 + 2r_2\sigma + 3r_3\sigma^2 + 4\sigma^3$ | $r_2 + 3r_3\sigma + 6\sigma^2$ |
| 5. | $r_0 + r_1\sigma + r_2\sigma^2 + r_3\sigma^3 + r_4\sigma^4 + \sigma^5$ | $r_1 + 2r_2\sigma + 3r_3\sigma^2 + 4r_4\sigma^3 + 5\sigma^4$ | $r_2 + 3r_3\sigma + 6r_4\sigma^2 + 10\sigma^3$ |
| 6. | $r_0 + r_1\sigma + r_2\sigma^2 + r_3\sigma^3 + r_4\sigma^4 + r_5\sigma^5 + \sigma^6$ | $r_1 + 2r_2\sigma + 3r_3\sigma^2 + 4r_4\sigma^3 + 5r_5\sigma^4 + 6\sigma^5$ | $r_2 + 3r_3\sigma + 6r_4\sigma^2 + 10r_5\sigma^3 + 15\sigma^4$ |

| | $a_3$ | $a_4$ | $a_5$ |
|---|---|---|---|
| 1. | — | — | — |
| 2. | — | — | — |
| 3. | — | — | — |
| 4. | $r_3 + 4\sigma$ | — | — |
| 5. | $r_3 + 4r_4\sigma + 10\sigma^2$ | $r_4 + 5\sigma$ | — |
| 6. | $r_3 + 4r_4\sigma + 10r_5\sigma^2 + 20\sigma^3$ | $r_4 + 5r_5\sigma + 15\sigma^2$ | $r_5 + 6\sigma$ |

TABLE 13.4–2

| Poles, Zero | $\omega^2 =$ | $-K'' = -K\dfrac{T_a T_b,\ \text{etc.}}{T_1 T_2 T_3,\ \text{etc.}}$ |
|---|---|---|
| (2, 1) | $[a_0 - b_0 a_1]$ | $a_1$ |
| (2, 2) | $\dfrac{[b_0 a_1 - b_1 a_0]}{[a_1 - b_1]}$ | $\dfrac{a_1}{b_1}$ |
| (3, 0) | $a_1$ | $[a_0 - a_2\omega^2]$ |
| (3, 1) | $\dfrac{[b_0 a_1 - a_0]}{[b_0 - a_2]}$ | $a_1 - \omega^2$ |
| (3, 2) | $\tfrac{1}{2}[(b_0 + a_1 - b_1 a_2) \pm \sqrt{(b_0 + a_1 - b_1 a_2)^2 - 4(b_0 a_1 - b_1 a_0)}\,]$ | $\dfrac{a_1 - \omega^2}{b_1}$ |
| (3, 3) | $\dfrac{1}{2(b_2 - a_2)}[(b_2 a_1 + b_0 - a_0 - b_1 a_2) \pm \sqrt{(b_2 a_1 + b_0 - a_0 - b_1 a_2)^2 - 4(b_2 - a_2)(b_0 a_1 - b_1 a_0)}\,]$ | $\dfrac{a_1 - \omega^2}{b_1 - \omega^2}$ |
| (4, 0) | $\left[\dfrac{a_1}{a_3}\right]$ | $[a_0 - a_2\omega^2 + \omega^4]$ |
| (4, 1) | $\tfrac{1}{2}[(a_2 - b_0 a_3) \pm \sqrt{(b_0 a_3 - a_2)^2 + 4(b_0 a_1 - a_0)}\,]$ | $a_1 - a_3\omega^2$ |
| (4, 2) | $\dfrac{1}{2(a_3 - b_1)}[(b_0 a_3 + a_1 - b_1 a_2) \pm \sqrt{(b_0 a_3 + a_1 - b_1 a_2)^2 - 4(a_3 - b_1)(b_0 a_1 - b_1 a_0)}\,]$ | $\dfrac{a_1 - a_3\omega^2}{b_1}$ |
| (5, 0) | $\tfrac{1}{2}[a_3 \pm \sqrt{a_3^2 - 4a_1}\,]$ | $[a_0 - a_2\omega^2 + a_4\omega^4]$ |
| (5, 1) | $\dfrac{1}{2(b_0 - a_4)}[(b_0 a_3 - a_2) \pm \sqrt{(b_0 a_3 - a_2)^2 - 4(b_0 - a_4)(b_0 a_1 - a_0)}\,]$ | $a_1 - a_3\omega^2 + a_5\omega^4$ |
| (6, 0) | $\dfrac{1}{2a_5}[a_3 \pm \sqrt{a_3^2 - 4a_1 a_5}\,]$ | $[+a_0 - a_2\omega^2 + a_4\omega^4 - \omega^6]$ |

Since a negative value for $\omega^2$ is not possible with a real value of $\omega$, the only value of $\omega^2$ that is significant is 22.64.

$$\omega = \pm 4.76$$

The gain $K''$ can be found from the expression

$$-K'' = a_1 - a_3\omega^2$$

$$= -71.67 - 16.01(22.64)$$

$$K'' = +434.17$$

Or in terms of actual gain,

$$K = \frac{434.17}{3.2} = 135.4$$

When more than one positive value of $\omega^2$ exists, then a value of $K''$ for each $\omega^2$ should be calculated. Occasionally, there will arise conditions when the computed value of $K''$ is negative despite the fact that $\omega^2$ is positive. Naturally, this also represents a condition of physical unrealizability in similar fashion to the cases when $\omega^2$ is negative.

In using this numerical method of Donahue's it is well to keep in mind the general shape of the root locus as obtained from the graphical and/or chart methods discussed earlier in this section. The three methods complement each other in providing detailed information about the location of the root locus.

## 13.5   Transient Response from Poles and Zeros

An added advantage to be gained from the root locus plot is the ability to derive quantitative information from which can be calculated the time response of the particular control system for which the poles and zeros are established. Thus, for a time response term of the $C_k e^{+s_k t}$ not only can be determined the quantitative value of the various exponential terms $e^{+s_k t}$ associated with the poles of the control system, but also the magnitude and phase of $C_k$ may also be fairly readily evaluated. This ability to calculate the transient response terms from the graphical data of the root locus plot represents an important added advantage for the root locus method. Although the fact that graphical data are used limits the accuracy of this technique, the results can be helpful for engineering purposes.

Referring to Section 4.5 where the method for performing the inverse Laplace transform was described, the process of obtaining the time response was given by the equation

$$f(t) = \mathcal{L}^{-1}[F(s)] = C_1 e^{+s_1 t} + C_2 e^{+s_2 t} + \cdots C_k e^{s_k t} + \cdots C_n e^{s_n t} \quad (13.5\text{-}1)$$

where

$$C_k = \left[ (s - s_k) \frac{A(s)}{B(s)} \right]_{s=s_k} \quad (13.5\text{-}2)$$

and

$$\frac{A(s)}{B(s)} = F(s) = \frac{(s - s_d)(s - s_e) \cdots (s - s_y)}{(s - s_1)(s - s_2) \cdots (s - s_k) \cdots (s - s_n)} \quad (13.5\text{-}3)$$

and the transform of the driving function has been included in $F(s)$ and $\dfrac{A(s)}{B(s)}$.

When one substitutes Equation 13.5–3 into Equation 13.5–2, the expression for $C_k$ is found to be

$$C_k = \frac{(s - s_d)(s - s_e) \cdots (s - s_y)}{(s - s_1)(s - s_2) \cdots (s - s_{k-1})(s - s_{k+1}) \cdots (s - s_n)} \bigg|_{s=s_k}$$

$$(13.5\text{-}4)$$

Equation 13.5–4 indicates that $C_k$ can be determined as the ratio of a product of terms $(s_k - s_d)(s_k - s_e) \cdots (s_k - s_y)$ divided by the product of terms $(s_k - s_1)(s_k - s_2) \cdots (s_k - s_{k-1})(s_k - s_{k+1}) \cdots (s_k - s_n)$.

In Figures 6.6–2 and 6.6–3 were shown how the graphical representation of a term $(s_k - s_1)$ corresponds in magnitude and angle to a vector from $s_1$ to $s_k$. Hence, by measuring on the root locus the magnitude and angle from $s_k$ to each of the poles and zeros representing the system and its driving function, the coefficient $C_k$ can be evaluated. Repeating this process will permit the evaluation of each of the $n$ coefficients $C_n$ in Equation 13.5–1.

*Example*

A control system in Section 13.2 has the open-loop transfer function given by Equation 13.2–4.

$$G = \frac{40 \times 3.2(s + \frac{1}{4})}{s(s + 4)(s + 16)(s + \frac{1}{80})} \quad (13.5\text{-}5)$$

for which the root locus plot has been drawn on Figure 13.2–3.

Determine the response of this system to a step-input of position.

Based on the value of open-loop transfer function of Equation 13.5–5 and the fact that the response to a step-function is sought, the Laplace transform of the $C/R$ $(s)$ can be written as

$$\frac{C}{R}(s) = \frac{1}{s} \times \frac{G(s)}{1 + G(s)} \tag{13.5-6}$$

$$\frac{C}{R}(s) = \frac{1 \times 40 \times 3.2(s + \frac{1}{4})}{s[s(s + 4)(s + 16)(s + \frac{1}{80}) + 40 \times 3.2(s + \frac{1}{4})]} \tag{13.5-7}$$

The root locus plot of Figure 13.2–3 has shown the values of factors of the denominator, i.e., the poles, to be $-0.286$, $-16.6$, $-1.56 \pm j2.08$. Placing these values into the bracketed term of Equation 13.5–7, one can write

$$\frac{C}{R}(s) = \frac{40 \times 3.2(s + \frac{1}{4})}{s(s + 16.6)(s + 1.56 - j2.08)(s + 1.56 + j2.08)(s + 0.286)} \tag{13.5-8}$$

So that the step response for $C/R$ $(t)$ as given by Equation 13.5–1 is

$$\frac{C}{R}(t) = C_1 + C_2 e^{-16.6t} + C_3 e^{(-1.56+j2.08)t} + C_4 e^{(-1.56-j2.08)t}$$
$$+ C_5 e^{-0.286t} \tag{13.5-9}$$

where

$$C_1 = \frac{40 \times 3.2(s_1 + 0.25)}{(s_1 + 16.6)(s_1 + 1.56 - j2.08)(s_1 + 1.56 + j2.08)(s_1 + 0.286)}\Big|_{s_1=0}$$

$$C_2 = \frac{40 \times 3.2(s_2 + 0.25)}{s_2(s_2 + 1.56 - j2.08)(s_2 + 1.56 + j2.08)(s_2 + 0.286)}\Big|_{s_2=-16.6}$$

$$C_3 = \frac{40 \times 3.2(s_3 + 0.25)}{s_3(s_3 + 16.6)(s_3 + 1.56 + j2.08)(s_3 + 0.286)}\Big|_{s_3=-1.56+j2.08}$$

$$C_4 = \frac{40 \times 3.2(s_4 + 0.25)}{s_4(s_4 + 16.6)(s_4 + 1.56 + j2.08)(s_4 + 0.286)}\Big|_{s_4=-1.56-j2.08}$$

$$C_5 = \frac{40 \times 3.2(s_5 + 0.25)}{s_5(s_5 + 16.6)(s_5 + 1.56 - j2.08)(s_5 + 1.56 + j2.08)}\Big|_{s_5=-0.286}$$

$$\tag{13.5-10}$$

Figures 13.5–1 and 13.5–2 show graphically the way the positions of the closed-loop poles on the root locus plots can be used to evaluate the coefficients of the transient response of the control system to the step-function input.

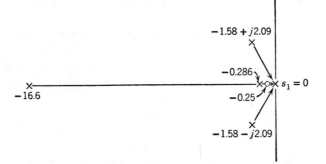

FIGURE 13.5–1.   Plot of vectors on root locus for evaluation of $C_1$ of Equation 13.5–9.

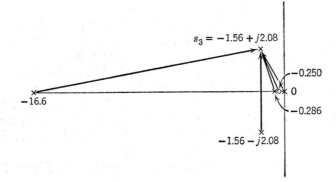

FIGURE 13.5–2.   Plot of vectors on root locus for evaluation of $C_3$ of Equation 13.5–9.

The coefficients of Equation 13.5–10 can also be evaluated analytically from which $C/R(t)$ is found to be

$$C/R(t) = 1.0 - 0.033e^{-16.6t}$$

$$+ 1.562e^{-1.56t} \cos (2.08t - 222.6°) + 0.166e^{-0.286t} \quad (13.5\text{–}11)$$

The effects of specific values of additional poles and zeros can be evaluated in the fashion described in the above example.   In general, the presence of poles and zeros near the origin or near the smallest poles and zeros tends to alter the coefficients most significantly.   Poles and zeros having large negative real parts compared to the dominant poles and zeros are not very effective in altering the transient response characteristics.

The above example serves to illustrate how knowledge of the root locus permits one to proceed quite directly with the calculation of the transient response of the system to specific reference inputs.

### 13.6  Control System Design for Desired Closed-Loop Performance

The material in the preceding sections has provided much knowledge of the closed-loop control system performance as a function of the location of the open-loop roots.  As such, it affords an excellent basis for the direct design of control systems having desired closed-loop control characteristics with a minimum of cut-and-try.

Extensive work by Truxal,[122] Guillemin,[10] and others has emphasized the root locus method as a basis for direct system design synthesis.  In the material that follows, a presentation is made of the general concepts involved in systems design using the desired closed-loop time response as a starting point.  Readers interested in advanced design work will find it worthwhile to refer to Truxal's book [122] for a more comprehensive treatment of the design problem.

In this section, two problems of design will be treated: (1) assuming that the desired closed-loop pole-zero configuration is known and that the characteristics of the power element are known, find the characteristics of the series compensating elements required to produce the desired closed-loop performance; (2) in the case of a, when the power element is such that internal feedback is desirable, find the characteristics of the internal feedback and the series stabilizing means.  The problem of relating the system performance requirements to the location of the closed-loop poles and zeros is also discussed briefly.

**Design Using Only Series Stabilizing Elements.**  On Figure 13.6–1

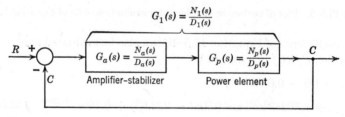

FIGURE 13.6–1.    System with power element and series stabilization.

is shown the block diagram of a system having a forward transfer function,

$$G_1(s) = \frac{N_1(s)}{D_1(s)} \qquad (13.6\text{–}1)$$

consisting of a power element

$$G_p(s) = \frac{N_p(s)}{D_p(s)} \qquad (13.6\text{–}2)$$

and a series amplifier-stabilizer

$$G_a(s) = \frac{N_a(s)}{D_a(s)} \qquad (13.6\text{-}3)$$

Since,

$$G_a(s) = \frac{G_1(s)}{G_p(s)} \qquad (13.6\text{-}4)$$

and since $G_p(s)$ is known initially, the design problem is that of determining the value of $G_1(s)$ so that $G_a(s)$ can be evaluated.

The closed-loop response for this system having unity feedback is

$$\frac{C(s)}{R(s)} = \frac{G_1(s)}{1 + G_1(s)} = \frac{N_1(s)}{D_1(s) + N_1(s)} \qquad (13.6\text{-}5)$$

Expressed in terms of the closed-loop itself for which the desired characteristics are known.

$$\frac{C(s)}{R(s)} = \frac{N_r(s)}{D_r(s)} \qquad (13.6\text{-}6)$$

Comparing Equations 13.6–5 and 13.6–6, one notes that $N_1(s)$, the zeros of the open-loop, and $N_r(s)$, the zeros of the closed-loop, are identical.

$$N_1(s) = N_r(s) \qquad (13.6\text{-}7)$$

Hence the numerator of the open-loop characteristic may be obtained by inspection.

By equating the denominators of Equations 13.6–5 and 13.6–6 and using the known values of $D_r(s)$ and $N_1(s)$, the expression for $D_1(s)$, the poles of the open loop, is

$$D_1(s) = D_r(s) - N_1(s) \qquad (13.6\text{-}8)$$

Although the solution of this equation may be obtained graphically as a function of $s$, the numerical solution for $D_1(s)$ is generally more direct and of greater accuracy. By setting $D_1(s)$ from Equation 13.6–8 equal to zero, the values of $s$ corresponding to the open-loop poles can be determined.

With $N_1(s)$ known from Equations 13.6–5 and 13.6–6, and $D_1(s)$ known from Equation 13.6–8, $G_1(s)$ in Equation 13.6–4 has been obtained. For any given $G_p(s)$, $G_a(s)$ can be evaluated by Equation 13.6–4.

It should be noted that starting with desired closed-loop specifications, the open-loop characteristics are established directly. Since there are a number of open-loop configurations that can yield approximately the same closed-loop response, it may be desirable to modify somewhat the open-loop characteristic as initially calculated to obtain a more readily realizable open-loop characteristic based on such practical considerations as cost and reliability.

*Example 1*

It is desired that the poles of the closed-loop system be located at $-10 \pm j15$, and $-40$ as shown on Figure 13.6–2. What is the open-loop characteristic that will produce this result?

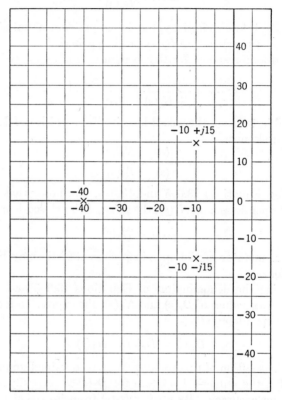

FɪɢURE 13.6–2.   Desired closed-loop pole configuration $-10 \pm j15, -40$.

$$D_r(s) = (s + 10 - j15)(s + 10 + j15)(s + 40) \quad (13.6\text{–}9)$$

$$D_r(s) = s^3 + 60s^2 + 1125s + 13{,}000 \quad (13.6\text{–}10)$$

Since there are no zeros indicated for the closed-loop

$$N_r(s) = K'' = N_1(s) \quad (13.6\text{–}11)$$

From Equations 13.6–8, 13.6–10, and 13.6–11

$$D_1(s) = s^3 + 60s^2 + 1125s + 13{,}000 - K'' \quad (13.6\text{–}12)$$

For the open-loop transfer function to be zero at $s = 0$, corresponding to a type 1 system,

$$K'' = 13{,}000 \quad (13.6\text{–}13)$$

Thus

$$D_1(s) = s(s^2 + 60s + 1125)$$

$$D_1(s) = s(s + 30 - j15)(s + 30 + j15) \qquad (13.6\text{--}14)$$

The open-loop transfer function $N_1(s)/D_1(s)$ from Equations 13.6–11, 13.6–13, and 13.6–14 is therefore

$$\frac{N_1(s)}{D_1(s)} = \frac{13{,}000}{s(s^2 + 60s + 1125)} \qquad (13.6\text{--}15)$$

$$\frac{N_1(s)}{D_1(s)} = \frac{11.52}{s(s^2/1125 + 60s/1125 + 1)} \qquad (13.6\text{--}16)$$

Figure 13.6–3 shows the root locus plot and indicates the desired closed-loop roots of $-10 \pm j15$ and $-40$.

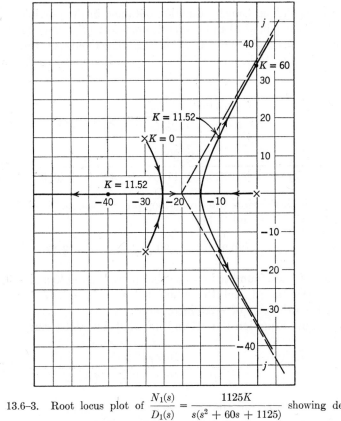

FIGURE 13.6–3.   Root locus plot of $\dfrac{N_1(s)}{D_1(s)} = \dfrac{1125K}{s(s^2 + 60s + 1125)}$ showing desired closed-loop poles at $-10 \pm j15, -40$.

Referring to Equation 13.6–14, one notes that the open-loop characteristic which has been found is one for which the denominator has complex roots. Although this characteristic is not one that is directly obtainable using series elements with real time constants, it can be realized through the use of feedback either around the amplifier stabilizer or around the power element. Despite the fact that some power elements may have oscillatory poles without feedback, it is generally not advantageous from a practical point of view to insist on specific values of oscillatory poles as a condition for design specifications. The sensitivity of such oscillatory poles to changes in manufacturing or operating conditions is frequently so critical as to make it attractive for the designer to use internal feedback to obtain the oscillatory characteristic if this is essential.

*Example 2*

To the open-loop transfer function obtained in the previous example, add additional gain of 10 and a series lag network $(T_1 s + 1)/(T_2 s + 1)$ in which $T_1 = 0.4$ and $T_2 = 4.0$. Compare the closed-loop transfer function obtained with the added gain and network (dipole) to that with the original system.

$$\frac{N_1'(s)}{D_1'(s)} = \frac{13,000(s + 2.5)}{s(s^2 + 60s + 1125)(s + 0.25)} \tag{13.6–17}$$

$$\frac{N_r'(s)}{D_r'(s)} = \frac{13,000s + 32,500}{s^4 + 60.25s^3 + 1140s^2 + 13,281s + 32,500} \tag{13.6–18}$$

By synthetic division, the closed-loop poles of the modified closed-loop characteristic are found to be,

$$s = -39.3, \qquad -8.89 \pm j13.5, \qquad -3.17$$

These poles are found to be somewhat more than $-40$ and $-10 \pm j15$ previously obtained and the additional pole of $-3.17$ is somewhat smaller than the zero of $-2.5$ introduced.

Expressing Equation 13.6–17 in somewhat different terms,

$$\frac{N_1'(s)}{D_1'(s)} = \frac{115.2(s/2.5 + 1)}{s(s^2/1125 + 60s/1125 + 1)(s/0.25 + 1)} \tag{13.6–19}$$

From this equation, the increase in velocity gain constant of $10/1$ over the previous value in Equation 13.6–16 is made apparent. Despite the marked change in velocity gain constant, the closed-loop poles have not changed at all proportionately.

*Example 3*

For closed-loop poles to be located at $-100$, $-60$, $-10 \pm j5$, and a closed-loop zero at $-40$, what is the open-loop characteristic required?

$$N_r(s) = K''(s + 40) = N_1(s) \tag{13.6-20}$$

$$D_r(s) = (s + 100)(s + 60)(s + 10 - j5)(s + 10 + j5) \tag{13.6-21}$$

Since $D_1(s) = D_r(s) - N_1(s)$,

$$D_1(s) = s^4 + 180s^3 + 9325s^2 + (140{,}000 - K'')s + (750{,}000 - 40K'') \tag{13.6-22}$$

For $D_1(0) = 0$, with $s = 0$

$$K'' = \frac{750{,}000}{40} = 18{,}750 \tag{13.6-23}$$

from which

$$D_1(s) = s(s^3 + 180s^2 + 9325s + 121{,}250) \tag{13.6-24}$$

This equation can be factored by synthetic division as was employed in Section 6.2 in determining the roots of a characteristic equation. Doing so, it is found that

$$D_1(s) = s(s + 97.3)(s + 62.7)(s + 20) \tag{13.6-25}$$

Combining Equations 13.6-20 and 13.6-25

$$\frac{N_1(s)}{D_1(s)} = \frac{18{,}750(s + 40)}{s(s + 97.3)(s + 62.7)(s + 20)} \tag{13.6-26}$$

or

$$\frac{N_1(s)}{D_1(s)} = \frac{6.15(s/40 + 1)}{s(s/97.3 + 1)(s/62.6 + 1)(s/20 + 1)} \tag{13.6-27}$$

Figure 13.6-4 shows the root locus plot for the open-loop characteristic of Equation 13.6-27 and the resultant closed-loop characteristic as originally sought. It will be noted that all real roots were obtained for the open-loop characteristic although there is an oscillatory closed-loop response. There has been only a small migration of the large negative open-loop poles to their closed-loop values. The smallest open-loop pole has teamed with the pole at the origin to yield the oscillatory closed-loop response.

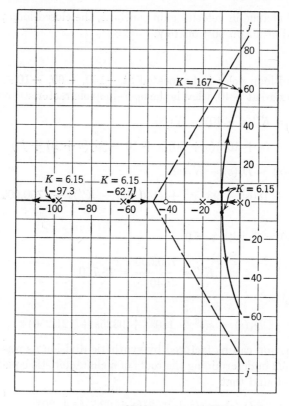

FIGURE 13.6-4. Root locus plot of $\dfrac{N_1(s)}{D_1(s)} = \dfrac{K''(s + 40)}{s(s + 97.3)(s + 62.7)(s + 20)}$ showing that desired closed-loop poles at $-100$, $-60$, $-10 \pm j5$ and zero at $-40$ are realized.

**Design Using Internal Feedback.** In similar fashion to the manner in which the closed-loop and open-loop zeros and poles were related in Equations 13.6–5 and 13.6–6 for series elements in the open loop, one can derive relationships between the closed-loop poles and zeros and the poles and zeros of the amplifier-stabilizer elements, the power element, and the internal feedback path. Referring to Figure 13.6–5, one is able to express the complete open-loop transfer function as

$$\frac{N_1(s)}{D_1(s)} = \frac{N_a(s)}{D_a(s)} \times \frac{N_p(s)/D_p(s)}{1 + N_p(s)N_H(s)/D_p(s)D_H(s)} \qquad (13.6\text{–}28)$$

$$\frac{N_1(s)}{D_1(s)} = \frac{N_a(s)}{D_a(s)} \times \frac{N_p(s)D_H(s)}{D_p(s)D_H(s) + N_p(s)N_H(s)} \qquad (13.6\text{–}29)$$

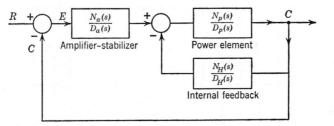

FIGURE 13.6–5.   System with power element, internal feedback, and series stabilization.

Since

$$\frac{C}{R}(s) = \frac{N_r(s)}{D_r(s)} = \frac{N_1(s)}{D_1(s) + N_1(s)} \qquad (13.6\text{--}30)$$

one readily observes that the relationship between the closed-loop poles
and zeros and the poles and zeros of the amplifier-stabilizer, the power
element, and the internal feedback is a fairly complex one. Certain
relationships are, of course, quite evident; for example, that closed-
loop zeros are obtained from the internal feedback poles. Because of
the general complexity, the direct synthesis approach is generally divided into three stages: (1) that of determining $N_1(s)$ and $D_1(s)$ as for
the case of the series elements; (2) that of deriving the series equivalent
of the power element with internal feedback as was done in Section 13.3;
and (3) that of deriving the amplifier-stabilizer characteristics knowing
the results of the first two steps. Although theoretically this solves the
problem, it is necessary to review the results obtained with the practical
considerations of manufacture, maintenance, and the effects of environ-
mental changes in mind. The determination of the series equivalent of
the power element with feedback and of the amplifier stabilizer characteristics is somewhat related to the procedure used with the attenuation-
frequency approach. It has the added feature of having the open-loop
requirements more definitely known in terms of the closed loop pole-
zero configurations they will produce.

*Example*

It is desired to determine the design requirements of a position control
system using tachometer feedback having closed-loop poles at $-4$, $-1.2$,
and $-10 \pm j15$ with a closed-loop zero at $-1.0$ as shown on Figure
13.6–6.

From the closed-loop pole requirements,

$$D_r(s) = s^4 + 25.2s^3 + 433.8s^2 + 1786s + 1560 \qquad (13.6\text{--}31)$$

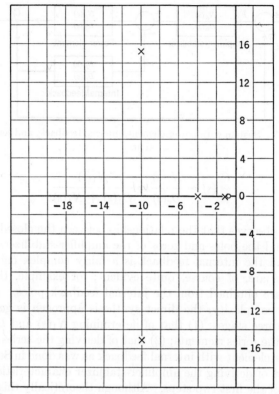

FIGURE 13.6–6.    Desired closed-loop pole zero locations.
$p = -1.2, -4.0, -10 \pm j15; z = -1.0.$

and from the closed-loop zero requirements

$$N_r(s) = K''(s + 1) = N_1(s) \qquad (13.6\text{–}32)$$

With the values of $D_r(s)$ and $N_r(s)$, the expression $D_1(s)$ is found to be

$$D_1(s) = s^4 + 25.2s^3 + 433.8s^2 + (1786 - K'')s + 1560 - K''$$

$$(13.6\text{–}33)$$

With $K'' = 1560$, corresponding to a type 1 control, $D_1(s)$ is factored
into

$$s(s + 0.537)(s + 12.33 - j16.35)(s + 12.33 + j16.35) \quad (13.6\text{–}34)$$

Expressed in terms of an open-loop transfer function, Equation 13.5–34
becomes

$$\frac{N_1(s)}{D_1(s)} = \frac{6.9(s+1)}{s(s/0.537+1)(s^2/421+24.7s/421+1)} \qquad (13.6\text{-}35)$$

as shown on the root locus plot of Figure 13.6–7.

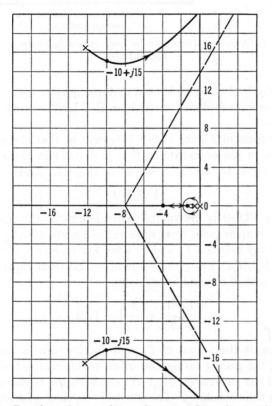

FIGURE 13.6–7.  Root locus for open-loop pole zero configuration required to produce desired closed-loop poles and zeros for Figure 13.6–6.

Since internal feedback is to be used, the block diagram configuration shown on Figure 13.3–2 can be employed for the combined power element—internal feedback portions of the control. The over-all open-loop control to be considered is that shown in Figure 13.6–8.

The forms of the transfer functions $G_p(s)$ and $H(s)$ are assumed to be

$$G_p(s) = \frac{K_1/T_m T_f}{s(s+1/T_m)(s+1/T_f)} \qquad (13.6\text{-}36)$$

$$H(s) = \frac{K_t s^2}{(s+1/T)} \qquad (13.6\text{-}37)$$

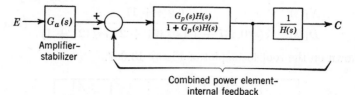

FIGURE 13.6–8. Open-loop control to be used to obtain characteristic shown on Figure 13.6–7.

which are physically realizable by a motor-generator control of position and by tachometer feedback through an R-C lead network as described in Section 13.3.

From the form of Figure 13.6–8 it is evident that the poles of $H(s)$ will be zeros in the open-loop so that $(s + 1/T)$ in Equation 13.6–37 must be set equal to $(s + 1)$ in Equation 13.6–35. Thus,

$$1/T = 1 \qquad (13.6\text{–}38)$$

On Figure 13.6–9 is drawn the general form of the $G_p(s)H(s)$ root locus. The complex poles lie along a vertical asymptote that is approximately midway between $T_m$ and $T_f$ since $1/T$ and 0 are small compared with $1/T_m + 1/T_f$. Using the value of $-12.3$ from Equation 13.6–34 for the real part of the oscillatory poles,

$$\frac{1}{2}\left(\frac{1}{T_m} + \frac{1}{T_f}\right) = 12.3 \qquad (13.6\text{–}39)$$

Depending on the values of $T_m$ and $T_f$ that can be obtained from machines of the proper rating and other qualifications, the selection of the larger of the two values $(T_m)$ will establish the requirement for the smaller $(T_f)$ time constant. The effect of the value of $K_1 K_t$ that is required to obtain the other pole near the origin (see Equation 13.6–42) may also affect the values of motor and field time constants that will be desired.

The value of the gain term $K_1 K_t$ will establish the values for the oscillatory portion of the poles $p_1$ and $p_2$ and also the real part of $p_3$. To determine values of $s$ along the $-12.3$ asymptote, the $G_p(s)H(s)$ function from Equations 13.6–36 and 13.6–37 is approximately

$$G_p(s)H(s) = \frac{K_t K_1 / T_m T_f}{s^2 + \left(\dfrac{T_m + T_f}{T_m T_f}\right) s + \dfrac{1}{T_m T_f}} \qquad (13.6\text{–}40)$$

from which the roots of $G_p(s)H(s)/[1 + G_p(s)H(s)]$ are obtained from

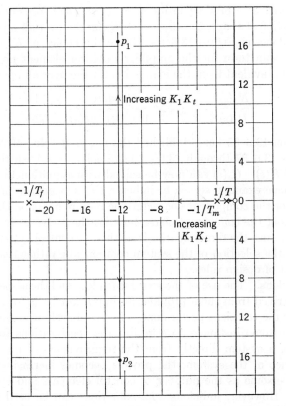

FIGURE 13.6–9.  Sketch showing general form of $G_p(s)H(s)$ root locus for Equations 13.6–36 and 13.6–37.

the characteristic equation

$$T_m T_f s^2 + (T_m + T_f)s + 1 + K_1 K_t = 0 \qquad (13.6\text{--}41)$$

Equating the oscillatory portion of Equations 13.6–41 to 16.3 as required by Equation 13.6–34 permits one to solve for $K_1 K_t$.

To determine the location of the pole between $1/T$ and 0, one lets $G_p(s)H(s) = \dfrac{K_1 K_t s}{(s + 1/T)}$ from which the pole 0.537 is equal to $1/T(1 + K_1 K_t)$. Thus,

$$K_1 K_t = 0.86 \qquad (13.6\text{--}42)$$

This value of $K_1 K_t$ will probably not be the same as that required for the desired oscillatory response, in which case it will be necessary to choose the value of $K_1 K_t$ that is the more critical; i.e., that has the most severe effect on the closed-loop requirements. Although the $K_1 K_t$

term appears as a product in its effect on the root locus considerations of Figure 13.6–9 above, the effect of $1/K_t$ on the over-all open-loop gain appears alone on Figure 13.6–8. Hence the choice of $K_t$ in $H(s)$ will affect the gain term for the amplifier-stabilizer element portion of the control as is evident from the expression for the over-all open-loop gain,

$$\frac{N_1(s)}{D_1(s)} = G_a(s) \times \frac{G_p(s)H(s)}{1 + G_p(s)H(s)} \times \frac{1}{H(s)} \qquad (13.6\text{–}43)$$

Equation 13.6–35 has established the required value of $N_1(s)/D_1(s)$. Equations 13.6–37 through 13.6–41 have helped establish the values of $G_p(s)$ and $H(s)$. $G_a(s)$ can now be solved with Equation 13.6–43.

The above example serves to indicate the dependence of the design solution for the component characteristic requirements on the nature of the values of the component characteristics themselves. It therefore is desirable to use the direct synthesis method of control system design as an aid to the selection of the system components, rather than as an inflexible set of design rules.

**Conclusions.** The use of the root locus plots and the associated information derived from them provides an important basis for understanding better the transient performance of control systems. Although it is possible in some instances to establish the specifications for the components of a system directly from the requirements of the closed-loop performance of the system, the process becomes increasingly complex and cumbersome as the number of control elements and control loops increase. However, judicious approximations can be used to simplify and speed up the calculations.

Use of the root locus and the attenuation-frequency methods,[118] each where it is most convenient, will provide the designer with a better knowledge of his system than could be obtained from either method alone.

# 14

## MULTIPLE-LOOP AND MULTIPLE-INPUT
## FEEDBACK CONTROL SYSTEMS

### 14.0 Introduction

In the preceding chapters emphasis has been placed on the analysis of comparatively simple series and feedback stabilized type 1 feedback control systems having a single input to the system. The general control system design or synthesis problem is not always as straightforward as this. In this chapter the design of more comprehensive systems and the design of systems having more than one input are discussed. In addition, representative problems are presented in conjunction with the design of systems having load regulation or load disturbance effects. Finally the design of systems to be used entirely as regulators with primary emphasis on minimizing output disturbance effects is considered.

Advantage is taken of the linear property of servomechanism and regulator systems having constant coefficients and unsaturated operation. The attenuation-frequency response of the controlled variable for each of the various inputs is determined separately. The resultant value of the controlled variable is determined from the combined effect of all the inputs. An effort is made to so choose and arrange the system parameters as to make the input-to-controlled-variable transmission function for each input that required by the dictates of the problem. Use is made of the superposition principle by representing an element or group of elements by one or more blocks in a block diagram. In this way the resultant equations describing the system performance are the same even though the block diagram representation differs somewhat from the physical configuration of the actual system. The object of so regrouping the system elements is to obtain a system the performance of which can be more readily determined than the performance of the original, more literal representation.

## 14.1   Design of More Complex Systems

The means used in preceding chapters to describe the performance of simple servomechanisms in terms of their attenuation and phase margin versus frequency characteristics can also be employed for more complex systems. The use of series and feedback arrangements of control elements and equalizing networks provides a means of analyzing and synthesizing more complex, multiple-loop systems. Instead of dealing solely with the attenuation and phase margin diagrams of individual elements, the corresponding diagrams for groups of elements are handled in the same fashion as single elements. The means employed to equalize partially a simple control element work with equal effectiveness when used on combinations of control and network elements. Before examples of the more general multi-loop control problem are considered, two illustrations of more complex systems will be described.

**Series Modification of Transfer Function.**   Referring to the example of Section 12.2, where the tachometer feedback means for stabilization is described, one sees the performance of the resultant system with the feedback loop closed indicated by the plot of the transfer function shown in Figure 12.2–5. Should it be desired to modify the transfer function further, another element may be placed in series with the $O/I = C/I$ transfer function. Such a modified system is indicated in Figure 14.1–1,

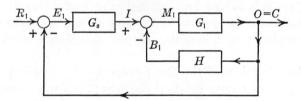

Figure 14.1–1.   Control elements shown in Figure 10.2–11 modified by the addition of control element $G_s$ and employing direct feedback.

where $I$ is the output of a series stabilizing network with transfer function $G_s$. The transfer function for such a system from $E_1$ to $C$ is

$$G = \frac{G_s G_1}{1 + G_1 H} \qquad (14.1-1)$$

To produce added gain at low frequencies without materially altering the stability of the system, phase lag networks and additional amplification with simple control elements can be used for $G_s$.

Figure 14.1–2 shows one way in which the attenuation-frequency diagram of the transfer function for $C/I$ could be changed by means of a phase lag network and added gain to give the desired characteristic.

It should be noted that, although a transfer function having the same attenuation-frequency characteristics as that shown in Figure 14.1–2 might be obtained by means of a two-stage $RC$ filter for the feedback function $H$, use of the series phase lag network may be desirable for practical reasons.  By using the $G_s$ network, different signal and impedance levels for $I$ are obtained and additional amplification of $E_1$ may be more readily available.  Furthermore, it should be stressed that loading, interaction between circuits and saturation effects, none of which

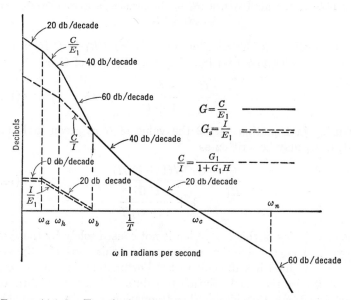

FIGURE 14.1–2.    Transfer function of composite system of Figure 14.1–1.

have yet been considered, may provide definite practical limits to the exclusive use of one or the other of the methods of providing equalization.

**Inclusion of a Servomechanism in a More Comprehensive Control System.**  In many cases a servomechanism is itself part of a series of control elements making up a more complete control system.  Certain control elements may combine to produce a signal at a low power level that it is desired to reproduce at a greatly increased power level.  For this purpose, the high-gain type 1 (velocity) system of Figure 14.1–1, for example, can be changed to a type 0 (position) system and made to take its place in the chain of control elements.  Figure 14.1–3 shows the block diagram for such a system using the servomechanism of Figure 14.1–1 for the type 0 power control element.

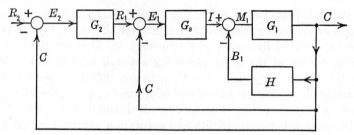

FIGURE 14.1-3. A control system ($R_2$ to $C$), including a servomechanism system ($R_1$ to $C$).

The expression for the transfer function from $R_1$ to $C$ for a control having an open-loop transfer function from $E_1$ to $C$ of $G$ is

$$\frac{C}{R_1} = \frac{G}{1 + G} \qquad (14.1\text{-}2)$$

By using in Equation 14.1-2 the value of $G$ as given in Equation 14.1-1, $C/R_1$ may be written as

$$\frac{C}{R_1} = \frac{G_sG_1/(1 + G_1H)}{1 + \dfrac{G_sG_1}{1 + G_1H}} \qquad (14.1\text{-}3)$$

The complexity of this expression is not caused solely by the symbols employed. To determine the performance for this portion of the system in an exact fashion is a difficult task. Fortunately, in most cases, one does not require the exact solution to gain a satisfactory picture of the system operation. Considering the attenuation-frequency approach, the approximate solution to this problem is comparatively simple.

The attenuation-frequency plot of Figure 14.1-2 represents the transfer function

$$\frac{G_sG_1}{1 + G_1H} = G$$

Using the same sort of approximations as those that were employed for representing simple single time constants, one may say to a fair degree of approximation that when $|G| > 1$

$$\frac{C}{R_1} \simeq 1 \qquad (14.1\text{-}4)$$

and when $|G| < 1$

$$\frac{C}{R_1} \simeq G \qquad (14.1\text{-}5)$$

Hence the attenuation-frequency diagram for $C/R_1$ of Figure 14.1–3 can be approximated as shown in Figure 14.1–4. From this it can be seen that the system is a type 0 control with good accuracy up to a frequency somewhat lower than $\omega_c$, after which the attenuation characteristic indicates that phase shift as well as a different amplitude of $C$ from that of $R_1$ is obtained.

Referring to the block diagram of Figure 14.1–3 and keeping in mind that the transfer function from $R_1$ to $C$ is essentially unity for frequencies below $\omega_c$, one realizes that the performance of the over-all control system

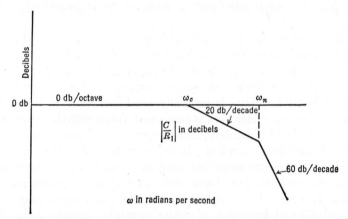

FIGURE 14.1–4.   Transfer function from $R_1$ to $C$ of Figure 14.1–3.

will be determined largely by the characteristics of $G_2$ in the region of frequencies less than $\omega_c$. Thus the design of the over-all system falls roughly into two parts:

1. The design of the high accuracy $C/R_1$ transfer function good out to frequency $\omega_c$.

2. The design of the $G_2$ transfer function having the desired characteristics of the over-all control system in the frequency range lower than that of $\omega_c$.

Once the broad framework of the approximate straight-line solution outlined above has been determined satisfactorily, the refinement process of obtaining the exact solution with the aid of the Nichols charts as was described in Sections 12.4 and 12.5 must be performed. This method of considering only the straight-line attenuation characteristics until the design has been pretty well formulated lends itself to system synthesis and provides a means whereby only a small number of systems must be analyzed before a suitable design is obtained.

## 14.2  Multiple Inputs and Load Disturbances

Frequently there is more than one input or type of input to a control system operating at a given time.  The resultant *performance of the system is judged on the ability of the control to reproduce accurately those inputs that it is desired to reproduce and to minimize the objectionable effects of the disturbance functions that it is desired not to reproduce.*  Although disturbance functions initially may not appear to be input signals since they may be expressed in different units or physical form from the reference input quantities, nevertheless, they generally can be converted into equivalent input units and, as such, analyzed as additional input terms.

In this section the simplified analysis of systems under the simultaneous action of more than one input will be described.  Since in many cases there is little or no relationship between the time at which each input occurs, the analysis of the system performance for the simultaneous action of multiple inputs is generally conducted only in literal form.  When detailed numerical work is performed, frequently the effect of each input is considered separately, and the principle of linear superposition of the various effects is applied.  In this way the problem becomes somewhat similar, as far as numerical analysis is concerned, to the case of a complex system having one input such as was described in the preceding section.  However, the transfer function for each input may be the result of different groupings of major elements, and, as such, only a certain amount of the numerical work is common for each of the various inputs.

Three specific examples will be used to illustrate these principles.  In the first example there are two position inputs and it is desired to separate the effect of one from the other.  The second example represents a portion of a system that is required to follow accurately a rapidly moving position input but to prevent mechanical load disturbances on the output element from introducing an error between input and output positions.  The third example is characteristic of the final stage of a regulator system in which the input changes may be comparatively unimportant but in which the effect of load regulation or the interaction of other control systems on the regulated output must be made a minimum.

**General Case of Multiple Inputs.**  Before considering specific problems of servomechanism operation under the action of multiple inputs, it is worth while to review briefly the general multiple input case that has been set forth so well by Brown and Campbell.[86]  Figure 14.2–1 illustrates such a servomechanism, in which $R_1$ and $R_2$ are independent position inputs.  $C$ is the output, while $G_1$, $G_2$, and $H$ are the transfer functions of the blocks indicated.

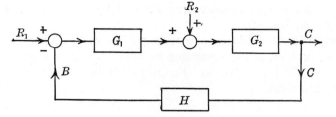

FIGURE 14.2-1.  Block diagram of a servomechanism having more than one input.

With each input considered separately, the output can be expressed in terms of each input as

$$\frac{C}{R_1} = \frac{G_1 G_2}{1 + G_1 G_2 H} \tag{14.2-1}$$

and

$$\frac{C}{R_2} = \frac{G_2}{1 + G_1 G_2 H} \tag{14.2-2}$$

If the two inputs are applied simultaneously and the principle of superposition is employed, the expression for the output is

$$C = \frac{G_1 G_2 R_1 + G_2 R_2}{1 + G_1 G_2 H} \tag{14.2-3}$$

Thus it will be noted that equal amounts of the inputs $R_1$ and $R_2$ may produce markedly different effects on the output, $C$, depending on the value of $G_1$.

In Equations 14.2-1 and 14.2-2.

$$\frac{C}{R_2} = \frac{1}{G_1}\left[\frac{C}{R_1}\right] \tag{14.2-4}$$

If $R_1$ is the input that must be transmitted, then $C/R_1$ will be approximately 1 for the low-frequency region.  This condition will help establish by means of Equation 14.2-1 the ratio of $G_1 G_2$ to $1 + G_1 G_2 H$.  Equation 14.2-4 will now help to indicate the nature that the $G_1$ function should have.  If it is desired that the $R_2$ motion should be reproduced in the output, then $G_1$ must also be very nearly equal to 1, at least for low frequencies.  On the other hand, if the $R_2$ motion to be present in the output is to be a minimum, then at low frequencies $G_1$ should be as large as possible.

Thus the condition that $C/R_1$ be unity places no restriction on the values of $G_1$ or $G_2$ but only on their product and its relationship to $1 + G_1 G_2 H$.  The limitation caused by the amount of $R_2$ desired in the output does, however, place an additional restraint on the values of $G_1$ and

$G_2$, which are acceptable since the value of $G_1G_2$ is already indicated by the $C/R_1$ requirements.

**Multiple-Position Inputs.** In some position-measuring systems the reference position of the measuring element is itself on a platform the position of which is changing. Figure 14.2–2 illustrates such a system in schematic form.

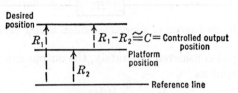

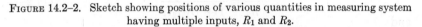

FIGURE 14.2–2.   Sketch showing positions of various quantities in measuring system having multiple inputs, $R_1$ and $R_2$.

$R_1$ is the desired position with respect to the reference line and $R_2$ is the position of the movable platform also with respect to the reference line. $C$ is the controlled position that endeavors to maintain the desired position $R_1$ despite movements of $R_1$ and $R_2$. An example of this can be found on shipboard where it may be desired to measure the location of a star in space with respect to the rolling deck of the ship. $R_1$ is the position of the star in space and is the quantity to be determined. $R_2$ is the angle of the deck with respect to space, and $R_1 - R_2$ is the apparent angle of the star with respect to the deck. $C$ is the angle of the controlled variable and is very nearly equal to $R_1 - R_2$.

Figure 14.2–3 shows a block diagram of a system that might be used for such an application. The net input to the system is $R_1 - R_2$. The position $R_2$, as determined by a separate measuring means, is introduced at another point in the system. In this way the position $P$, can be made to be very nearly equal to $R_1$ as is shown below.

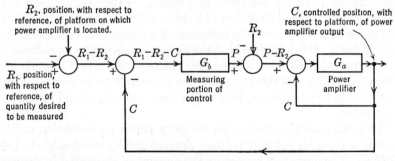

FIGURE 14.2–3.   Block diagram showing measuring system of Figure 14.2–2 having multiple-position inputs.

The transfer functions $G_a$ and $G_b$ are in reality combinations of more simple transfer functions, and each can be considered to have a high gain. Considering the power amplifier portion of the controller, the output expressed in terms of the input to it is

$$C = \frac{G_a}{1 + G_a} (P - R_2) \cong P - R_2 \qquad (14.2\text{-}5)$$

The transfer function of the measuring portion of the control is

$$P = G_b[R_1 - R_2 - C] \qquad (14.2\text{-}6)$$

Using the approximate value of $P$ from Equation 14.2–5 in Equation 14.2–6, one obtains

$$C + R_2 \cong G_b[R_1 - R_2 - C] \qquad (14.2\text{-}7)$$

or

$$C + R_2 \cong \frac{G_b R_1}{1 + G_b} \qquad (14.2\text{-}8)$$

When Equations 14.2–5 and 14.2–8 are compared, the result is

$$P \cong \frac{G_b}{1 + G_b} R_1 \cong R_1 \qquad (14.2\text{-}9)$$

Thus, by the use of the two inputs $R_1 - R_2$ and $R_2$, it has been possible to determine the value of $R_1$, the quantity that it is desired to measure.

The exact values for the quantities $P$ and $C$ in terms of the two transfer functions $G_a$ and $G_b$ are found to be

$$P = \frac{G_b R_1}{1 + \dfrac{G_a G_b}{1 + G_a}} - \frac{G_b \left[ 1 - \dfrac{G_a}{1 + G_a} \right] R_2}{1 + \dfrac{G_a G_b}{1 + G_a}} \qquad (14.2\text{-}10)$$

and

$$C = \frac{\dfrac{G_a G_b}{1 + G_a} R_1 - \dfrac{G_a(1 + G_b)}{1 + G_a} R_2}{1 + \dfrac{G_a G_b}{1 + G_a}} \qquad (14.2\text{-}11)$$

Note that, with large values for $G_a$ and $G_b$, these expressions for $P$ and $C$ reduce to the approximate values given by Equations 14.2–9 and 14.2–8, respectively.

In passing it is worth while to observe the similarity between the control systems of Figure 14.1–3 and Figure 14.2–3. With the input

$R_2$ of Figure 14.2–3 set equal to zero, the two systems are identical if

$$G_2 = G_b$$

and

$$\frac{G_s G_1}{1 + G_1 H} = G_a$$

It is evident that other control systems previously considered might also be similar to portions of more complicated, multiple-input systems.

**Response to Input Signal and Load Disturbance.** In some control systems the controlled variable is acted upon by a combination of an electrical input signal and a mechanical load disturbance. An example of such a system is a position or speed control being driven by an electric motor and subjected to external mechanical load torques. Treatment of such a problem is frequently facilitated by the use of an "equivalent" electromechanical system in which both electrical and mechanical inputs and control elements are represented.

The idea of representing actual elements in an electrical machine or circuit by their equivalents having the same performance has long been used for such devices as transformers, induction motors, and electronic tubes. The more recent work of Kron and others has extended the equivalent circuit concept to mechanical and other types of systems. In the analysis of complex servomechanisms as well, it is frequently advantageous to describe a certain grouping of parameters and operators as an equivalent transfer function for a particular element. Although the numerical calculations that result from the equivalent block diagram representation seldom differ appreciably from those otherwise obtained, there is frequently an advantage to be gained from the simpler presentation of the problem that results.

The problem of combined electrical and mechanical inputs is illustrated in one of its more simple forms in Figure 14.2–4, where the load

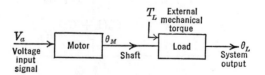

FIGURE 14.2–4.   Schematic diagram of motor and load with external load torque applied.

and motor are rigidly interconnected. To determine the nature of the transfer function involved and of the equivalent inputs to the transfer function, it is necessary to write the equations describing the electrical and mechanical portions of the system. From these equations one may arrange a block diagram of the transfer functions and the inputs.   The performance equations for the equivalent block diagram must be the same as for the actual system.

The voltage and torque equations for the d-c motor in transform form are, respectively,

$$V_a = IR + K_e s \theta_M \qquad (14.2\text{–}12)$$

and

$$K_T I + T_L = J_{ML} s^2 \theta_M \qquad (14.2\text{–}13)$$

where $V_a$ = terminal voltage impressed on the motor armature,

$I$ = motor armature current,

$R$ = motor armature circuit resistance,

$K_e$ = motor-induced voltage per radian per second of motor,

$K_T$ = pound-feet torque on motor rotor per ampere of armature current,

$T_L$ = external torque applied, foot-pounds,

$J_{ML}$ = motor and load combined moment of inertia in slug feet squared,

$\theta_M$ = position of motor rotor in radians, and

$\theta_L$ = position of load in radians.

Solving these equations simultaneously for $\theta_M$ gives

$$\theta_M = \frac{V_a + \dfrac{R}{K_T} T_L}{K_e s [T_m s + 1]} \qquad (14.2\text{–}14)$$

where $T_m = J_{ML} R / K_T K_e$.

The block diagram corresponding to this equation is shown in Figure 14.2–5.

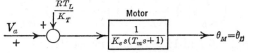

FIGURE 14.2–5.   Block diagram of equivalent system of motor and load with external load torque applied.

In addition to the voltage $V_a$ impressed on the usual motor transfer function, an equivalent voltage $RT_L/K_T$ that is proportional to the load torque is also added to $V_a$ to form the net input.

A position control system having such a characteristic and subjected to an external torque load is described more fully in Section 14.4.

A more complicated variation of this problem is shown schematically in Figure 14.2–6, where the electric motor drives its load through an elastic shaft and the external torque is applied to the load.

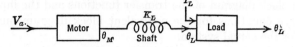

FIGURE 14.2–6.   Schematic diagram of motor connected to load through springy shaft with external load torque applied.

Here the voltage Equation 14.2–12 is still valid, but the torque equation for the motor rotor is

$$K_T I + K_L(\theta_L - \theta_M) = J_M s^2 \theta_M \qquad (14.2\text{–}15)$$

where $K_L$ = pound-feet torque per radian twist of shaft.

By eliminating $I$ from Equations 14.2–12 and 14.2–15 and grouping all the $\theta_M$ terms together, the following relationship between $\theta_M$, $\theta_L$, and $V_a$ is obtained:

$$\frac{K_L R}{K_T}\left[\frac{J_M}{K_L}s^2 + \frac{K_e K_T}{K_L R}s + 1\right]\theta_M = V_a + \frac{K_L R}{K_T}\theta_L \qquad (14.2\text{–}16)$$

The torque equation for the load sums the external load torque $(T_L)$, the spring torque, and a viscous friction torque of the load $(Ds\theta_L)$, and equates them to the acceleration of the load inertia.  Note that a positive torque $T_L$ produces a positive acceleration of the load.

$$J_L s^2 \theta_L = T_L + K_L(\theta_M - \theta_L) - Ds\theta_L \qquad (14.2\text{–}17)$$

where $J_L$ = load moment of inertia in slug feet squared and referred to the motor shaft, and

$D$ = pound-feet torque per radian per second of load.

Grouping together the $\theta_L$ terms gives

$$\left(\frac{J_L}{K_L}s^2 + \frac{D}{K_L}s + 1\right)\theta_L = \theta_M + \frac{T_L}{K_L} \qquad (14.2\text{–}18)$$

Equations 14.2–16 and 14.2–18 may be written as

$$\theta_M = \frac{V_a + \dfrac{K_L R}{K_T}\theta_L}{\dfrac{K_L R}{K_T}\left[\dfrac{J_M}{K_L}s^2 + \dfrac{K_e K_T}{K_L R}s + 1\right]} \qquad (14.2\text{–}19)$$

$$\theta_L = \frac{\theta_M + \dfrac{T_L}{K_L}}{\left[\dfrac{J_L}{K_L}s^2 + \dfrac{D}{K_L}s + 1\right]} \qquad (14.2\text{–}20)$$

The equations presented in this form suggest that the variables in the numerators that are functions of time are the driving functions or inputs to the system transfer functions. The remaining portions of these equations are functions only of the characteristic parameters of the system and are considered as "equivalent" transfer functions. Thus both the motor and the load elements have an equivalent transfer function that is influenced by the common springy shaft and have two input quantities, one of which is an independent variable $V_a$ or $T_L$, and the other of which is a dependent variable $\theta_L$ or $\theta_M$. A block diagram demonstrating the simultaneous relations expressed by Equations 14.2–19 and 14.2–20 is shown in Figure 14.2–7.

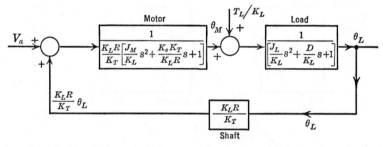

FIGURE 14.2–7.   Equivalent block diagram of motor connected to springy shaft with external load torque applied.

It will be noted that the inputs to each element are expressed in a common set of units, volts for the motor input and radians for the load. Thus, despite the apparent incongruity of having electrical and mechanical input quantities to a single element, by utilizing the proper factor for performing the conversion of units both quantities may be expressed in the same dimensions.

Also worthy of mention is the fact that the two inputs to each element are added together as a *summing* process rather than as in a *differencing* device similar to the differential of an error-sensing device. For this reason especial care must be taken when determining the "closed-loop" performance of this type of equivalent circuit.

**A Regulator-Type Problem.**   The extensive use of regulators in industry to control such varied quantities [82, 95, 98, 104] as speed, voltage, and torque makes it worth while to consider in detail some of the characteristics of this type of controller. Since speed and torque controllers represent variations of the position control problems discussed in the preceding sections, the output portion of a voltage regulator will be described to indicate how the effects of external disturbances may be treated for the voltage-regulator problem.

Figure 14.2–8 is a sketch of a d-c generator in which the exciter voltage $E_x$ supplies the generator field. The generator rotor is driven through its drive shaft at speed $S$ by an external source of power that may not be capable of maintaining a constant speed. The generator internal voltage $E_g$ supplies the load voltage $E_L$ through the generator internal resistance $R_g$ and the line resistance $R_L$. The generator terminal voltage $E_t$ represents the controlled variable signal for use by the voltage regulator itself. The nature of the load being fed is such that $E_L$ may have a time variation quite independent of the remainder of the system.

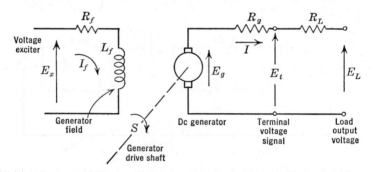

FIGURE 14.2–8. Schematic diagram of d-c generator with variable speed drive and load variations.

Thus, from these physical considerations alone, it appears that the terminal voltage $E_t$ is a function of the various inputs $E_x$, $S$, and $E_L$, of which $E_x$ and, to a much lesser extent, $S$ and $E_L$ may be changed as a result of a change in $E_t$. The transform equations below indicate in a quantitative fashion the relationship between the change in $E_t$ and the change in each of the three variables, $E_x$, $S$, and $E_L$.

The generator field current $I_f$ can be expressed in terms of $E_x$ as

$$I_f = \frac{E_x}{R_f(T_f s + 1)} \tag{14.2-21}$$

where $T_f = L_f/R_f$.

The generator internal voltage $E_g$ is proportional to the product of the field current and the generator rotor speed,

$$E_g = K_g S I_f$$

or

$$E_g = \frac{K_g S E_x}{R_f(T_f s + 1)} \tag{14.2-22}$$

$E_t$ can be expressed as

$$E_t = E_g - IR_g \qquad (14.2\text{-}23)$$

where $I$, the armature current, is

$$I = \frac{E_g - E_L}{R_g + R_L} \qquad (14.2\text{-}24)$$

From the two equations above,

$$E_t = \frac{R_L K_g S E_x}{(R_g + R_L)R_f(T_f s + 1)} + \frac{R_g E_L}{R_g + R_L} \qquad (14.2\text{-}25)$$

By considering only small variations in the quantities $E_f$, $S$, $E_x$, and $E_t$ the change in $E_t$ of Equation 14.2-25 may be expressed as

$$\Delta E_t = \frac{R_L K_g S_o \Delta E_x}{(R_g + R_L)R_f(T_f s + 1)} + \frac{R_L K_g E_{x_o} \Delta S}{(R_g + R_L)R_f} + \frac{R_g \Delta E_L}{R_g + R_L} \qquad (14.2\text{-}26)$$

where $\Delta E_t$ is the deviation of $E_t$ from its nominal value $E_{t_o}$,
  $\Delta E_L$ is the deviation of $E_L$ from its nominal value $E_{L_o}$,
  $E_{x_o}$ is the nominal value of $E_x$,
  $\Delta E_x$ is the deviation of $E_x$ from $E_{x_o}$,
  $S_o$ is the nominal value of $S$, and
  $\Delta S$ is the deviation of $S$ from $S_o$.

A block diagram corresponding to the relationships indicated by Equation 14.2-26 is shown in Figure 14.2-9. The quantitative effect of each of the three inputs $\Delta E_L$, $\Delta S$, and $\Delta E_x$ is thus illustrated. It should,

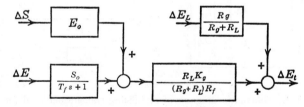

FIGURE 14.2-9.  Equivalent block diagram of d-c generator shown in Figure 14.2-8.

of course, be understood that the remainder of the control system must be connected so that only a small change, $\Delta E_t$, will be occasioned by a change of any of these inputs. The point of interest at present is that the system equations representing common regulator systems may have present external disturbances over and above the reference signal, and a block diagram representing the complete system can generally be drawn.

## 14.3   Equivalent Block Diagram Representation

Often the analysis of control systems having multiple loops is made cumbersome by the presence of interconnected loops having common elements. The complications that arise are due to two major causes:

Loading or interaction effects of interconnected elements make the transfer function of one element dependent on the parameters of another element.

Multiple feedback circuits may be so interrelated that it is difficult to reduce the system to a simple form without eliminating the variables that are of interest.

An artifice that may be used to advantage to handle such problems is to obtain an equivalent block diagram for the system. Some examples of the representation by equivalent transfer functions and block diagrams of regulation or interaction effects have been described in the previous section. Another important example of a common problem of this sort is the stabilizing transformer used for feedback purposes. This is described in the following section.

**Equivalent Block Diagram of Stabilizing Transformer.**   In some electrical regulator systems the effect of a rate signal such as produced by a tachometer in a position control is obtained by use of a stabilizing transformer signal.[77]   As shown in Figure 14.3–1, a voltage $E_2$ impressed on

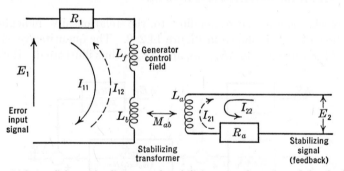

FIGURE 14.3–1.   Schematic diagram of stabilizing transformer used for feedback.

the stabilizing transformer primary produces a current in the secondary of the transformer and in the control field of the generator. This current opposes the error signal current in the control field caused by the error voltage $E_1$. Because of the coupling between primary and secondary of the transformer, the error signal input $E_1$ produces a current $(I_{11})$ in the control field that is a function of the impedance of the control field, the transformer, and the rest of the network from which the transformer signal is derived.  In similar fashion, the transfer function between a signal ($E_2$) on the stabilizing transformer and a current ($I_{12}$) in the control field is likewise a function of these three impedances.

With only the error signal $E_1$ considered, the following transform voltage equations can be written:

$$E_1 = [R_1 + (L_f + L_b)s]I_{11} - M_{ab}sI_{21} \qquad (14.3\text{–}1)$$

$$0 = - M_{ab}sI_{11} + (R_a + L_a s)I_{21} \qquad (14.3\text{–}2)$$

where $R_1$ = total series resistance in ohms of input circuit,

$L_f$ = inductance in henries of control field,

$L_b$ = self-inductance in henries of secondary of stabilizing transformer,

$L_a$ = self-inductance in henries of primary of stabilizing transformer,

$M_{ab}$ = mutual inductance in henries of stabilizing transformer,

$R_a$ = total series resistance in ohms of stabilizing transformer primary and associated network,

$I_{11}$ = current of control field in amperes caused by voltage $E_1$, and

$I_{21}$ = current of stabilizing field primary in amperes caused by voltage $E_1$.

By solving these two equations for $I_{11}$, the current in the control field produced by an error input signal is found to be

$$\frac{I_{11}}{E_1} = \frac{\left[1 + \dfrac{L_a}{R_a}s\right]}{R_1\left\{1 + s\left(\dfrac{L_f + L_b}{R_1} + \dfrac{L_a}{R_a}\right) + s^2\left[\dfrac{L_a}{R_a}\dfrac{(L_f + L_b)}{R_1} - \dfrac{M_{ab}^2}{R_1 R_a}\right]\right\}}$$

or

$$\qquad (14.3\text{–}3)$$

$$\frac{I_{11}}{E_1} = \frac{1 + T_a s}{R_1[1 + T_x s][1 + T_y s]} \qquad (14.3\text{–}4)$$

where $T_a = L_a/R_a$, and
$T_x$ and $T_y$ are equivalent time constants for denominator of Equation 14.3–3.

Now considering the feedback signal $E_2$, the corresponding voltage equations are

$$0 = [R_1 + (L_b + L_f)s]I_{12} - M_{ab}sI_{22} \qquad (14.3\text{–}5)$$

$$E_2 = - M_{ab}sI_{12} + (R_a + L_a s)I_{22} \qquad (14.3\text{–}6)$$

where $I_{12}$ = current of control field in amperes caused by voltage $E_2$, and

$I_{22}$ = current of stabilizing field primary in amperes caused by voltage $E_2$.

From these equations

$$\frac{I_{12}}{E_2} = \frac{M_{ab}s}{R_a R_1 [1 + T_x s][1 + T_y s]} \tag{14.3-7}$$

where $T_x$ and $T_y$ are defined above. Equation 14.3–7 indicates that $I_{12}$ is proportional to $sE_2$ so that, to a first approximation, the output current is proportional to the rate of change of the voltage $E_2$.

Combining the transfer functions, Equations 14.3–4 and 14.3–7, into a single equivalent block diagram results in Figure 14.3–2. Although

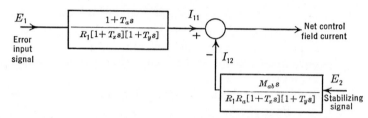

FIGURE 14.3–2.   Equivalent block diagram for combined input and stabilizing circuits of Figure 14.3–1.

the loading effect of the two circuits still exists between the two transfer functions shown, each transfer function may be considered separately from the other.

**Simplifying Interconnected Multiple-Loop Systems.** The problem of multiple-loop systems that are interconnected in an intricate fashion can be illustrated by means of Figure 14.3–3, where the ratio of the output $C$ to the input $R$ is sought. The process of simplifying loop 2 so that it

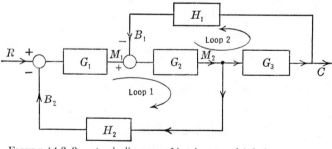

FIGURE 14.3–3.   Block diagram of intricate multiple-loop system.

may be included in loop 1 tends to eliminate the control variable $C$. This difficulty can be overcome by rearranging the block diagram of the system in the fashion shown in Figure 14.3–4.

By use of the superposition principle it is possible to represent any transfer function by more than one block without altering the equations of performance of the system, provided the system remains within its

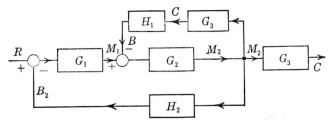

FIGURE 14.3–4.   Rearranged diagram of multiple-loop system of Figure 14.3–3.

linear region of operation.   Using this technique, the $G_3$ transfer function is properly indicated twice on Figure 14.3–4, which is merely a rearrangement of the block diagram of Figure 14.3–3.

The representation shown in Figure 14.3–4 is in such a form that the resultant function from $M_1$ to $M_2$ may be obtained quite directly by the use of closed-loop analysis methods.   This is shown as follows:

$$\frac{M_2}{M_1} = \frac{G_2}{1 + G_2 G_3 H_1} \qquad (14.3\text{–}8)$$

The transfer function from $R$ to $M_2$ can now be written as

$$\frac{M_2}{R} = \frac{\dfrac{G_1 G_2}{1 + G_2 G_3 H_1}}{1 + \dfrac{G_1 G_2 H_2}{1 + G_2 G_3 H_1}} \qquad (14.3\text{–}9)$$

Simplifying this equation and modifying by $G_3$, the over-all transfer function from $R$ to $C$ is

$$\frac{C}{R} = \frac{G_1 G_2 G_3}{1 + G_2 G_3 H_1 + G_1 G_2 H_2} \qquad (14.3\text{–}10)$$

This result is the same as the one that would be obtained by less direct methods.

Although no major change has been produced by including the $G_3$ transfer function twice on the block diagram, nevertheless a more direct attack on the analysis has been made available.

There are no inherent limitations to the rearrangement methods indicated; the equivalent block diagrams must, however, yield the same system equations as the original physical system. It should be noted that the "equivalent" transfer functions may not always yield intermediate results that are physically obtainable, although the over-all results must be the same as for the original system.

## 14.4 Position Control System with Load Disturbance

As a means of indicating the details of the analysis of a control system subjected to both input position and load disturbances, an illustrative position control system will be described. The system is one that has been designed with primary emphasis on its position control requirements. However, consideration has also been placed on the needs of the control to respond properly to the application of a disturbance load torque.

Shown in Figure 14.4–1 is a block diagram representing the system being considered. $R$, the position input, is compared to the controlled variable position, $C$, in a selsyn control transformer, and the difference $E$ appears as an a-c voltage signal. A discriminator-amplifier rectifies and amplifies $E$ to produce $M_1$, from which is subtracted $B_1$; the feedback voltage $M_2$, the net signal, is amplified by an amplifier and an amplidyne, the voltage of which, $M_3$, is impressed on the d-c motor with attached load. A disturbance load torque $T_L$ is also applied to the load. A tachometer and an acceleration generator supply d-c voltages to the filter, the output of which is the feedback voltage $B_1$. It is desired to determine the output motion as a function of frequency both for the sinusoidal motion of $R$ and for the application of sinusoidal torques $T_L$.

By making use of the equivalent block diagram developed in Section 14.2 for a motor with electrical and mechanical inputs applied, Figure 14.4–1 may be redrawn as is done in Figure 14.4–2, where, in addition, the feedback circuit is shown in somewhat simplified form. For reasons of abbreviating the nomenclature, the literal form of a transfer function is shown above the block to which it refers.

Since the system is assumed to be linear, superposition of the effects of the two inputs may be applied; thus the output response as a function of frequency for each input may be determined independently. The various steps in the process of regrouping the transfer function blocks for each input are described below, and the attenuation and phase diagrams corresponding to these various arrangements are also shown.

**Determination of $C/R$.** For this purpose the load torque $T_L$ is set equal to zero and $s$ is replaced by $j\omega$. The elements $G_2$ and $G_3$ are combined in series to form $G_7$, and the block diagram appears in the form shown in Figure 14.4–3. The effect of feeding $H_1$ around $G_7$ results in the effective transfer function $G_8$, which is shown in Figure 14.4–4. The process of determining the $C/R$ as a function of frequency from Figure

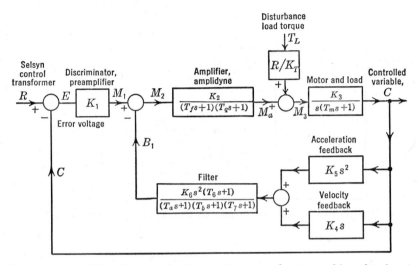

FIGURE 14.4–1. Block diagram showing position control system subjected to input position motion and disturbance load torque.

$K_1 = 14.8$ volts/radian
$K_2 = 2300$ volts/volt
$K_3 = 0.526$ radian per second/volt
$K_4 = 0.98$ volt/radian per second
$K_5 = 0.01368$ volt/radian per second$^2$
$K_6 = 0.193$ second$^2$
$T_f = 1/31.5 = 0.0317$ second
$T_q = 1/17.6 = 0.0569$ second
$T_m = 1/9.1 = 0.110$ second
$T_a = 1/0.986 = 1.014$ seconds
$T_b = 1/5.26 = 0.19$ second
$T_6 = 0.016$ second
$T_7 = 0.0016$ second
$\dfrac{K_5}{K_4} = 1/71.5 = 0.0140$ second
$\dfrac{R}{K_T} = 0.855$ volt/pound-foot

14.4–4 is quite straightforward. A tabulation of various transfer functions indicated in Figures 14.4–2, 14.4–3, and 14.4–4 is made in Table 14.4–1. Also shown is the figure number corresponding to the attenuation and phase diagrams for each of these transfer functions.

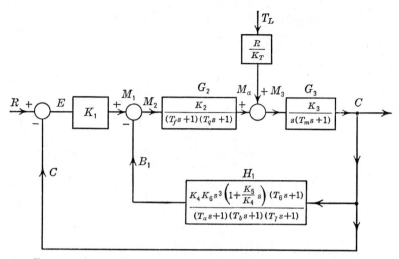

FIGURE 14.4–2. Alternate representation of system of Figure 14.4–1.

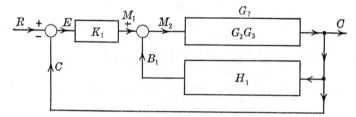

FIGURE 14.4–3. Simplified block diagram of system of Figure 14.4–2 (with $T_L = 0$).

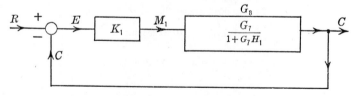

FIGURE 14.4–4. Further simplification of block diagram of system of Figure 14.4–3 (with $T_L = 0$).

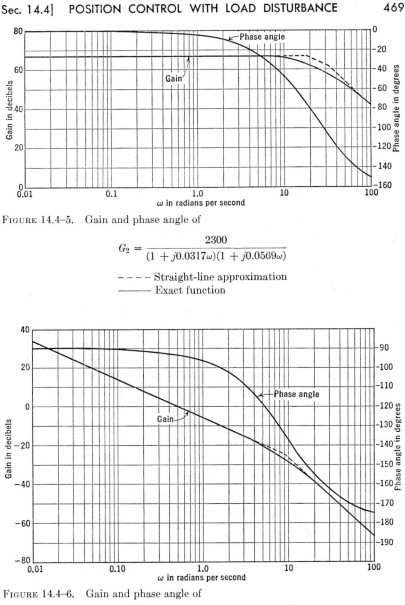

FIGURE 14.4–5.   Gain and phase angle of

$$G_2 = \frac{2300}{(1 + j0.0317\omega)(1 + j0.0569\omega)}$$

– – – – Straight-line approximation
———— Exact function

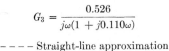

FIGURE 14.4–6.   Gain and phase angle of

$$G_3 = \frac{0.526}{j\omega(1 + j0.110\omega)}$$

– – – – Straight-line approximation
———— Exact function

TABLE 14.4–1

TABLE OF TRANSFER FUNCTIONS AND THE CORRESPONDING FIGURES ON WHICH
THE ATTENUATION AND PHASE DIAGRAMS ARE SHOWN ($C/R$ CASE)

| Transfer Function | Figure Number |
|---|---|
| $G_2$ | 14.4–5 |
| $G_3$ | 14.4–6 |
| $G_7$ | 14.4–7 |
| $H_1$ | 14.4–8 |
| $G_7H_1$ | 14.4–9 |
| $K_1G_8$ | 14.4–10 |
| $C/R$ | 14.4–11 |

The forward-loop transfer function $G_7$ shown in Figure 14.4–7 has a
high gain at low frequencies and is composed of three time constants in

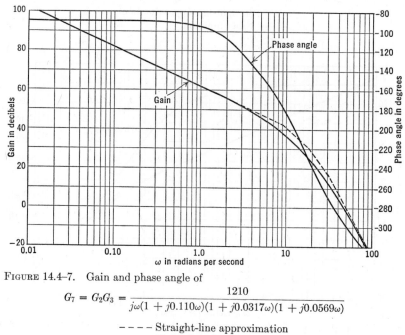

FIGURE 14.4–7.   Gain and phase angle of

$$G_7 = G_2G_3 = \frac{1210}{j\omega(1 + j0.110\omega)(1 + j0.0317\omega)(1 + j0.0569\omega)}$$

– – – – Straight-line approximation
———— Exact function

addition to the integrating action of the motor.   The feedback transfer
function $H_1$ has extremely low values of gain at low frequencies as shown
in Figure 14.4–8.   The gain rate initially is 60 decibels per decade, decreasing to 40 then 20 decibels at the filter time constants $T_a = 1/0.986$

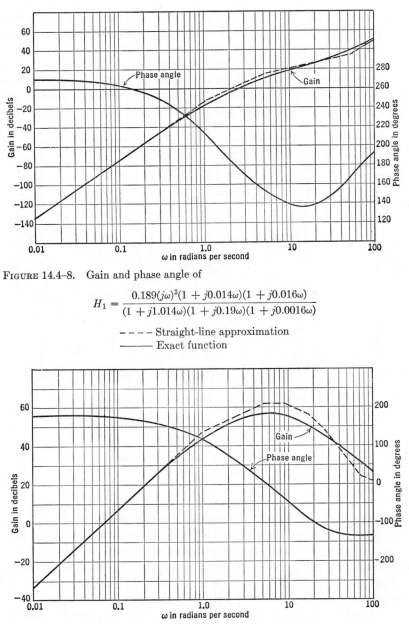

FIGURE 14.4–8. Gain and phase angle of

$$H_1 = \frac{0.189(j\omega)^3(1 + j0.014\omega)(1 + j0.016\omega)}{(1 + j1.014\omega)(1 + j0.19\omega)(1 + j0.0016\omega)}$$

– – – – Straight-line approximation
———— Exact function

FIGURE 14.4–9. Gain and phase angle of $G_7H_1$.

– – – – Straight-line approximation
———— Exact function

and $T_b = 1/5.26$. At $\omega = 62.5$ and 70 radians per second the gain rate is increased by 20 decibels per decade at each frequency because of the presence of a filter time constant and the acceleration feedback. Figure 14.4–9 shows the over-all loop transfer function $G_7 H_1$ and indicates that over a range of frequencies from $\omega = 0.069$ to more than 100 radians per second this loop gain is substantially greater than 1. The forward gain function of the complete system, $K_1 G_8$, shown in Figure 14.4–10 is

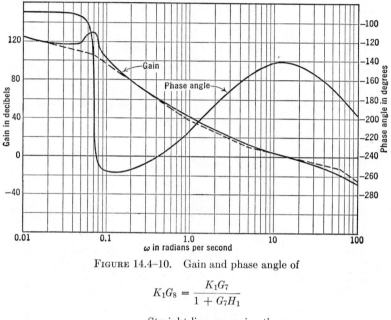

FIGURE 14.4–10.    Gain and phase angle of

$$K_1 G_8 = \frac{K_1 G_7}{1 + G_7 H_1}$$

– – – – Straight-line approximation
———— Exact function

seen to have essentially the reciprocal characteristic of the feedback circuit over the broad range of frequencies indicated above. Included in this range is the frequency at which the open-loop attenuation is 0 decibels and at which the attenuation rate is 20 decibels per decade. The resultant over-all closed-loop transfer function for $C/R$ is shown in Figure 14.4–11. The $C/R$ curve is approximately 0 decibels for the low frequencies, peaks to about +4 decibels at $\omega = 12$ radians per second, after which it attenuates rapidly as the value of $C/R$ approximates the value of the $K_1 G_8$ transfer function for higher frequencies.

**Determination of $C/T_L$.** When the effect of load torque disturbances is considered, the position input $R$ is set equal to zero and the block di-

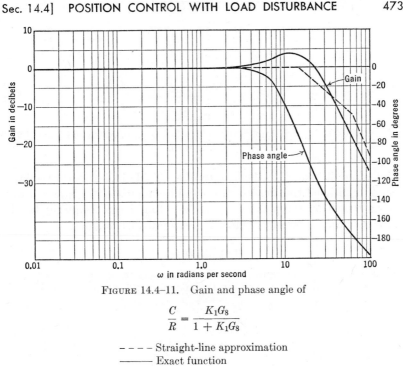

FIGURE 14.4–11.   Gain and phase angle of

$$\frac{C}{R} = \frac{K_1 G_8}{1 + K_1 G_8}$$

– – – – Straight-line approximation
——— Exact function

agram appears as shown in Figure 14.4–12.   In this figure the feedback
function $H_1$ and the error amplification $K_1$ form a parallel grouping of
elements, the effective transfer function of which is called $H_2$.   $H_2$ and $G_2$
combine in series to provide the total feedback quantity for the forward

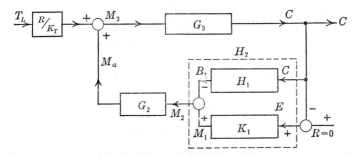

FIGURE 14.4–12.   Simplified block diagram of system of Figure 14.4–2 (with $R = 0$).

function $G_3$, as shown in Figure 14.4–13.   The process of determining
the ratio of $C/T_L$ for the block diagram shown in Figure 14.4–13 becomes
analogous to that for the normal feedback case when it is realized that
the polarity of the feedback quantity is reversed before it appears at the

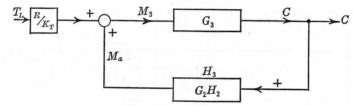

FIGURE 14.4–13.   Further simplification of block diagram of system of Figure 14.4–12
(with $R = 0$).

point where it "adds" to the load torque.   Table 14.4–2 shows a tabulation of additional transfer functions and the figures on which are drawn their attenuation and phase diagrams as a function of frequency for the block diagrams shown in Figures 14.4–12 and 14.4–13.

TABLE 14.4–2

TABLE OF TRANSFER FUNCTIONS AND THE CORRESPONDING FIGURES ON WHICH
THE ATTENUATION AND PHASE DIAGRAMS ARE SHOWN ($C/T_L$ CASE)

| Transfer Function | Figure Number |
|---|---|
| $H_2$ | 14.4–14 |
| $H_3$ | 14.4–15 |
| $G_3 H_3$ | 14.4–16 |
| $\dfrac{C}{R T_L / K_T}$ | 14.4–17 |

The gain and phase shift of $H_2$ are shown in Figure 14.4–14.   The parallel grouping of $H_1$ and $K_1$ is very nearly equal to the position feedback component $K_1$ for the frequencies lower than $\omega = 14.5$ radians per second.   For frequencies in the region of $\omega = 14.5$ to $\omega = 70$ radians per second the velocity term dominates; at higher frequencies the acceleration term is predominant.   The low-frequency feedback filter time constants do not appear directly in this figure, for, as indicated in Figure 14.4–8, they no longer serve to attenuate for frequencies above 5.26 radians per second.

Figure 14.4–15 shows the series combination of $G_2$ and $H_2$ and indicates the feedback function to be of extremely high gain at low frequencies.   It is also of interest to note that the phase angle of $H_3$ at $\omega = 0$ is 180°, indicating the action of negative feedback associated with the tachometer and output feedback circuits.   The attenuation effect of $G_2$ at higher frequencies (Figure 14.4–5) is compensated for by the increased gain at higher frequencies of $H_2$ due to velocity and acceleration.   Thus the feedback is relatively independent of frequency, and the rate of change

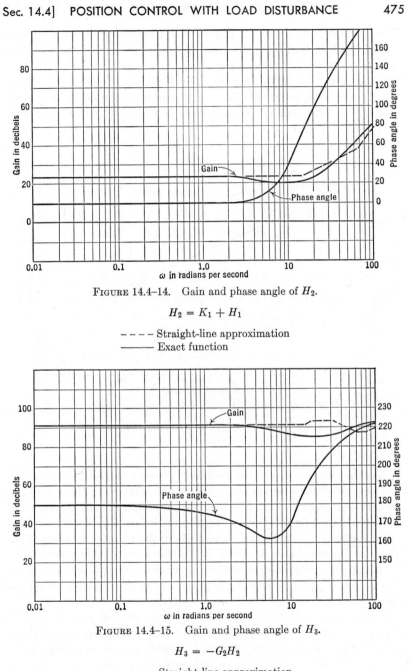

FIGURE 14.4–14.   Gain and phase angle of $H_2$.

$$H_2 = K_1 + H_1$$

– – – – Straight-line approximation
———— Exact function

FIGURE 14.4–15.   Gain and phase angle of $H_3$.

$$H_3 = -G_2 H_2$$

– – – – Straight-line approximation
———— Exact function

of attenuation is quite small.  Figure 14.4–16 showing the over-all loop transfer function $G_3H_3$ indicates that the loop gain exceeds zero for frequencies less than 100 radians per second.

The resultant $C/(RT_L/K_T)$ transfer function is shown in Figure 14.4–17, where the motor displacement for a given torque input is comparatively independent of the frequency of the input torque.  Despite

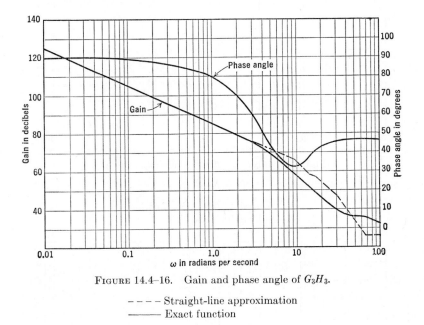

FIGURE 14.4–16.   Gain and phase angle of $G_3H_3$.

– – – – Straight-line approximation

———— Exact function

the fact that an increase in the load displacement of about 2/1 over the low-frequency values occurs for torques of frequencies in the vicinity of $\omega = 20$ radians per second, this is not an appreciable load motion compared to what might be obtained if the amplifier portion of the controller were not effective.  In Figure 14.4–6, where the transfer function $G_3$ of the motor alone is shown, it is evident that because of its low gain above $\omega = 0.5$ much greater motion of the motor would occur if it were not for the effectiveness of the controller in producing an electromagnetic torque that opposes the external load torque applied.

Although the load torque that the control is called upon to restrain is seldom sinusoidal, nevertheless the relative effectiveness of two types of control in opposing load torques may be readily compared on this basis. Furthermore, the sinusoidal approach provides a means whereby the steps necessary to improve system performance can be more readily

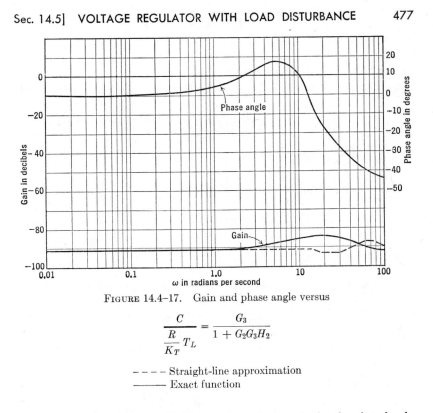

FIGURE 14.4–17.   Gain and phase angle versus

$$\frac{C}{\dfrac{R}{K_T}T_L} = \frac{G_3}{1 + G_2G_3H_2}$$

– – – – Straight-line approximation
———— Exact function

ascertained than they would be for a transient analysis of so involved a system.

## 14.5   Voltage Regulator with Load Disturbance

The problem of regulating the terminal voltage of an alternator, as is commonly encountered in central station practice, may also be readily handled by means of the attenuation-frequency techniques previously described. Although in years past the performance of such an equipment would not customarily be analyzed on the basis of sinusoidally varying inputs and loads, here this approach will be used.

Figure 14.5–1 shows a schematic diagram representing the regulator system being considered. The desired voltage $V$ is set into the voltage reference unit, the output of which is $R$. $E_T$, the terminal voltage of the alternator, is measured by a potential transformer that is assumed to have no error. $E_T$ is compared with $R$ to produce the actuating voltage $E$. The resultant current in the control field of the amplidyne is the difference of the currents obtained from $E$ and from the main exciter voltage $E_x$, as modified by the feedback through the stabilizing transformer.

The amplidyne voltage $E_a$ serves as a control signal to the exciter field, which is provided with self-excitation from the main exciter. $E_x$, the exciter voltage, also supplies excitation for the alternator field. The internal generator voltage is $E_G$, whereas $E_T$ is the terminal voltage of the

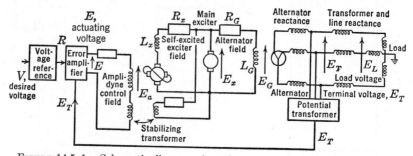

FIGURE 14.5-1.  Schematic diagram of an alternator voltage regulator system.

generator. $E_L$ is the terminal voltage on the load and is the indirectly controlled quantity, $Q$. It is desired to determine the nature of the terminal voltage for independent sinusoidal inputs to $V$ and $E_L$.

In Figure 14.5-2 the block diagram equivalent of Figure 14.5-1 is drawn. From this block diagram the regulator can be recognized as a

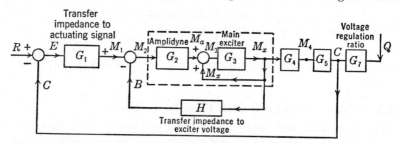

FIGURE 14.5-2.  Block diagram of regulator system shown in Figure 14.5-1.

$M_1$ = amplidyne control field current per volt of actuating signal
$B$ = amplidyne control field current per volt of exciter voltage
$M_2 = M_1 - B$ = resultant control field current
$M_a$ = amplidyne terminal voltage, $E_a$
$M_x$ = exciter terminal voltage, $E_x$
$M_4$ = generator internal voltage, $E_G$
$C$ = generator terminal voltage, $E_T$
$Q$ = load terminal voltage, $E_L$

multiple-loop system having two internal loops.  The transfer impedance functions $G_1$ and $H$ are similar to those developed in Section 14.3 for the stabilizing transformer.  The effect of self-excitation of the main exciter field appears as a direct regenerative feedback around $G_3$.  Since the main exciter transfer function is essentially that of a single time constant element having a regenerative loop gain less than unity, this internal loop may be simplified directly and a combined transfer function from $M_2$ to $M_x$ can readily be obtained. $G_6$ is this combined transfer function.

$G_4$ is the transfer function from exciter voltage to the generator voltage. The transfer function from the generated voltage to the terminal voltage of the generator is $G_5$. The effect of load regulation is represented by the transfer function $G_7$, which relates the load voltage $E_L$ to the terminal voltage $E_T$. $G_7$ can be determined in a fashion similar to that described in Section 14.2 for a d-c regulator.

**Determination of $C/R = (E_T/V)$.** For this case the alternator is assumed to be unloaded so that $Q$ is equal to $C$ and $G_5 = 1$. Figure 14.5–3

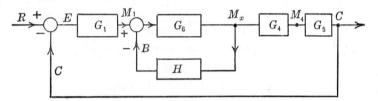

FIGURE 14.5–3.   Simplified block diagram of system of Figure 14.5–2 with no load disturbance.

$$G_1 = \frac{(1 + 0.163s)}{48.4(1 + 0.487s)(1 + 0.0189s)}$$

$$G_6 = \frac{3750}{(1 + 0.133s)(1 + 0.795s)}$$

$$H = \frac{s}{550(1 + 0.68s)(1 + 0.0214s)}$$

$$G_4 = \frac{1}{1.25(1 + 7.2s)}$$

$$G_5 = 1$$

is the simplified block diagram of the system shown in Figure 14.5–2 with the amplidyne exciter elements combined. In Table 14.5–1 is a tabulation of the various transfer functions indicated on Figure 14.5–3 and a listing of the numbers of the figures on which are located the attenuation and phase diagrams for these transfer functions.

The amplidyne-exciter transfer function $G_6$ shown in Figure 14.5–4 has high gain at low frequencies and indicates the presence of the effective time constants of the amplidyne and the exciter. $H$, the feedback transfer function through the stabilizing transformer and the control field, is shown in Figure 14.5–5. The initial 20 decibels per decade gain rate at low frequencies due to the stabilizing transformer is reduced to 0 and

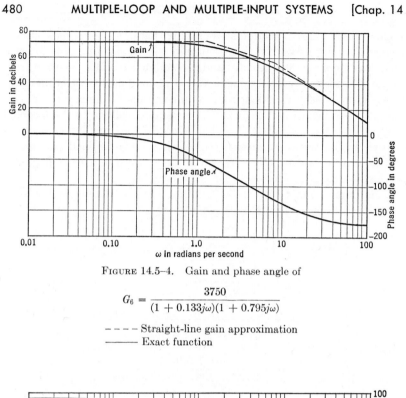

Figure 14.5–4. Gain and phase angle of

$$G_6 = \frac{3750}{(1 + 0.133j\omega)(1 + 0.795j\omega)}$$

– – – – Straight-line gain approximation
———— Exact function

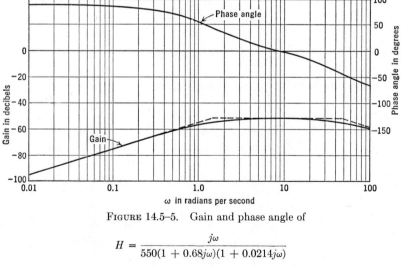

Figure 14.5–5. Gain and phase angle of

$$H = \frac{j\omega}{550(1 + 0.68j\omega)(1 + 0.0214j\omega)}$$

– – – – Straight-line gain approximation
———— Exact function

TABLE 14.5-1

Table of Transfer Functions and the Corresponding Figures on Which
are Shown the Attenuation and Phase Diagrams

| Transfer Function | Figure Number |
|---|---|
| $G_6$ | 14.5–4 |
| $H$ | 14.5–5 |
| $G_6H$ | 14.5–6 |
| $\dfrac{G_6}{1 + G_6H}$ | 14.5–7 |
| $G_1G_4G_5$ | 14.5–8 |
| $\dfrac{G_1G_4G_5G_6}{1 + G_6H} = G_8$ | 14.5–9 |
| $G$ | 14.5–10 |

finally to a 20 decibels per decade loss rate as the resultant time constants of the transformer windings and the control field become effective in the vicinity of $\omega = 1.5$ and $\omega = 46$ radians per second.

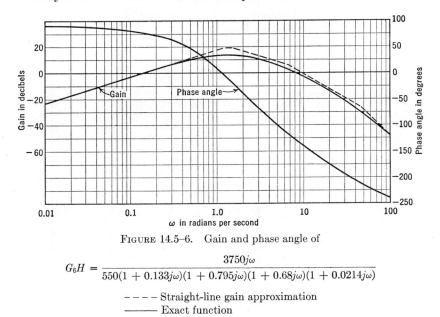

Figure 14.5–6.   Gain and phase angle of

$$G_6H = \frac{3750j\omega}{550(1 + 0.133j\omega)(1 + 0.795j\omega)(1 + 0.68j\omega)(1 + 0.0214j\omega)}$$

– – – – Straight-line gain approximation
———— Exact function

Figure 14.5–6, showing the loop gain $G_6H$, indicates that in the region of frequencies from $\omega = 0.15$ to $9.0$ radians per second the gain is somewhat greater than unity.   The closed-loop transfer function $G_6/(1 + G_6H)$ is shown in Figure 14.5–7 and is seen to be similar to $G_6$

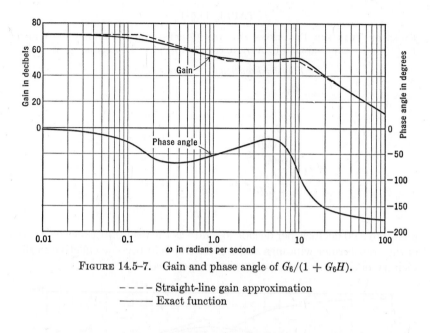

FIGURE 14.5–7.    Gain and phase angle of $G_6/(1 + G_6H)$.

– – – – Straight-line gain approximation
———— Exact function

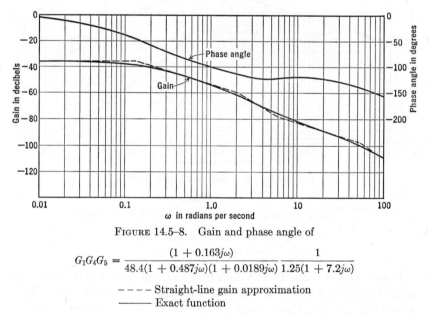

FIGURE 14.5–8.    Gain and phase angle of

$$G_1G_4G_5 = \frac{(1 + 0.163j\omega)}{48.4(1 + 0.487j\omega)(1 + 0.0189j\omega)} \frac{1}{1.25(1 + 7.2j\omega)}$$

– – – – Straight-line gain approximation
———— Exact function

except for the range of frequencies $\omega = 0.15$ to $9.0$ radians per second noted above.  Figure 14.5–8 shows the combined series transfer function of $G_1G_4G_5$ and indicates the gain of these elements of the system to be low.  It is interesting to note that there is the effect of a "lead" element produced in the frequency range from $\omega = 6$ to $50$ radians per second. This effect is caused by the action of the stabilizing transformer as indicated in Section 14.3 and Equation 14.3–4.

The transfer function of the combined open-loop transfer function $G_8$ is shown in Figure 14.5–9.  The gain at low frequencies is 36 decibels or

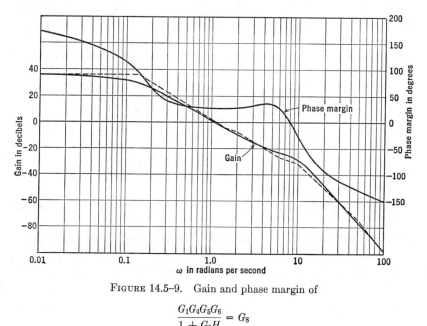

FIGURE 14.5–9.   Gain and phase margin of

$$\frac{G_1G_4G_5G_6}{1 + G_6H} = G_8$$

– – – – Straight-line gain approximation
——— Exact function

a gain of about 60, and zero attenuation rate is maintained out to a little more than 0.1 radian per second.  Although the attenuation rate at 0 decibels is 40 decibels per decade, the presence of occasional sections of 20 decibels per decade slope results in a phase margin of about 25° in the frequency range near 0 decibels.  It will be noted that the phase margin is positive over a substantial range of frequencies so that an over-all gain change should not produce instability.  The closed-loop transfer function for the system is shown in Figure 14.5–10 and indicates an amplification

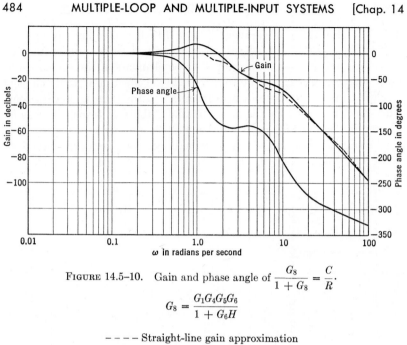

FIGURE 14.5–10.   Gain and phase angle of $\dfrac{G_8}{1+G_8} = \dfrac{C}{R}$.

$$G_8 = \frac{G_1 G_4 G_5 G_6}{1 + G_6 H}$$

– – – – Straight-line gain approximation
———— Exact function

peak of 7 decibels or slightly greater than 2 in the vicinity of 1 radian per second.

**Determination of $C/Q = (E_T/E_L)$.**   When the effect of load voltage disturbances is considered, the reference voltage $R$ is set equal to zero and the block diagram appears as shown on Figure 14.5–11, where the signal $E$ is equal to $-C$.   Since

$$C = G_7 Q - G_8 C \tag{14.5-1}$$

$$\frac{C}{Q} = \frac{G_7}{1 + G_8} \tag{14.5-2}$$

With the load present, the alternator reactance produces a regulation effect that makes $G_5 = X_L/(X_L + X_G)$, and alters the previous value of $G_8$.   Figure 14.5–12 shows a plot of Equation 14.5–2 and shows the response of the regulator to be effective in attenuating load disturbances of low frequencies, $-42$ decibels at $\omega = 0.01$ radian per second.   As the frequencies of the load disturbances increase above $\omega = 0.15$ radian per second, the regulator is less effective in reducing the disturbances until, for frequencies of 1 radian per second and greater, the regulator is no longer able to assist in maintaining the terminal voltage and this voltage

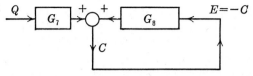

FIGURE 14.5–11.   Simplified block diagram of system of Figure 14.5–2 with only load disturbance applied.

$$G_7 = \frac{X_G}{X_L + X_G} = 0.5$$

$$G_8 = \frac{G_1 G_4 G_5 G_6}{1 + G_6 H} \text{ (shown in Figure 14.5–9 for } G_5 = 1.0)$$

$$G_5 = \frac{X_L}{X_L + X_G} = 0.5$$

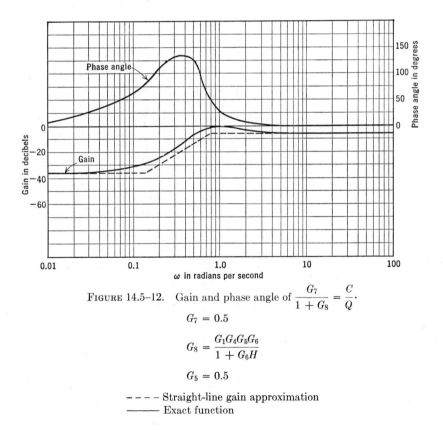

FIGURE 14.5–12.   Gain and phase angle of $\dfrac{G_7}{1 + G_8} = \dfrac{C}{Q}$.

$$G_7 = 0.5$$

$$G_8 = \frac{G_1 G_4 G_5 G_6}{1 + G_6 H}$$

$$G_5 = 0.5$$

– – – – Straight-line gain approximation
———— Exact function

becomes equal to the load voltage. For signals of higher frequencies, the inherent regulation of the system as described by the transfer function, $G_7 = 0.5$, is alone responsible for preventing the terminal voltage $C$ following the load voltage $Q$.

Although the load voltage disturbance variations are not normally considered on the basis of their frequency characteristics, a comparison of the performance of two different regulators to load disturbances may be made conveniently on the basis of their response to sinusoidal disturbances. It is apparent that response of the control shown in Figure 14.5–12 is somewhat limited in its ability to resist rapidly changing load voltage disturbances.

# 15

## COMPARISON OF STEADY-STATE AND
## TRANSIENT PERFORMANCE OF SERVOMECHANISMS

### 15.0 Introduction

The preceding chapters have presented the analysis and synthesis of servomechanisms and other feedback control systems from the point of view of both attenuation-frequency and root locus methods. As such, there has been a conscious effort to relate in a general way both steady-state and transient performance of a number of control systems. However, no particular effort was made in a detailed fashion to relate these two aspects of system performance quantitatively.

In this chapter two methods will be used to provide the quantitative comparison desired. One will be to relate the closed-loop poles and zeros of a feedback control system to its open-loop attenuation frequency characteristic. The other method will be an empirical comparison presented in chart form of the numerical results of a large number of specific control systems expressed in terms of steady-state and transient performance.

The simplicity of the attenuation-frequency methods of feedback control system design is a result of the ease with which the open-loop characteristics may be represented graphically and the speed with which closed-loop performance as a function of frequency can be determined from the M-contours or the Nichols charts. However, as has been noted before, the performance of a control system is frequently judged on the basis of its response to a transient input consisting of a step-function of position. Since abrupt changes in the desired input or the introduction of disturbance forces represent important conditions under which the system response is of interest, knowledge of the performance of a system on the basis of sinusoidal input alone is not always sufficient. Furthermore, because of the ease with which the response of a system to a transient input may be determined experimentally with limited equipment, it is desirable to be able to check the design results against system performance. The works of Biernson [117] and later Chen [130] have provided simple approximate methods for enabling the control system designer to determine quantitatively the closed-loop poles and zeros from the open-loop characteristics. As such, the designer can obtain directly from the open-loop attenuation-frequency plot information from which the closed-loop poles and zeros can be calculated. Thus both steady-state and transient performance of feedback control systems can be obtained.

The other method of determining and comparing the steady-state and transient response of a servomechanism system which will be described in this chapter involves the use of a series of charts that require no detailed calculations. These charts relate the open-loop attenuation-frequency characteristic and the closed-loop response to either a sinusoidal input signal or to an input that is a step input of position. In addition, the non-dimensionalized form in which the charts are presented serves to emphasize the interrelationship of the response requirements as time functions and as frequency functions. These charts present data similar to those described by Herr and Gerst,[66] who indicated the kind of open-loop attenuation curves required to produce certain closed-loop responses.

The designer will readily recognize the value of this method of comparing steady-state and transient responses as described above. The method is tailored to meet his needs. Generally he is given a set of specifications from which he can determine the required steady-state frequency response and/or the transient response to a step input. His problem is to determine the approximate form of the open-loop attenuation characteristic that will provide the desired performance; with this he is in a position to start his more detailed design and to have a fairly definite, although not an absolute, goal toward which he must shape his design. With the design and synthesis techniques described in the preceding chapters, plus a knowledge of the primary control system elements, the designer can determine the remainder of the components necessary to obtain a suitable open-loop characteristic.

Since such practical limitations as non-ideal components, cost, and weight will probably necessitate deviations from the theoretical open-loop attenuation characteristic initially chosen, it is not essential that the open-loop characteristic be determined with particularly great precision. It is essential, however, to have this open-loop characteristic reasonably close to the necessary form. In addition, the quantitative effect of changes in the various parameters in terms of the steady-state and transient performance should be understood so as to indicate a method of refining the system design to meet the exact specification requirements.

As a means for meeting the needs outlined above, a series of charts has been prepared that show the steady-state and transient response of ideal linear servomechanisms in terms of the open-loop attenuation characteristics that are necessary to obtain the response.

## 15.1  Estimation of Closed-Loop Poles from Open-Loop Attenuation Characteristics

Review of the material on the use of the root locus method of control system design and synthesis will serve to point out that the open-loop zeros of a feedback control system are the same as the closed-loop zeros for a system consisting of a series of elements.  For systems having internal loops, the methods for obtaining the "series equivalent" of such loops in terms of their open-loop poles and zeros have also been indicated. The problem that remains therefore is that of determining the closed-loop poles of a control system from its open-loop attenuation characteristic.

**Description of the Method.**  In Section 6.6, it was indicated that the closed-loop poles start from the open-loop pole and move to the open-loop zeros along the root loci as the gain increases from zero to infinity.  Use of the gain information offered by the straight line approximations to the attenuation-frequency plots enables one to determine quickly which closed-loop poles are near the open-loop poles, which are near the open-loop zeros, and which are in the middle of their path along the root locus line.  By dividing the closed-loop poles into three groups based on open-loop system gain, the location of the closed-loop poles can be estimated with very little effort.  The following material is based largely on the presentation of Chen.[130]

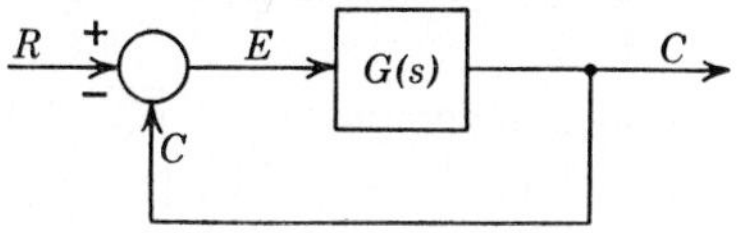

FIGURE 15.1–1.  Control system with direct feedback.

Consider the feedback control system to have the simple form shown in Figure 15.1–1 in which the transfer function $G(s)$ is

$$G(s) = \frac{C(s)}{E(s)} = \frac{K(T_a s + 1)}{s(T_1 s + 1)(T_2 s + 1)(T_3 s + 1)} \qquad (15.1\text{–}1)$$

or in terms of its poles and zeroes

$$G(s) = \frac{K''(s + z_a)}{s(s + p_1)(s + p_2)(s + p_3)} \qquad (15.1\text{–}2)$$

where $K'' = \dfrac{K p_1 p_2 p_3}{z_a}$ $\qquad (15.1\text{–}3)$

The straight line approximation to the attenuation-frequency plot for $G(s)$ is shown in Figure 15.1–2. Indicated on this figure are dotted lines at $\pm 15$ db which have been chosen arbitrarily to divide the attenuation scale into three gain regions: a low-gain region for $|G(\omega)| < -15$ db, a

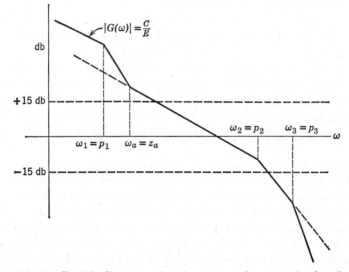

FIGURE 15.1–2. Straight line approximation to open-loop transfer function $G(\omega)$ having direct feedback. Dotted lines at $+15$ db and $-15$ db indicated.

higher-gain region $|G(\omega)| > +15$ db, and the intermediate-gain region where $+15$ db $> |G(\omega)| > -15$ db. The values of $+15$ db $= 5.63$ and $-15$ db $= 0.178$ have been selected as gain-boundary lines on somewhat of a heuristic basis with the thought that the conditions $|G(\omega)| \gg 1$ and $|G(\omega)| \ll 1$ will generally be obtained in the high-gain and low-gain areas respectively. Further, the choice of $\pm 15$ db serves to simplify the evaluation of the closed-loop poles in the intermediate-gain region between $\pm 15$ db as described below.

Having divided the open-loop attenuation-frequency plot into three gain regions, the next step consists of assuming that the high, low, and intermediate gain conditions establish what is happening in the corresponding frequency and, therefore, time domains associated with these gain conditions. For example, the low-gain region occurs at frequencies somewhat above $\omega_2$, and therefore describes conditions that take place at times corresponding to less than $T_2 = \dfrac{1}{\omega_2}$. The high-gain region occurs at frequencies of from slightly greater than $\omega_a$ down to zero, and therefore provides information on the longer time constants ranging from $\infty$ down to slightly less than $T_a = \dfrac{1}{\omega_a}$. The intermediate range of times is described by the intermediate region of gains.

Shown in Figure 15.1–3($a$) and ($b$) are two forms of the root locus for

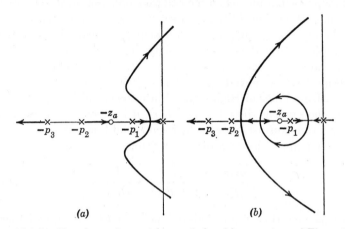

(a)                                              (b)

FIGURE 15.1–3.   Two forms for root locus of closed-loop system of Figure 15.1–2, depending on open-loop pole-zero orientation.

the closed-loop system of Figure 15.1–2, depending on the relative locations of the open-loop poles and zeros.   The root locus plots are similar to some of those shown more exactly in Chapters 6 and 13 and merely help to illustrate more clearly the comparison between the attenuation-frequency and the root locus methods.   The plot is not needed to determine the values of the closed-loop poles themselves.

**Closed-Loop Poles for Low Gain.**   For low values of gain $\left| G(\omega) \right| \ll 1$, one may approximate the closed-loop response as

$$\frac{C(s)}{R(s)} = \frac{G(s)}{1 + G(s)} \simeq G(s) \qquad (15.1\text{–}4)$$

Under this condition, the closed-loop poles of $C(s)/R(s)$ are approximately the open-loop poles of $G(s)$.   The condition of $\left| G(\omega) \right| \ll -15$ db is not critical but does provide a satisfactory gain division point subject to modification as noted below in connection with the closed-loop poles in the region of intermediate gain.

Referring to Figure 15.1–2, one notes from Equation 15.1–4 that one approximate closed-loop pole is at $-p_3$ since this break in the attenuation-frequency plot represents a pole of $G(s)$ and is under the

$-15$ db line. In terms of the root loci plots, Figure 15.1–3, the low value of gain means that the closed-loop pole which starts from $-p_3$ has not moved far from $-p_3$ for the gain, $K''$. As a matter of interest, consideration of the root locus characteristic along the negative real axis as can be done by the rules of Section 6.6 will indicate whether this closed-loop pole has moved on the real axis higher or lower than its open-loop value, depending on the number of poles and zeros on the axis to the right of $-p_3$. Since the closed-loop pole near $-p_3$ corresponds to a transient term that decays rapidly, it will not affect the over-all system transient response very much if the closed-loop pole is considered not to have moved from $-p_3$ at all.

**Closed-Loop Poles at High Gain.** Since the closed-loop poles of $C(s)/R(s)$ are the same as those for $E(s)/R(s)$, it is more convenient to work with the latter expression for the high-gain condition. With $|G(\omega)| \gg 1$, the following approximation may be written

$$\frac{E(s)}{R(s)} = \frac{1}{1 + G(s)} \simeq \frac{1}{G(s)} \tag{15.1–5}$$

Under this condition, the closed-loop poles of $E(s)/R(s)$, and therefore $C(s)/R(s)$ are approximately the open-loop zeros of $G(s)$. Referring to Figure 15.1–2, one approximate closed-loop pole is near $z_a$ since this break corresponds to a zero and is above the $|G(s)| = +15$ db line. In terms of the root locus, this means that one closed-loop pole, corresponding to a rather long time constant, has moved very close to $-z_a$, but has not yet reached it. On Figure 15.1–4 is shown a straight line approxima-

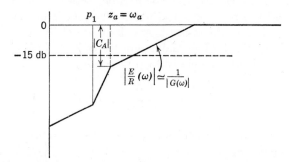

FIGURE 15.1–4. Straight line approximation to closed-loop error function $E/R(\omega)$ for system with open-loop characteristic as shown on Figure 15.1–2. Dotted line at $-15$ db indicated.

tion to $|E/R(s)|$ from which may be seen the effect of a pole corresponding to the downward break produced at $z_a$.

Since $-z_a$ is also a closed-loop zero, there is a dipole formed by the closed-loop zero and the closed-loop pole in close proximity to each other at $-z_a$. The presence of a dipole has a significant effect on the settling time of the system since it produces a slowly decaying transient term which, though small in magnitude, may give a perceptible "tail" to the system response.

Because of the significance of the slowly decaying tail, the dipole should not be neglected by assuming the open-loop zero to be canceled by the closed-loop pole for $|G(s)| \ll 1$. Fortunately, it is possible to determine the separation between the zero and the pole of the dipole quickly in an approximate manner. The magnitude, $C_a$, of the corresponding transient term (residue) for both $c(t)$ and $e(t)$ is the same at the pole of interest for a step-input of position. Referring to the methods of evaluating the inverse Laplace transform of section 4.5, one is able to write the approximate expression for $C_a$ with a step input of position, $(1/s)$, as

$$C_a = \left| \frac{(s + 1/T_a)}{s[G(s) + 1]} \right|_{s=-1/T_a} \simeq \left| \frac{(s + 1/T_a)}{sG(s)} \right|_{s=1/T_a} \quad (15.1\text{-}6)$$

Since it is the magnitude of $C_a$ that is of interest, and since $1/T_a = \omega_a$, the substitutions $s = j\omega_a$ rather than $s = 1/T_a$ can be made in Equation 15.1-6. When this is done, $C_a$ is found to be

$$C_a = \frac{\sqrt{2}}{G(\omega_a)} \quad (15.1\text{-}7)$$

which is equal in magnitude to the amplitude of the asymptote to the $\left| \frac{E}{R}(\omega) \right|$ function evaluated at $\omega_a$ (see Figure 15.1-4).

Truxal has shown that if the closed-loop pole $(-p_1)$ and the closed-loop zero $(-z_a)$ of a dipole are much closer to the origin of a root locus plot than any other closed-loop poles and zeros, which is normally the case, the magnitude of the residue $Kp_i$ is given approximately by

$$Kp_i = -1 + \frac{p_i}{z_i} \quad (15.1\text{-}8)$$

Expressed in terms of the symbols being used here,

$$C_a = 1 - \frac{p_i}{z_a} \quad (15.1\text{-}9)$$

From this equation, the location of the pole of the dipole can be expressed as

$$p_i = z_a - z_a C_a \qquad (15.1\text{-}10)$$

Whether $p_i$ is greater or less than $z_a$ can be readily determined by considering the root loci that lie on the real axis. Since from Equation 15.1–1 and from Figure 15.1–3 no poles can lie between $-p_1$ and $-z_a$, the closed-loop pole near $-z_a$ lies to the left of it and is located at

$$s = (1 + C_a)z_a \qquad (15.1\text{-}11)$$

where $C_a$ is evaluated from the straight line frequency approximation for $\left| \dfrac{1}{G(\omega_a)} \right|$ as on Figure 15.1–4. Since at the frequency $\omega_a$, the magnitude of $\left| G(\omega_a) \right|$ and $\left| 1/G(\omega_a) \right|$ are merely reciprocals, the value of $C_a$ may be determined satisfactorily using Figure 15.1–2 alone rather than also using Figure 15.1–4.

**Closed-Loop Poles at Intermediate Values of Gain.** The methods described in the preceding sections have permitted the evaluation of the closed-loop poles and zeros outside the region of gain $-15$ db $< \left| G(\omega) \right|$ $< +15$ db. For determining approximately the closed-loop poles and zeros contributed by the open-loop poles and zeros inside the $\pm15$ db band, the effect of the open-loop poles and zeros outside the $\pm15$ db band is ignored. Since the number of breaks inside the $\pm15$ db band is usually much smaller than the total number of breaks, the problem of determining the roots of the simplified characteristic equation that results is greatly reduced.

For instance, the open-loop transfer function $G(s)$ of Equation 15.1–2 as represented in Figures 15.1–2 and 15.1–3 in this intermediate region of gain is

$$G(s) = \frac{K''(s + z_a)}{s(s + p_1)(s + p_2)(s + p_3)} \simeq \frac{K''/p_3}{s(s + p_2)} \qquad (15.1\text{-}12)$$

since, for within the $\pm15$ db band, it may be considered that $p_1 = z_a$, and $s \ll p_3$.

The corresponding closed-loop transfer function is

$$\frac{G(s)}{1 + G(s)} = \frac{K''/p_3}{s(s + p_2) + K''/p_3} \qquad (15.1\text{-}13)$$

The original quartic characteristic equation has thus been reduced to a quadratic equation that may be easily solved. Note that the approximation given by Equation 15.1–13 is equivalent to approximating this attenuation-frequency plot of Figure 15.1–2 outside of the $\pm15$ db band by the slant lines which are extensions of the actual asymptotes crossing the ±15 db lines.

Of course, approximation within the ±15 db band does not result in a quadratic characteristic equation for every system.  However, if the system is designed for satisfactory stability, the straight line approximations to the attenuation-frequency characteristics near 0 db usually assume a fairly simple form, generally a cubic or less.

Figure 15.1–5 shows some typical forms which the attenuation-

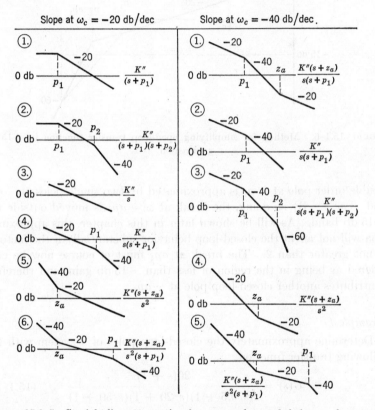

FIGURE 15.1–5.  Straight line attenuation-frequency plots and their open-loop transfer functions near the region of 0 db.

frequency characteristics may have in the region of gain ±15 db and the equivalent transfer functions which describe these characteristics.  In general, an effort should be made to simplify the expression for the transfer function within ±15 db band so as to reduce the order of the equation to be solved.  As an example of some of the means that may be employed, consider the attenuation-frequency plot shown on Figure 15.1–6 where a double order open-loop pole occurs at $s = -p_1$. The number of breaks within the $\pm 15$ db band may be reduced by one if the

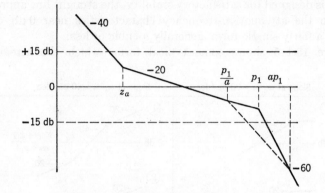

FIGURE 15.1–6.    Method for simplifying open-loop transfer function in +15 db gain region.

double order pole at $-p_1$ is approximated by two single poles at $-ap_1$ and $-p_1/a$. By so doing, the break at $\omega = ap_1$ is moved outside the $\pm 15$ db band. As will be shown later in this chapter, this approximation will not affect the closed-loop behavior substantially if the factor $a$ is not greater than 2. The break at $ap_1$ must of course now be considered as being in the region of less than $-15$ db gain, and therefore contributes another closed-loop pole at $-ap_1$.

*Example 1*

Determine approximately the closed-loop poles of a system with the following transfer function.

$$G(s) = \frac{20(s+1)}{s(s/0.5 + 1)(s/20 + 1)(s/50 + 1)} \qquad (15.1\text{–}14)$$

Figure 15.1–7 shows the straight line attenuation-frequency diagram for Equation 15.1–14. The break at $\omega = 50$ is below the $-15$ db line, so one approximate closed-loop pole is at $s = -50$. The upward break at $\omega = 1$ is above the $+15$ db line and the gain at this point is 20 db or 10. Using Equation 15.1–11, one is able to establish that another approximate closed-loop pole, which is to the left of $-1$ in the $s$ plane, is at $s = -1(1 + \frac{1}{10}) = -1.1$.

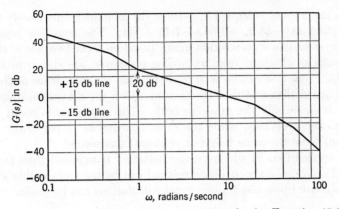

FIGURE 15.1–7.  Attenuation frequency asymptote plot for Equation 15.1–14.

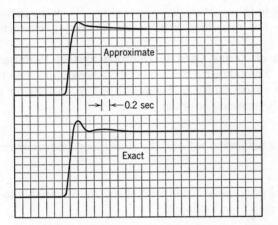

FIGURE 15.1–8.  Approximate and exact transient responses to a step input for system of Equation 15.1–14.

Within the ±15 db band,

$$G(s) \simeq \frac{20s}{s(s/0.5)(s/20 + 1)(1)} = \frac{10}{s(s/20 + 1)} \qquad (15.1\text{–}15)$$

and

$$\frac{G(s)}{1 + G(s)} \simeq \frac{10}{s(0.05s + 1) + 10} \qquad (15.1\text{–}16)$$

Setting the denominator equal to zero, one finds the corresponding approximate closed-loop poles at $s = -10 \pm j10$.  These four approximate poles at $-50$, $-1.1$, $-10 \pm j10$ compare rather closely to the exact poles at $-55.2$, $-1.06$, $-7.15 \pm j11$. The transient responses of the system to a step-position input, based on these two sets of closed-loop poles as obtained from an analog computer, are shown in Figure 15.1–7. From this can be seen that the time characteristics of the two curves are similar and that the time at which the maximum overshoot occurs is essentially the same for both. The approximate result has a 12 per cent overshoot, while the exact solution is 17 per cent. Both solutions have the same long tail of almost one second.

For applications in which greater accuracy is required than that indicated above, the approximate method can be used to provide a good first estimate upon which more exact calculations can be made.

## 15.2   Description of Servomechanism Being Considered

The nomenclature that will be used to define the closed-loop system performance in the charts is described below. Then the parameters used to describe the open-loop attenuation frequency characteristics are presented.

**Definition of Terms Used to Describe System Performance Characteristics.** The following definitions have been applied to the symbols used on the charts shown in Figures 15.4–7 to 15.4–24 for purposes of describing the system performance.

$\left. \dfrac{C}{R} \right|_m$ = the maximum ratio of the closed-loop frequency response,

$\left. \dfrac{C}{R} \right|_p$ = the peak value of the ratio of controlled variable to input for a step function input,

$\dfrac{\omega_m}{\omega_c}$ = the ratio of the frequency $\omega_m$ at which $\left. \dfrac{C}{R} \right|_m$ occurs to the frequency $\omega_c$ at which the straight-line approximation of the open-loop response is 0 decibels,

$\dfrac{\omega_t}{\omega_c}$ = the ratio of $\omega_t$, the lowest frequency of oscillation for a step input to $\omega_c$, the frequency at which the straight-line approximation of the open-loop response is 0 decibels,

$\omega_c t_p$ = $\omega_c$, the frequency at which the straight-line approximation of the open-loop response is 0 decibels times $t_p$, the response time from the start of the step function until $\left. \dfrac{C}{R} \right|_p$ occurs, and

$\omega_c t_s = \omega_c$, the frequency at which the straight-line approximation of the open-loop response is 0 decibels times $t_s$, the settling time from the start of the step function until the output continues to differ from the input by less than 5 per cent.

Indicated in Figures 15.2–1a, 15.2–1b, and 15.2–1c are these various

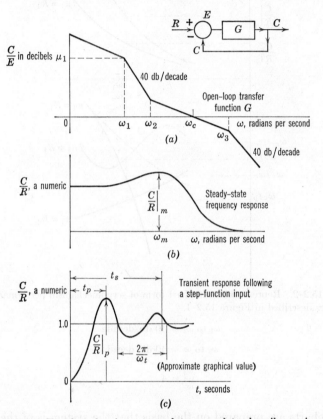

FIGURE 15.2–1.   Sketches showing nomenclature used to describe various characteristics of servomechanism performance.

characteristics in terms of the familiar curves of the open-loop transfer function, the frequency response, and the transient response to a step input.  In Figure 15.2–2 are shown how the same characteristics are indicated on the charts merely as a function of the ratio $\omega_1/\omega_c$ and $\mu_1$, where $\mu_1$ is constant at some value $K_1$ as shown.  Instead of the more customary curves of Figures 15.2–1a, 15.2–1b, and 15.2–1c, only significant preformance parameters have been plotted and these in terms of the open-loop attenuation characteristic that will produce them.

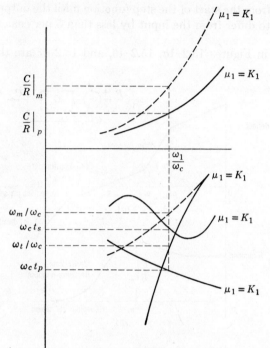

FIGURE 15.2–2.  Representation in chart form of servomechanism performance characteristics described in Figure 15.2–1.

$$\omega_1 \text{ to } \omega_2 = 40 \text{ db/decade}$$

$$\omega_3 \text{ to } \infty = 40 \text{ db/decad}$$

$$\frac{\omega_3}{\omega_c} = 4$$

The charts are prepared on the basis that the system is of the type 1 variety containing a single integrating element so that at very low frequencies the open-loop attenuation characteristic has a slope of 20 decibels per decade. However, as is discussed later, the major factor influencing the performance of the system is the attenuation characteristic in the vicinity of 0 decibels. Hence the charts may also be used to provide worth-while information on the performance of regulating systems (type 0) that have zero attenuation rate at low frequencies, as well as torque-motor type systems (type 2) that have an attenuation rate of 40 decibels per decade at low frequencies. The performance comparison

of these various systems will be good, provided the attenuation-frequency
characteristics of these systems in the vicinity of 0 decibels are comparable to the attenuation characteristic of the system shown on the
chart that has the desired performance.

**Open-Loop Attenuation-Frequency Characteristics.** In Figure 15.2–1
are shown the significant parameters that have been used to define the
idealized attenuation diagrams for which the steady-state and transient
performance have been determined. Although the attenuation characteristic and the block diagram of the system indicate that only series
elements are considered as making up the control system, it is apparent
that feedback loops may be included within the control provided the
resultant attenuation characteristic approaches that for an equivalent
system containing only series elements. Basically the attenuation diagram considered is one in which:

1. The attenuation slope is 20 decibels per decade in the vicinity of
0 decibels, which gain occurs at the frequency $\omega_c$. This type of attenuation characteristic is desirable from the standpoint of providing
adequate stability.

2. The attenuation slope increases to 40 or 60 decibels per decade
at some higher frequency $\omega_3$ for which the equivalent time constant is
$T_3$, that is, $T_3 = 1/\omega_3$. This may correspond to the presence of the
power element time constant or to the condition obtained when the
loop gain around a feedback loop falls below unity. In addition, this
characteristic may be deliberately inserted to help attenuate undesirable higher frequency input signals.

3. The attenuation rate is 40 to 60 decibels per decade in the region
of frequencies from $\omega_1$ to $\omega_2$ for which the equivalent time constants
are $T_1$ and $T_2$, respectively. Thus

$$T_1 = \frac{1}{\omega_1} \quad \text{and} \quad T_2 = \frac{1}{\omega_2}$$

4. The attenuation rate is 20 decibels per decade from zero fre-
quency to the frequency $\omega_1$. The system gain at $\omega_1$ is defined as $\mu_1$
on the straight-line approximation to the attenuation diagram. The
actual gain will be 3 decibels or 6 decibels lower at this frequency, depending on whether the attenuation rate from $\omega_1$ to $\omega_2$ is 40 or 60 decibels per decade.

In some cases certain of the time constants take on limiting values
so that the attenuation diagram appears to have a different form from
that shown in Figure 15.2–3. For example, if $T_1 = T_2$, the slope of 20

decibels per decade extending from low frequencies continues constant until the frequency $\omega_3$. This case is represented on the charts by the data at $\omega_1/\omega_c = 0.1$ and $\mu_1 = 20$ decibels. As another example, consider the case where $T_3 = 0$ so that the 20 decibels per decade slope at $\omega_c$ is maintained from $\omega_c$ on out to $\infty$. These data are contained on those charts where $\omega_3/\omega_c = \infty$.

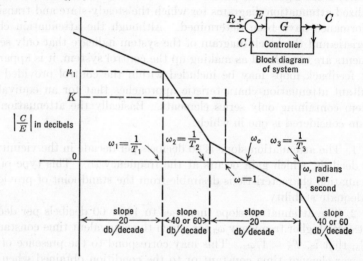

FIGURE 15.2–3. Straight-line approximation to open-loop attenuation characteristic, showing significant values of gain, time constants, and frequencies of attenuation slope breaks.

Figure 15.2–3 shows that $\mu_1$ in general *is not the same as the system gain* $K$, which is the value of the gain obtained at $\omega = 1$ if the initial slope from 0 to $\omega_1$ were to be maintained at 20 decibels per decade.

The method employed on the charts to define a given attenuation characteristic is to indicate the nature of the slope between $\omega_1$ and $\omega_2$ as 40 or 60 decibels per decade and also to indicate the slope between $\omega_3$ and $\infty$ as 40 or 60 decibels per decade. Each chart is then drawn up for a constant value of the ratio $\omega_3/\omega_c$. The other parameters used to define uniquely the specific attenuation characteristic are the gain $\mu_1$ in decibels and the frequency ratio $\omega_1/\omega_c$. Since $\mu_1$ and $\omega_1$ are definitely related to the servomechanism specification requirements of a certain maximum actuating signal at a specific signal frequency, these are particularly significant parameters from the viewpoint of system needs as well as of their usefulness to the designers.

The use of the dimensionless ratio $\omega_1/\omega_c$ as the abscissa serves to broaden the utility of the data while permitting the designer to determine the performance of the system if $\omega_1/\omega_c$ is already established or to determine the $\omega_1/\omega_c$ ratio if the performance of the system is selected as the independent condition for system design. Although it might appear that broad increments of $\mu_1$ have been chosen for the family of curves plotted against $\omega_1/\omega_c$, there are sufficient curves shown to permit fairly straightforward interpolation in most cases.

It should be pointed out that, although for convenience purposes the attenuation characteristics are represented by their straight-line approximations, the exact attenuation characteristic has been used in the calculations for the charts.

## 15.3 Effect of Value of $\omega_c$ on Frequency Response and Transient Response

The preceding section has served to emphasize the importance of the shape of the attenuation-frequency diagram in the vicinity of 0 decibels. Although Bode's work has pointed out the importance of this characteristic on stability considerations, its effect on the steady-state and transient response of a servomechanism has not been so clearly emphasized. Consider the case shown in Figure 15.3–1, where two similar attenuation-frequency characteristics are drawn. Both have the same value of $\mu_1$

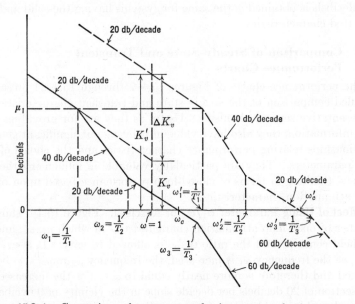

FIGURE 15.3–1. Comparison of two servomechanism systems having attenuation-frequency characteristics of similar shape but shifted in frequency by the ratio $\omega'_c/\omega_c$.

and both have the same rate of change of attenuation with frequency in the region near 0 decibel; however, the values of the frequencies $\omega'_c$, $\omega'_1$, $\omega'_2$, and $\omega'_3$ on the dotted curve are $\omega'_c/\omega_c$ times higher than the comparable $\omega_c$, $\omega_1$, $\omega_2$, and $\omega_3$ on the solid curve.

By means of the Laplace transformation, it can be shown that for the two attenuation characteristics described by Figure 15.3–1:

The velocity gain constant for the dotted curve is $\omega'_c/\omega_c$ times that for the solid curve.

The response time and the settling time for the system represented by the dotted curve to the same step function input are altered by the ratio $\omega_c/\omega'_c$ times their values for the system illustrated by the solid curve.

The ratio of the magnitude of the peak overshoot to the initial transient input is the same for systems represented by the solid and by the dotted curves.

The ratio of the maximum magnitude of the steady-state response to the input sinusoid is the same for the systems represented by the solid and by the dotted characteristics.

The ratio of the frequencies at which maximum output to input ratio of the steady-state response occurs and the frequency at which 0 decibels is obtained is the same for systems having the solid and the dotted characteristics.

## 15.4 Comparison of Steady-State and Transient Performance Charts

The performance charts of Figures 15.4–7 through 15.4–24 present a detailed comparison of the steady-state and transient characteristics of representative servomechanisms. Useful as they are for providing specific information, they also have value in pointing out significant general relationships relating performance characteristics and the choice of design parameters. They are particularly valuable in influencing the designers' thinking in terms of closed-loop performance based upon open-loop attenuation characteristics.

**Effect of Using Parameter $\omega_1/\omega_c$ for Abscissa.** Figure 15.4–1 shows a number of open-loop attenuation characteristics in which $\mu_1$, $\omega_c$, and $\omega_3$ are held constant and the ratio $\omega_1/\omega_c$ is allowed to vary. It is evident that, as the frequency $\omega_1$ is increased, the frequency $\omega_2$ must also be increased and therefore is more nearly equal to $\omega_c$. For the increased $\omega_2$, the section of 20 decibels per decade slope in the vicinity of 0 decibels is reduced, and it would appear from a qualitative point of view that a less stable system would result, that is, one having a higher value of $C/R \big|_m$ (steady-state) and a higher value of $C/R \big|_p$ (transient). This result is indicated quantitatively in the curves of $C/R \big|_m$ and $C/R \big|_p$ as a function of $\omega_1/\omega_c$ for $\mu_1$ and $\omega_c$ constant.

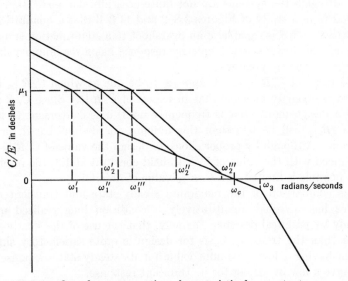

FIGURE 15.4–1.   Open-loop attenuation characteristic for constant $\mu_1$, $\omega_c$, and $\omega_3$ but with $\omega_1/\omega_c$ allowed to vary.

It might appear that fairly broad interpolation would be required to obtain performance figures at values of $\mu_1$ other than those specifically calculated. Actually the $C/R$ values for values of $\mu_1$ greater than 40 seem to be determined largely by the values of $\omega_2$ so that the effect of going to higher values of $\mu_1$ is to reduce $\omega_1/\omega_c$ to a lower value for the corresponding servomechanism performance. Reference to Figure 15.4–24, which has the same ordinates as Figure 15.4–18 but has $\omega_2/\omega_c$ as its abscissa, indicates that there can be a close dependence of the transient and steady-state performance on $\omega_2/\omega_c$, and that there may be a relatively small effect on the system performance for changes of $\mu_1$ as long as the value of $\mu_1$ is large, for instance, 60 decibels or greater.

**Comparison of Maximum Steady-State Value $[C/R|_m]$ and Peak Transient Value $[C/R|_p]$ of Output-Input Ratio.** Study of the data presented on the upper portions of Figures 15.4–7 to 15.4–24 reveals that the maximum steady-state value $C/R \big|_m$ generally exceeds the peak value of the transient $C/R \big|_p$ for most values of $\omega_1/\omega_c$, although this is not universally true. It is only for systems that have a low value of $C/R \big|_m$, that is, less than 1.3, that $C/R \big|_p$ may exceed $C/R \big|_m$. For these systems the maximum value of both the steady state or transient is low, and the transient peak seems not to exceed the steady-state maximum by more than 5 per cent of the input in any case. Systems such as these are exceptionally stable ones for which the degree of damping is fairly high, although the systems are not quite critically damped. It will be recalled from a study of Figures 3.8–2 and 11.3–6 that a quadratic system with $\zeta = 0.8$ is capable of an overshoot to a step-function transient although the steady-state frequency response has a maximum value of 1.0 or only slightly greater.

The value of $C/R \big|_m = 1.3$ appears to be one at which $C/R \big|_m$ for a system is equal to or somewhat in excess of $C/R \big|_p$. Since $C/R \big|_m = 1.3$ is a design figure that is frequently used, it is convenient to know that $C/R \big|_p$ will be less than this amount for designs based on this criterion. Although by proper choice of design the value of $C/R \big|_p$ may be reduced with the value of $C/R \big|_m$ held constant at 1.3, the improvement possible is limited to a $C/R \big|_p$ value of about 1.2.

This comparison of the maximum steady-state and transient magnitudes has revealed quantitatively a condition long realized qualitatively by practical designers, namely, that the use of the steady-state rather than the transient basis for design is quite satisfactory since a system having a low maximum value for its steady-state response will also have a low overshoot for its transient response.

**Comparison of Frequency $\omega_m$ at Which $C/R|_m$ Occurs to $\omega_t$, the Lowest Frequency Oscillatory Term of the Transient Response.** The curves presented on the lower portion of Figures 15.4–7 to 15.4–24 compare plots of $\omega_m/\omega_c$ and $\omega_t/\omega_c$ for the systems having the $C/R \big|_m$ and $C/R \big|_p$ values shown in the upper portion of these charts. As such, these data may be used for the purpose of rapidly determining the frequency characteristics of a contemplated design. Since, as is generally the case, the actual frequency of $\omega_m$ is given as a specification requirement, the $\omega_m/\omega_c$ ratio is useful in establishing the frequency $\omega_c$ that will be required to obtain the value of $\omega_m$ desired.

In addition, these frequency data presented in the charts can be used to indicate certain trends in performance that result from the selection of one or another design, both of which may have comparable values for $C/R \big|_m$ or $C/R \big|_p$. If $\omega_m/\omega_c$ and $\omega_t/\omega_c$ be compared for the same system, then a direct comparison of $\omega_m$ and $\omega_t$ can be made. From such a comparison the following generalities are indicated.

*Effect of $\omega_3/\omega_c$.* Systems in which $1 < \omega_3/\omega_c < 4$ correspond to fairly oscillatory systems with little damping. The lowest frequency of transient oscillation $\omega_t$ is greater than the frequency $\omega_m$ at which the steady-state response is a maximum. The variation of the values of $\omega_t/\omega_c$ and $\omega_m/\omega_c$ is fairly small and the values of each are about 1.0.

For systems having higher values of the $\omega_3/\omega_c$ ratio, that is, $\omega_3/\omega_c >$ 4, $\omega_m$ exceeds $\omega_t$. There can be a wide variation of both the values of $\omega_t$ and $\omega_m$ as $\omega_1/\omega_c$ is changed. The values range from about 1 for each when $\omega_1/\omega_c$ is large for a given $\mu_1$, that is, fairly oscillatory systems to 0 for $\omega_t$ at low values of $\omega_1/\omega_c$ when the systems are so stable as to have all real roots. The oscillatory and stable systems correspond to values of $\omega_2/\omega_c$, which are near 1.0 and near 0.1, respectively.

*Effect of Change in* $\mu_1$. The shape of the $\omega_t/\omega_c$ and $\omega_m/\omega_c$ curves for a constant $\mu_1$ and over a range of $\omega_1/\omega_c$ bears a close resemblance to these same curves for a different $\mu_1$ but the same $\omega_3/\omega_c$. This tends to indicate that, if $\omega_3/\omega_c$ and $\omega_2/\omega_c$ are fixed and $\mu_1$ and $\omega_1$ alone are changed, the changes in $\omega_m/\omega_c$ and $\omega_t/\omega_c$ are not great. However, it is evident from the curves that the effect of reducing the gain $\mu_1$ is to increase the $\omega_m/\omega_c$ and $\omega_t/\omega_c$ ratio.

*Effect of Attenuation Slope* $\omega_3$ *to* $\infty$. For systems in which the attenuation slope from $\omega_3$ to infinite frequency is 60 decibels per decade rather than 40 decibels per decade, the values of $\omega_m/\omega_c$ are higher. That is, the frequency at the steady-state maximum is more nearly that of $\omega_c$ when a 60 decibels per decade slope at the higher frequencies is employed. From the point of view of decreasing the transmission of the system at higher frequencies, this appears desirable, but transient considerations discussed in the following section may be of greater importance.

**Time $t_p$ at Which Peak Overshoot Occurs.** Figures 15.4–7 to 15.4–23 show that, for the lower values of $\omega_3/\omega_c$ in the range from $1 < \omega_3/\omega_c <$ 4, the value of $\omega_c t_p$ is approximately equal to 3 and is relatively unaffected by changes in $\mu_1$ or $\omega_1/\omega_c$ for a constant value of $\omega_c$. However, since the ordinate of these curves is $\omega_c t_p$ the value of $t_p$, the elapsed time from the application of a step function until the peak overshoot, is inversely proportional to $\omega_c$. Therefore it is primarily by increasing $\omega_c$ that the time $t_p$ can be reduced.

When $\omega_3/\omega_c \leq 8$, $\omega_c t_p$ tends to vary over a wider range and to decrease as $\omega_1/\omega_c$ takes on larger values with $\mu_1$, $\omega_c$, and $\omega_3$ constant. This may be verified in a qualitative way by reference to Figure 15.4–1, where, as $\omega_1$ takes on increasing values, the actual gain of the system is increased for the frequencies lower than $\omega_2$ and a shorter time should be required for the initial step displacement to be reduced to zero. Figures 15.4–2 and 15.3–3, comparing the actual transient response as a function of time for constant values of $\mu_1$, $\omega_c$, and $\omega_3$, indicate in a quantitative fashion the decrease in time required for the higher gain, lower $\omega_1/\omega_c$ systems to reach their transient peak although the peak attained is higher.

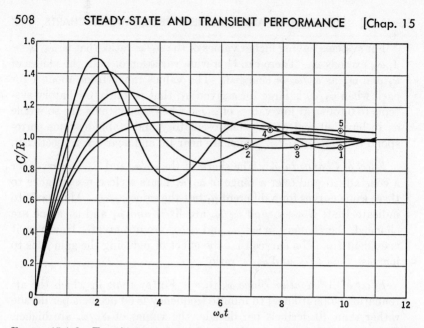

FIGURE 15.4–2. Transient response following step function position input disturbance for various values of $\omega_1/\omega_c$.

$$\omega_1 \text{ to } \omega_2 = 60 \text{ db/decade}$$

$$\omega_3 \text{ to } \infty = 40 \text{ db/decade}$$

$$\frac{\omega_3}{\omega_c} = \infty$$

$$\mu_1 = 60$$

Curves labeled at $t_s$

| Curve | $\dfrac{\omega_1}{\omega_c}$ |
|-------|-------|
| 1 | 0.1000 |
| 2 | 0.0788 |
| 3 | 0.0543 |
| 4 | 0.0342 |
| 5 | 0.0215 |

**Settling Time $t_s$ to Reach 5 Per Cent of Final Value.**  If the magnitude of the peak overshoot can be made less than the allowable limit, then the time $t_p$ alone is of interest.  However, when the initial overshoot exceeds the desirable operating value of the output, the performance may still be satisfactory if the succeeding overshoots can be brought within acceptable limits within a tolerable length of time.

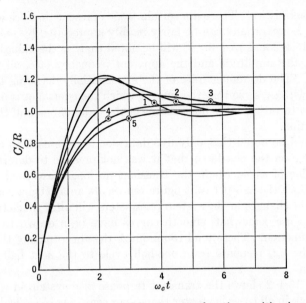

FIGURE 15.4–3.   Transient response following step function position input disturbance for various values of $\omega_1/\omega_c$.

$$\omega_1 \text{ to } \omega_2 = 60 \text{ db/decade}$$

$$\omega_3 \text{ to } \infty = 40 \text{ db/decade}$$

$$\frac{\omega_3}{\omega_c} = \infty$$

$$\mu_1 = 20$$

Curves labeled at $t_s$

| Curve | $\dfrac{\omega_1}{\omega_c}$ |
|-------|------|
| 1 | 0.464 |
| 2 | 0.366 |
| 3 | 0.252 |
| 4 | 0.159 |
| 5 | 0.1 |

The acceptable error limit that has been selected is ±5 per cent from the desired step input. Since most high-performance servomechanism systems tend not to be linear for large displacements, the step input for which this analysis is valid is likewise small. Consequently 5 per cent of this magnitude is probably a small enough error to be acceptable.

No simple over-all statement can be made concerning the shape of the

$\omega_c t_s$ characteristics. There are certain trends present that are worthy of mention, however, and can be fairly readily appreciated by reference to Figures 15.4–2 and 15.4–3. It will be noted that, as the values of $\omega_1/\omega_c$ decrease, the amplitude and the apparent frequency of oscillation also decrease. The decrement rate of the exponentially decaying term also changes with $\omega_1/\omega_c$ so that the time at which the overshoot is 5 per cent is subject to rather large fluctuations of the order of one-half the period of oscillation.

It should be noted that only five data points were used to construct each curve on the charts so that it was not possible to determine the exact value of $\omega_1/\omega_c$ where the transient no longer exceeded 1.050 or 0.950. Since the $\pm5$ per cent figure represents an arbitrary value, and since slight changes in the system parameters will alter the actual transient response somewhat, smooth curves have been drawn to indicate the $\omega_c t_s$ function. These tend to minimize the abruptness of the transition of the $\omega_c t_s$ response from one-half cycle to the next half cycle of oscillation.

Figure 15.4–2 shows the transient response of a system in which the initial peak in all cases is greater than 5 per cent. As $\omega_1/\omega_c$ is decreased from its highest value, $\omega_c t_s$ first decreases as the peak overshoot decreases and the decrement rate remains fairly high. As $\omega_1/\omega_c$ further decreases, the frequency of oscillation is lowered and the decrement rate is also decreased; hence the initial overshoot is maintained for a longer period. Therefore $\omega_c t_s$ is increased again as $\omega_1/\omega_c$ is further reduced.

Curves 1, 2, and 3 of Figure 15.4–3 indicate a continuation of the trend noticed in Figure 15.4–2 toward higher values of $\omega_c t_s$ as $\omega_1/\omega_c$ is decreased. However, as $\omega_1/\omega_c$ is further decreased, the peak overshoot falls below 1.05, and for curve 4 the output remains within 5 per cent of the input after it reaches $C/R = 0.95$ at $\omega_c t = 2.35$ seconds. A further decrease in the $\omega_1/\omega_c$ ratio as shown by curve 5 causes the system to be more heavily damped and the time required to get to $C/R = 0.95$ is again increased.

Perhaps the situation can be stated as follows: For a system having $\mu_1$, $\omega_c$, and $\omega_3$ fixed, the time after which the error to a step-position input remains less than a small amount can be decreased only so far by decreasing $\omega_1$. A further decrease in $\omega_1$ merely causes the system to become too sluggish. Quantitative data are provided by Figures 15.4–7 to 15.4–23, which indicate whether an improvement in system performance will be realized by such a decrease in $\omega_1/\omega_c$.

The beneficial effect of increasing the frequency $\omega_c$ mentioned in conjunction with $t_p$ is also realized for $t_s$ since the time ordinates on Figures 15.4–7 to 15.4–23 are $\omega_c t$.

**Use of Figures 15.4–7 to 15.4–23 for Systems Other than Those Having a Single Integrating Element in the Controller.**   Although the results presented in Figures 15.4–7 to 15.4–23 are valid only for systems having the attenuation diagrams specified, they are also of considerable use for predicting the performance of systems having quite different attenuation-frequency characteristics at low frequencies but identical attenuation characteristics for frequencies for which the open-loop characteristic is in the vicinity of 0 decibels, and for all higher frequencies.   Figure 15.4–4

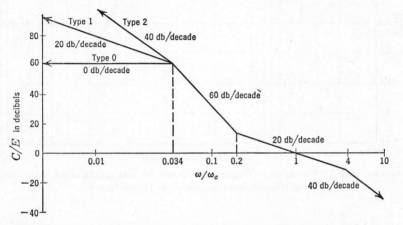

FIGURE 15.4–4.   Open-loop transfer function for three different type servomechanism systems having identical attenuation characteristics at higher frequencies.

shows three such systems, and Figure 15.4–5 indicates the frequency response of each.   It is evident that there is a close comparison among these three systems as far as the frequency response is concerned.   The type 0 system has a slightly lower maximum value than the type 1 system, and the type 2 system has a slightly higher maximum value than the type 1 system.   It would appear that this relationship between the magnitude of the response of systems of these various types is fairly general although it is not probable that the frequency of the maximum of the frequency response will be the same for each in the general case.

Figure 15.4–6, comparing the transient response to a step function of these three seemingly different systems, also reveals that there is a close relationship among them.   It is doubtful that so close a comparison will be obtained for the more general case, where the attenuation characteristics are dissimilar until the gain is lower than that for the three systems considered.   However, the possibilities of the performance results for a type 1 system in providing a ceiling indication for the type 0 system and a lower limit value for the type 2 system are apparent.

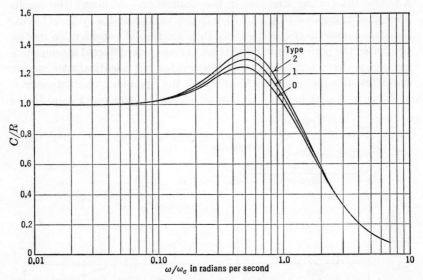

FIGURE 15.4–5.   Steady-state frequency response for servomechanisms with open-loop transfer functions shown in Figure 15.4–4.

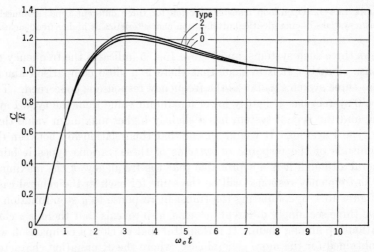

FIGURE 15.4–6.   Transient response to a step function for servomechanisms with open-loop transfer functions shown in Figure 15.4–4.

For type 2 systems in which the initial attenuation rate is 40 decibels per decade at very low frequencies, followed by a section of 20 decibels per decade attenuation rate in the region of $\omega_c$, the question arises as to which values of $\mu_1$ and $\omega_1/\omega_c$ should be used with which charts. The charts to be used are those for which the attenuation rate from $\omega_1$ to $\omega_2$ is 40 decibels per decade and those for which the proper value of $\omega_3/\omega_c$ and attenuation rate from $\omega_3$ to $\infty$ are obtained. Select the $\mu_1 = 80$ decibels characteristics and use the value of $\omega_1$ determined at $\mu_1 = 80$ decibels for the actual transfer function attenuation characteristic. The values of the performance parameters indicated should most closely approximate those actually obtained for the 40 decibels per decade type 2 system.

**Effect of Having Non-Multiple Breaks in Open-Loop Attenuation Characteristics.** In the interest of presenting a fairly complete picture of the performance of representative servomechanism systems with a limited number of charts, it was considered necessary not to include systems in which there are intermediate breaks in the attenuation diagram. For example, the ideal cases represented in the charts by multiple breaks, where in the open-loop diagram the attenuation rates change abruptly from 20 decibels per decade to 60 decibels per decade or vice versa, are generally realized in practice by two adjacent breaks so that there is an intermediate section of 40 decibels per decade. Fortunately design methods are such that frequently this 40 decibels per decade attenuation section is limited to a short range of frequencies. In this way the attenuation and phase shift of the system at some frequency remote from this range of frequencies are essentially the same whether multiple breaks occur, for example, at the frequency $\omega_1$, or two separate breaks occur at somewhat higher and somewhat lower frequencies than $\omega_1$. As a general rule, two different but neighboring time constants $T_a$ and $T_b$ may be replaced by two equal time constants of value $T_{ab}$, which are defined as

$$T_{ab} = \sqrt{T_a T_b}$$

This approximation may be verified in a qualitative fashion by a comparison of the terms

$$(1 + T_a s)(1 + T_b s) = 1 + (T_a + T_b)s + T_a T_b s^2$$

and

$$(1 + T_{ab}s)^2 = 1 + 2\sqrt{T_a T_b}\,s + T_a T_b s^2$$

The difference between the two is that the coefficients of the $s$ term are $T_a + T_b$ and $2\sqrt{T_a T_b}$, respectively. When $T_a = T_b$, the ratio of $(T_a + T_b)/2\sqrt{T_a T_b}$ is 1.0; when $T_a$ is as much as $4T_b$, the ratio of

$(T_a + T_b)/2\sqrt{T_{ab}}$ is only $5/4 = 1.25$, and the maximum variation between the two amplitude characteristics is only about 2 decibels.

The intermediate frequency $\omega_{ab}$ corresponding to the intermediate time constant $T_{ab}$ can be located graphically merely by extending, until they intersect, the sections of 20 decibels per decade and 60 decibels per decade slope on either side of the 40 decibels per decade slope and noting the frequency at the intersection. If this frequency is used for an equivalent $\omega_1$, $\omega_2$, or $\omega_3$, as the case requires, reasonably good agreement should be realized between the actual results and those indicated by the accompanying charts.

It is of interest to note that transfer functions having quadratic terms with complex factors may also be represented by two equal factors for purposes of using the charts. Thus, approximately,

$$(1 + 2\zeta Ts + T^2s^2) \simeq (1 + Ts)(1 + Ts)$$

which yields the same value as that given by $T_{ab}$ in the preceding discussion.

**Choice of Attenuation Rates between $\omega_1$ and $\omega_2$, and $\omega_3$ and $\infty$.** For systems in which the parameters $\mu_1$, $\omega_1$, and $\omega_3$ are fixed and the attenuation rate from $\omega_1$ to $\omega_2$ alone is a design choice to be made, use of a steeper slope (60 decibels per decade) produces lower values of $C/R \mid_m$ and $C/R \mid_p$ than use of the less steep (40 decibels per decade) slope. However, it will be noticed that despite the lower initial transient peak for the 60 decibels per decade slope, the time required for the transient to settle to 5 per cent of the magnitude of the step input may not be less for this case. The choice is not clear-cut for all cases, and the relative importance of maximum magnitude of transient or settling time must be considered.

Where all other system parameters are chosen except the slope of the open-loop attenuation characteristic between $\omega_3$ and $\infty$, use of an attenuation rate of 60 decibels per decade rather than 40 decibels per decade increases $C/R \mid_m$ and $C/R \mid_p$. In addition, the time for the transient error to settle to 5 per cent of its original value may also be increased somewhat by use of the steeper slope. It should be noted, however, that use of the higher attenuation rate may be advantageous in eliminating undesirable noise signals in the higher frequency region of the spectrum. In a sense the inability of the 60 decibels per decade system to respond rapidly to transient inputs may not be a liability for, in so doing, the system is also made insensitive to the extraneous high-frequency noise signals as well.

FIGURES 15.4–7 THROUGH 15.4–24. COMPARISON OF STEADY-STATE FREQUENCY RESPONSE CHARACTERISTICS AND TRANSIENT RESPONSE FOLLOWING A STEP FUNCTION OF INPUT AS A FUNCTION OF $\omega_1/\omega_c$.

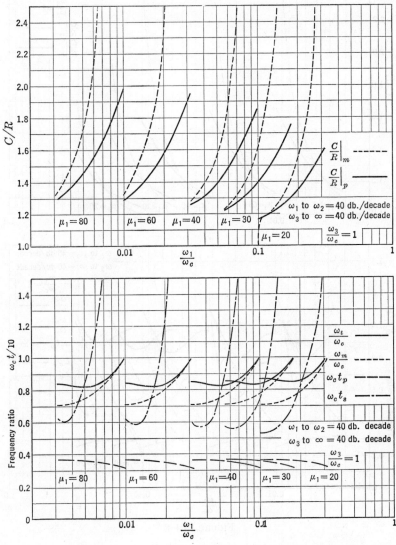

FIGURE 15.4–7

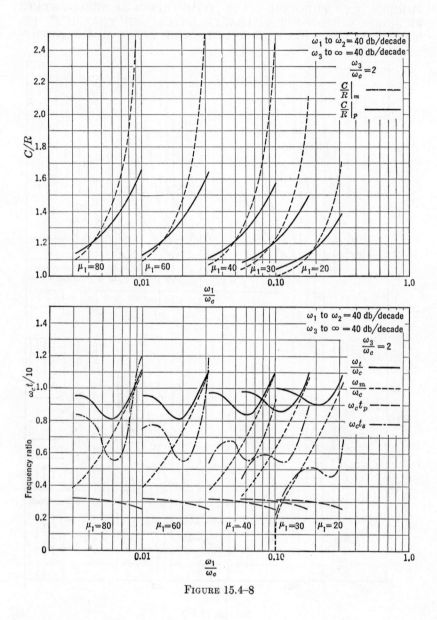

FIGURE 15.4–8

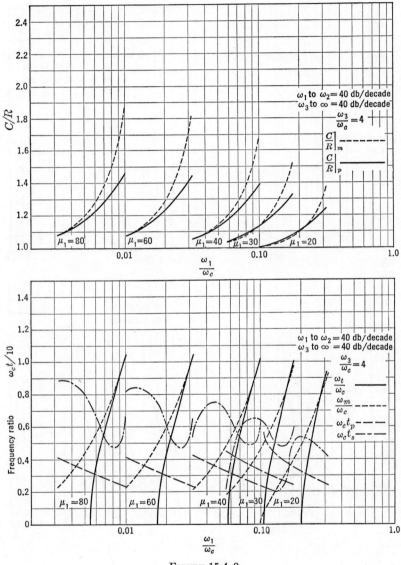

FIGURE 15.4–9

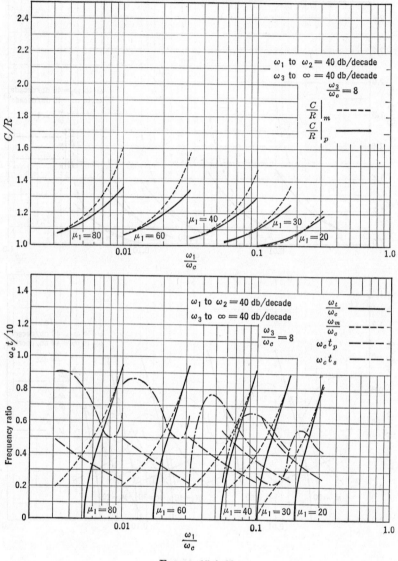

FIGURE 15.4–10

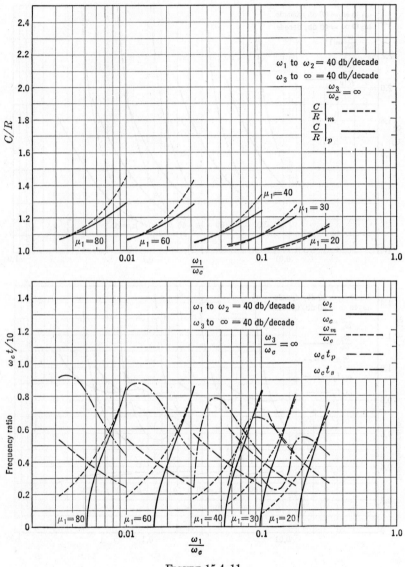

FIGURE 15.4–11

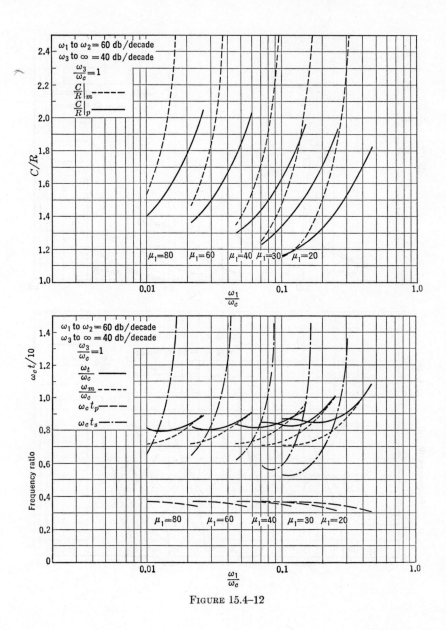

FIGURE 15.4–12

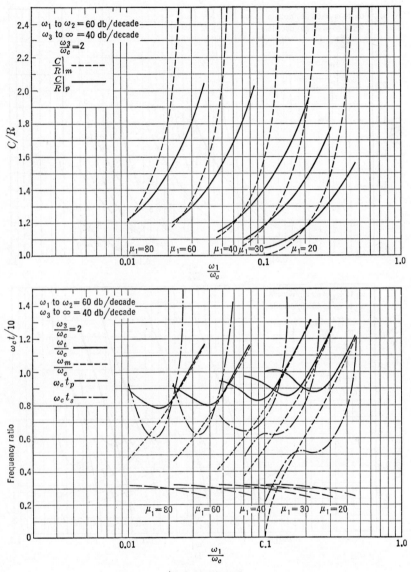

FIGURE 15.4–13

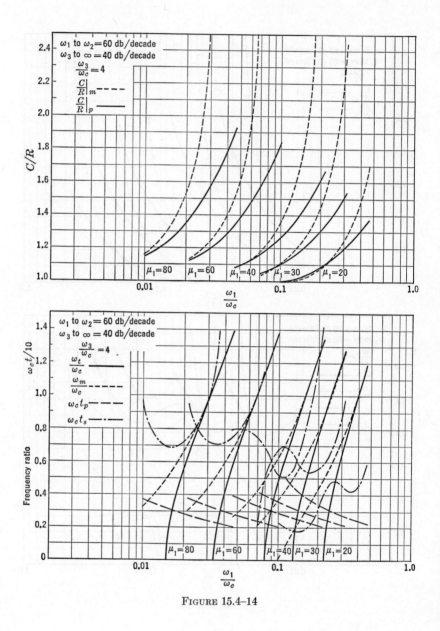

FIGURE 15.4–14

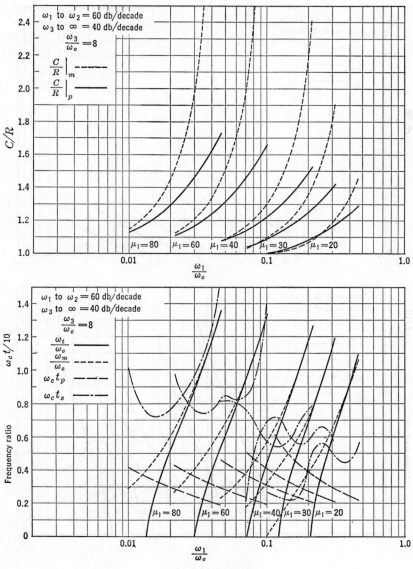

FIGURE 15.4–15

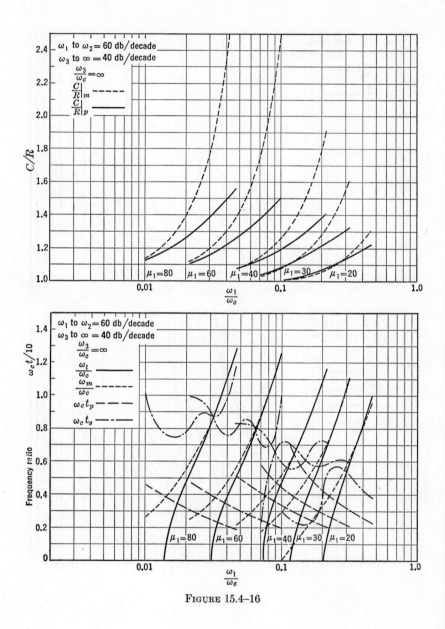

FIGURE 15.4-16

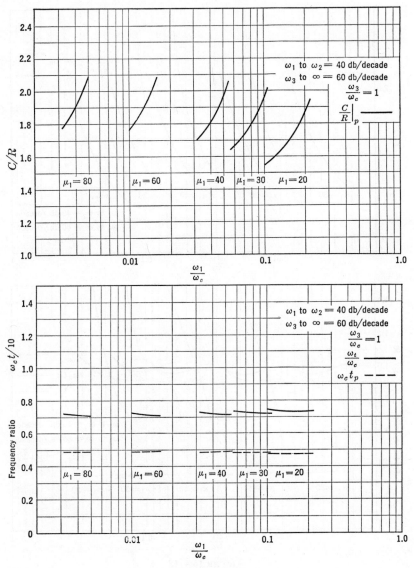

FIGURE 15.4–17

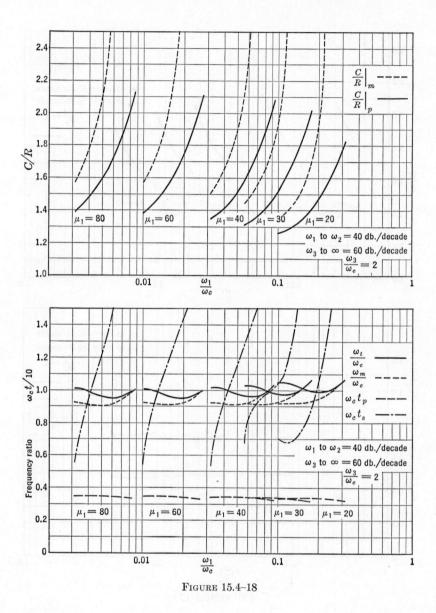

FIGURE 15.4–18

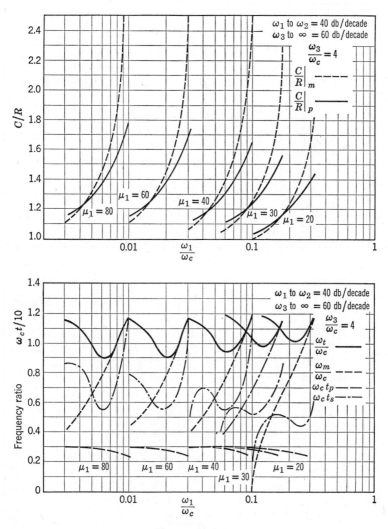

FIGURE 15.4–19

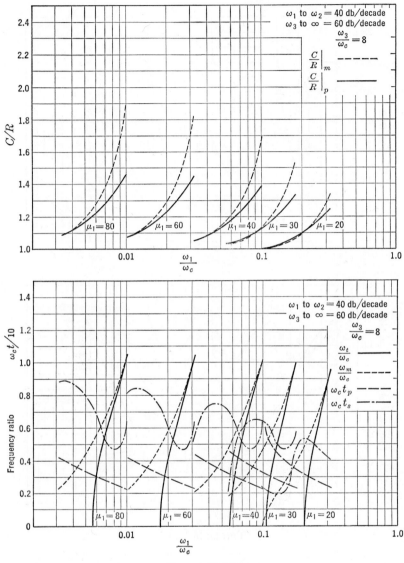

FIGURE 15.4–20

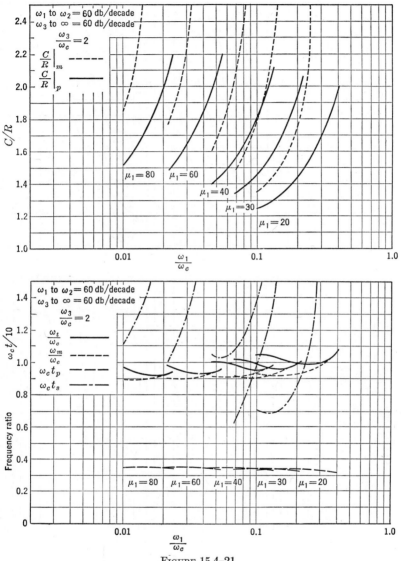

FIGURE 15.4–21

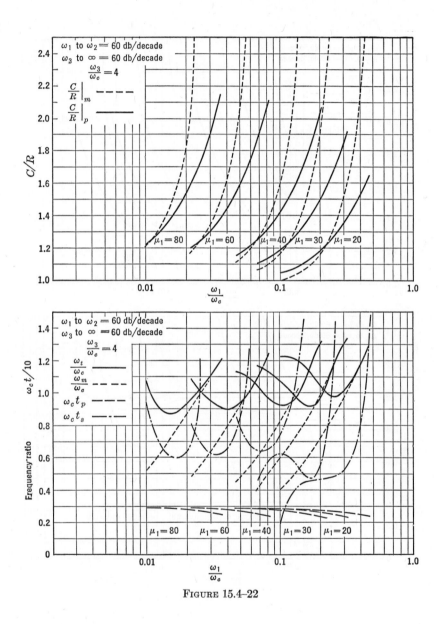

FIGURE 15.4–22

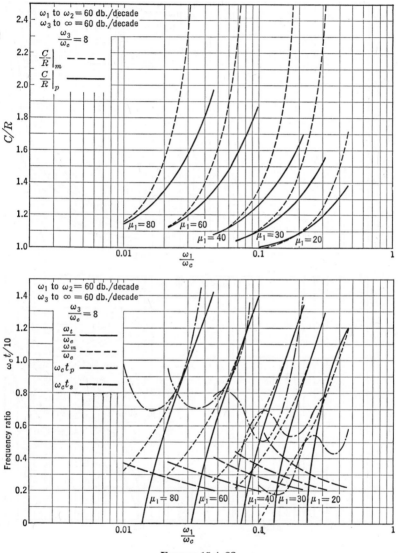

FIGURE 15.4–23

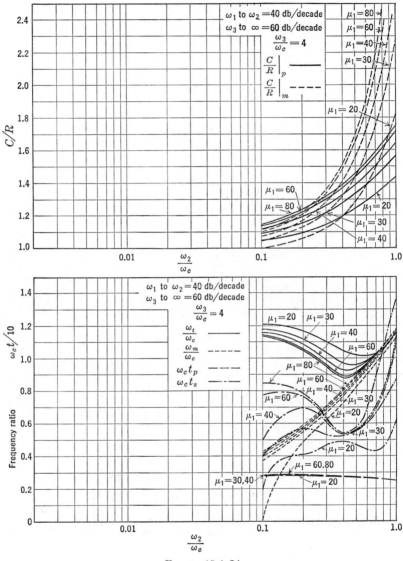

FIGURE 15.4–24

## 15.5  Examples

The information presented in Figures 15.4–7 to 15.4–23 is useful either for purposes of analysis, that is, determining the response of systems already designed, or for purposes of synthesis, that is, determining what sort of system will be required to do a specified job. Typical examples of each of these uses are illustrated in the following.

### Charts Used for System Analysis

*Case 1*

Determine, approximately, the value of the maximum value of $C/R$ and the frequency at which it occurs, and the magnitude of the peak overshoot to a step-function input and the time when it occurs for a system having the transfer function,

$$\frac{C}{E} = \frac{4}{s(1 + 0.1s)(1 + 0.025s)}$$

which is drawn in Figure 15.5–1. Also drawn in Figure 15.5–1 for purposes of check is the frequency response from which $C/R \mid_m$ and $\omega_m/\omega_c$ are found to be 1.00 and 0, respectively.

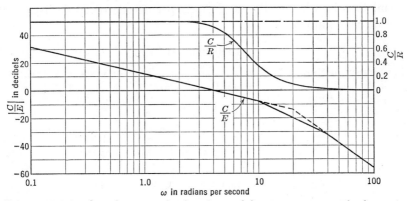

FIGURE 15.5–1. Open-loop transfer function and frequency response for low gain system of Case 1.

$$\frac{C}{E} = \frac{4}{s(1 + 0.1s)(1 + 0.025s)}$$

From Figure 15.5–1 the information necessary to specify the various parameters for use of the charts can be obtained. Thus

$$\omega_c = 4$$
$$\mu_1 = 20 \text{ db}$$
$$\omega_1 = 0.4 \quad ( = \omega_2); \quad \frac{\omega_1}{\omega_c} = 0.1$$

$$\omega_3 = 10 \quad \text{and} \quad \frac{\omega_3}{\omega_c} = 2.5 \quad \text{(if slope is 40 db per decade, } \omega_3 \text{ to } \infty\text{)}$$

or

$$\omega_3 = 20 \quad \text{and} \quad \frac{\omega_3}{\omega_c} = 5.0 \quad \text{(if slope is 60 db per decade, } \omega_3 \text{ to } \infty\text{)}$$

Since no section of either 40 decibels per decade or 60 decibels per decade occurs before 0 decibels, the charts for which the attenuation rate from $\omega_1$ to $\omega_2$ is 40 decibels per decade may be used with the data obtained at $\mu_1 = 20$ and $\omega_1/\omega_c = 0.1$.

Two alternatives present themselves for selecting the attenuation rate from $\omega_3/\omega_c$ to $\infty$. By choosing this rate to be 40 decibels per decade and $\omega_3/\omega_c = 2.5$, a system performance somewhat more optimistic than will be actually realized will be determined. By choosing the attenuation rate to be 60 decibels per decade and using a value of $T_3 = T_{ab}$, then $\omega_3/\omega_c = 5$, and more realistic values of system performance should be determined. Tabulated below is a comparison of the values of the desired performance quantities based on these two assumptions as well as the actual values obtained by direct calculation. It is evident that these results are essentially independent of the method used to obtain them, that is, whether the 40 decibels per decade or 60 decibels per decade charts are used.

TABLE 15.5–1

COMPARISON OF SYSTEM PERFORMANCE OBTAINED FROM CHARTS AND ACTUAL SYSTEM CALCULATIONS

| | $\dfrac{\omega_3}{\omega_c} = 2.5$ | $\dfrac{\omega_3}{\omega_c} = 5.0$ | |
|---|---|---|---|
| | *Figures 15.4–8 and 15.4–9* | *Figures 15.4–19 and 15.4–20* | *Actual System Performance* |
| (a) $\left.\dfrac{C}{R}\right|_m$ | 1.00 | 1.00 | 1.00 |
| $\omega_m$ | 0 | 0 | 0 |
| (b) $\left.\dfrac{C}{R}\right|_p$ | 1.02 | 1.02 | 1.04 |
| $t_p$ | 0.75 | 0.75 | 0.74 |

*Case 2*

For the high gain system shown in Figure 15.5–2, in which the solid line indicates the actual open-loop transfer functions and the dotted lines indicate the straight-line approximations to this transfer function, find the values of $C/R\ |_m$, $C/R\ |_p$, $\omega_m$, and $t_p$.

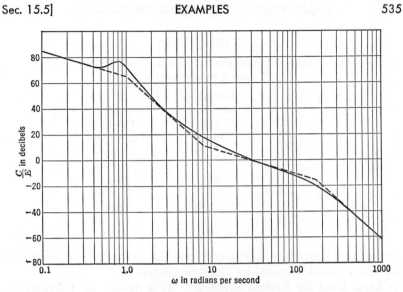

FIGURE 15.5–2. Actual and approximate open-loop transfer function for high gain system of Case 2.

$$\frac{C}{E} = \frac{1780(0.0156s^2 + 0.25s + 1)}{0.000039s^5 + 0.012s^4 + 1.03s^3 + 0.375s^2 + s}$$

The information necessary to determine the proper charts and performance is found in Figure 15.5–2 to be

$$\omega_c = 28 \text{ radians per second}$$

$$\omega_1 = 1 \text{ radian per second}$$

$$\mu_1 = 65 \text{ db}$$

$$\omega'_3 = 168 \text{ radians per second}$$

$$\omega_1 \text{ to } \omega_2 = 60 \text{ db per decade}$$

$$\omega'_3 \text{ to } \infty = 60 \text{ db per decade}$$

$$\frac{\omega_1}{\omega_c} = 0.035$$

$$\frac{\omega'_3}{\omega_c} = 6.00$$

It will be noted that the value of $\omega'_3$ is an equivalent value and is obtained by use of the approximate methods described previously. Hence Figures 15.4–22 and 15.4–23 must be used. In Table 15.5–2 the desired

TABLE 15.5–2

COMPARISON OF SYSTEM PERFORMANCE OBTAINED FROM CHARTS AND ACTUAL
SYSTEM CALCULATIONS

|  | Performance from Figures 15.4–22 and 15.4–23 | Actual System Performance |
|---|---|---|
| $\dfrac{C}{R}\Big|_m$ | 1.56 | 1.57 |
| $\omega_m$ | 20 | 20 |
| $\dfrac{C}{R}\Big|_p$ | 1.42 | 1.40 |
| $t_p$ | 0.1 | 0.1 |

performance quantities as obtained from the charts are compared with the actual values obtained by direct calculation.

**Charts Used for System Synthesis.** It is desired to determine an open-loop attenuation frequency characteristic for which the maximum value of the frequency response is 1.4 or less and occurs at frequency greater than 3 cycles per second. The ratio of output to error for a sinusoidal input of 1 radian per second should be at least 500. The attenuation rate for frequencies in excess of 120 radians per second will probably be 60 decibels per decade.

From the above data the following preliminary values of design parameters may be selected:

$\omega_m = 3 \times 2\pi = 18.8$ radians per second

$\mu_1 = 60$ db (which produces the proper actual gain at $\omega_1$)

$\omega_1 = 1$ radian per second

$\omega_3 = 120$ radians per second

Since the attenuation rate from $\omega_3$ to $\infty$ is to be 60 decibels per decade, and since high system performance is desired, Figures 15.4–21 to 15.4–23 will be used. Figure 15.4–22, for which $\omega_3/\omega_c = 4$, shows that for $\mu_1 = 60$ and $\dfrac{C}{R}\Big|_m = 1.4$, $\omega_1/\omega_c = 0.033$ and $\omega_m/\omega_c = 0.68$. For these conditions then, $\omega_c = \dfrac{18.8}{0.68} = 27.6$ radians per second. This indicates that a value of $\omega_c = 30$ can be used and the values of $\omega_1$ and $\omega_3$ above are satisfactory. The value of $\omega_m$ obtained is $\dfrac{0.68 \times 30}{2\pi} = 3.25$ cycles per second and is greater than the minimum allowable value. From this it appears that the specifications have been met. Therefore, an open-loop attenuation characteristic for which the system performance is satisfactory is

$$\frac{C}{E} = \frac{1000(1 + 0.17s)^2}{s(1 + s)^2(1 + 0.0083s)^2}$$

Since the most convenient means for obtaining this transfer function practically may not be such that the exact time constants indicated above are realized, it is probably not worth while to determine the transfer function more precisely from the charts.

In conjunction with the use of Figures 15.4–7 through 15.4–23, the designer is assisted materially by the knowledge of the values for the gain $\mu_1$ or the frequency $\omega_1$ corresponding to $\mu_1$. In Volume II, where the influence of the input characteristics will be discussed, methods for obtaining data on these quantities from the requirements of the problem will be presented. However, in those synthesis problems where this information may not be available, the designer may arbitrarily select open-loop attenuation characteristics that he thinks will be adequate, and by means of these charts check to see what characteristics are necessary to approximate the desired closed-loop performance. Having this approximate information, refinements can be made, using the charts with greater effectiveness.

## 15.6 Relationship between Phase Margin and Damping Ratio

Because the phase margin at 0 db is frequently used as a criterion of the performance of a system design using the steady-state methods of analysis, it is desirable to show the relationship between the phase margin and the damping ratio $\zeta$ for a simple quadratic system. Although this relationship is not strictly valid for systems of higher order, the qualitative correlation is generally correct and useful as a rule-of-thumb.

Consider the open-loop transfer function of a second-order system to be

$$G = \frac{K}{s(Ts + 1)} \tag{15.6-1}$$

for which the closed-loop transfer function is

$$\frac{C}{R} = \frac{K/T}{s^2 + s/T + K/T} \tag{15.6-2}$$

Expressed in terms of damping ratio and undamped natural frequency

$$\frac{C}{R} = \frac{\omega_0{}^2}{s^2 + 2\zeta\omega_0 s + \omega_0{}^2} \tag{15.6-3}$$

Comparing 15.6–2 and 15.6–3, one notes that

$$\omega_0 = \sqrt{K/T} \qquad (15.6\text{–}4)$$

and

$$2\zeta\omega_0 = 1/T$$

From this it can be shown that

$$KT = \frac{1}{4\zeta^2} \qquad (15.6\text{–}5)$$

Figure 15.6–1 shows a plot of $G = 1/s(Ts + 1)$ for various values of

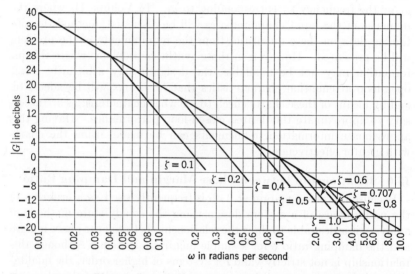

FIGURE 15.6–1.  Plot of $G = 1/s(Ts + 1)$, for various values of damping ratios, $\zeta$, where $T = 1/4\zeta^2$.

damping ratios $\zeta$ where $T$ has been calculated from Equation 15.6–5. Using these curves, one is able to determine the frequency for which the the open-loop attenuation is zero for the actual characteristic as well as for its straight line approximation.  The phase shift and phase margin at this frequency may also readily be calculated.  Figure 15.6–2 shows a plot of the phase margin in degrees thus obtained as a function of the damping ratio, $\zeta$, for the straight-line and actual attenuation characteristics.

Correlating this phase margin and damping ratio information with the step-function transient information contained in Figure 3.8–2, one observes that the peak overshoots of 10 to 20 per cent obtained from $\zeta = 0.6$ and $\zeta = 0.4$ correspond to phase margins of about 60° to 40°, respectively. These are values of phase margin that have generally been considered as good design objectives for many systems of higher order.

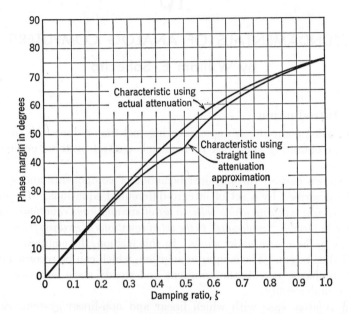

FIGURE 15.6–2.   Phase Margin at 0 db versus damping ratio for second-order systems shown in Figure 15.6–1 for 0 db obtained from actual and approximate attenuation characteristics.

The various methods of relating system performance from a steady-state and transient point of view are all helpful to the designer to understand alternate ways of accomplishing his system's design. Although exact and simple correlations are not easily obtained, a number of the approximate relationships described in the preceding sections can be very helpful.

# 16

## FUNDAMENTALS OF ANALOG COMPUTERS
### by William E. Sollecito

### 16.0 Introduction

An analog computer is an engineering tool that reduces the time and effort in obtaining solutions to feedback control systems engineering problems.

As shown earlier, the physical behavior of components and systems can be described by a set of integro-differential equations. *The analog computer is a machine which solves a set of simultaneous equations that are similar in form or "analogous" to the set of equations describing the dynamic behavior of the system under study.* In this fashion, the computer "simulates" the system. The computer solution, which can be recorded easily on strip charts, reveals the transient and steady state behavior of the system under study.

The relative ease with which linear and non-linear systems can be simulated allows analysis and design calculations which would be otherwise practically impossible.

The electronic computer is an electrical model of a system. The model can easily be changed and rearranged, a host of systems analyzed, and the optimum system selected for construction. Electronic analog computers are also called differential analyzers because their purpose is to solve differential equations.

The analysis and synthesis of control systems can be broken down into three main parts: problem definition, equation solution, and solution evaluation.

Problem definition is that portion related to the initial uncovering of the need to do a certain job, the equipment that can do the job, and the application of mathematics and the technology-based sciences to reduce the hardware to equations and graphs. The equation solution is that part which obtains the response functions for prescribed inputs. The solution evaluation is then devoted to interpretation of results, modification of equations where required, and translation of the equation modifications back into hardware.

It is in the area of equation solution that computers are invaluable. They not only greatly shrink the time and effort involved to solve those equations that can be solved by hand calculations, but they bring into the realm of feasibility a host of equation solutions which by hand calculation are for practical purposes unsolvable.

Paper analysis techniques and analog computers complement one another in that the former can be used to obtain a general "feel" for a problem and point the way for more detailed study, whereas the latter can be used to obtain complete solutions to specific problems. Hand calculations provide check solutions which can be used to insure proper computer operation.

This chapter shows what analog computers are and how they can be used to study control systems problems.

## 16.1  Analogs and Block Diagrams

*Different physical systems whose dynamic performance can be described by similar or "analogous" equations are analogs of one another.* Figure 16.1–1 shows the symbolic representation of a mechanical and an electrical system.

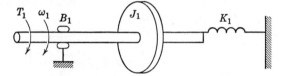

$$T_1 = B_1\omega_1 + J_1\frac{d\omega_1}{dt} + K_1\int\omega_1\,dt$$

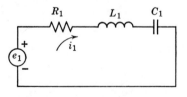

$$e_1 = R_1 i_1 + L_1\frac{di_1}{dt} + \frac{1}{C_1}\int i_1\,dt$$

FIGURE 16.1–1.   Analogous systems.

The equations defining the physical behavior of the two systems are given as:

$$T_1 = B_1\omega_1 + J_1\frac{d\omega_1}{dt} + K_1\int\omega_1\,dt \qquad (16.1\text{–}1)$$

$$e_1 = R_1 i_1 + L_1 \frac{di_1}{dt} + \frac{1}{C_1} \int i_1 \, dt \qquad (16.1\text{-}2)$$

The equations are identical in form and if $e_1$ is made proportional to $T_1$, $i_1$ proportional to $\omega_1$, $R_1$ proportional to $B_1$, $L_1$ proportional to $J_1$, and $C_1$ proportional to $K_1^{-1}$, solution of Equation 16.1–2 provides the solution to Equation 16.1–1. In other words, the solution of a mathematical equation is independent of the physical meaning attached to each of the parameters in the equation.

The opportunities afforded by the existence of analogs are pointed up by Figure 16.1–1. If it were desirable to build the mechanical system by "experimentation and evaluation" procedures, many dampers, springs, and inertias would have to be constructed to study many different situations. The relative ease of obtaining and interconnecting different values of $R_1$, $L_1$, and $C_1$ shows that an experimental study of the electrical system is much simpler than the experimental study of the mechanical system.

The analysis techniques presented earlier tend to remove the need for "experimentation and evaluation" procedures. For simple linear

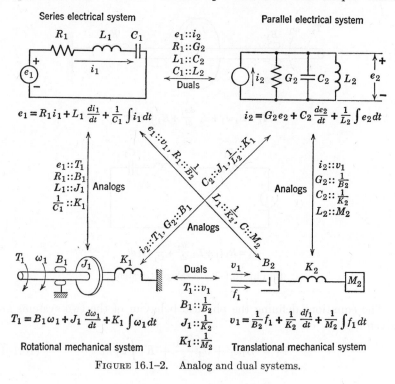

FIGURE 16.1–2.   Analog and dual systems.

systems this is true.  When complex, non-linear systems are encountered, the "experimentation and evaluation" procedure is again useful.  The analysis techniques are extremely valuable in guiding the experimentation and evaluation.  The analog computer allows use of the principles of this procedure without the attendant time-consuming and expensive hardware building.  In effect, simulated hardware is constructed on the computer.

Figure 16.1–2 shows four analogous systems.  When two of them are of the same type, that is, both electrical or both mechanical, they have been called duals.  For the work covered here, the electronic computer will be considered as an analog of any system under study.

**Block Diagram Representation of System Equations.**  *A block diagram is a pictorial method of describing system interrelationships or writing system equations.*

To illustrate the development of a block diagram, consider the mechanical system of Figure 16.1–1 whose equations of motion were given by

$$T_1 = B_1\omega_1 + J_1 \frac{d\omega_1}{dt} + K_1 \int \omega_1 \, dt \qquad (16.1\text{–}1)$$

In this system, $T_1$ is the applied torque and is the independent variable or reference or command, whereas $\omega_1$ is the dependent variable or the controlled variable.

Rearrangement of Equation 16.1–1 yields

$$J_1 \frac{d\omega_1}{dt} = T_1 - B_1\omega_1 - K_1 \int \omega_1 \, dt \qquad (16.1\text{–}3)$$

In Figure 16.1–3, this equation is found at the output of the summing point.

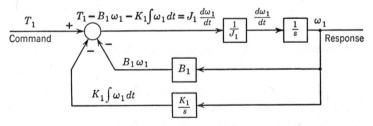

FIGURE 16.1–3.   Block diagram of mechanical system of Figure 16.1–1.

The output of the summing point, $J_1 \, d\omega_1/dt$, is equal to the summation of all the inputs.  Multiplication by $1/J_1$ yields $d\omega_1/dt$.  Integration of

$d\omega_1/dt$ yields $\omega_1$. Multiplication of $\omega_1$ by $B_1$ yields $B_1\omega_1$, while integration and multiplication by $K_1$ yield $K_1 \int \omega_1 \, dt$. These terms are then returned to the summing point with negative signs.

Inspection of this diagram reveals that three distinct operations are performed:

(1) Multiplication by a coefficient.
(2) Integration.
(3) Summation.

Generation of these operations by electronic means forms the basis for electronic analog computation.

## 16.2   Simulation of Blocks

*The heart of a d-c electronic analog computer is a high gain d-c amplifier* [116] as shown in Figure 16.2–1. Because it is used to generate the

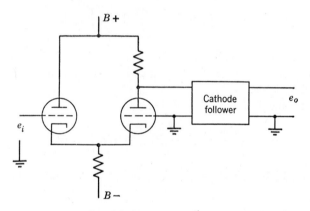

FIGURE 16.2–1.   Simplified version of d-c operational amplifier.

previously mentioned operations, it is commonly called an operational amplifier. Some points to remember are:

(1) The input voltage is applied directly to a grid.
(2) The output impedance is low.
(3) The amplifier introduces a phase inversion.
(4) The output has definite voltage and power limitations.
(5) d-c amplifiers have drift problems.
(6) The amplifier gain ranges from 10,000 to greater than 1,000,000 depending on the manufacturer.

The symbol for the operational amplifier is shown in Figure 16.2–2.

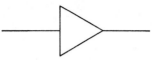

FIGURE 16.2–2.   High-gain operational amplifier symbol.

By introducing input and feedback impedances to the amplifier, certain operations can be generated.   Consider the arrangement shown in Figure 16.2–3.

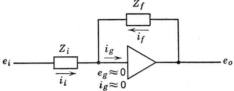

FIGURE 16.2–3.   Operational amplifier with input and feedback impedances.

$e_i$ is the input voltage supplied by a voltage source.   $e_o$ is the output voltage which supplies a high impedance load.   Because the amplifier gain is very high, it will be assumed that the grid voltage necessary to produce any output voltage, $e_o$, within the voltage limitations of the amplifier is negligibly small; therefore, $e_g \approx 0$.   Because the input to the amplifier is applied directly to the grid, it will also be assumed that $i_g \approx 0$.   These assumptions simplify the analysis without introducing appreciable error for the usual application.   Should it be necessary, one can consider $e_g$ and $i_g$ not equal to zero and thereby calculate the exact performance characteristics.   The error terms neglected here are inversely proportional to amplifier gain.

Summation of currents at the amplifier input node yields:

$$i_i + i_f = i_g = 0 \qquad (16.2\text{--}1)$$

$$\frac{e_i - e_g}{Z_i} + \frac{e_o - e_g}{Z_f} = 0 \qquad (16.2\text{--}2)$$

$$\text{for } e_g = 0$$

$$\frac{e_i}{Z_i} + \frac{e_o}{Z_f} = 0 \qquad (16.2\text{--}3)$$

Therefore

$$e_o = -\frac{Z_f}{Z_i} e_i \qquad (16.2\text{--}4)$$

Equation 16.2–4 shows that *the output voltage is equal to minus the input voltage times the ratio of the feedback impedance to the input impedance.* If the impedances are now taken as pure resistors, that is, $Z_f = R_f$ and $Z_i = R_i$, then

$$e_o = -\frac{R_f}{R_i}e_i \qquad (16.2\text{–}5)$$

It is now apparent that the ratio of $R_f$ to $R_i$ can be a number which corresponds to the value of a circuit parameter such as $B_1$, $K_1$, etc. Therefore, an operational amplifier with pure resistive input and feedback impedances generates the operation of multiplication by a coefficient. A phase inversion is also generated.

The impedance of a capacitor is

$$Z_c = \frac{1}{Cs} \qquad (16.2\text{–}6)$$

Therefore, if the feedback element is a capacitor and the input element is a resistor, the operation is that of integration and multiplication by a constant:

$$e_0 = -\frac{Z_f}{Z_i}e_i = -\frac{1/C_f s}{R_i}e_i = -\frac{1}{R_i C_f s}e_i \qquad (16.2\text{–}7)$$

Note that the gain coefficient is inversely proportional to the product of $R_i$ and $C_f$.

The multiplication by a coefficient and the integration operations are shown in Figure 16.2–4.

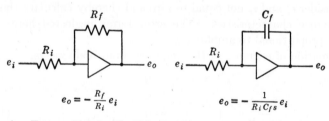

$$e_0 = -\frac{R_f}{R_i}e_i \qquad\qquad e_0 = -\frac{1}{R_i C_f s}e_i$$

FIGURE 16.2–4.   Coefficient and integration operations.

For the summation operation consider the setup shown in Figure 16.2–5.

Summation of currents at the amplifier input node yields

$$i_1 + i_2 + i_3 + i_f = i_g = 0 \qquad (16.2\text{–}8)$$

$$\frac{e_1}{R_1} + \frac{e_2}{R_2} + \frac{e_3}{R_3} + \frac{e_o}{R_f} = 0 \quad \text{for } e_g \approx 0 \qquad (16.2\text{–}9)$$

Therefore

$$e_o = -\left[\frac{R_f}{R_1}e_1 + \frac{R_f}{R_2}e_2 + \frac{R_f}{R_3}e_3\right] \qquad (16.2\text{--}10)$$

Equation 16.2–10 shows that the output voltage is equal to minus the sum of the input voltages, each input voltage multiplied by the usual ratio of feedback resistance to each respective input resistance.

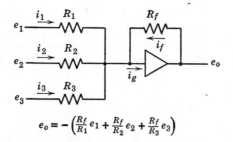

$$e_o = -\left(\frac{R_f}{R_1}e_1 + \frac{R_f}{R_2}e_2 + \frac{R_f}{R_3}e_3\right)$$

FIGURE 16.2–5.   Summation operation.

The reader should note that only resistors and capacitors were used to generate the required operations shown in Figures 16.2–4 and 16.2–5. It is fortunate that inductors are not necessary because these elements exhibit non-linear characteristics when magnetic core materials are used to obtain the required range of inductance.

The computer setup for the mechanical system shown in block diagram form in Figure 16.1–3 is shown in Figure 16.2–6. *All resistors are in terms of megohms and all capacitors are in terms of microfarads.*

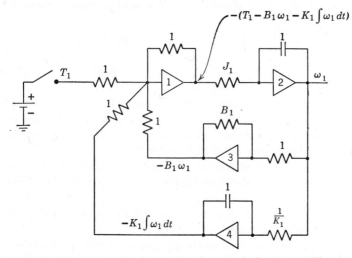

FIGURE 16.2–6.   Computer setup for rotational mechanical system of Figures 16.1–1 and 16.1–3.

This system, with $J_1 = 1$, $B_1 = 0.4$, $K_1 = 1$, was set up on a computer and the response recorded for a unit-step input of torque. The applied torque, $T_1$, and angular position, $\theta_1 = \int \omega_1 \, dt$, are shown in Figure 16.2–7. The angular position can be recorded as the output of amplifier #4.

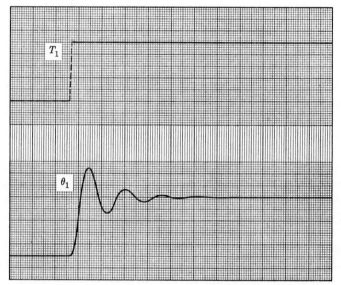

FIGURE 16.2–7.  Computer record for unit step input of torque to setup of Figure 16.2–6.

The equation relating input torque to output angular position is

$$T_1 = J_1 \frac{d^2\theta_1}{dt^2} + B_1 \frac{d\theta_1}{dt} + K_1\theta_1 \qquad (16.2\text{–}11)$$

This equation is the same form as Equation 3.8–1 of Chapter 3. Since $\zeta = 0.2$ for the particular values of $J_1$, $B_1$, and $K_1$ used, the angular position recording of Figure 16.2–7 is exactly the same shape as the $\zeta = 0.2$ curve of Figure 3.8–2 of Chapter 3.

If $T_1$ were a sinusoid instead of a unit-step function, the computer recording would be as shown in Figure 16.2–8 where steady-state conditions exist.

By comparing the relative magnitudes of $T_1$ and $\theta_1$ and also the relative phase angle, the curves for $\zeta = 0.2$ in Figures 11.3–6 and 11.3–7 of Chapter 11 can be measured on the computer. Since the computer setup represents the actual hardware, a frequency response of the hardware can be measured on the computer.

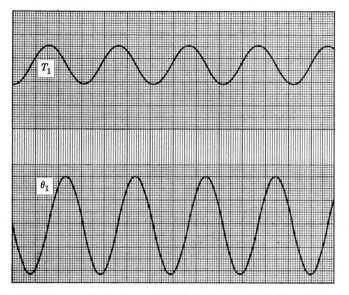

FɪɢURE 16.2–8.   Computer recording for steady-state sinusoidal input.

## 16.3   Differential Equation Method of Simulation

In general there are two basic approaches to setting up a computer to simulate a system—the differential equation method and the transfer function method. The first allows easy recognition of all the parameters of a system in terms of some resistance or capacitance. The computer setup shown in Figure 16.2–6 was generated in this fashion. Each parameter can be varied by changing the value of the capacitor or resistor that is associated with it.

The second method generates entire transfer functions by using complex input and feedback impedances. It affects a saving in computer amplifiers required but suffers from the loss of one to one correspondence between a resistor or capacitor and a system parameter. It also suffers from the increased difficulty in inserting initial conditions. In practice, both approaches are used in arriving upon the optimum computer setup.

In the differential equation method it is customary to rearrange the given equation such that the highest order derivative is set equal to the rest of the terms in the equation. The next step is to assume that all the rest of the terms in the equation are available and that upon summation, they produce the highest order derivative term. Refer to Equation 16.1–3 and the summing point shown in Figure 16.1–3.

With the highest order derivative in hand, successive integration yields the rest of the lower order terms. Multiplication of the lower order terms by the appropriate coefficients yields the terms that were assumed available at the start of the process. The reference input is injected at the summation point and the block diagram is complete. Review of the steps taken to develop the block diagram of Figure 16.1–3 clearly illustrates the differential equation method of setting up a computer diagram. Generation of the blocks then follows the procedure of 16.2. In closing the loops it may turn out that the available term is of polarity opposite to that required. In this event a sign changer is used. A sign changer is a coefficient amplifier with unity gain. This corresponds to the coefficient operation of Figure 16.2–4 where $R_f = R_i$ and therefore $e_o = -e_i$. *To check quickly a computer setup for proper polarity of feedback, count the number of amplifiers in a loop. An odd number indicates negative feedback whereas an even number indicates positive feedback.* The polarity of feedback should correspond to that indicated in the block diagram of the system.

For systems described by a set of simultaneous equations, the procedure follows the same ground rules. For every independent equation there will be a distinct summing point.

As an example consider the system shown in Figure 10.2–12 of Chapter 10 which is reproduced in Figure 16.3–1.

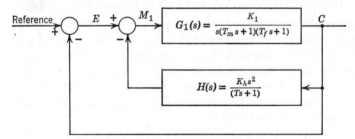

FIGURE 16.3–1.    System shown in Figure 10.2–12.

The equations of this system were given as

$$K_1 M_1(s) = [T_m T_f s^3 + (T_m + T_f)s^2 + s]C(s) \qquad (16.3\text{–}1)$$

$$K_h s^2 C(s) = (Ts + 1)B(s) \qquad (16.3\text{–}2)$$

$$E(s) = R(s) - C(s) \qquad (16.3\text{–}3)$$

$$M(s) = E(s) - B(s) \qquad (16.3\text{–}4)$$

Rewriting Equations 16.3–1 and 16.3–2,

$$T_m T_f s^3 C(s) = K_1 M_1(s) - [(T_m + T_f)s^2 + s]C(s) \qquad (16.3\text{–}5)$$

$$TsB(s) = K_h s^2 C(s) - B(s) \qquad (16.3\text{–}6)$$

These equations yield the block diagram of Figure 16.3–2.

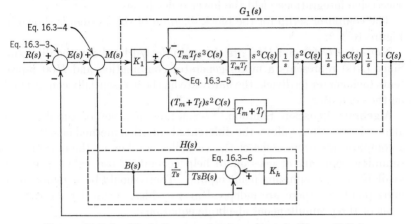

FIGURE 16.3–2.   Block diagram of system shown in Figure 16.3–1.

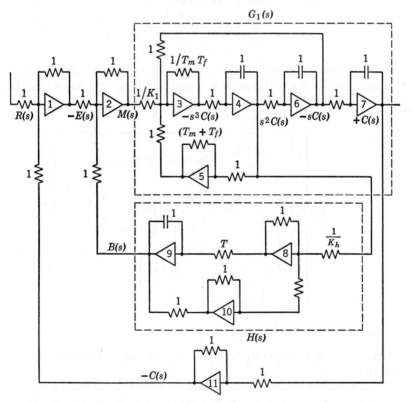

FIGURE 16.3–3.   Computer setup for the system shown in Figure 16.3–2.

Note that each equation is represented by a summing point and that successive integrations yield the lower order terms.

The computer setup for the block diagram of this system is shown in Figure 16.3–3.

Note that $G_1(s)$ and $H(s)$ are shown in dotted blocks in the diagram. Since $G_1(s)$ represents a motor-generator combination and $H(s)$ represents tachometer feedback, the hardware has been essentially constructed on the computer.

**Algebraic Equation Solution.**[129]   Solution of a set of simultaneous algebraic equations follows the differential equation method of setting up a computer diagram.   One of the variables is taken as the output of a summing point and it goes on to help generate those values assumed available at the summing point inputs.   There should be as many summing points as there are independent variables.   Consider the case of a set of three simultaneous algebraic equations:

$$a_1x + b_1y + c_1z = A_1 \qquad (16.3\text{–}7)$$

$$a_2x + b_2y + c_2z = A_2 \qquad (16.3\text{–}8)$$

$$a_3x + b_3y + c_3z = A_3 \qquad (16.3\text{–}9)$$

The computer will obtain those values of $x$, $y$, and $z$ which satisfy the equations for the particular $a$, $b$, $c$, and $A$ values.   The block diagram of this setup is shown in Figure 16.3–4.

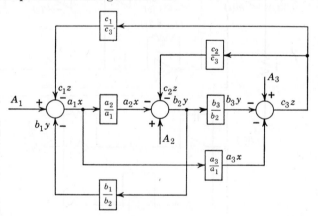

FIGURE 16.3–4.   Block diagram of three simultaneous algebraic equations.

Generation of the operations follows the standard procedure of Section 16.2.

The d-c analog computer can yield solutions only for those equations whose solutions are real numbers.   When no real solution exists, the computer will either oscillate or the voltages will tend toward infinity and thereby cause amplifier saturation.

When a loop occurs in a setup where no capacitors are involved, an algebraic loop has been set up. These algebraic loops can cause oscillations when several amplifiers and high gain are present in the loop. This oscillation is due to the fact that the amplifiers have attenuation and phase shift at high frequencies. With no other lag circuits in the loop, gain crossover can occur at a negative phase margin when several amplifiers and high gain are present in the loop. This trouble can sometimes be cured by placing a small capacitor in parallel with the normal feedback resistor of one of the amplifiers. This effects a gain crossover in the region before the phase shift reaches $-180°$.

Figure 16.3–5 shows insertion of a stabilizing capacitor in an algebraic loop.

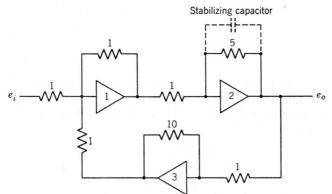

FIGURE 16.3–5. Insertion of a stabilizing capacitor in an algebraic loop.

## 16.4 Transfer Function Method of Simulation

In generating the simple operations of multiplication by a coefficient, integration, and summation, simple impedance structures for $Z_i$ and $Z_f$ were used. If complex structures are considered, then more complex transfer functions can be generated with a single operational amplifier. The transfer function method is different from the differential equation method of simulation in that one operational amplifier with complex impedances is used to generate transfer functions wholly or in part.

Consider the transfer function of Equation 16.2–11 in Laplace transform notation.

$$\frac{\theta_1(s)}{T_1(s)} = \frac{1/J_1}{s^2 + \dfrac{B_1}{J_1}s + \dfrac{K_1}{J_1}} \tag{16.4-1}$$

In the standard form this becomes

$$\frac{\theta_1(s)}{T_1(s)} = \frac{K}{s^2 + 2\zeta\omega_0 s + \omega_0{}^2} \tag{16.4-2}$$

To generate this transfer function, consider the circuit shown in Figure 16.4-1.

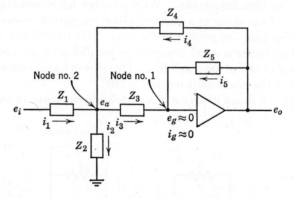

FIGURE 16.4-1.  A specific complex computer circuit.

Under the usual assumption that $e_g \approx 0$ and $i_g \approx 0$, the current summation equation at node 1 yields:

$$i_3 + i_5 = 0 \tag{16.4-3}$$

$$\frac{e_a}{Z_3} + \frac{e_o}{Z_5} = 0 \tag{16.4-4}$$

$$e_a = -\frac{Z_3}{Z_5} e_o \tag{16.4-5}$$

The current summation equation at node 2 yields:

$$i_1 + i_4 = i_3 + i_2 \tag{16.4-6}$$

$$\frac{e_i - e_a}{Z_1} + \frac{e_o - e_a}{Z_4} = \frac{e_a}{Z_3} + \frac{e_a}{Z_2} \tag{16.4-7}$$

$$\frac{e_i}{Z_1} + \frac{e_o}{Z_4} = e_a \left[ \frac{1}{Z_3} + \frac{1}{Z_2} + \frac{1}{Z_1} + \frac{1}{Z_4} \right] \tag{16.4-8}$$

Substitution for $e_a$ from Equation 16.4-5 yields

$$\frac{e_i}{Z_1} + \frac{e_o}{Z_4} = -\frac{Z_3}{Z_5} \left[ \frac{1}{Z_3} + \frac{1}{Z_2} + \frac{1}{Z_1} + \frac{1}{Z_4} \right] e_o \tag{16.4-9}$$

This reduces to

$$\frac{e_o}{e_i} = -\frac{Z_2 Z_4 Z_5}{Z_1 Z_2 Z_3 + Z_1 Z_2 Z_4 + Z_1 Z_3 Z_4 + Z_2 Z_3 Z_4 + Z_1 Z_2 Z_5} \quad (16.4\text{--}10)$$

For the purpose at hand, this is rewritten

$$\frac{e_o}{e_i} = -\frac{Z_4}{\dfrac{Z_1 Z_3 Z_4}{Z_2 Z_5} + \dfrac{Z_3 Z_4}{Z_5} + \dfrac{Z_1 Z_3}{Z_5} + \dfrac{Z_1 Z_4}{Z_5} + Z_1} \quad (16.4\text{--}11)$$

It now becomes apparent that if

$$Z = R_1 \qquad Z_3 = R_3 \qquad Z_4 = R_4 \qquad (16.4\text{--}12)$$

$$Z_2 = \frac{1}{C_2 s} \qquad Z_5 = \frac{1}{C_5 s}$$

The transfer function becomes

$$\frac{e_o(s)}{e_i(s)} = -\frac{R_4}{R_1 R_3 R_4 C_2 C_5 s^2 + (R_3 R_4 + R_1 R_4 + R_1 R_3) C_5 s + R_1} \quad (16.4\text{--}13)$$

or

$$\frac{e_o(s)}{e_i(s)} = -\frac{1/R_1 R_3 C_2 C_5}{s^2 + \dfrac{R_3 R_4 + R_1 R_4 + R_1 R_3}{R_1 R_3 R_4 C_2} s + \dfrac{1}{R_3 R_4 C_2 C_5}} \quad (16.4\text{--}14)$$

Equating like terms among Equations 16.4–1, 16.4–2, and 16.4–14 yields:

$$\frac{1}{J_1} = K_1 = \frac{1}{R_1 R_3 C_2 C_5} \quad (16.4\text{--}15)$$

$$\frac{K_1}{J_1} = \omega_0{}^2 = \frac{1}{R_3 R_4 C_2 C_5} \quad (16.4\text{--}16)$$

$$\frac{B_1}{J_1} = 2 \zeta \omega_0 = \frac{R_3 R_4 + R_1 R_4 + R_1 R_3}{R_1 R_3 R_4 C_2} \quad (16.4\text{--}17)$$

For the previously selected values of $J_1 = 1$, $K_1 = 1$, and $B_1 = 0.4$, the computer resistor and capacitor values can be selected as follows. *All capacitors are in microfarads and all resistors are in megohms.*

From Equations 16.4–15, 16.4–16, and 16.4–17

$$\frac{1}{R_1 R_3 C_2 C_5} = 1 \qquad (16.4\text{–}18)$$

$$\frac{1}{R_3 R_4 C_2 C_5} = 1 \qquad (16.4\text{–}19)$$

$$\frac{1}{C_2}\left(\frac{1}{R_1} + \frac{1}{R_3} + \frac{1}{R_4}\right) = 0.4 \qquad (16.4\text{–}20)$$

From Equations 16.4–18 and 16.4–19

$$\frac{1}{R_3} = R_1 C_2 C_5 = R_4 C_2 C_5 \qquad (16.4\text{–}21)$$

Therefore
$$R_1 = R_4 \qquad (16.4\text{–}22)$$

Substituting Equations 16.4–21 and 16.4–22 into 16.4–20

$$\frac{1}{C_2}\left(\frac{1}{R_4} + R_4 C_2 C_5 + \frac{1}{R_4}\right) = 0.4 \qquad (16.4\text{–}23)$$

This yields
$$C_2 C_5 R_4{}^2 - 0.4 C_2 R_4 + 2 = 0 \qquad (16.4\text{–}24)$$

Solution for $R_4$ yields

$$R_4 = \frac{0.4 C_2 \pm \sqrt{(0.4 C_2)^2 - 8 C_2 C_5}}{2 C_2 C_5} \qquad (16.4\text{–}25)$$

The square root term is real when
$$C_2 > 50 C_5 \qquad (16.4\text{–}26)$$

Arbitrarily setting $C_2 = 50 C_5 = 1$
$$C_5 = 0.02 \qquad (16.4\text{–}27)$$

From Equations 16.4–22 and 16.4–25

$$R_4 = R_1 = \frac{0.4 C_2}{2 C_2 C_5} = \frac{0.4}{2 C_5} = 10 \qquad (16.4\text{–}28)$$

From Equation (16.4–21)

$$R_3 = \frac{1}{R_4 C_2 C_5} = 5 \qquad (16.4\text{–}29)$$

The computer setup for this system is shown in Figure 16.4–2.

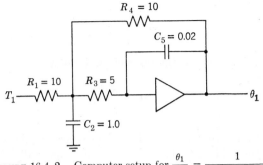

FIGURE 16.4–2.    Computer setup for $\dfrac{\theta_1}{T_1 s} = \dfrac{1}{s^2 + 0.4s + 1}$.

Comparison of Figures 16.2–6 and 16.4–2 shows that the differential equation method

(1) Requires more amplifiers.
(2) Allows measurement of all the variables in the system.
(3) Allows one to one correspondence between a system parameter and a computer resistor or capacitor. This saves time when studying effects of parameter changes.

The transfer function method

(1) Saves amplifiers.
(2) Allows measurement of less variables.
(3) Increases computational work.

It is apparent, therefore, that both methods should be considered in setting up a computer to take advantage of the most convenient setup arrangement.

The circuit of Figure 16.4–1 was fairly complex in that an additional feedback loop was included (the one containing $Z_4$). Normally such complexity is unwarranted and it suffices to merely consider noninteracting feedback and input impedances. For the simple circuit shown in Figure 16.2–3, many transfer functions can be generated by letting $Z_i$ and $Z_f$ represent the *transfer impedance* of a resistor-capacitor network.

The terms transfer impedance and driving point impedance may be defined with reference to Figure 16.4–3.

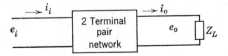

FIGURE 16.4–3.    Standard 2 terminal pair network.

The *driving point impedance* is the ratio of the input voltage divided by the input current.

$$Z_{DP} = \frac{e_i}{i_i} \qquad (16.4\text{--}30)$$

The *transfer impedance* is the ratio of the input voltage divided by the output current.

$$Z_T = \frac{e_i}{i_o} \qquad (16.4\text{--}31)$$

In a computer setup, transfer impedances are required because the current into the grid node due to a voltage at more distant node is of importance. In many situations $Z_{DP} = Z_T$; therefore this case can introduce no error. When they are not equal, use of driving point impedances causes erroneous results.

To illustrate calculation of transfer impedances, consider the network shown in Figure 16.4–4.

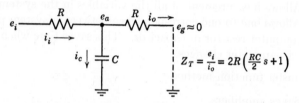

FIGURE 16.4–4.   Transfer impedance of simple $RC$ network.

Since a network usually terminates on the input of an operational amplifier, the output end of the network is considered at ground potential, that is, $e_g = 0$.

$$i_i = i_o + i_c \qquad (16.4\text{--}32)$$

$$\frac{e_i - e_a}{R} = \frac{e_a}{R} + e_a C s \qquad (16.4\text{--}33)$$

$$\frac{e_i}{R} = \frac{e_a}{R}(2 + RCs) \qquad (16.4\text{--}34)$$

Because

$$i_o = \frac{e_a}{R} \qquad (16.4\text{--}35)$$

$$\frac{e_i}{R} = 2i_o\left(\frac{RCs}{2} + 1\right) \qquad (16.4\text{--}36)$$

Therefore

$$Z_T = \frac{e_i}{i_o} = 2R\left(\frac{RCs}{2} + 1\right) \qquad (16.4\text{--}37)$$

This network can be used either as the input impedance $(Z_i)$ or feedback impedance $(Z_f)$ of an amplifier. Figure 16.4–5 shows the different connections and the resulting transfer functions.

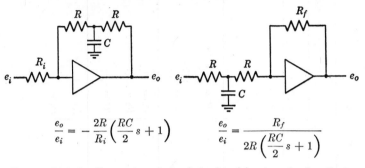

$$\frac{e_o}{e_i} = -\frac{2R}{R_i}\left(\frac{RC}{2}s + 1\right) \qquad \frac{e_o}{e_i} = \frac{R_f}{2R\left(\dfrac{RC}{2}s + 1\right)}$$

FIGURE 16.4–5.   Generation of simple lead and lag transfer functions.

There are many possible networks that can be used. A set that covers most of the cases encountered in practice is shown in Table 16.4–1.[127] The column titled "relations" expresses the transfer impedance coefficients in terms of the network parameters while the "inverse relations" column expresses the network parameters in terms of the transfer impedance coefficients. The $RC$ network of Figure 16.4–5 is 3 in the table.

*Example 1*

Consider the amplidyne and motor of Figure 10.1–5 of Chapter 10. The amplidyne and motor are reproduced in Figure 16.4–6.

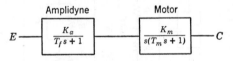

FIGURE 16.4–6.   Amplidyne and motor of Figure 10.1–5.

To simulate these transfer functions several choices are available. A possible setup which preserves one to one correspondence between amplifiers and hardware and also allows recording of more of the important variables is shown in Figure 16.4–7.

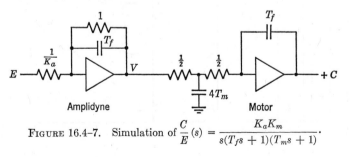

FIGURE 16.4–7.   Simulation of $\dfrac{C}{E}(s) = \dfrac{K_a K_m}{s(T_f s + 1)(T_m s + 1)}.$

TABLE 16.4-1

TRANSFER IMPEDANCE FUNCTIONS OF R-C INPUT AND OUTPUT NETWORKS

| Transfer-impedance Function | Network | Relations | Inverse Relations |
| --- | --- | --- | --- |
| (1) $A$ | | $A = R$ | $R = A$ |
| (2) $\dfrac{A}{Ts+1}$ | | $A = R$<br>$T = RC$ | $R = A$<br>$C = \dfrac{T}{A}$ |
| (3) $A(Ts+1)$ | | $A = 2R$<br>$T = \dfrac{RC}{2}$ | $R = \dfrac{A}{2}$<br>$C = \dfrac{4T}{A}$ |
| (4) $A\left(\dfrac{\theta Ts+1}{Ts+1}\right)$<br>$\theta < 1$ | | $A = R_1 + R_2$<br>$T = R_2 C$<br>$\theta = \dfrac{R_1}{R_1+R_2}$ | $R_1 = A\theta$<br>$R_2 = A(1-\theta)$<br>$C = \dfrac{T}{A(1-\theta)}$ |
| | | $A = R_1$<br>$T = (R_1+R_2)C$<br>$\theta = \dfrac{R_2}{R_1+R_2}$ | $R_1 = A$<br>$R_2 = \dfrac{A\theta}{1-\theta}$<br>$C = \dfrac{T(1-\theta)}{A}$ |

TABLE 16.4-1 (Continued)

TRANSFER IMPEDANCE FUNCTIONS OF R-C INPUT AND OUTPUT NETWORKS

| Transfer-impedance Function | Network | Relations | Inverse Relations |
|---|---|---|---|
| (5) $A\left(\dfrac{Ts+1}{\theta Ts+1}\right)$ <br> $\theta < 1$ | | $A = \dfrac{2R_1 R_2}{2R_1 + R_2}$ <br><br> $T = \dfrac{R_1 C}{2}$ <br><br> $\theta = \dfrac{2R_1}{2R_1 + R_2}$ | $R_1 = \dfrac{A}{2(1-\theta)}$ <br><br> $R_2 = \dfrac{A}{\theta}$ <br><br> $C = \dfrac{4T(1-\theta)}{A}$ |
| | | $A = 2R_1$ <br><br> $T = \left(R_2 + \dfrac{R_1}{2}\right) C$ <br><br> $\theta = \dfrac{2R_2}{2R_2 + R_1}$ | $R_1 = \dfrac{A}{2}$ <br><br> $R_2 = \dfrac{A\theta}{4(1-\theta)}$ <br><br> $C = \dfrac{4T(1-\theta)}{A}$ |
| | | $A = 2R$ <br><br> $T = \dfrac{R}{2}(C_1 + C_2)$ <br><br> $\theta = \dfrac{2C_2}{C_1 + C_2}$ | $R = \dfrac{A}{2}$ <br><br> $C_1 = \dfrac{2T(2-\theta)}{A}$ <br><br> $C_2 = \dfrac{2T\theta}{A}$ |

TABLE 16.4-1 (*Continued*)

TRANSFER IMPEDANCE FUNCTIONS OF R-C INPUT AND OUTPUT NETWORKS

| Transfer-impedance Function | Network | Relations | Inverse Relations |
|---|---|---|---|
| (6) $\dfrac{1}{Bs}\left[\dfrac{(T_1 s + 1)(T_3 s + 1)}{T_2 s + 1}\right]$ <br><br> $T_1 < T_2 < T_3$ | | $B = C_1$ <br><br> $T_2 = (R_1 + R_2)C_2$ <br><br> $T_1 T_3 = R_1 R_2 C_1 C_2$ <br><br> $T_1 + T_3 = R_1 C_1 + R_2 C_2 + R_1 C_2$ | $R_1 = \dfrac{T_1 + T_3 - T_2}{B}$ <br><br> $R_2 = \dfrac{T_1 T_3 (T_1 + T_3 - T_2)}{B(T_3 - T_2)(T_2 - T_1)}$ <br><br> $C_1 = B$ <br><br> $C_2 = \dfrac{B(T_3 - T_2)(T_2 - T_1)}{(T_1 + T_3 - T_2)^2}$ |
| | | $B = C_1 + C_2$ <br><br> $T_2 = R_2\left(\dfrac{C_1 C_2}{C_1 + C_2}\right)$ <br><br> $T_1 T_3 = R_1 R_2 C_1 C_2$ <br><br> $T_1 + T_3 = R_1 C_1 + R_2 C_2 + R_1 C_2$ | $R_1 = \dfrac{T_1 T_3}{B T_2}$ <br><br> $R_2 = \dfrac{(T_1 T_2 + T_2 T_3 - T_1 T_3)^2}{B T_2^2(T_3 - T_2)(T_2 - T_1)}$ <br><br> $C_1 = \dfrac{T_1 T_2 + T_2 T_3 - T_1 T_3}{B T_2^2}$ <br><br> $C_2 = \dfrac{B(T_3 - T_2)(T_2 - T_1)}{T_1 T_2 + T_2 T_3 - T_1 T_3}$ |
| | | $B = C_1$ <br><br> $T_2 = R_2 C_2$ <br><br> $T_1 T_3 = R_1 R_2 C_1 C_2$ <br><br> $T_1 + T_3 = R_1 C_1 + R_2 C_2 + R_2 C_1$ | $R_1 = \dfrac{T_1 T_3}{B T_2}$ <br><br> $R_2 = \dfrac{(T_3 - T_2)(T_2 - T_1)}{B T_2}$ <br><br> $C_1 = B$ <br><br> $C_2 = \dfrac{B T_2^2}{(T_3 - T_2)(T_2 - T_1)}$ |

TABLE 16.4–1 (Continued)

TRANSFER IMPEDANCE FUNCTIONS OF R-C INPUT AND OUTPUT NETWORKS

| Transfer-impedance Function | Network | Relations | Inverse Relations |
|---|---|---|---|
| (6) $\dfrac{1}{Bs}\left[\dfrac{(T_1s+1)(T_3s+1)}{T_2s+1}\right]$ $T_1 < T_2 < T_3$ | | $B = C_1$ $T_2 = R_2C_2$ $T_1T_3 = R_1R_2C_1C_2$ $T_1 + T_3 = R_1C_1 + R_2C_2 + R_1C_2$ | $R_1 = \dfrac{T_1T_3}{BT_2}$ $R_2 = \dfrac{T_1T_2T_3}{B(T_3-T_2)(T_2-T_1)}$ $C_1 = B$ $C_2 = \dfrac{B(T_3-T_2)(T_2-T_1)}{T_1T_3}$ |
| (7) $\dfrac{1}{Bs}(1+T_1s)(1+T_2s)$ $T_1 \neq T_2$ | | $B = C_2$ $T_1T_2 = R_1R_2C_1C_2$ $T_1 + T_2 = R_1C_1 + R_2C_2 + R_1C_2$ | $R_1 = \dfrac{(\sqrt{T_1} - \sqrt{T_2})^2}{B}$ $R_2 = \dfrac{\sqrt{T_1T_2}}{B}$ $C_1 = \dfrac{B\sqrt{T_1T_2}}{(\sqrt{T_1} - \sqrt{T_2})^2}$ $C_2 = B$ |
| (8) $\dfrac{1}{Bs}\left[\dfrac{(1+T_1s)(1+T_2s)}{\sqrt{T_1T_2}\,s}\right]$ $T_1 \neq T_2$ | | $B = C_2$ $T_1T_2 = R_1R_2C_1C_2$ $T_1 + T_2 = R_1C_1 + R_2C_2 + R_1C_2$ | $R = \dfrac{(\sqrt{T_1} - \sqrt{T_2})^2}{B}$ $R_2 = \dfrac{\sqrt{T_1T_2}}{B}$ $C_1 = \dfrac{B\sqrt{T_1T_2}}{(\sqrt{T_1} - \sqrt{T_2})^2}$ $C_2 = B$ |

TABLE 16.4-1 (*Continued*)

Transfer Impedance Functions of R-C Input and Output Networks

| Transfer-impedance Function | Network | Relations | Inverse Relations |
|---|---|---|---|
| (9) $\dfrac{1}{Bs}\left[\dfrac{(T_1s+1)(T_2s+1)}{T_1T_2s^2}\right]$<br>$T_1 < T_2$ | | $B = \dfrac{C_1C_2}{C_1+2C_2}$<br>$T_1 = RC_1$<br>$T_2 = R(C_1+2C_2)$ | $R = \dfrac{T_1(T_2-T_1)}{2BT_2}$<br>$C_1 = \dfrac{2BT_2}{T_2-T_1}$<br>$C_2 = \dfrac{BT_2}{T_1}$ |
| (10) $A\left(\dfrac{T_1s+1}{T_1T_2s^2+1}\right)$ | $R_1C_1 = 4R_2C_2$ | $A = 2R_1$<br>$T_1 = \dfrac{R_1C_1}{2} = 2R_2C_2$<br>$T_2 = R_1C_2$ | $R_1 = \dfrac{A}{2}$<br>$R_2 = \dfrac{AT_1}{4T_2}$<br>$C_1 = \dfrac{4T_1}{A}$<br>$C_2 = \dfrac{2T_2}{A}$ |
| (11) $\dfrac{1}{Bs}$ | | $B = C$ | $C = B$ |
| (12) $\dfrac{(Ts+1)}{Bs}$ | | $B = C$<br>$T = RC$ | $R = \dfrac{T}{B}$<br>$C = B$ |

TABLE 16.4-1 (Continued)

Transfer Impedance Functions of R-C Input and Output Networks

| Transfer-impedance Function | Network | Relations | Inverse Relations |
|---|---|---|---|
| (13) $\dfrac{1}{Bs}\left(\dfrac{Ts+1}{Ts}\right)$ | | $B = \dfrac{C}{2}$<br>$T = 2RC$ | $R = \dfrac{T}{4B}$<br>$C = 2B$ |
| (14) $\dfrac{1}{Bs}\left(\dfrac{Ts+1}{\theta Ts+1}\right)$<br>$\theta < 1$ | | $B = C_1$<br>$T = R(C_1 + C_2)$<br>$\theta = \dfrac{C_2}{C_1 + C_2}$ | $R = \dfrac{T(1-\theta)}{B}$<br>$C_1 = B$<br>$C_2 = \dfrac{B\theta}{1-\theta}$ |
|  | | $B = C_1 + C$<br>$T = RC_2$<br>$\theta = \dfrac{C_1}{C_1 + C_2}$ | $R = \dfrac{T}{B(1-\theta)}$<br>$C_1 = B\theta$<br>$C_2 = B(1-\theta)$ |
| (15) $\dfrac{1}{Bs}\left[\dfrac{(T_1s+1)(T_3s+1)}{T_2s+1}\right]$<br>$T_1 < T_2 < T_3$ | | $B = C_1 + C_2$<br>$T_1 = R_1C_1$<br>$T_2 = (R_1 + R_2)\left(\dfrac{C_1C_2}{C_1 + C_2}\right)$<br>$T_3 = R_2C_2$ | $R_1 = \dfrac{T_1(T_3 - T_1)}{B(T_2 - T_1)}$<br>$R_2 = \dfrac{T_3(T_3 - T_1)}{B(T_3 - T_2)}$<br>$C_1 = \dfrac{T_2 - T_1}{T_3 - T_1}$<br>$C_2 = \dfrac{B(T_3 - T_2)}{T_3 - T_1}$ |

## TABLE 16.4-1 (Continued)

### TRANSFER IMPEDANCE FUNCTIONS OF R-C INPUT AND OUTPUT NETWORK

| Transfer-impedance Function | Network | Relations | Inverse Relations |
|---|---|---|---|
| (16) $A\left(\dfrac{T_1 s + 1}{T_1 T_2 s^2 + T_1 s + 1}\right)$ | | $A = R_2$<br>$T_1 = 2R_1 C$<br>$T_2 = \dfrac{R_2 C}{2}$ | $R_1 = \dfrac{A T_1}{4 T_2}$<br>$R_2 = A$<br>$C = \dfrac{2 T_2}{A}$ |
| (17) $A\left(\dfrac{T_2 s + 1}{T_1 T_2 s^2 + T_1 s + 1}\right)$ | | $A = 2R$<br>$T_1 = 2R C_2$<br>$T_2 = \dfrac{R C_1}{2}$ | $R = \dfrac{A}{2}$<br>$C_1 = \dfrac{4 T_2}{A}$<br>$C_2 = \dfrac{T_1}{A}$ |
| (18) $A\left[\dfrac{T_3 s + 1}{T_1 T_2 s^2 + T_1 s + 1}\right]$<br>$T_2 > \dfrac{T_1}{4}$ (complex roots)<br>$T_3 > T_2$ | | $A = \dfrac{2 R_1 R_2}{(2 R_1 + R_2)}$<br>$T_1 = \dfrac{R_1(R_1 C_1 + 2 R_2 C_2)}{2 R_1 + R_2}$<br>$T_2 = \dfrac{R_1 R_2 C_1 C_2}{R_1 C_1 + 2 R_2 C_2}$<br>$T_3 = \dfrac{R_1 C_1}{2}$ | $R_1 = \dfrac{A T_3^2}{2[T_3^2 - T_1(T_3 - T_2)]}$<br>$R_2 = \dfrac{A T_3^2}{T_1(T_3 - T_2)}$<br>$C_1 = \dfrac{4[T_3^2 - T_1(T_3 - T_2)]}{A T_3}$<br>$C_2 = \dfrac{T_1 T_2}{A T_3}$ |

**TABLE 16.4–1 (Continued)**

TRANSFER IMPEDANCE FUNCTIONS OF R-C INPUT AND OUTPUT NETWORKS

| Transfer-impedance Function | Network | Relations | Inverse Relations |
|---|---|---|---|
| (18) $A\left[\dfrac{T_3 s + 1}{T_1 T_2 s^2 + T_1 s + 1}\right]$ <br> $T_2 > \dfrac{T_1}{4}$ (complex roots) <br> $T_3 > T_2$ | | $A = 2R_1$ <br> $T_1 = R_2 C_1 + 2R_1 C_2$ <br> $T_2 = \dfrac{R_1(R_1 + 2R_2)C_1 C_2}{R_2 C_1 + 2R_1 C_2}$ <br> $T_3 = \left(R_2 + \dfrac{R_1}{2}\right)C_1$ | $R_1 = \dfrac{A}{2}$ <br> $R_2 = \dfrac{AT_1(T_3 - T_2)}{4[T_3^2 - T_1(T_3 - T_2)]}$ <br> $C_1 = \dfrac{4[T_3^2 - T_1(T_3 - T_2)]}{AT_3}$ <br> $C_2 = \dfrac{T_1 T_2}{AT_3}$ |
| | | $A = 2R$ <br> $T_1 = R(C_2 + 2C_3)$ <br> $T_2 = \dfrac{RC_3(C_1 + C_2)}{C_2 + 2C_3}$ <br> $T_3 = \dfrac{R}{2}(C_1 + C_2)$ | $R = \dfrac{A}{2}$ <br> $C_1 = \dfrac{2[2T_3^2 - T_1(T_3 - T_2)]}{AT_3}$ <br> $C_2 = \dfrac{2T_1(T_3 - T_2)}{AT_3}$ <br> $C_3 = \dfrac{T_1 T_2}{AT_3}$ |
| (19) $A\left[\dfrac{T_3 s + 1}{T_1 T_2 s^2 + T_1 s + 1}\right]$ <br> $T_2 > \dfrac{T_1}{4}$ (complex roots) <br> $T_3 < T_1$ | | $A = R_2$ <br> $T_1 = 2R_1 C_1 + R_2 C_2$ <br> $T_2 = \dfrac{R_1 R_2 C_1(C_1 + 2C_2)}{2R_1 C_1 + R_2 C_2}$ <br> $T_3 = 2R_1 C_1$ | $R_1 = \dfrac{AT_3^2}{4[T_1 T_2 - T_3(T_1 - T_3)]}$ <br> $R_2 = A$ <br> $C_1 = \dfrac{2[T_1 T_2 - T_3(T_1 - T_3)]}{AT_3}$ <br> $C_2 = \dfrac{(T_1 - T_3)}{A}$ |

TABLE 16.4-1 (Continued)

TRANSFER IMPEDANCE FUNCTIONS OF R-C INPUT AND OUTPUT NETWORKS

| Transfer-impedance Function | Network | Relations | Inverse Relations |
|---|---|---|---|
| (19) $A\left[\dfrac{T_3 s + 1}{T_1 T_2 s^2 + T_1 s + 1}\right]$ <br><br> $T_2 > \dfrac{T_1}{4}$ (complex roots) <br><br> $T_3 < T_1$ | | $A = R_2$ <br><br> $T_1 = \dfrac{C_1(2R_1C_2 + R_2C_1)}{2C_1 + C_2}$ <br><br> $T_2 = \dfrac{R_1R_2C_1C_2}{2R_1C_2 + R_2C_1}$ <br><br> $T_3 = \dfrac{2R_1C_1C_2}{(2C_1 + C_2)}$ | $R_1 = \dfrac{AT_3^2}{4[T_1T_2 - T_3(T_1 - T_3)]}$ <br><br> $R_2 = A$ <br><br> $C_1 = \dfrac{2T_1T_2}{AT_3}$ <br><br> $C_2 = \dfrac{4T_1T_2[T_1T_2 - T_3(T_1 - T_3)]}{AT_3^2(T_1 - T_3)}$ |
|  | | $A = R_3$ <br><br> $T_1 = \dfrac{R_1(2R_2 + R_3)C}{R_1 + R_2}$ <br><br> $T_2 = \dfrac{R_2R_3C}{(2R_2 + R_3)}$ <br><br> $T_3 = \dfrac{2R_1R_2C}{(R_1 + R_2)}$ | $R_1 = \dfrac{AT_3^2}{2[2T_1T_2 - T_3(T_1 - T_3)]}$ <br><br> $R_2 = \dfrac{AT_3}{2(T_1 - T_3)}$ <br><br> $R_3 = A$ <br><br> $C = \dfrac{2T_1T_2}{AT_3}$ |
| (20) $A(T_1 s + 1)(T_2 s + 1)$ <br><br> $T_1 < T_2$ | | $A = 2R_1 + R_2$ <br><br> $T_1 = \left(\dfrac{R_1R_2}{2R_1 + R_2}\right)C$ <br><br> $T_2 = R_1 C$ | $R_1 = A\left(\dfrac{T_2 - T_1}{2T_2}\right)$ <br><br> $R_2 = A\dfrac{T_1}{T_2}$ <br><br> $C = \dfrac{2T_2^2}{A(T_2 - T_1)}$ |

TABLE 16.4-1 (Continued)

TRANSFER IMPEDANCE FUNCTIONS OF R-C INPUT AND OUTPUT NETWORKS

| Transfer-impedance function | Network | Relations | Inverse relations |
|---|---|---|---|
| (21) $\dfrac{1}{Bs}\left(\dfrac{\theta Ts + 1}{Ts + 1}\right)$  $\theta < 1$ | | $B = C_2$ $T = RC_1\left(\dfrac{2C_2 + C_1}{C_2}\right)$ $\theta = \dfrac{2C_2}{2C_2 + C_1}$ | $R = \dfrac{T\theta^2}{4B(1 - \theta)}$ $C_1 = \dfrac{2B(1 - \theta)}{\theta}$ $C_2 = B$ |
| | | $B = \dfrac{C_1^2}{2C_1 + C_2}$ $T = RC_2$ $\theta = \dfrac{2C_1}{2C_1 + C_2}$ | $R = \dfrac{T\theta^2}{4B(1 - \theta)}$ $C_1 = \dfrac{2B}{\theta}$ $C_2 = \dfrac{4B(1 - \theta)}{\theta^2}$ |
| | | $B = \left(\dfrac{R_1}{R_1 + R_2}\right)C$ $T = R_2C$ $\theta = \dfrac{2R_1}{R_1 + R_2}$ | $R_1 = \dfrac{T\theta^2}{2B(2 - \theta)}$ $R_2 = \dfrac{T\theta}{2B}$ $C = \dfrac{2B}{\theta}$ |

## TABLE 16.4-1 (Continued)

### TRANSFER IMPEDANCE FUNCTIONS OF R-C INPUT AND OUTPUT NETWORKS

| Transfer-impedance function | Network | Relations | Inverse relations |
|---|---|---|---|
| (22) $A\left[\dfrac{T_2 s + 1}{(T_1 s + 1)(T_3 s + 1)}\right]$ <br> $T_1 < T_2 < T_3$ | | $A = R_1 + R_2$ <br><br> $T_1 = R_1 C_1$ <br><br> $T_2 = \left(\dfrac{R_1 R_2}{R_1 + R_2}\right)(C_1 + C_2)$ <br><br> $T_3 = R_2 C_2$ | $R_1 = \dfrac{A(T_2 - T_1)}{T_3 - T_1}$ <br><br> $R_2 = \dfrac{A(T_3 - T_2)}{T_3 - T_1}$ <br><br> $C_1 = \dfrac{T_1(T_3 - T_1)}{A(T_2 - T_1)}$ <br><br> $C_2 = \dfrac{T_3(T_3 - T_1)}{A(T_3 - T_2)}$ |
| | | $A = R_2$ <br><br> $T_2 = R_1 C_1$ <br><br> $T_1 T_3 = R_1 R_2 C_1 C_2$ <br><br> $T_1 + T_3 = R_1 C_1 + R_2 C_2 + R_2 C_1$ | $R_1 = \dfrac{A T_2^2}{(T_3 - T_2)(T_2 - T_1)}$ <br><br> $R_2 = A$ <br><br> $C_1 = \dfrac{(T_3 - T_2)(T_2 - T_1)}{A T_2}$ <br><br> $C_2 = \dfrac{T_1 T_3}{A T_2}$ |
| | | $A = R_1 + R_2$ <br><br> $T_2 = \left(\dfrac{R_1 R_2}{R_1 + R_2}\right) C_2$ <br><br> $T_1 T_3 = R_1 R_2 C_1 C_2$ <br><br> $T_1 + T_3 = R_1 C_1 + R_2 C_2 + R_2 C_1$ | $R_1 = \dfrac{A T_2^2}{T_1 T_2 + T_2 T_3 - T_1 T_3}$ <br><br> $R_2 = \dfrac{A(T_3 - T_2)(T_2 - T_1)}{T_1 T_2 + T_2 T_3 - T_1 T_3}$ <br><br> $C_1 = \dfrac{T_1 T_3}{A T_2}$ <br><br> $C_2 = \dfrac{(T_1 T_2 + T_2 T_3 - T_1 T_3)^2}{A T_2(T_3 - T_2)(T_2 - T_1)}$ |

TABLE 16.4-1 (*Continued*)

TRANSFER IMPEDANCE FUNCTIONS OF R-C INPUT AND OUTPUT NETWORKS

| Transfer-impedance function | Network | Relations | Inverse relations |
|---|---|---|---|
| (22) $A\left[\dfrac{T_2s+1}{(T_1s+1)(T_3s+1)}\right]$ <br> $T_1 < T_2 < T_3$ | | $A = R_1$ <br><br> $T_2 = R_2(C_1 + C_2)$ <br><br> $T_1T_3 = R_1R_2C_1C_2$ <br><br> $T_1 + T_3 = R_1C_1 + R_2C_2 + R_2C_1$ | $R_1 = A$ <br><br> $R_2 = \dfrac{A(T_3 - T_2)(T_2 - T_1)}{(T_1 + T_3 - T_2)^2}$ <br><br> $C_1 = \dfrac{T_1 + T_3 - T_2}{A}$ <br><br> $C_2 = \dfrac{T_1T_3(T_1 + T_3 - T_2)}{A(T_3 - T_2)(T_2 - T_1)}$ |
| (23) $A\left[\dfrac{T_2s+1}{(T_1s+1)(T_3s+1)}\right]$ <br> $T_2 \le T_1 \le T_3$ | | $A = 2R_1 + \dfrac{R_1^2}{R_2}$ <br><br> $T_1 = R_1C_1$ <br><br> $T_2 = \left(\dfrac{R_1R_2}{R_1 + 2R_2}\right)(C_1 + C_2)$ <br><br> $T_3 = R_1C_2$ | $R_1 = \dfrac{AT_2}{(T_1 + T_3)}$ <br><br> $R_2 = \dfrac{AT_2^2}{(T_1 + T_3)(T_1 + T_3 - 2T_2)}$ <br><br> $C_1 = \dfrac{T_1(T_1 + T_3)}{AT_2}$ <br><br> $C_2 = \dfrac{T_3(T_1 + T_3)}{AT_2}$ |
| (24) $A\left[\dfrac{T_2s+1}{(T_1s+1)(T_3s+1)}\right]$ <br> $T_1 \le T_3 \le T_2$ | | $A = R_1 + R_2$ <br><br> $T_1 = R_1C_1$ <br><br> $T_2 = \dfrac{R_1R_2}{R_1 + R_2}(2C_1 + C_2)$ <br><br> $T_3 = R_2C_1$ | $R_1 = \dfrac{AT_1}{(T_1 + T_3)}$ <br><br> $R_2 = \dfrac{AT_3}{(T_1 + T_3)}$ <br><br> $C_1 = \dfrac{(T_1 + T_3)}{A}$ <br><br> $C_2 = \dfrac{(T_1 + T_3)}{A}\left(\dfrac{T_2}{T_3} + \dfrac{T_2}{T_1} - 2\right)$ |

Reprinted, by permission, from the April 1952 issue of *Electronics*, a McGraw-Hill Publication, copyright 1952. This table was developed by S. Godet of the Reeves Instrument Corporation, New York City.

An alternate possible setup that requires only one amplifier to simulate both the amplidyne and motor is shown in Figure 16.4–8.

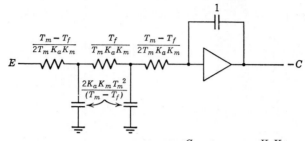

FIGURE 16.4–8.   Alternate simulation of $\dfrac{C}{E}(s) = \dfrac{K_a K_m}{s(T_f s + 1)(T_m s + 1)}$.

This setup requires a maximum of calculations and introduces a polarity reversal.

*Example 2*

Consider the system shown in Figure 16.3–1 where

$$G_1(s) = \frac{K_1}{s(T_m s + 1)(T_f s + 1)} \qquad (16.4\text{–}38)$$

$$H(s) = \frac{K_h s^2}{(T s + 1)} \qquad (16.4\text{–}39)$$

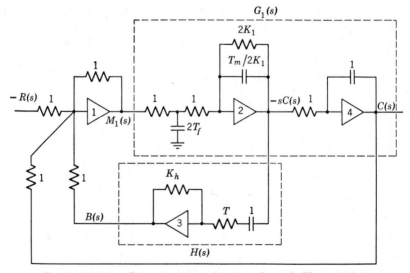

FIGURE 16.4–9.   Computer setup of system shown in Figure 16.3–1.

It is possible to simulate this entire system with one amplifier, but because of the complexity of the circuitry this approach will not be used here. Instead the approach will be used which more nearly preserves correspondence between computer amplifiers and system hardware. This system setup is shown in Figure 16.4–9.

This setup should be compared with that of Figure 16.3–3. Note the saving in computer amplifiers and the loss of component internal variables as the output of amplifiers. Both methods allow blocking out of system components.

**Circuitry Selection to Minimize Effect of Noise.** When selecting networks to generate a given transfer function, it is wise to avoid use of networks like 2 and 11 from Table 16.4–1 as input impedances to an amplifier because of noise transmission as is described below. Figure 16.4–10

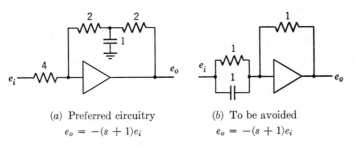

(a) Preferred circuitry
$e_o = -(s + 1)e_i$

(b) To be avoided
$e_o = -(s + 1)e_i$

FIGURE 16.4–10.    Preferred and non-recommended choices for simulation of a simple lead.

shows two ways to generate a simple lead transfer function. The (a) circuit is preferred, and the (b) circuit should be avoided.

These same networks which are to be avoided as input impedances can be used as feedback impedances without harmful effects. The circuits shown in Figure 16.4–11 are both recommended.

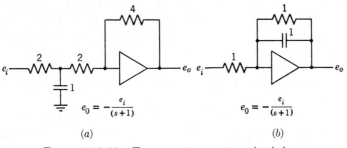

$$e_0 = -\frac{e_i}{(s+1)}$$

(a)

$$e_0 = -\frac{e_i}{(s+1)}$$

(b)

FIGURE 16.4–11.    Two ways to generate a simple lag.

The reason for this circuitry selection can be explained by reference to the noise generator and computer circuit of Figure 16.4–12.

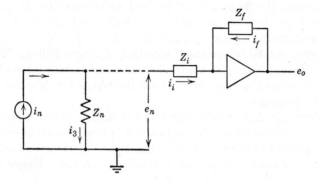

FIGURE 16.4–12.   Noise equivalent circuit in a computer setup.

The noise generator, which can come about by inductive, capacitive and conductive coupling to leads throughout the computer, can be considered a standard current source, $i_n$, with shunt internal impedance, $Z_n$. The noise generator output voltage, $e_n$, appears at the input to the operational amplifier. $i_i$ is the amplifier input current due to $i_n$ and is equal to

$$i_i = \frac{Z_n}{Z_n + Z_i} i_n \qquad (16.4\text{–}40)$$

This current must be balanced by $i_f$; therefore

$$i_f = -i_i \qquad (16.4\text{–}41)$$

$$\frac{e_o}{Z_f} = -\frac{Z_n i_n}{Z_n + Z_i} \qquad (16.4\text{–}42)$$

$$e_o = -\frac{Z_f Z_n}{Z_n + Z_i} i_n \qquad (16.4\text{–}43)$$

Since it is desirable to keep low the $e_o$ due to noise, inspection of Equation 16.4–43 shows that it is desirable to keep $Z_i$ as high as possible. Since a resistor's value is independent of frequency and that of a capacitor reduces with increasing frequency, and since noise is of higher frequencies, it is apparent that the ($a$) circuit is preferred over the ($b$) circuit in Figure 16.4–10. *It is important to note that it is always desirable to have some series resistive impedance as part of $Z_i$.*

It is not necessary to have some series resistive impedance as part of $Z_f$ as shown in Figure 16.4–11($b$) because the negative feedback causes a cancellation of the noise effects.

High noise levels are undesirable because

(1) Noise obscures the signal that is to be observed.

(2) Amplifiers saturate and upon saturation produce undesirable effects.

In some instances the operation of differentiation is unavoidable. Rather than using the circuit of Figure 16.4–13 the circuit of Figure

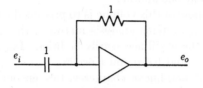

FIGURE 16.4–13.  Differentiation circuit.  $e_o = se_i$.

16.4–14($b$) is recommended.  The block diagram in Figure 16.4–14($a$) shows the functional operations performed.

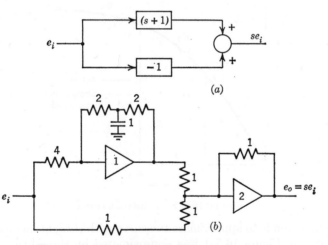

FIGURE 16.4–14.  Preferred differentiation circuit.

## 16.5   Simulation of Non-linearities

Linear systems analysis techniques have been developed to the point where usage of analog computers affects only a saving in time and labor in obtaining linear system time responses.  In the area of non-linear systems analysis where analytical techniques are limited, the computer really comes into its own.

*Computer simulation of non-linear equations is almost as simple as simulation of linear ones.*  This fact leads some to question the wisdom of expending the tremendous effort applied to the paper analysis of non-linear systems. Despite the many and varied advantages of computers, *they do not replace engineering judgment*. Engineering judgment depends heavily on experience and analytical techniques. The computer is merely an engineering tool. Paper analysis techniques are engineering tools. The wise engineer should have enough tools available so that he can use those which best fit a given situation. Computers and paper analyses complement one another.

Because the purpose of this volume is to present the fundamentals and application of linear systems analysis methods, the non-linear systems simulation covered here will necessarily be brief. For further details see books by Johnson [126] and Korn and Korn.[127]

The majority of non-linear characteristics encountered in practice exhibit magnitude dependency. To simulate this broad class of non-linearities, unilateral elements such as the biased electronic diode are used.

**Saturation.** Consider the saturation curve shown in Figure 16.5–1.

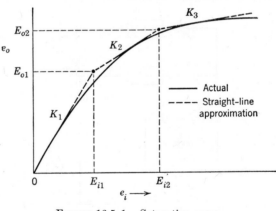

FIGURE 16.5–1.    Saturation curve.

The first step is to approximate the curve with straight line segments. The curve in Figure 16.5–1 was approximated by three line segments having slopes or gains of $K_1$, $K_2$, and $K_3$. A computer setup that will generate the approximate curve is shown in Figure 16.5–2.

Amplifier 1 is used merely as a sign changer so that $+e_i$ produces $+e_o$. As long as $e_o$ is less than $E_{o1}$, the biased diodes (1) and (2) are non-conducting. The amplification is in the linear range and is equal to $K_1$. When $e_o$ is greater than $E_{o1}$ but less than $E_{o2}$, diode (1) conducts which places $R_2$ in parallel with $R_1$. The combination produces a gain of $K_2$. When $e_o$ exceeds $E_{o2}$, both diodes conduct, $R_1$, $R_2$, and $R_3$ are in parallel, and the combination produces the gain $K_3$.

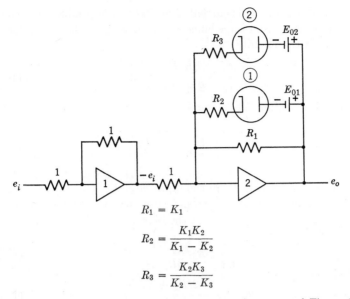

FIGURE 16.5–2.  Computer setup to generate saturation curve of Figure 16.5–1.

The same saturation curve can be generated by the computer setup of Figure 16.5–3.

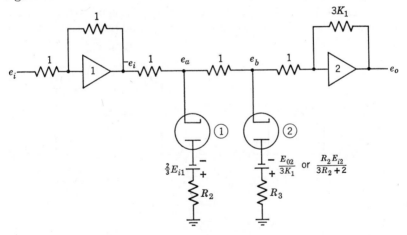

FIGURE 16.5–3.  Alternate setup to generate saturation curve of Figure 16.5–1.

Until the voltage $e_i$ exceeds $E_{i1}$, both biased diodes are non-conducting and the gain of the amplifier is $3K_i$ divided by 3 which equals $K_1$. When $e_i$ exceeds $E_{i1}$ but is less than $E_{i2}$, $e_a$ exceeds $\frac{2}{3}E_{i1}$, diode (1) conducts and places $R_2$ in the input circuit.  This shunt resistance diverts current away from the grid. This current shunting action produces an effective increased input transfer impedance which thereby produces a lower gain. With $R_2$ in the circuit

$$\frac{e_o}{e_i} = \frac{3K_1 R_2}{2 + 3R_2} = K_2 \qquad (16.5\text{-}1)$$

From this equation $R_2$ becomes

$$R_2 = \frac{2K_2}{3(K_1 - K_2)} \qquad (16.5\text{-}2)$$

In a similar fashion, when $e_i$ exceeds $E_{i2}$, $e_b$ exceeds $E_{o2}/3K_1$ and diode 2 conducts placing $R_3$ in the input circuit. This further increases the input transfer impedance to decrease the gain to $K_3$. A detailed analysis of the circuit reveals that the bias on diode number 2 is

$$\frac{E_{o2}}{3K_1} \quad \text{or} \quad \frac{R_2}{3R_2 + 2} E_{i2} \qquad (16.5\text{-}3)$$

and that

$$R_3 = \frac{2(R_2 + 1)K_3}{6K_1 - (3K_2 + 2)K_3} \qquad (16.5\text{-}4)$$

*Series and Shunt Method of Diode Connection.* There are basically two ways to connect biased diodes in a circuit. The first is the series method used in Figure 16.5-2. When a series diode conducts, additional current *goes into* the input node of the amplifier and produces an effective

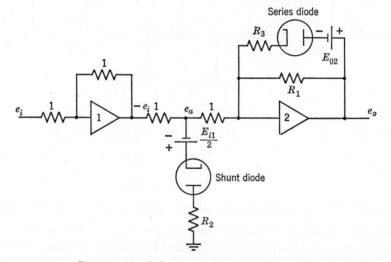

FIGURE 16.5-4. Combination of shunt and series diodes to produce the saturation curve of Figure 16.5-1.

*decrease* in transfer impedance. The second way to connect a diode is the shunt method used in Figure 16.5–3. When a shunt diode conducts, current is *diverted away* from the amplifier input node and produces an effective *increase* in transfer impedance. Figures 16.5–2 and 16.5–3 show that to produce a decreasing gain characteristic, series diodes can be used in the feedback path and shunt diodes can be used in the input path. A combination of both methods shown in Figure 16.5–4 can be used and usually results in easier calculations for the bias voltages and shunt resistors.

If it were desirable to generate an increasing gain characteristic, a combination of series diodes in the input circuit and shunt diodes in the feedback circuit could be used. This is illustrated in Figure 16.5–5.

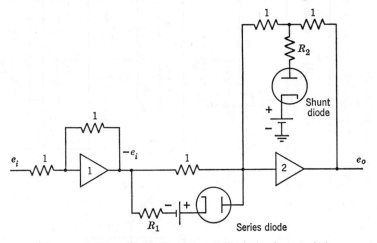

FIGURE 16.5–5.  Generation of increasing gain characteristic.

To avoid use of batteries, voltage divider networks may be employed as shown in Figure 16.5–6.

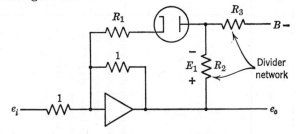

FIGURE 16.5–6.  Divider network to obtain bias voltages.

When the diode conducts, $R_2$ is in series with $R_1$. Because $R_1$ is in the order of megohms and $R_2$ and $R_3$ are in the order of kilohms, $R_2$ can

TABLE 16.5-1

NON-LINEAR CIRCUITS FOR SPECIAL APPLICATIONS [127]

All formulae are derived for negligible source impedance and infinite amplifier gain.

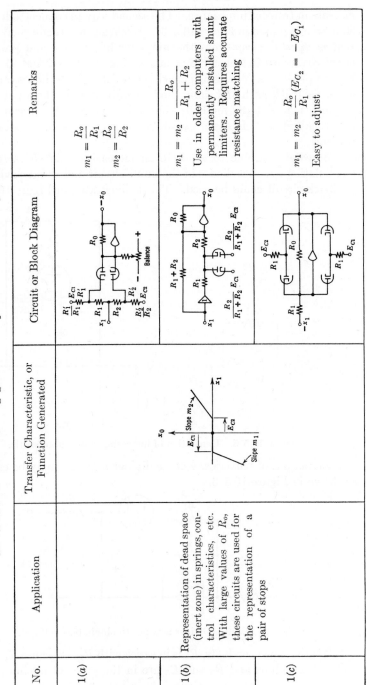

| No. | Application | Transfer Characteristic, or Function Generated | Circuit or Block Diagram | Remarks |
|---|---|---|---|---|
| 1(a) | Representation of dead space (inert zone) in springs, control characteristics, etc. With large values of $R_o$, these circuits are used for the representation of a pair of stops | | | $m_1 = \dfrac{R_o}{R_1}$ $m_2 = \dfrac{R_o}{R_2}$ |
| 1(b) | | | | $m_1 = m_2 = \dfrac{R_o}{R_1 + R_2}$ Use in older computers with permanently installed shunt limiters. Requires accurate resistance matching |
| 1(c) | | | | $m_1 = m_2 = \dfrac{R_o}{R_1} \ (E_{C_2} = -E_{C_1})$ Easy to adjust |

| No. | Application | Transfer Characteristic, or Function Generated | Circuit or Block Diagram | Remarks |
|---|---|---|---|---|
| 2 | Approximate representation of backlash in gears, linkages, process-control error detectors, etc. (assuming inelastic stops); see 9 below | (Output displacement), $x_1$, Slope $\approx b$, $B$ | $E$, $ar$, $r$, $R$, $C$, $x$, $-x$, $x_1$, $-E$ | $B \approx \dfrac{2aE}{b(1-a)}\,(ar+R)C \ll 1$ <br> Typical values: <br> $r = R = 50K$ <br> $C = 1\,\mu f$ <br> $b = 1$ <br> $E = 200\,v$ |
| 3 | Approximate representation of granularity (e.g., potentiometer granularity) [1,2] | $x$ | $R_1 = 0.1M$, $200\,M$, $C_1 = 0.001\,\mu F$, $C_0 = 1\,\mu F$, $1K$, $1K$, Ne51, $R_3 = 0.1M$, $R_2 = 0.25M$, $R_0 = 6.5M$, $1M$, $x$, $V$ | Average slope $= \dfrac{R_2}{R_0 R_1}$ <br> Step height $\approx \dfrac{R_2}{20}$ <br> $R_3 C_0$ controls the step rise time and thus the permissible stepping rate. For a more accurate representation, a pair of thyratrons or diodes may replace the neon bulb [2] |
| 4 | Approximate representation of starting friction and coulomb friction | $F_F$, $F_0$, $-PX$, $F_0$ | $0.02\,M$, $40\,M$, $0.5\,M$, $0.5\,M$, $0.5\,M$, $1\,M$, $R_1 = 1\,M$, $F_F$, Ne51, $-PX$ | $F_o \approx 130 R_o$ volts |
| 5 | Precision absolute-value device (linear full-wave rectifier) [3] | $x_0$, $x_0 = |x_1|$, $x_1$ | $x_0$, $0.5\,M$, $0.5\,M$, $0.5\,M$, $50\,K$, $300\,K$, $-300\,v$, $x_1$ | Obtain $-|x_1|$ by reversing diodes and bias voltage |

**TABLE 16.5–1** (*Continued*)

NON-LINEAR CIRCUITS FOR SPECIAL APPLICATIONS

All formulae are derived for negligible source impedance and infinite amplifier gain.

| No. | Application | Transfer Characteristic, or Function Generated | Circuit or Block Diagram | Remarks |
|---|---|---|---|---|
| 6 | Comparator circuit [3] (also used to represent coulomb friction) | | | Useful in many switching applications<br>Drives relays<br>A small feedback capacitor may be required for stability |
| 7 | Bistable multivibrator [3] | | | |
| 8 | Free-running multivibrator [3] | | | $$T_1 = \frac{1}{ab}\left(1 + \frac{E_{C_1}}{E_{C_2}}\right)$$ $$T_2 = \frac{1}{ab}\left(1 + \frac{E_{C_2}}{E_{C_1}}\right)$$ |

[1] GEDA Simulation Study of a Carrier-type Instrument Servomechanism, *Report GER-5779*, Goodyear Aircraft Corporation, Akron, Ohio, April 21, 1954.

[2] Meneley, C. A., and C. D. Morrill, Application of Electronic Differential Analyzers to Engineering Problems, *Proc. IRE*, **41**: 1487, 1953.

[3] Morrill, C. D., and R. V. Baum, Diode Limiters Simulate Mechanical Phenomena, *Electronics*, **25**: 122, November, 1952.

| No. | Application | Transfer Characteristic, or Function Generated | Circuit or Block Diagram | Remarks |
|---|---|---|---|---|
| 9 | Simple approximate representation of backlash; see 2 | (Output displacement) $x$, $x_1$, Slope $\approx b$, $B$ | $R_1$, $R_2$, $C_1$, $x_1$, $x_0$, $E_1$ $E_1$, Zener diodes | $B \approx 2E_1$ <br> $b = \dfrac{R_2}{R_1}$ |
| 10 | Electronic switch | $x_1$ — $x_0$, $x_c$ | Comparator, $x_c$, Germanium diodes, $R_4$, $R_6$, $R_5$, $R_1$, $R_1$, $R_2$, $R_3$, $x_1$, $x_0$ | Polarity of $X_c$ actuates the switch <br> Typical values: comparator output $= \pm25V$ <br> $R_1 = R_4 = 0.5$ Meg. <br> $R_2 = R_6 = 2$ Meg. <br> $R_3 = R_5 = 1$ Meg. |
| 11 | Square loop hysteresis | $x_0$, $E_1$, $E_2$, $x_1$, $E_1$, $-E_2$, $-E_1$ | $-x_1$, Comparator $+E_1$/$-E_1$, $R_1$, $1$, $x_0$ | $R_1 = \dfrac{E_2}{E_1}$ |
| 12 | Variable time constant with constant gain | $G(s) = \dfrac{K_1}{Ts+1} = \dfrac{R_2/R_1}{C\left[R_2 + \dfrac{R_3}{R_1}(R_1+R_2)\right]s+1}$ | $R_1$, $R_2$, $R_2$, $C_1$, $x_1$, $x_0$ | For $R_1 = R_2$ <br> $G(s) = \dfrac{1}{C(R_1 + 2R_3)s + 1}$ |

normally be neglected. In the cases where it is not negligible, $R_1$ can be decreased to offset its effect.

A recent addition to the computer components family is the Zener diode.[137] This diode has characteristics similar to normal diodes except that at a set voltage in the reverse direction, the diode breaks down and conducts. Upon decrease of the reverse excitation, the diode ceases to conduct. In the reverse direction, a Zener diode behaves as a normal diode with a built-in battery. Zener diodes with different breakdown voltage are available.

Figure 16.5–7 shows a saturation curve setup using Zener diodes.

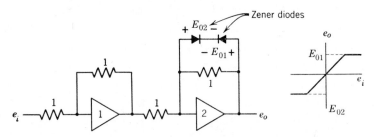

FIGURE 16.5–7.    Saturation curve generation using zener diodes.

These diodes are used back-to-back because if only one were used it would conduct in the forward direction. Letting $E_{o2}$ go to zero shows the effect of only one Zener diode in the feedback path.

**Multiplication.** A second commonly encountered non-linear behavior is that of multiplication. A fairly straightforward electromechanical method of multiplication is that shown in Figure 16.5–8.

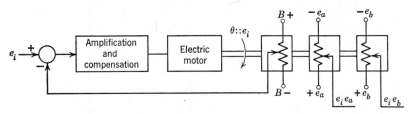

FIGURE 16.5–8.    Electromechanical multiplier.

The motor position is determined by $e_i$. All potentiometer shafts follow the motor position. The first potentiometer is used for feedback and has a constant voltage applied across it. The second potentiometer has a variable voltage, $e_a$, applied across it and the voltage at the arm is proportional to the product of arm rotation and voltage excitation. This produces the desired product $e_i e_a$. Additional potentiometers can be used for other products involving $e_i$.

For high speed operation, several types of electronic multipliers are available.   For details of electronic multiplier circuitry, see Korn and Korn.[127]

Table 16.5–1 represents some non-linear circuits for special computer applications.   No effort is made to describe the details of circuit performance.

## 16.6   Scale Factors, Time Scaling, Initial Conditions and Checking the Computer Setup

The variable in an electronic analog computer is voltage.   The ways in which this voltage varies in time depict the dynamic behavior of the several variables in the system under study.   The magnitudes of these computer voltages are related to the magnitudes of the variables in the system.

**Scale Factors.**[136]   *Scale factors are merely the proportionality ratios between computer voltages and system variables.*   For example, if the voltage output of an amplifier represents a force in pounds, then each volt must represent a certain number of pounds.   If the scale factor is $\frac{1}{50}$ volt per pound, then an amplifier output of 10 volts represents a force of 500 pounds.

To avoid the necessity of describing each scale factor of each amplifier in terms of the dimensions of the particular variable being represented, an additional term is introduced—units.   A unit is a certain amount of a given variable and is so chosen as to reduce or amplify the quantities so that reasonable numbers for scale factors can be used.   For example, suppose an equation was given as

$$R = KF \qquad (16.6\text{–}1)$$

where $K = \frac{1}{5}$ lb/ft
$\quad R = $ range in ft
$\quad F = $ force in lb

$$R = \tfrac{1}{5}F \qquad (16.6\text{–}2)$$

If in the system under study the force is in the order of 50,000 pounds, the range will be in the order of 10,000 feet.   The unit legend may therefore be arbitrarily taken as:

| | |
|---|---|
| 1 unit of length = 1000 ft | Range = 10 units |
| 1 unit of force  = 5000 lb | Force = 10 units |

This choice of units necessitates a change in the constant of the equation:

$$K' = \frac{R}{F} = \frac{10 \text{ units of range}}{10 \text{ units of force}} = 1 \text{ unit/unit} \qquad (16.6\text{–}3)$$

Therefore, the modified equation is:

$$R = F \qquad (16.6\text{-}4)$$

where $R$ = range in units of 1000 ft
$F$ = force in units of 5000 lb

Note that if the unit of force had been chosen as 1000 pounds, the constant $K$ would have remained unchanged.

In this fashion, the physical dimensions are set up in terms of units of that particular dimension. The constants in the equation are modified if necessary. The scale factors then relate computer volts to units of the physical dimensions. The unit concept is introduced to remove the necessity of carrying dimensions such as pounds, feet, radians, etc., around on a computer diagram.

In using a computer, it is desirable to utilize the full range of the amplifiers to minimize the effect of extraneous signals such as noise and amplifier drift. It is also desirable to stay in the linear range of the amplifiers because when unintentional saturation is introduced, the simulation is in error. The probability of using the amplifiers properly is directly proportional to how well the engineer can guess the maximum values of the variables. Fortunately, if the first guess is incorrect, the scale factors can be modified at the computer location to remove amplifier saturation.

Before setting up a problem, a paper analysis should be made as far as is profitable. In so doing, a feel for the results can be obtained with regard to probable maximum values of the variables and the general form of the transient response. With this information in hand, assignment of scale factors is fairly routine where the scale factor is defined as

$$\text{Scale factor} = \frac{\text{Maximum amplifier volts}}{\text{Maximum number of units}} = \text{volts/unit} = \text{v/u}$$

$$(16.6\text{-}5)$$

It is possible to invert the definition to obtain scale factors in terms of units per volt. It matters little which definition is used provided one is consistent.

*Upon use of scale factors, it will be shown that when scale factors are changed, the change effects only a shift in gain around a loop. It does not and cannot change the gain around a loop. This gain is governed only by the equations defining the physical system.*

Before citing an example, one new term will be defined: channel gain. *Channel gain is the actual gain of an amplifier (channel) after scale factors have been introduced.*  For scale factor as defined in Equation 16.6–5:

$$\text{Channel gain} = \frac{\text{output scale factor}}{\text{input scale factor}} \times \text{gain desired} \quad (16.6\text{–}6)$$

*Example 1*

Consider a computer study of the linear system shown in Figure 16.3–1.  A likely computer setup is that shown in Figure 16.4–9.  The first step is to perform the paper analysis shown in Section 10.2 or an approximate Bode diagram analysis along the lines of Section 12.2, for motor-generator time constants of

$$T_m = 0.25 \text{ second}$$
$$T_f = 0.0625 \text{ second}$$

and with

$$K_1 = 100$$
$$K_h = 0.167$$
$$T = 0.8$$

For these values, Figure 10.2–13 shows that the open-loop complex plane plot crosses the unit circle with a phase margin of $+32°$.  This indicates an underdamped system and for a unit-step input, reference to Figure 15.6–2 shows that the transient overshoot will be approximately 40 per cent.  This amount of paper analysis should be sufficient for this study.

The next step is to decide the nominal voltage levels of the input and

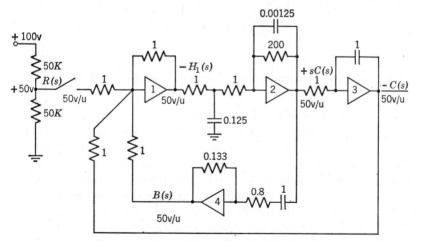

FIGURE 16.6–1.   Computer setup of Figure 16.4–9 with all scale factors at 50 volts per unit.

output.  If the computer amplifiers have linear ranges up to ±100 volts, a good nominal range to use would be 50 volts.  Assuming a unit-step input, the scale factors could be set at 50 volts per unit for $R(s)$ and $C(s)$.  If it were assumed that all amplifier scale factors would be set at 50 volts per unit, the computer setup would be shown in Figure 16.6–1.

An undesirable feature about this setup is that the feedback resistor around amplifier 2 is much too high and the associated capacitor is too low.  The high resistance produces a very high amplifier gain, whereas the low capacitance is in the range of lead stray capacitance.  By changing the output scale factor of amplifier 1, the total gain of amplifiers 1 and 2 remains the same although the individual amplifier gains are changed inversely.  A reasonable setup is shown in Figure 16.6–2.  Note that both input and feedback impedances of amplifier 2 were changed.

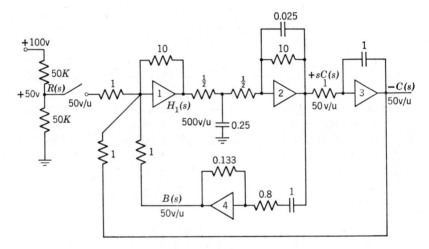

FIGURE 16.6–2.  Computer setup of Figure 16.6–1 with changed scale factors.

Upon application of a unit-step input, the output of amplifiers 1, 2, and 4 should be monitored to insure that they do not exceed ±100 volts.  If, for example, it was found that amplifier 4 was overloading, its output scale factor could be reduced by reducing the feedback resistor.  To increase the channel gain of amplifier 1 the resistor from the output of amplifier 4 to the input of amplifier 1 could be decreased by the same proportion.  The channel gains of amplifiers 4 and 1 would change inversely, whereas the total gain would remain constant.  For this reason, *changing scale factors merely shifts gain around the loop without changing total loop gain.*

*Example 2*

Non-linear system. Consider a turbine speed control system shown in Figure 16.6–3.

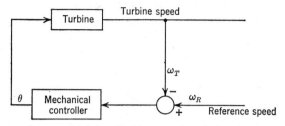

FIGURE 16.6–3. Turbine speed control system.

The turbine equations are given as:

Turbine speed    $\omega_T = \int \dot{\omega}_T \, dt$ rad/sec      (16.6–7)

Turbine acceleration

$$\dot{\omega}_T = \frac{1}{J}[T_D - T_L - B\omega_T] \text{ radian/sec}^2 \qquad (16.6-8)$$

Turbine inertia    $J = \frac{1}{40}$ lb-in.-sec$^2$      (16.6–9)

Load torque    $T_L = 50$ lb-in.      (16.6–10)

Turbine speed damping coefficient

$$B = 0.1 \text{ lb-in./rad/sec} \qquad (16.6-11)$$

Turbine developed torque

$$T_D = f(\theta) \text{ lb-in.} \qquad (16.6-12)$$

The turbine developed torque is a function of the air inlet valve position, $\theta$, and is shown in Figure 16.6–4.

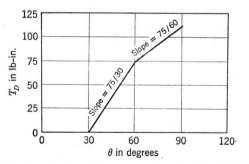

FIGURE 16.6–4. Turbine developed torque as a function of air inlet valve position.

The mechanical controller consists of a pilot piston and ram type servo valve combination whose equations are given by:

Pilot piston displacement $x = K_x(\omega_R - \omega_T)$ mils       (16.6–13)

Reference speed        $\omega_R = 3600$ rpm         (16.6–14)

Pilot piston gain      $K_x = 0.05$ mils/rad/sec      (16.6–15)

Air inlet valve position    $\theta = K_\theta \int x \, dt$ degrees      (16.6–16)

Valve angle gain      $K_\theta = 2°/\text{mil}$           (16.6–17)

The maximum air inlet valve angle = 90°.

It is desired to investigate the transient behavior of the system during startup and during subsequent application of load torque. The variations of $T_D$, $\omega_T$, $\dot{\omega}_T$, $x$, and $\theta$ are to be recorded.

The equations are drawn in block diagram form in Figure 16.6–5.

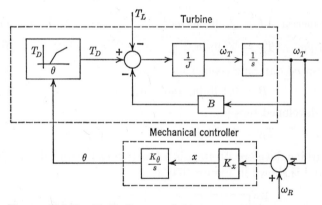

Figure 16.6–5.   Block diagram of the system of Figure 16.6–3.

Because all the variables are to be recorded, the differential equation method of setting up the computer will be used. To assign scale factors the maximum values of amplifier outputs must be determined.

From the problem statement $\omega_T$ is initially at zero and then $\omega_R$ is applied. This step input can cause an overshoot in $\omega_T$ depending on the system characteristics. The later application of $T_L$ will reduce $\omega_T$; therefore, the maximum $\omega_T$ occurs due to the step input of $\omega_R$. To estimate the peak overshoot, a Bode diagram will be drawn for the system after the non-linear torque-valve angle has been linearized.  Because the transfer function from $\omega_R$ to $\omega_T$ is of the form:

$$G(s) = \frac{K_1}{s(Ts + 1)} \qquad (16.6\text{--}18)$$

an increasing gain should cause an increasing overshoot; therefore, the torque-valve angle curve will be conservatively linearized by assuming that the maximum slope occurs everywhere.  This slope is

$$K_D = \frac{75 \text{ lb-in.}}{30°} = 2.5 \text{ lb-in.}/° \qquad (16.6\text{--}19)$$

The linearized block diagram is shown in Figure 16.6–6.

$$G(s) = K_x \frac{K_\theta}{s} K_D \frac{1/B}{(J/Bs + 1)} = \frac{2.5}{s(0.25s + 1)} \qquad (16.6\text{--}20)$$

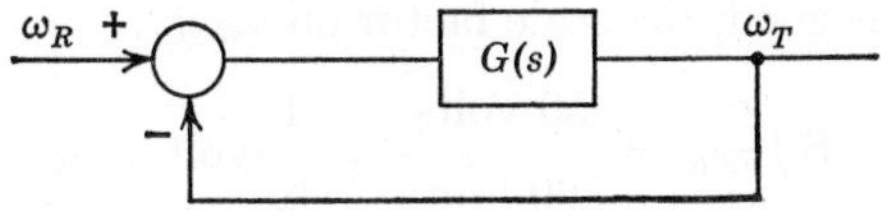

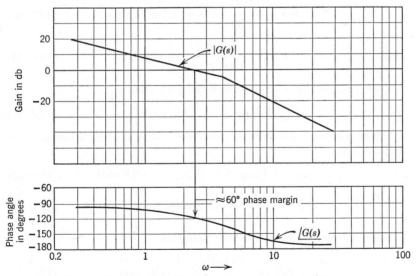

FIGURE 16.6–6.   Linearized block diagram of system of Figure 16.6–5.

The Bode diagram of this system is shown in Figure 16.6–7.

FIGURE 16.6–7.   Bode diagram of system of Figure 16.6–3.

The phase margin at gain crossover is $60°$ so the system is very stable. The overshoot will be roughly about 10 to 20 per cent. This amount of paper analysis should be sufficient.

The units must be set up prior to assignment of scale factors. Since all the dimensions are relatively small, the following legend should suffice:

1 unit of speed = 1 rad/sec
1 unit of time = 1 sec
1 unit of acceleration = 1 rad/sec$^2$
1 unit of torque = 1 lb-in.
1 unit of valve angle = $1°$
1 unit of pilot piston displacement = 1 mil

With this choice of units, the original constants in the equations need not be altered.

$\omega_R$ was given as 3600 rpm which is approximately equal to 360 radians per second which now is 360 units of speed. Since operation around 50 volts is good, the scale factor on $\omega_R$ is

$$\text{S.F.}_{\omega_R} = \frac{50 \text{ volts}}{360 \text{ units}} \approx \frac{1}{10} \text{ volt/unit} \qquad (16.6\text{--}21)$$

since it is advisable to use nice round numbers.

$$T_L = 50 \text{ lb-in.} = 50 \text{ units} \qquad (16.6\text{--}22)$$

Therefore

$$\text{S.F.}_{T_L} = \frac{50 \text{ volts}}{50 \text{ units}} = 1 \text{ volt/unit} \qquad (16.6\text{--}23)$$

Also

$$\text{S.F.}_{T_D} = \frac{50 \text{ volts}}{100 \text{ units}} = \frac{1}{2} \text{ volt/unit} \qquad (16.6\text{--}24)$$

Since $\omega_{T\max}$ will not be too much different from $\omega_R$

$$\text{S.F.}_{\omega_T} = \tfrac{1}{10} \text{ volt/unit} \qquad (16.6\text{--}25)$$

The maximum pilot valve displacement, $x$, will occur when $\omega_T = 0$. At this time

$$x_{\max} = K_x \omega_R = 0.05 \times 360 = 18 \text{ mils} \qquad (16.6\text{--}26)$$

$$\text{S.F.}_x = \frac{50 \text{ volts}}{18 \text{ units}} \approx 2 \text{ volts/unit} \qquad (16.6\text{--}27)$$

The maximum value of $\theta$ is $90°$; therefore

$$\text{S.F.}_\theta = \frac{50 \text{ volts}}{90 \text{ units}} \approx \frac{1}{2} \text{ volt/unit} \qquad (16.6\text{--}28)$$

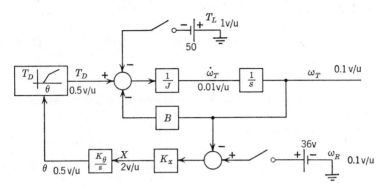

FIGURE 16.6–8.   Block diagram of system of Figure 16.6–3 with scale factors.

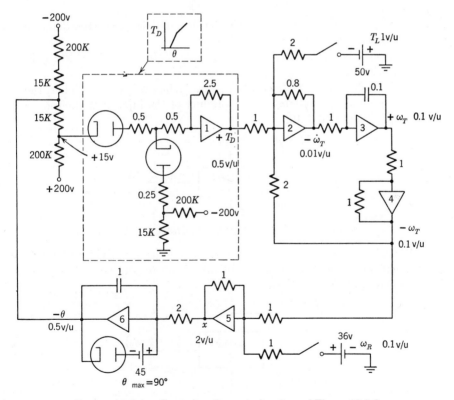

FIGURE 16.6–9.   Computer diagram of system of Figure 16.6–3.

The maximum value of $\dot{\omega}_T$ can be estimated by assuming that all the developed torque is used to accelerate the inertia.

$$\dot{\omega}_{T\max} = \frac{T_{D\max}}{J} = 40 \times 100 = 4000 \text{ units} \qquad (16.6\text{--}29)$$

$$\text{S.F.}\dot{\omega}_T = \tfrac{50}{4000} \approx 0.01 \text{ volt/unit} \qquad (16.6\text{--}30)$$

The block diagram of Figure 16.6–5 can be redrawn as shown in Figure 16.6–8.

The channel gain of the $x$ to $\theta$ amplifier is

$$\text{C.G.} = \frac{\text{S.F.}_\theta}{\text{S.F.}_x} K_\theta = \frac{\frac{1}{2}}{2} K_\theta = \frac{1}{4} K_\theta = \frac{1}{4} \times 2 = \frac{1}{2} \qquad (16.6\text{--}31)$$

The channel gain of the $\omega_R$ to $x$ amplifier (same also for $\omega_T$ to $x$) is

$$\text{C.G.} = \frac{\text{S.F.}_x}{\text{S.F.}\omega_R} K_x = \frac{2}{\frac{1}{10}} 0.05 = 1 \qquad (16.6\text{--}32)$$

After all the channel gains have been calculated, the computer diagram can be drawn as shown in Figure 16.6–9.

It should be noted that changing scale factors merely shifts gain around the loop.

*Scale Factors When Using a Multiplier.* When using a multiplier, the output scale factor is equal to the product of the input scale factors as shown in Figure 16.6–10.

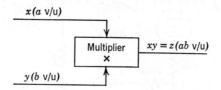

FIGURE 16.6–10. Scale factors when using a multiplier.

*Scale Factors When Using a Divider.* When using a divider, the output scale factor is equal to the quotient of the respective scale factors as shown in Figure 16.6–11.

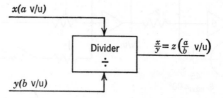

FIGURE 16.6–11. Scale factors when using a divider.

**Time Scaling.** Real time is the actual time it takes for real events to happen. The dynamic behavior of physical equipment is related only to real time.

A computer can be considered as a technique for solving a set of equations. In solving equations, time can be non-dimensionalized. The time scale is the proportionality ratio between computer time and real time. When a time scale is two to one it means that 2 seconds of computer time are equivalent to 1 second of real time. A two to one time scale change means the computer has been slowed down by a factor of two to one. There are definite advantages in being able to change the time scale of a problem. If the daily heating of a home by the sun were to be investigated, a one to one time scale would mean that it would take a day to make a run. In this case, a speed-up of 1440 times allows a day to be compressed into a minute.

On the other end of the time scale are those events which occur in the order of microseconds. Here a slowing down of the process is required to allow the computer equipment to function properly.

If real time is taken as $t$ and computer time is taken as $\tau$:

$$\tau = at \tag{16.6--33}$$

Where $a$ is the time scale change

$$d\tau = a\,dt \tag{16.6--34}$$

In real time

$$s = \frac{d}{dt} = \text{differentiation in real time} \tag{16.6--35}$$

In computer time

$$s' = \frac{d}{d\tau} = \text{differentiation in computer time} \tag{16.6--36}$$

$$s' = \frac{d}{a\,dt} = \frac{1}{a}s \tag{16.6--37}$$

Therefore

$$s = as' \tag{16.6--38}$$

The only computer element affected by the time scale is the capacitor.

$$Z_c = \frac{1}{Cs} = \frac{1}{aCs'} = \frac{1}{C's'} \tag{16.6--39}$$

The above relationship shows that $C'$ is in computer time what $C$ is in real time. To maintain a given $Z_c$ as the time scale is changed:

$$C' = aC \tag{16.6--40}$$

When slowing down a problem, $a$ is greater than one. Therefore, to effect a given time scale change of $a$, change all the capacitors in the setup by $a$. In other words, if it is desirable to slow down a problem by a factor of 3 to 1, all the capacitors should be increased by a factor of 3.

In some cases, a large increase in capacitance may require very large, unwieldy capacitors. It should be noted that in any of the circuits of Table 16.4–1, the coefficient of $s$ always involves an $RC$ product. Therefore, $R$ can be changed to affect a time scale change. In Table 16.4–1 it will also be observed that a change in the coefficient of the transfer impedance accompanies the change in resistor values. When affecting time scale changes by resistance changes, care should be exercised in making sure the gain is returned to its normal value by changing another resistor in the setup.

**Initial Conditions.** Initial conditions usually occur as initial charges on capacitors at the time of starting a run. A standard means of introducing initial conditions is to place a charge on the feedback capacitor of an integrator. The required switching circuits are part of standard machines. Because in the differential equation method capacitors appear only in integrators, this method of setup allows easy insertion of initial conditions.

Initial conditions could be placed on the capacitors in the complex networks used in the transfer function method of setup. This would require special switching arrangements not provided on standard machines and is therefore not recommended.

If a problem is so set up that the computer generates the initial conditions and proceeds from there, both methods of setup produce these initial conditions as charges on capacitors.

**Checking the Computer Setup.** A computer behaves according to the fundamental laws of nature which pertain to the construction of the machine and the external interconnections of wires, resistors, and capacitors. There is no guarantee that because a computer diagram was drawn correctly, the computer setup representing it is correct. It is good practice to assume a setup is in error until it has shown itself to be correct by actual test. There are three parts to setup checking:

1. Visual Inspection.
2. Static Checking.
3. Dynamic Checking.

Visual inspection assumes that all components are in working order and merely checks to ascertain that they are interconnected as prescribed by the computer diagram.

Static checking is carried out by calculating the d-c voltage ouputs that occur when a d-c voltage input is applied. Actual application of the d-c voltage input should then produce the calculated d-c voltage outputs. This static check can be carried out in an open-loop or closed-loop fashion. This procedure checks proper interconnections, proper values of resistors, and proper amplifier operation. Capacitor values are not checked by this technique.

Dynamic checking is carried out by applying a dynamic test condition for which a solution is known. The computer should reproduce this calculated check solution. A simple dynamic check is that of applying a step input to a simple lag circuit and recording the input and output. The output should reach 63% of its final value in one time constant.

A sinusoidal input can be used and the record of input and output should show the proper phase shift and attenuation.

In a lengthy, complex, non-linear system simulation, it is common practice to hand, or digital computer, calculate the exact solution for a nominal condition. The analog computer setup should then reproduce this calculated check solution. Great pains must be taken to insure that the initial setup is correct. As parameter changes are made, the computer results can be expected to be right if from time to time the check solution is reproduced properly.

When involved in long computer studies it is good practice to record a run at the end of the day. This run serves as a check solution at the beginning of the next day to insure that nothing has changed in the meantime.

In some instances, actual test data are available. This type of information is most valuable in that it serves as a check not only on the computer setup but also on the engineering assumptions made in first describing the dynamic behavior of the system in terms of integro-differential equations.

## 16.7   Types of Computers and Methods of Application

Besides size, a striking difference between commercially available d-c analog computers is the way in which the operational amplifiers are normally used. There are the committed and uncommitted amplifier type machines.

The committed amplifier machine is one wherein each amplifier normally performs a given operation. Input and feedback impedances are built-in. This usage leads to additional operational amplifier symbolism as shown in Figure 16.7–1.

The committed amplifier operation can be changed, but normally involves additional equipment to the basic machine or suffers from inconvenience.

Initial
condition

Uncommitted          Summing          Integrating
amplifier          amplifier          amplifier

FIGURE 16.7–1.   Operational amplifier symbolism for committed amplifier type
machines.

The uncommitted amplifier machine is one wherein the input and feedback impedances to each amplifier can be chosen at will. This type machine allows more complex problem setup with a given number of amplifiers, but requires extra work when the normal simple operations of summation, integration, and multiplication by a coefficient are performed.

The committed amplifier type machines are usually more accurate in that resistors and capacitors are factory selected and can be mounted in temperature controlled ovens. The components are fixed in place and do not suffer from handling operations.

Figure 16.7–2 shows a large committed amplifier type machine. The inputs and outputs of the operational amplifiers are brought to a main terminal board—the patch panel—where they can easily be connected in accordance with the computer diagram.

Figure 16.7–3 shows a desk-top type uncommitted amplifier machine. The patch panel is the horizontal plug-in board.

The plug-in board or patch panel is removable in both types of machines. A long lasting simulation can be set up on one board and the board removed while a second problem is simulated by use of a second problem board.

A second difference between commercially available d-c analog computers is the way in which system inputs are applied and the way in which system outputs are recorded. There are the repetitive type and the non-repetitive type machines. The repetitive type machines are those in which the input functions are applied at periodic intervals and the repetitive outputs can be viewed on an oscilloscope. The non-repetitive type machines are those in which the input functions are applied at will and the outputs recorded on a strip chart recorder such as a Sanborn recorder.

A third difference between commercially available d-c analog computers is the way in which the machine is basically constructed. Some machines come essentially as a lump package. Other machines are available in separate pieces or modules. The latter approach allows a computer facility to start out on a very small scale and to grow as the occasion warrants.

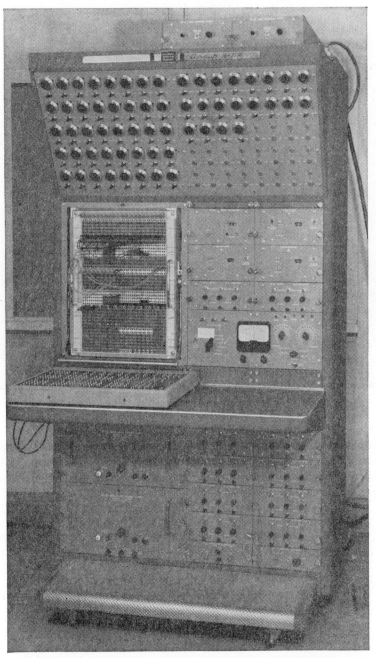

FIGURE 16.7–2.   Large committed amplifier type machine.

FIGURE 16.7–3.  Desk top type uncommitted amplifier type machine.

**Methods of Application.**  Normally a basic feedback control system is made up of three parts as shown in Figure 16.7–4.  These are (1) the control elements, (2) the controlled system or process, and (3) the measurement devices.

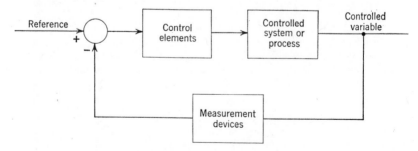

FIGURE 16.7–4.  Basic feedback control system.

The control elements act upon the difference of the reference with respect to the controlled output and perform the subsequent amplification and compensation functions. The controlled system or process contains the power element and/or the characteristics of the system. The measurement devices are necessary to feed back an indication of what the controlled output is doing. Large, complex systems have many interconnected loops, but basically these loops can be reduced to the one shown in Figure 16.7–4.

In the proposal or preconstruction stage, the analog computer can be used to simulate all parts of the system shown in Figure 16.7–4. This kind of study indicates system feasibility and possible optimum system design. It helps to establish the requirements for the control elements.

Once the requirements of the control elements and the measurement devices are established, it is usually possible for the prototypes of these equipments to be made available before the controlled system or process. With these control elements and measurement devices in hand, the system simulation can take on the form shown in Figure 16.7–5. The actual

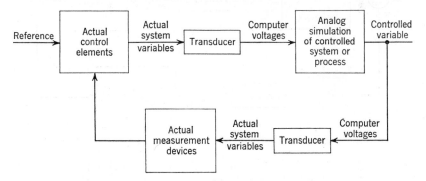

FIGURE 16.7–5.   Partial hardware—partial computer simulation technique.

control elements and measurement devices are used, whereas the controlled system or process is simulated on the computer. Transducers, which convert one physical variable or dimension to another physical variable or dimension, are required to tie together hardware variables to the analog computer voltages. These transducers must supply the appropriate power levels because computer signals are of relatively low power. For example, if a computer voltage represents a valve position which controls the fuel flow to a jet engine, a voltage to position transducer is required. This simulation procedure is useful in checking the control element design. Further, the same sort of arrangement can serve as a quality check on production units of the control elements if the controlled system or process is expensive or difficult to obtain.

When the controlled system or process becomes available, it can be incorporated directly with the rest of the actual system. The actual controlled system can be tested with simulated controls as shown in Figure 16.7–6 when the actual control elements are not available. This simulation approach can serve as a useful way of developing or checking the controller design. It has the advantage of using the actual controlled system characteristic.

It is unfortunate that in many cases the controlled system is unavailable when designing the controller. The simulation technique using the actual controlled system is valuable in that there are usually many variables in the controlled system that can be used for control. Because of noise generation and non-linear system behavior, some of the variables are more useful in control than others. This simulation technique shown in Figure 16.7–6 is very close to the final actual system in that the portion

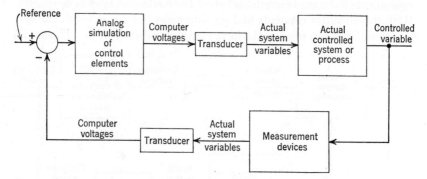

FIGURE 16.7–6. Second partial hardware—partial computer simulation technique.

of the system which is least predictable is incorporated in final form and that portion which is simulated can more readily be constructed to behave as designed.

Although the analog computer removes much of the labor in making prescribed calculations, it should be apparent that a computer cannot be substituted for good engineering judgment. The computer is a valuable tool which lessens an engineer's work load and leaves him free to do more and better engineering in the various stages of control systems production.

This chapter has served to acquaint the reader with the fundamentals and usage of d-c electronic analog computers. It is realized that there are many interesting and useful aspects that were not covered in detail or not covered at all. The intent of the book has been slanted toward control system analysis and design and not primarily toward analog computers per se. The analog computer is one of the many engineering tools that the systems designer has available and one that he cannot afford to be unaware of.

For a more complete treatment of analog computers, the books by Korn and Korn [127] and Johnson [126] are highly recommended.

## Conclusion to Volume I

The preceding chapters have described the nature of the feedback control system problem and have presented an analytical approach to servomechanism and regulator design. Emphasis has been placed on the complex plane, the attenuation-frequency, and root-locus methods of control system analysis of both simple and more complex systems. In conjunction with the multiple-loop systems, techniques have been described for handling complicated control problems with simplified analysis methods. The use of such methods enables the designer to arrive at a workable design fairly readily and to use more exact means only to refine a design that has promise of being suitable for the job. The charts presented in Chapter 15 permit the designer to select an open-loop attenuation characteristic that will provide a closed-loop response of the desired transient or steady-state performance. In Volume II, the design problems associated with the determination of the choice of system to be used for a particular application and the practical considerations of how to obtain this system will be discussed.

# BIBLIOGRAPHY

The following references are listed by title in approximately the chronological order in which they were published. The list is by no means complete, although it does present a large segment of the available literature useful in the study of servomechanisms and regulators. There are some items in the bibliography that should be useful to the reader although they may not have been referred to specifically in this book. References that pertain primarily to material contained in Volume II are listed in that volume.

1. "Directional Stability of Automatically Steered Bodies," by N. Minorsky, *Jour. Am. Soc. Naval Engrs.*, Vol. 34, p. 280, May, 1922.
2. *Advanced Part of the Dynamics of a System of Rigid Bodies*, Vol. II, 6th Edition, by E. J. Routh, Macmillan and Company, London, 1930.
3. "Automatic Steering Tests," by N. Minorsky, *Jour. Am. Soc. Naval Engrs.*, Vol. 42, pp. 285–310, May, 1930.
4. "The Differential Analyzer," by V. Bush, *Jour. Franklin Inst.*, Vol. 212, pp. 447–488, October, 1931.
5. *Communication Engineering*, by W. L. Everitt, McGraw-Hill Book Company, New York, 1932 (Chapter II, "Network Theorems").
6. "Regeneration Theory," by H. Nyquist, *Bell System Tech. Jour.*, Vol. 11, pp. 126–147, January, 1932.
7. "Stabilized Feedback Amplifiers," by H. S. Black, *Bell System Tech. Jour.*, Vol. 13, pp. 1–18, January, 1934.
8. "Theory of Servomechanisms," by H. L. Hazen, *Jour. Franklin Inst.*, Vol. 218, pp. 279–331, September, 1934.
9. "Design and Test of a High-Performance Servomechanism," by H. L. Hazen, *Jour. Franklin Inst.*, Vol. 218, pp. 543–580, November, 1934.
10. *Communication Networks*, Vol. II, by Ernst A. Guillemin, John Wiley & Sons, New York, 1935.
11. "Time Lag in a Control System," by D. R. Hartree, A. Porter, and A. Callender, *Trans. Roy. Soc., Phil.*, Vol. 235A, pp. 415–444, July 21, 1936.
12. *Mathematics of Modern Engineering*, by Robert E. Doherty and Ernest G. Keller, John Wiley & Sons, New York, 1936.
13. "An Automatic Curve Follower," by H. L. Hazen, J. J. Jaeger, and G. S. Brown, *Rev. Sci. Instruments*, Vol. 7, pp. 353–357, September, 1936.
14. "Amplifiers," by H. W. Bode, Patent 2,123,178 (1938).
15. "Constant Speed Control Theory," by H. K. Weiss, *Jour. Aero. Sci.*, Vol. 6, pp. 147–152, February, 1939.
16. "Theory of Automatic Control of Airplanes," by H. K. Weiss, *NACA Technical Notes*, No. 700, Washington, D. C., 47, 1939.
17. "General Principles of Instrument Analysis," by C. S. Draper and G. V. Schliestett, *Instruments*, Vol. XII, pp. 137–144, 1939.

18. "Recent Developments in Generator Voltage Regulation," by C. R. Hanna, K. A. Oplinger, and C. E. Valentine, *Trans. AIEE*, Vol. 58, pp. 838–844, 1939.

19. *Electric Circuits*, by the Electrical Engineering Staff, Massachusetts Institute of Technology, The Technology Press and John Wiley & Sons, New York, 1940.

20. "The Amplidyne Generator, a Dynamoelectric Amplifier for Power Control," by E. F. W. Alexanderson, M. A. Edwards, and K. K. Bowman, *G. E. Rev.*, Vol. 43, p. 104, March, 1940, *Trans. AIEE*, Supplement, Vol. 59, pp. 937–939, December, 1940.

21. "Industrial Applications of Amplidyne Generators," by D. R. Shoults, M. A. Edwards, and F. E. Crever, *G. E. Rev.*, Vol. 43, p. 114, March, 1940, *Trans. AIEE*, Supplement, Vol. 59, pp. 944–949, December, 1940.

22. "Direct-Acting Generator Voltage Regulator," by W. K. Boice, S. B. Crary, G. Kron, and L. Thompson, *Trans. AIEE*, Vol. 59, p. 149, March, 1940.

23. "Automatic Control in the Presence of Process Lags," by C. E. Mason and G. A. Philbrick, *Trans. ASME*, Vol. 62, pp. 295–308, May, 1940.

24. "Design Factors Controlling the Dynamic Performance of Instruments," by C. S. Draper and A. P. Bentley, *Trans. ASME*, Vol. 62, pp. 421–432, July, 1940.

25. "Recent Developments in Speed Regulation," by C. R. Hanna, K. A. Oplinger, and S. J. Mikina, *Trans. AIEE*, Vol. 59, pp. 692–700, 1940.

26. "The Analysis and Design of Servomechanisms," by H. Harris, *OSRD Report*, 454, December, 1941.

27. "Servomechanisms," by Y. J. Liu. Charts for verifying their stability and for finding the roots of their third and fourth degree characteristic equations. Massachusetts Institute of Technology, Cambridge, Mass., 1941.

28. "Stabilization of Servomechanisms," by D. C. Bomberger and B. T. Weber, Restricted Publication of Bell Telephone Laboratories, Inc., December, 1941.

29. *Transients in Linear Systems*, by M. F. Gardner and J. L. Barnes, John Wiley & Sons, New York, 1942.

30. "Process Lags in Automatic Control Circuits," by J. G. Ziegler and N. B. Nichols, *Trans. ASME*, Vol. 64, p. 759, October, 1942.

31. *Analysis and Synthesis of Linear Servomechanisms*, by Albert C. Hall, Technology Press, Cambridge, Mass., 1943.

32. *Alternating-Current Circuits*, 2nd Edition, by R. M. Kerchner and G. F. Corcoran, John Wiley & Sons, New York, 1943.

33. *Applied Electronics*, Chapter IX, by the Electrical Engineering Staff, Massachusetts Institute of Technology, The Technology Press and John Wiley & Sons, New York, 1943.

34. "Experimental and Analytical Studies on Oil Gears M3B1" by Servomechanisms Laboratory, Massachusetts Institute of Technology, 1943. (See also U. S. Patent 2,409,190.)

35. *Automatic Control Engineering*, by Ed. S. Smith, McGraw-Hill Book Company, New York, 1944.

36. "Electric Automatic Pilots for Aircraft," by P. Halpert and O. E. Esval, *Trans. AIEE*, Vol. 63, pp. 861–866, 1944.

37. "Polarized Light Servo-System," by T. M. Berry, *Elec. Engg.*, Vol. 63, pp. 195–198, Transactions, April, 1944.

38. *Modern Operational Mathematics in Engineering*, by R. V. Churchill, McGraw-Hill Book Company, 1944.

39. "Gyroscopic Stabilizer for Tank Guns," by C. R. Hanna and L. B. Lynn, *Elec. Engg.*, Vol. 63, pp. 355–360, April, 1944.

40. "Considerations in Servomechanism Design," by S. W. Herwald, *Trans. AIEE*, Vol. 63, pp. 871–877, December, 1944.

41. *Fundamental Theory of Servomechanims*, by Leroy A. MacColl, D. Van Nostrand Company, New York, 1945.

42. *Principles of Industrial Process Control*, by Donald P. Eckman, John Wiley & Sons, New York, 1945.

43. *Network Analysis and Feedback Amplifier Design*, by H. W. Bode, D. Van Nostrand Company, New York, 1945.

44. "Tracer Controlled Position Regulator for Propeller Milling Machine," by C. R. Hanna, W. O. Osbon, and R. A. Hartley, *Trans. AIEE.*, Vol. 64, p. 201, 1945.

45. "Operational Methods in Servomechanism Design," by William E. Restemeyer, *Jour. Aero. Sci.*, Vol. 12, pp. 313–319, July, 1945.

46. "The Servo Problem as a Transmission Problem," by E. B. Ferrell, *Proc. IRE*, Vol. 33, pp. 763–767, October, 1945.

47. "Selsyn Design and Application," by T. C. Johnson, *Trans. AIEE*, Vol. 64, pp. 703–708, October, 1945.

48. "A New Type of Differential Analyzer," by V. Bush and S. H. Caldwell, *Jour. Franklin Inst.*, Vol. 240, pp. 255–326, October, 1945.

49. "Electrical Analogy Methods Applied to Servomechanisms Problems," by S. W. Herwald and G. D. McCann, *Trans. AIEE*, Vol. 65, pp. 91–96, February, 1946.

50. "Fundamentals of Servomechanisms; How to Select and Apply Them," by S. W. Herwald, *Prod. Engg.*, Vol. 17, pp. 464–470, June, 1946.

51. "Analysis of Relay Servomechanisms," by H. K. Weiss, *Jour. Aero. Sci.*, Vol. 13, No. 7, pp. 364–376, July, 1946.

52. "Dynamic Behavior and Design of Servomechanisms," by Gordon S. Brown and Albert C. Hall, *Trans. ASME*, Vol. 68, pp. 503–524, July, 1946.

53. "Parallel Circuits in Servomechanisms," by H. Tyler Marcy, *Trans. AIEE*, Vol. 65, pp. 521–529, 1946.

54. "Frequency Response of Automatic Control Systems," by H. Harris, Jr., *Trans. AIEE*, Vol. 65, pp. 539–545, 1946.

55. "Theory of Servo Systems, with Particular Reference to Stabilization," by A. L. Whiteley, *Jour. Inst. Elec. Engg.*, Vol. 93, Part II, pp. 353–367, August, 1946.

56. "Linear Servo Theory," by Robert E. Graham, *Bell System Tech. Jour.*, Vol. XXV, No. 4, pp. 616–651, October, 1946.

57. "Application of Circuit Theory to the Design of Servomechanisms," by Albert C. Hall, *Jour. Franklin Inst.*, Vol. 242, pp. 279–307, October, 1946.

58. "Electronic Register Control for Multicolor Printing," by W. D. Cockrell, *Trans. AIEE*, Vol. 65, pp. 617–622, 1946.

59. "Dimensionless Analysis of Angular-Position Servomechanisms," by S. W. Herwald and G. D. McCann, *Trans. AIEE*, Vol. 65, pp. 636–639, October, 1946.

60. *Servomechanism Fundamentals*, by Henri Lauer, Robert Lesnick, and Leslie E. Matson, McGraw-Hill Book Company, New York, 1947.

61. *Automatic Regulation*, by W. R. Ahrendt and John F. Taplin, P.O. 4673, Washington, D. C., 1947.

62. *Theory of Servomechanisms*, by Hubert M. James, Nathaniel B. Nichols, and Ralph S. Phillips, McGraw-Hill Book Company, New York, 1947.

63. "Instrument to Measure Servomechanism Performance," by H. I. Tarpley, *Rev. Sci. Instruments*, Vol. 18, pp. 39–43, January, 1947.

64. "The Application of Lead Networks and Sinusoidal Analysis to Automatic Control Systems," by G. Schwartz, *Trans. AIEE*, Vol. 66, pp. 69–77, 1947.

65. "A Comparison of Two Basic Servomechanisms Types," by H. Harris, *Trans. AIEE*, Vol. 66, pp. 83–93, 1947.

66. "The Analysis and an Optimum Synthesis of Linear Servomechanisms," by Donald Herr and Irving Gerst, *Trans. AIEE*, Vol. 66, pp. 959–970, 1947.

67. "Laboratory Aids for Electromechanical System Developments," by G. C. Newton, Jr., and W. T. White, *Trans. AIEE*, Vol. 66, pp. 315–319, 1947.

68. "Electro-Hydraulic Control of Diesel Electric Drives," by M. A. Edwards and C. B. Lewis, *Diesel Power*, Vol. 25, pp. 72–74, 96, February, 1947.

69. "Analysis and Design of Servomechanisms," by H. Harris, *Trans. ASME*, Vol. 69, pp. 267–280, April, 1947.

70. "Electronic Servo Simulators," by F. C. Williams and F. J. R. Ritson, *Jour. IEE*, Part IIA, No. 1, Vol. 94, pp. 112–129, 1947.

71. "Constant Current Control Systems," by O. W. Livingston, *G. E. Rev.*, Vol. 50, pp. 38–44, May, 1947.

72. "Hydraulic Variable Speed Transmissions as Servomotors," by G. C. Newton, Jr., *Jour. Franklin Inst.*, Vol. 243, No. 6, pp. 439–470, June, 1947.

73. "Designing Hydraulic Servos," by H. Ziebolz, *Mach. Design*, Vol. 19, pp. 123–126, July, 1947.

74. "Electrical Positioning System of High Accuracy for Industrial Use," by D. E. Garr, *G. E. Rev.*, Vol. 50, pp. 17–24, July, 1947.

75. "Designing Pneumatic and Electric Servos," by H. Ziebolz, *Mach. Design*, Vol. 19, pp. 132–138, September, 1947.

76. "Progress in Dynamic Stability and Control Research," by W. F. Milliken, Jr., *Jour. Aero. Sci.*, Vol. 14, No. 9, pp. 493–519, September, 1947.

77. "Solution of the General Voltage Regulator Problem by Electrical Analogy," by E. L. Harder, *Trans. AIEE*, Vol. 66, pp. 815–825, 1947.

78. "Fundamental Principles of Automatic Regulators and Servomechanisms," by A. L. Whiteley, *Jour. IEE*, Part IIA, No. 1, Vol. 94, pp. 5–22, 1947.

79. "Elements of Position Control," by K. A. Hayes, *Jour. IEE*, Part IIA, No. 2, Vol. 94, pp. 161–176, 1947.

80. "Naval Applications of Electrical Remote-Positional Controllers," by V. E. C. Lampert, *Jour. IEE*, Part IIA, No. 2, Vol. 94, pp. 236–251, 1947.

81. "Some Characteristics of a Human Operator," by J. A. V. Bates, *Jour. IEE*, Part IIA, No. 2, Vol. 94, pp. 298–304, 1947.

82. "General Analysis of Speed Regulators under Impact Loads," by G. D. McCann, W. O. Osbon, and H. S. Kirschbaum, *Trans. AIEE*, Vol. 66, pp. 1243–1252, 1947.

83. "Analysis of Problems in Dynamics by Electronic Circuits," by J. R. Ragazzini, R. H. Randall, and F. A. Russell, *Proc. IRE*, Vol. 35, pp. 442–452, 1947.

84. "Obtaining Attenuation Frequency Characteristics for Servomechanisms," by H. Chestnut, *G. E. Rev.*, Vol. 50, pp. 38–44, December, 1947.

85. *Dynamics of Automatic Controls*, by R. C. Oldenbourg and H. Sartorius, translated and edited by H. L. Mason, ASME, New York, 1948.

86. *Principles of Servomechanisms*, by G. S. Brown and D. P. Campbell, John Wiley & Sons, New York, 1948.

87. "Application of the Performance Operator to Aircraft Automatic Control," by R. C. Seamans, B. G. Bromberg, L. E. Payne, *Jour. Aero. Sci.*, Vol. 15, No. 9, pp. 535–555, September, 1948.
88. "Stabilitats Kriterium insbesondere von Regelkreisen," by A. Leonard, *Archiv für Electrotechnik*, Vol. 42, pp. 100–107, September, 1948.
89. "Aircraft Accessory Systems," by T. B. Holliday, *Product Engg.*, Vol. 19, pp. 119–121, November, 1948.
90. "Relation between Amplitude and Phase in Electrical Networks," by T. Murakami and M. S. Corrington, *RCA Rev.*, Vol. IX, No. 4, pp. 602–631, December, 1948.
91. "Valve Characteristics and Process Control," by J. G. Ziegler and N. B. Nichols, *Instruments*, Vol. 22, No. 1, pp. 75–81, January, 1949.
92. "Application of Servo Systems to Aircraft," by J. R. Moore, *Aero. Engg. Rev.*, Vol. 8, pp. 32–43, January, 1949.
93. "Selecting Electric Servomotors," by Robert S. Edwards, *Mach. Design*, Vol. 21, pp. 104–109, January, 1949.
94. "Probability Criterion for the Design of Servomechanisms," by J. R. Ragizzini and A. Z. Lofti, *Jour. App. Physics*, Vol. 20, pp. 141–144, February, 1949.
95. "Industrial Applications of Rotating Regulators," by M. H. Fisher, *Power Generation*, Vol. 53, pp. 66–68, April, 1949.
96. "Transfer Functions for R-C and R-L Equalizer Networks," by E. W. Tschudi, *Electronics*, Vol. 22, pp. 116–120, May, 1949.
97. "Comparison of Steady-State and Transient Performance of Servomechanisms," by H. Chestnut and R. W. Mayer, *Trans. AIEE*, Vol. 68, pp. 765–777, 1949.
98. "Three Control Systems for D-C Adjustable Speed Drives," by W. L. O. Graves and E. H. Dinger, *Electrical Manufacturing*, Vol. 44, pp. 82–87, July, 1949.
99. "More Differential Analyzer Applications," by A. C. Cook and F. J. Maginniss, *G. E. Rev.*, Vol. 52, No. 8, pp. 14–20, August, 1949.
100. "Transient Response of Filters," by M. S. Corrington, *RCA Rev.*, Vol. X, No. 3, pp. 397–429, September, 1949.
101. "Planning for Automatic Process Control," *Electronics*, Vol. 22, pp. 72–79, October, 1949.
102. "Amplidyne Control of Tension in the Metal Industries," by W. Spence, *BTH Activities*, Vol. 20, pp. 185–189, November-December, 1949.
103. "Applications of Network Theorems in Transient Analysis," by Y. P. Yu, *Jour. Franklin Inst.*, Vol. 248, No. 5, pp. 381–398, November, 1949.
104. "Electronic Regulators and Regulating Systems," by W. G. Roman, *Mach. Design*, Vol. 21, No. 12, pp. 147–149, December, 1949.
105. "Control System Synthesis by Locus Methods," by W. R. Evans, *AIEE Preprint*, 50–51, January, 1950.
106. "A Frequency Response Method for Analyzing and Synthesizing Contactor Servomechanisms," by R. J. Kochenburger, *AIEE Preprint*, 50–44, January, 1950.
107. "A Generalized Analogue Computer for Flight Simulation," by A. C. Hall, *AIEE Preprint*, 50–48, January, 1950.
108. "An Electronic Simulator for Nonlinear Servomechanisms," by C. M. Edwards and E. C. Johnson, *AIEE Preprint*, 50–47, January, 1950.
109. "The Pulse Method for the Determination of Aircraft Dynamic Performance," by R. C. Seamans, Jr., B. P. Blasingame, and G. C. Clementson, *Jour. Aero. Sci.*, Vol. 17, No. 1, pp. 22–38, January, 1950.

110. "Report on Terminology and Nomenclature," by a Subcommittee of the Feedback-Control Systems Committee, AIEE, January, 1950.

111. "Analog Computers for Servo Problems," by Donald McDonald, *Rev. of Sci. Instr.*, Vol. 21, pp. 154–157, February, 1950.

112. "Instrument Engineering," by G. S. Brown and D. P. Campbell, *Mechanical Engg.*, Vol. 72, No. 2, pp. 124–127, 136, February, 1950.

113. "Transducers, Sending Elements for Servos," by J. R. Stovall, *Electrical Manufacturing*, Vol. 45, No. 4, pp. 88–92, 176–184, April, 1950.

114. "Electrical Pickoffs for Instrumentation of Pilotless Aircraft," by Jack Andresen, *Instruments*, Vol. 23, No. 4, pp. 347–349, April, 1950.

115. *Automatic Feedback Control*, by W. R. Ahrendt and John Taplin, McGraw-Hill Book Company, New York, 1951.

116. *Driftless D-C Amplifier*, by F. R. Bradley and R. McCoy, *Electronics*, April, 1952, McGraw-Hill Book Company, New York.

117. "Quick Methods for Evaluating the Closed-Loop Poles of Feedback Control Systems," by G. Biernson, AIEE Applications and Industry No. 6, pp. 53–70, May, 1953.

118. "Correlation Between Frequency and Transient Responses of Feedback Control Systems," by Yaohan Chu, AIEE Applications and Industry, pp. 81–92, May, 1953.

119. *Servomechanism Practice*, by W. R. Ahrendt, McGraw-Hill Book Company, New York, 1954.

120. *Control-System Dynamics*, by Walter R. Evans, McGraw-Hill Book Company, New York, 1954.

121. "Study of Transients in Linear Feedback System by Conformal Mapping and the Root-Locus Method," by Victor C. M. Yeh, *Trans. ASME*, Vol. 76, pp. 349–361, April, 1954.

122. *Automatic Feedback Control System Synthesis*, by John G. Truxal, McGraw-Hill Book Company, New York, 1955.

123. "A General Theory for Determination of the Stability of Linear Lumped-Parameter Multiple-Loop Servomechanisms (and other Feedback Systems)," by Thomas S. Amlie and Thomas J. Higgins, AIEE Applications and Industry, pp. 134–147, July, 1955.

124. "Simple Method for Calculating the Time Response of a System to an Arbitrary Input," by G. A. Biernson, AIEE Applications and Industry, pp. 227–245, September, 1955.

125. *Frequency Response*, by Rufus Oldenburger, Macmillan, New York, 1956.

126. *Analog Computer Techniques*, by C. L. Johnson, McGraw-Hill Book Company, New York, 1956.

127. *Electronic Analog Computer*, by G. A. Korn and T. M. Korn, McGraw-Hill Book Company, New York, 1956.

128. "Synthesis of Feedback Control Systems by Gain-Contour and Root-Contour Methods," by Victor C. M. Yeh, AIEE Applications and Industry, pp. 85–96, May, 1956.

129. "Solution of Algebraic Equations on an Analog-Computer," by C. R. Cahn, *Review of Scientific Instruments*, Vol. 27, pp. 856–858, October, 1956.

130. "Quick Method for Estimating Closed-Loop Poles of Control Systems," by Kan Chen, AIEE Applications and Industry, pp. 80–87, May, 1957.

131. *Introduction to the Design of Servomechanisms*, by John L. Bower and Peter M. Schultheiss, John Wiley and Sons, New York, 1958.

132. *Process Dynamics*, by D. P. Campbell, John Wiley and Sons, New York, 1958.

133. *Automatic Process Control*, by D. P. Eckman, John Wiley and Sons, New York, 1958.
134. *Handbook of Automation, Computation, and Control*, edited by E. M. Grabbe, Simon Ramo, and Dean E. Wooldridge, John Wiley and Sons, New York, 1958.
135. *Control Engineers' Handbook*, by John G. Truxal, McGraw-Hill Book Company, New York, 1958.
136. "Method of Scaling and Checking Computer Circuits," by L. Jubin Lane, AIEE Applications and Industry, pp. 67–70, May, 1958.
137. "Silicon Zener Diodes," George Porter, *Electrical Journal*, Vol. 161, pp. 570–571, August 29, 1958.

# PROBLEMS

## Chapter 2

**2.1**  The ratio of the controlled variable $C$ to the actuating error $E$ of a control system is frequently expressed as a complex number that is a function of the sinusoidal frequency $\omega$.   Consider the two values for this ratio given below:

$$(a)\quad \frac{C}{E} = \frac{20}{j\omega(1 + j0.5\omega)(1 + j0\,04\omega)}$$

$$(b)\quad \frac{C}{E} = \frac{10}{(j\omega)^2(1 + j0.25\omega)(1 + j0.0625\omega)}$$

For $\omega = 2$, 4, and 10, express in polar form the three values of $C/E$ for each case. Plot each group of $C/E$ values on the complex plane to a common scale for each case.

**2.2**  The expression for the controlled variable to reference input ratio of a feedback control system can be written as

$$\frac{C}{R} = \frac{\dfrac{C}{E}}{1 + \dfrac{C}{E}}$$

Using the equations for $C/E$ of Problem 2.1, find the value $C/R$ in polar form for $\omega = 0.2$, 2.0, and 20.   Indicate the results on the complex plane.

**2.3**  The controlled variable to reference input ratio, $C/R$, is sometimes expressed as

$$\frac{C}{R} = \frac{G_1}{1 + G_1 H}$$

With

$$G_1 = \frac{60}{j\omega(1 + j0.25\omega)(1 + j0.08\omega)}$$

and

$$H = \frac{0.4(j\omega)^2}{(1 + j2.0\omega)}$$

find the value of $C/R$ for $\omega = 0.5$, and 5.0.

**2.4**  In the solution for the response of a servomechanism controlled variable as a function of time, it may be necessary to determine the exponential form of a complex number.   To illustrate this problem, determine as a single complex number in exponential and polar forms the following complex expressions:

$$(a)\quad \frac{(1 + j2)}{(8 - j5)(8 + j7)}$$

$$(b)\quad \frac{3(-2 + j5) + 16}{(-2 + j5)(2j5)}$$

$$(c)\quad \frac{3 + j4}{2(1 + j3)}$$

$$(d)\quad \frac{(2 + j11)}{j7(16 + j7)(16 - j13)}$$

**2.5**   In performing the inverse Laplace transform it is necessary to determine, as a single magnitude and an angle, the resultant complex number that is obtained from a complicated grouping of complex numbers.   Perform such a simplification on the following groupings:

$$(a)\quad \frac{24(-16 + j9)}{(112 - j384)} + \frac{(16 + j9)}{9}$$

$$(b)\quad \frac{(4 + j7)(9 + j7)}{j4(3 + j5)(3 - j9)}$$

**2.6**   Express the following exponential terms in their sine and/or cosine form to the extent to which this is possible:

$$(a)\quad Ae^{-\alpha t}e^{j(\psi + \beta t)} + Ae^{-\alpha t}e^{-j(\psi + \beta t)}$$

$$(b)\quad Be^{j\omega t} + Ce^{-j\omega t}$$

$$(c)\quad 3e^{j5t}e^{-2t} - 4e^{-2t}e^{-j3t}$$

$$(d)\quad 5e^{j(\pi/3)}e^{j\omega t}$$

**2.7**   The ease with which complex numbers may be manipulated in their exponential form makes it desirable to be able to convert sine and cosine functions into this form.   Determine the exponential equivalents of the following trigonometric expressions:

$$(a)\quad \cos(\omega t + \phi)$$

$$(b)\quad e^{-\alpha t}\sin(\beta t + \psi)$$

$$(c)\quad A\sin\omega t + B\cos\omega t$$

**2.8**  The evaluation of the time response of a control system may require the substitution of a complex value of $s$ into an expression containing both real and complex numbers.  Determine the value for $C_3$ in the following equation for the value of $s = -1.56 + j2.08$

$$C_3 = \frac{40 \times 3.2(s + 0.25)}{s(s + 16.6)(s + 1.56 + j2.08)(s + 0.286)}$$

**2.9**  When determining the stability and performance of control systems, use is frequently made of the substitution $s = j\omega$.  In a control system with

$$G = \frac{375}{(1 + 0.14s)(1 + 0.79s)}$$

and

$$H = \frac{s}{55(1 + 0.68s)(1 + 0.021s)}$$

evaluate as complex numbers $GH$ and $\dfrac{GH}{1 + GH}$ for $\omega = 1$ and $\omega = 4$.

### Chapter 3

**3.1**  A constant d-c voltage $E$ is impressed upon the resistances and inductance shown.  The switch $S_1$ is initially closed, and steady-state conditions have been obtained.  What is the current flowing through the inductance $L$ at this time? What is the current through $R_1$ at this time?

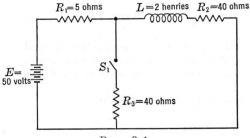

PROB. 3–1

The switch $S_1$ is then opened and left open.  What is the current through $R_1$ immediately after switching?  Write the differential equation for the voltages in the circuit after switching.  Determine the current through the inductance as a function of time after switching.  What is the time constant of this circuit with the switch open?

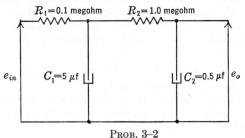

PROB. 3–2

**3.2** Resistor-capacitor networks of the type shown here have desirable properties for certain servomechanism applications. For this network, with the capacitors initially uncharged, determine the value of the output voltage $e_o$ as a function of time with an input voltage, $e_{in} = 10t$. What is the expression for the steady-state component of the output voltage? What are the time constants of this network?

**3.3** A common form of servomechanism positioning system is shown in the accompanying diagram. This system is similar to that shown in Figure 3.8-1, and the symbols used here are the same as those for Figure 3.8-1.

The torques acting on the motor are:

$$\text{Torque from amplifier current} = Ke$$

$$\text{Motor inertia and damping torques} = J\frac{d^2c}{dt^2} + D\frac{dc}{dt}$$

where $e$ = actuating signal in radians = $r - c$,
$\quad r$ = reference input in radians, and
$\quad c$ = controlled variable in radians.

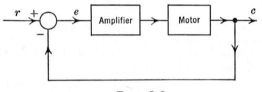

PROB. 3–3

$K$ = pound-feet/radian of actuating signal
$J$ = slug feet$^2$ inertia of motor and load
$D$ = pound-feet/radian per second of motor

$$\omega_0 = \sqrt{\frac{K}{J}} = 4.0 \text{ radians/sec}$$

$$\zeta = \frac{D}{2\sqrt{KJ}} = 0.8$$

With the reference input $r$ moving sinusoidally,

$$r = R_0 \sin \omega t, \text{ radians}$$

determine the magnitude and angular position with respect to $r$ of the steady-state value of the controlled variable $c$. The initial conditions and transient response of $c$ may be neglected. Also neglect other external torques acting on motor or load.

**3.4** Another important type of reference input to the control system described in Problem 3.3 is one in which the input is initially zero but is made to increase linearly with time. Thus,

$$r = R_1 t$$

where $R_1$ has the units of radians per second.

With the motor initially at rest with zero displacement, determine the expression for the controlled variable position $c$ in radians as a function of time, with the values of $\omega_0$ and $\zeta$ given in Problem 3.3.

**3.5**  The problem of a motor synchronizing on a fixed reference signal as described in Section 3.8 is frequently made more complicated by the fact that the motor at a displacement $+C_0$ radians may not be initially at rest.  In addition to the initial displacement, the motor may be moving with an initial velocity, $-C_1$ radians per second, in the direction of the stationary reference position.  It is desired to determine the value of $-C_1$ that will cause the motor position $c(t)$ to have a maximum overshoot of an amount $-C_0$, that is, equal in magnitude to the original positive displacement.  Use values of $\omega_0 = 10$ radians per second and $\zeta = 0.6$.

**3.6**  The presence of external torques acting on the motor or load of a servomechanism system of the type described in Problem 3.3 produces a modified form of response to that obtained with only reference input displacement.  The net torque applied to the motor (see Problem 3.3) can be expressed as

$$\text{Net torque} = Ke + T(t)$$

where $T(t)$ is the external torque and may be a function of time.  The remaining equations are the same as those for Problem 3.3.

Compare the response of the controlled variable $c$ for the system initially at rest for the two input conditions:

(a) Reference input zero, $T(t) = 0$      $t < 0$

$$T(t) = KT_0 \qquad t > 0$$

(b) $T(t)$ zero,            $r = 0$      $t < 0$

$$r = R_0 \qquad t > 0$$

Determine the controlled variable response in terms of the undamped natural frequency $\omega_0$ and the damping ratio $\zeta$ for an underdamped oscillatory system.

**3.7**  The voltage regulator shown in simplified schematic form in the diagram below is used to maintain the terminal voltage in correspondence with the reference input voltage.  The main generator field is supplied by a constant bus voltage $e_B$ and an exciter in series.  The bus voltage provides sufficient field current $i_{f_0}$ to maintain the terminal voltage at its nominal value $e_{c_0}$.  Thus, $i_{f_0} = e_B/R_2$ and $K_2 i_{f_0} = e_{c_0}$.  The exciter provides the remaining current $i_f$ that is necessary to produce at the generator terminals the desired voltage.

The reference voltage can be expressed as $e_{r_0} + e_r$, where $e_{r_0}$ is the nominal value and $e_r$ is the change in the reference voltage from its nominal value.  The terminal

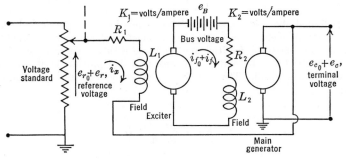

PROB. 3–7

voltage can be expressed as $e_{c_0} + e_c$, where $e_c$ represents the change in terminal voltage from its nominal value.

The difference between the reference and terminal voltages appears across the exciter field to produce a current $i_x$. The current $i_x$ generates an exciter voltage that acts to produce the $i_f$ component of generator field current described above. $i_f$ produces the change in terminal voltage $e_c$.

Write the differential equation for $e_c$ in terms of $e_r$. Consider the reference and terminal voltages to be set initially at their nominal value and the control system to be at rest. The reference voltage is suddenly changed by $e_r = 4$ volts. It is desired to determine the change in the terminal voltage $e_c$ as a function of time following this input change.

*System Constants*

| | |
|---|---|
| $R_1 = 160$ ohms | $R_2 = 5$ ohms |
| $L_1 = 32$ henries | $L_2 = 5$ henries |
| $K_1 = 320$ volts/amp | $K_2 = 25$ volts/amp |

Consider the internal resistance of the voltage standard and the battery to be included in the resistances $R_1$ and $R_2$. Consider the main generator to be unloaded.

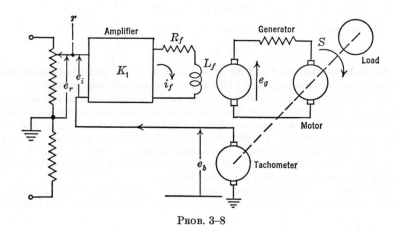

PROB. 3–8

**3.8** Indicated above is a speed regulator system in which the desired speed is set in as a potentiometer voltage $e_r$, and a tachometer voltage $e_b$ proportional to the controlled motor speed $S$ is fed back and compared with $e_r$. The voltage difference, $e_i$, is amplified and used to excite a generator field that provides excitation for the motor and attached load. The following equations describe the operation of the system:

$$e_r - e_b = e_i$$

$$K_1 e_i = \frac{L_f}{R_f} \frac{di_f}{dt} + i_f$$

$$K_f i_f = e_g$$

$$K_s e_g = T_m \frac{dS}{dt} + S$$

$$e_b = K_h S$$

Data

$$\frac{L_f}{R_f} = T_f = 0.04 \text{ sec}$$

$$T_m = 0.80 \text{ sec}$$
$$K_1 = 4 \text{ amp/volt}$$
$$K_f = 50 \text{ volts/amp}$$
$$K_s = 0.25 \text{ radian/sec/volt}$$
$$K_h = 0.2 \text{ volt/radian/sec}$$

Initially $S$ is 5 radians per second, and steady-state conditions are obtained. What are the values of $e_g$, $i_f$, and $e_r$?

If $e_r$ is suddenly decreased to zero, how does the motor speed change as a function of time?

**3.9** It is desired to determine the expression for the output voltage $e_o$ as a function of time with the input voltage $e_{in} = E \cos \omega t$ impressed on this network. Steady-state conditions alone are of interest so that transient effects can be neglected.

Draw on the complex plane the relative positions of the input and output voltages for

$$\omega = 40 \text{ rad/sec} \qquad R_2 = 0.0278 \text{ meg}$$
$$R_1 = 1.0 \text{ meg} \qquad C_2 = 0.18 \ \mu\text{f}$$
$$C_1 = 0.2 \ \mu\text{f}$$

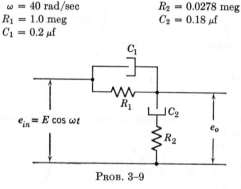

PROB. 3–9

**3.10** The accompanying figure shows a disk with inertia $J$ lb-ft² fastened to a torsion rod of stiffness, $S$ lb-ft/rad.

The viscous damping on the disk exerts $D$ lb-ft/radian per second. Develop the differential equations for the torques acting on the disk.

With the disk initially held at rest a small angle, $A$, from its equilibrium position, determine $\theta$, the position of the disk as a function of time from the instant the disk is released.

$$J = 12.88 \text{ lb-ft}^2$$

$$S = 25.6 \text{ lb-ft/rad}$$

$$D = 1.28 \text{ lb-ft/rad/sec.}$$

How many seconds will have elapsed from the time of release before the disk will remain within 10 per cent of the initial displacement, $A$?

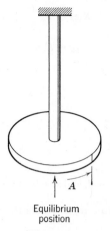

Equilibrium
position

Prob. 3–10

## Chapter 4

**4.1** From the definition of the Laplace transform,

$$F(s) = \mathcal{L}[f(t)] = \int_0^\infty f(t)e^{-st}\, dt$$

derive $F(s)$ for the following values of $f(t)$:

    (a) $f(t) = \sin(\omega t + \phi)$
    (b) $f(t) = e^{-4t}$
    (c) $f(t) = e^{-\beta t} \cos \omega t$
    (d) $f(t) = (1 - e^{-\alpha t})$
    (e) $f(t)$ = positive triangular pulse starting at $t = 0$ and reaching its maximum
        of 4 at $t = 2$ seconds.

$$f(t) = 0 \qquad t < 0$$
$$f(t) = 2t \qquad 0 < t < 2$$
$$f(t) = 8 - 2t \qquad 2 < t < 4$$
$$f(t) = 0 \qquad t > 4$$

**4.2** Obtain the direct Laplace transform for the differential and integral equations
listed below:

    (a) $L\dfrac{di(t)}{dt} + Ri(t) + \dfrac{1}{C}\displaystyle\int i(t)\, dt = e(t)$

    (b) $M\dfrac{d^2x(t)}{dt^2} + D\dfrac{dx(t)}{dt} + Kx(t) = F_2 t^2$

    (c) $T_m\dfrac{d^2\theta(t)}{dt^2} + \dfrac{d\theta(t)}{dt} = \theta_M \sin \omega t$

    (d) $Dv(t) + K\displaystyle\int v(t)\, dt = F_1 t$

**4.3** Perform the partial fraction expansion and determine the coefficients of the
following values of $F(s)$:

(a) $F(s) = \dfrac{2}{(s+1)(s+3)}$

(b) $F(s) = \dfrac{s+3}{s(s+2)(s+4)^2}$

(c) $F(s) = \dfrac{(s+1)}{(s+5)[(s+2)^2+9]}$

(d) $F(s) = \dfrac{24(s+0.75)}{s(s+1.04)(s^2+6.46s+17.3)}$

(e) $F(s) = \dfrac{(s+0.7)^2}{s(s+0.590)(s+0.870)(s^2+0.272s+0.955)}$

**4.4** Obtain the time functions corresponding to the values of $F(s)$ in Problem 4.3 by means of the inverse Laplace transform.

**4.5** Solve any of the problems of Chapter 3 by means of the direct and the inverse Laplace transformation.

**4.6** Write the differential equations for the network shown below to obtain an expression for the output voltage $e_o(t)$.

Take the Laplace transform of these equations and obtain the expression for $E_o(s)$, the transform of $e_o(t)$ in terms of the driving and the initial excitation functions and of the circuit parameters.

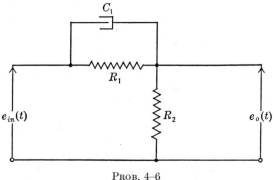

PROB. 4–6

For the circuit initially in the steady state, with $e_{in}(t) = E_I$, determine the time expression for $e_o(t)$ following the instant when $e_{in}(t) = 0$.

**4.7** A simple form of remote position indicator is shown below. It consists of a selsyn transmitter (generator), a selsyn repeater (motor) with a light aluminum indicating dial fastened to the repeater rotor, and a permanent magnet that serves as an eddy-current brake on the dial. The selsyns resemble small synchronous machines with three-winding stators that are electrically connected together, and single-winding rotors energized from an a-c source. For the purposes of this problem it is adequate to consider the transmitter-repeater combination as a torque generator. When properly "zeroed" and energized, the two rotors tend always to assume the same angular position. If the transmitter rotor is displaced, a torque is produced on the repeater rotor tending to make it "follow" the transmitter. The magnitude

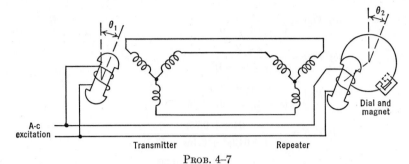

of the torque on the repeater is given approximately by the relation:

$$T(t) = K_T \sin [\theta_1(t) - \theta_2(t)]$$

Or, if the angular error $e(t) = [\theta_1(t) - \theta_2(t)]$ is small,

$$T(t) = K_T[\theta_1(t) - \theta_2(t)] = K_T e(t)$$

where $K_T$ is the torque gradient, or torque per unit error.

The magnetic brake produces a retarding torque on the repeater rotor proportional to its speed,

$$T_F(t) = -D \frac{d\theta_2(t)}{dt}$$

where $D$ is the retarding torque for a unit velocity, or viscous damping coefficient.

1. Assume a system of two similar selsyns each having moment of inertia, $J$. Assume that all bearing friction and viscous damping *other than that of the magnetic brake* are negligible. Assume the system initially at rest with $\theta_1 = \theta_2 = 0$. A sudden angular displacement $\Delta$ is given to the transmitter rotor. Write the differential equation of motion of the repeater rotor. Obtain the complete solution for $\theta_2(t)$ as a function of time. What is the steady-state error in position $[\theta_1(t) - \theta_2(t)]$? Obtain numerical answers for $\Delta = 0.5$ radian. Sketch the result $\theta_2(t)$.

2. Assume that the transmitter is turning with constant angular velocity $S$, and that enough time has elapsed for all transients to have died away to practically zero. What is the steady-state velocity of the repeater rotor? What is the steady-state error $[\theta_1(t) - \theta_2(t)]$ under constant velocity input? Obtain numerical results for $S = 10$ revolutions per minute.

*Data*

$J = 2.4$ lb-in.$^2$ (inertia of each rotor)      lb (mass)
$K_T = 3.4$ oz-in./degree error (torque gradient)      oz (force)
$D = 22.1$ oz-in./revolution per second (frictional drag of magnetic brake)

**4.8** A schematic diagram of a form of tension regulator is shown below. In this regulator a continuous sheet of material is unrolled from the wind-off roll and rewound onto the wind-up roll. The operation of the wind-up roll motor control is such as to attempt to maintain constant the tension in the material during this transfer. A measure of the tension in the material is obtained by having the material threaded through three rollers as shown, the center roller of which is maintained in position by a spring. The force exerted by the spring is proportional to the displacement of the center roller from its nominal position.

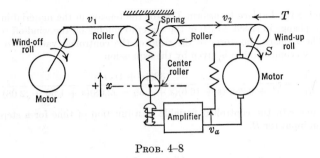

PROB. 4–8

Attached to the center roller is a reactor that puts out a signal that is also proportional to the displacement of this roller from its nominal position. The reactor signal is amplified to drive the motor that controls the wind-up reel speed. By control of this motor speed, the tension in the material is regulated.

The following equations, which describe the operation of this system, are based on the assumption that there is a constant stretch in the material from the wind-off roll to the wind-up roll. The inertia of the center roller can also be neglected for purposes of this analysis.

$$\text{Position of center roll} = x(t) = \tfrac{1}{2} \int [v_2(t) - v_1(t)] \, dt$$

where $v_1(t)$ = velocity of material from wind-off reel, feet per second, and
$v_2(t)$ = velocity of material onto wind-up reel, feet per second.

$$K_2 S(t) = v_2(t)$$

where $S(t)$ = angular speed of wind-up motor in radians per second, and
$K_2$ = feet per radian.

The voltage from the reactor is $K_1 x(t)$, where $K_1$ = volts per foot.
The change in motor terminal voltage $v_a(t)$ is related to $K_1 x(t)$ as

$$T_1 \frac{dv_a(t)}{dt} + v_a(t) = -K_1 x(t)$$

where $T_1$ is a control time constant in seconds.
The change in motor terminal voltage is also equal to

$$v_a(t) = K_m \left[ T_m \frac{dS(t)}{dt} + S(t) \right] + K_3 T(t)$$

where $K_m$ = volts per radian per second,
$T_m$ = motor time constant, seconds,
$T(t)$ = change in tension in material from the nominal value, pounds, and
$K_3$ = equivalent motor volts per pound tension.

The spring force restraining the dancer roll is equal to $2T(t)$ and is proportional to the position of the floating roll.

$$2T(t) = K_4 x(t)$$

$$K_4 = \text{pounds per foot}$$

Determine the Laplace transform $T(s)$ for the tension in the material in terms of an abrupt change in speed $\Delta V_1(t)$ of the material coming off the wind-off roll.

**4.9** The Laplace transform of the ratio of the controlled variable to reference input of a servomechanism is given by the expression

$$\frac{C(s)}{R(s)} = \frac{32(4s+1)}{(s+0.286)(s+16.6)(s+1.56-j2.08)(s+1.56+j2.08)}$$

Determine $c(t)$, the controlled variable as a function of time for a step-function of position input for $R$.

## Chapter 5

**5.1** Two networks used occasionally to stabilize servomechanism and regulating systems are shown here. Figure $a$ shows a phase-lead type network; Figure $b$ shows a double $RC$ lead network.

(a) For each network determine the ratio $E_o/E_{in}(j\omega)$ in terms of the principal time constant, $T = RC$.

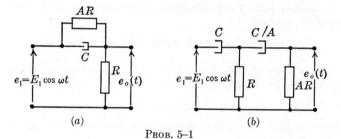

$$e_1 = E_1 \cos \omega t \qquad e_o(t)$$

(a)

$$e_1 = E_1 \cos \omega t \qquad e_o(t)$$

(b)

PROB. 5–1

(b) With $A = 5.0$, calculate the complex value of $E_o/E_{in}(j\omega)$ for each network for $\omega T = 0, 0.2, 0.5, 1.0,$ and $\infty$.

(c) Using the data in part $b$, for each network sketch the complex plane plot of $E_o/E_{in}(j\omega)$ for $0 \leq \omega T \leq \infty$.

**5.2** Utilizing the impedance concepts, derive the relationship for $E_o/E_{in}(j\omega)$ for the bridged-T type network shown below.

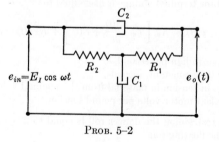

$$e_{in} = E_I \cos \omega t \qquad e_o(t)$$

PROB. 5–2

**5.3** The differential equation expressing the output $x(t)$ of a mechanical system in terms of its input $y(t)$ is

$$y(t) = A\frac{d^3x(t)}{dt^3} + B\frac{d^2x(t)}{dt^2} + C\frac{dx(t)}{dt}$$

Determine the ratio $X/Y(j\omega)$ for a sinusoidal input motion. With the values of $A$, $B$, and $C$ given below, plot the $X/Y(j\omega)$ ratio on the complex plane

$$A = 0.01$$

$$B = 0.06$$

$$C = 0.25$$

**5.4** Frequently in regulator systems in which no electronic tubes are used, stabilizing action is obtained by the use of a "stabilizing transformer." On the following page is a diagram showing such an application.

The net current $i(t)$ in the inductance $L_f$ determines the field flux, which in turn produces the amplidyne control field signal. The current $i(t)$ is produced by the combined action of the input voltage $e_{in}(t)$ and the stabilizing transformer voltage $e_b(t)$. Select a suitable polarity for the stabilizing transformer windings. Considering the internal impedance of the input source and of the amplidyne armature circuit

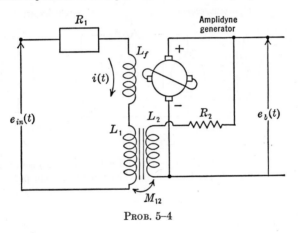

PROB. 5–4

negligible, derive the expression for $I(s)$ in terms of $E_{in}(s)$ and $E_b(s)$ and the circuit parameters, where

$$I(s) = \mathcal{L}[i(t)]$$

$$E_{in}(s) = \mathcal{L}[e_{in}(t)]$$

$$E_b(s) = \mathcal{L}[e_b(t)]$$

$R_1$ and $R_2$ represent the total resistance in their respective loop circuits.

The superposition principle may be advantageous in handling this problem.

Discuss the effect of connecting the stabilizing transformer with the opposite polarity to that you have chosen.

**5.5** For the electrical circuit shown in Figure $a$, below, determine by use of Thevenin's theorem the equivalent source voltage $e$ and the equivalent source impedance $Z'$ shown in Figure $b$.

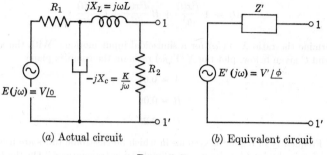

$R_1$ $\quad jX_L = j\omega L$ $\qquad\qquad\qquad$ $Z'$

$-jX_c = \dfrac{K}{j\omega}$ $\qquad R_2$

$E(j\omega) = V\underline{/0}$ $\qquad\qquad\qquad$ $E'(j\omega) = V'\underline{/\phi}$

$\qquad$ (a) Actual circuit $\qquad\qquad$ (b) Equivalent circuit

Prob. 5–5

**5.6** A portion of a d-c generator control system is shown here. The input voltage $e_{in}(t)$ controls the field of the exciter; the exciter generated voltage $e_x(t)$ is impressed on the field of the main generator.

The exciter voltage is equal to $K_x$ times the exciter field current $i_x(t)$, whereas the generator voltage is equal to $K_g$ times the generator field current $i_g(t)$.

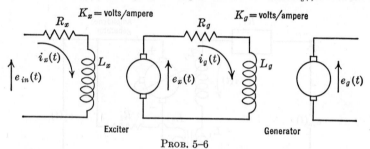

$K_x$ = volts/ampere $\qquad\qquad\qquad\qquad K_g$ = volts/ampere

$R_x$ $\qquad\qquad\qquad\qquad\qquad R_g$

$i_x(t)$ $\qquad L_x$ $\qquad\qquad\qquad i_g(t)$ $\qquad L_g$

$e_{in}(t)$ $\qquad\qquad\qquad\qquad e_x(t)$ $\qquad\qquad\qquad\qquad e_g(t)$

$\qquad\qquad$ Exciter $\qquad\qquad\qquad\qquad\qquad$ Generator

Prob. 5–6

With the system constants given below, and with $e_{in}(t) = E_I \cos \omega t$, plot on the complex plane the ratio $E_g/E_{in}(j\omega)$ for the values of the system parameters given below.

*Data*

$\qquad R_x = 1000$ ohms
$\qquad R_g = 10$ ohms
$\qquad L_x = 50$ henries
$\qquad L_g = 2$ henries
$\qquad K_x = 2000$ volts/amp
$\qquad K_g = 50$ volts/amp
$\qquad \omega$ from 0 to 20 radians/sec

**5.7** Plot the attenuation (decibels) and phase characteristics as a function of frequency to a logarithmic scale for the functions given below. Emphasis should be placed upon these characteristics in the range $0.1 < \omega < 10$ radians per second.

$$(a) \quad \frac{C}{E}(j\omega) = \frac{5}{(1 + j0.25\omega)(1 + j2.0\omega)}$$

$$(b) \quad \frac{C}{E}(j\omega) = \frac{40}{j\omega(1 + j4\omega)}$$

(c) $\dfrac{C}{E}(j\omega) = \dfrac{0.2(j\omega)^2}{(1 + j\omega)}$

(d) $\dfrac{C}{R}(j\omega) = \dfrac{1}{1 + j1.2\omega + (j\omega)^2}$

**5.8** Express in terms of amplitude in decibels and phase in degrees the following transfer functions for values of $\omega = 1, 4, 10$, and $40$:

$$G(s) = \dfrac{121}{j\omega(1 + j0.110\omega)(1 + j0.0317\omega)(1 + j0.0569\omega)}$$

$$H(s) = \dfrac{0.189(j\omega)^3(1 + j0.014\omega)(1 + j0.016\omega)}{(1 + j1.0\omega)(1 + j0.19\omega)(1 + j0.0016\omega)}$$

$$G(s) = \dfrac{40(1 + j\omega)}{j\omega(1 + j10\omega)(1 + j0.0625\omega)(1 + j0.025\omega)}$$

**5.9** Develop the expression for the ratio of the output to input voltages, $E_o/E_{in}(j\omega)$, for each of the networks shown below. Where possible, identify the time constants with convenient resistance-capacitance groupings.

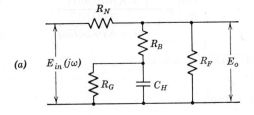

(a)   $E_{in}(j\omega)$

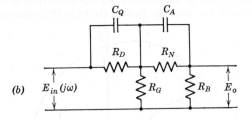

(b)   $E_{in}(j\omega)$

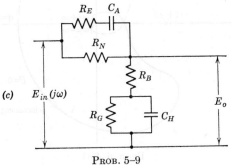

(c)   $E_{in}(j\omega)$

PROB. 5–9

## Chapter 6

**6.1** Determine the roots of the following characteristic equations:

$$(a) \qquad\qquad s^3 + 2s^2 + 9s + 68 = 0$$
$$(b) \quad s^5 + 10s^4 + 36s^3 + 60s^2 + 52s + 16 = 0$$
$$(c) \qquad s^4 + 3.2s^3 + 68.8s^2 + 131s + 129 = 0$$
$$(d) \qquad\qquad 5s^4 + 11s^3 + 7s^2 + 6s + 2 = 0$$

**6.2** Determine by means of Routh's stability criterion whether the systems having the following characteristic equations are stable or not:

$$(a) \qquad\qquad 5s^3 + 6s^2 + 6s + 2 = 0$$
$$(b) \qquad 3.78s^4 + 8.56s^3 + 5.78s^2 + 4.78s + 2.65 = 0$$
$$(c) \quad 0.290s^5 + 2.59s^4 + 6.86s^3 + 9.45s^2 + 10.28s + 4.64 = 0$$
$$(d) \qquad 25s^5 + 105s^4 + 120s^3 + 121s^2 + 21s + 1 = 0$$

**6.3** The Laplace transform of the ratio of the controlled variable to the reference input of a servomechanism can be written as

$$\frac{C(s)}{R(s)} = \frac{\dfrac{500G_b(s)}{1 + K_T G_b(s) H(s)}}{1 + \dfrac{500G_b(s)}{1 + K_T G_b(s) H(s)}}$$

where $G_b(s) = \dfrac{1}{s(1 + 0.5s)(1 + 0.08s)}$

$$H(s) = \frac{s^3}{(1 + 0.4s)^2}$$

Over what range of values for the constant $K_T$ will the system be stable?

**6.4** The sketches below show the form of the $G(j\omega)H(j\omega)$ functions for a number

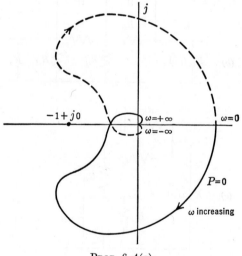

PROB. 6–4(a)

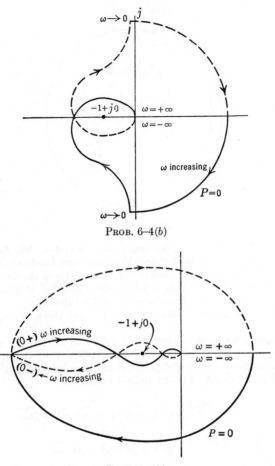

$\omega \rightarrow 0$ $j$

$-1+j0$    $\omega = +\infty$
           $\omega = -\infty$

$\omega$ increasing

$P = 0$

$\omega \rightarrow 0$

PROB. 6–4(b)

$(0+)$ $\omega$ increasing    $-1+j0$

$\omega = +\infty$
$\omega = -\infty$

$(0-)$ $\omega$ increasing

$P = 0$

PROB. 6–4(c)

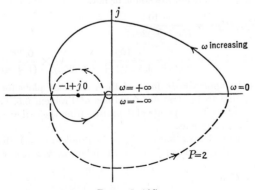

$j$

$\omega$ increasing

$-1+j0$    $\omega = +\infty$    $\omega = 0$
           $\omega = -\infty$

$P = 2$

PROB. 6–4(d)

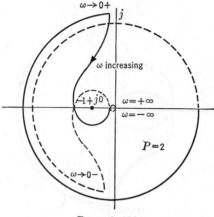

PROB. 6–4(e)

of closed-loop control systems over the range $-\infty < \omega < +\infty$. The solid lines show the values $0 < \omega < +\infty$; the dotted lines show the same functions over the range $-\infty < \omega < 0$. $P$, the number of roots of the denominator of the function $G(s)H(s)$ having positive real parts as determined by Routh's criterion, is indicated for each system. The arrows show the direction of increasing values of $\omega$.

State whether each system is stable or unstable, and indicate the reason for your selection.

**6.5** By means of the complex plane plots, determine whether the systems represented by the following values of $G(j\omega)H(j\omega)$ are stable. Note that it is not necessary to plot exactly the values of $G(j\omega)H(j\omega)$ for all values of frequency. Only a few significant values of $\omega$ need be determined accurately.

$$(a)\ \ G(j\omega)H(j\omega) = \frac{50}{(1 + j0.2\omega)(1 + j0.5\omega)(1 + j2\omega)}$$

$$(b)\ \ G(j\omega)H(j\omega) = \frac{100}{j\omega(1 + j0.8\omega)(1 + j0.25\omega)}$$

**6.6** Determine from complex plane plots whether the two systems having the values of $G(j\omega)H(j\omega)$ listed below are stable or not.

$$(a)\ \ G(j\omega)H(j\omega) = \frac{-10}{j2\omega(1 - j20\omega)}$$

$$(b)\ \ G(j\omega)H(j\omega) = \frac{100}{j\omega(1 + j0.25\omega)(1 + j0.0625\omega)} \times \frac{0.200(j\omega)^2}{(1 + j0.8\omega)}$$

**6.7(a)** Sketch the approximate form of the root locus plots for the values of $G(s)H(s)$ corresponding to the transfer functions of Problem 6.5. Show such significant data as the asymptotes, points of departure from the real axis, and the intersections with the imaginary axis.

**6.7(b)** In similar fashion to that employed in Problem 6.7(a) above, sketch the approximate form of the root locus plots for the following values of $G(s)H(s)$.

$$G(s)H(s) = \frac{200(0.4s + 1)(0.5s + 1)}{s(2.0s + 1)(1.6s + 1)(0.025s + 1)}$$

$$G(s)H(s) = \frac{20(0.218s + 1)}{s(5s + 1)(s/80 + 1)(s/200 + 1)}$$

**6.7**(c)   For a transfer function such as

$$G(s) = \frac{K}{s(T_1s + 1)(T_2s + 1)}$$

establish in a general form the expression for the location at which the root locus will intersect the imaginary axis. What will the value of $K$ be at that point?

**6.8**   As was mentioned in Section 6.4, John R. Moore and A. Leonhard have each pointed out a useful extension to the Nyquist complex plane approach to the subject of system stability. In Section 6.4 it has been shown that the presence of factors in the characteristic equation having positive real parts can be determined by substituting $s = j\omega$ in $G(s)H(s)$ and allowing $\omega$ to take on all values from $-\infty$ to $+\infty$. The net number of counterclockwise rotations $[R]$ is compared with the number of poles $[P]$ of $G(s)H(s)$ as described in Equations 6.4–12, 6.4–15. When $[R] = [P]$ the system is stable, having no factors of the characteristic equation with real parts in the positive portion of the complex plane.

Moore and Leonard suggest that, instead of letting $s = j\omega$, the substitution $s = -b + j\omega$ should be made in the expression for $G(s)H(s)$. If the same criteria are applied as when $s = j\omega$, the presence of factors of the characteristic equation that are more positive than $-b$ will be indicated. Thus if it is desired that transient terms decay to $e^{-1}$ of their original value in a time that is faster than a certain specific number of seconds $\tau$, then $[R]$ must be equal to $[P]$ for $G(s)H(s)$ when the substitution $s = -b + j\omega$ is made with $b = 1/\tau$.

Using this criterion that Moore and Leonard suggest, determine whether the following $G(s)H(s)$ functions have decrement times, $\tau$, less than 0.1 second.

(a)  $G(s)H(s) = \dfrac{100}{s(0.02s + 1)(0.005s + 1)}$

(b)  $G(s)H(s) = \dfrac{20}{s(0.2s + 1)(0.05s + 1)}$

(c)  $G(s)H(s) = \dfrac{40}{(0.5s + 1)(2s + 1)(0.01s + 1)}$

**6.9**   There is a counterpart of the method described in Problem 6.8 for use with Nyquist's complex plane stability criterion that can be used with the Routh stability criterion. The Routh's criterion counterpart involves working with the characteristic equation rather than with the $G(s)H(s)$ function, as is done in the Nyquist method.

In the Nyquist method we replace $s$ by $-b + j\omega$ in $G(s)H(s)$ and allow $\omega$ to vary from $-\infty$ to $+\infty$. In the Routh method we substitute for $s$ in the original characteristic equation,

$$s = \lambda - b$$

where $\lambda$ is a new variable similar in nature to $s$. To the modified characteristic equation in terms of $\lambda$ that is obtained, apply Routh's criterion. If the modified characteristic is "stable," the most positive root of the original characteristic equation is more negative than $-b$, and the largest time constant is less than $1/b$ seconds. If the modified characteristic equation is "unstable," the most positive root of the original characteristic equation is more positive than $-b$, and the largest time constant is less than $1/b$.

For the following characteristic equations, determine if the largest value of time constants is greater or less than 1.0 sec.

$$(a) \qquad 4.64s^4 + 8.95s^3 + 9.95s^2 + 10.28s + 4.64 = 0$$

$$(b) \quad 6.25s^5 + 51.25s^4 + 110.1s^3 + 120.5s^2 + 21s + 1 = 0$$

$$(c) \qquad 36.6s^4 + 81.7s^3 + 90.7s^2 + 59.5s + 11.7 = 0$$

## Chapter 7

**7.1** On the table shown in the accompanying diagram is spring-mounted a platform with equipment attached having a combined mass of $M$ slugs. The spring coupling between the platform and table has a coefficient of $K$ pounds per foot. A viscous damper is attached to the table and the platform and develops $D$ pounds per foot per second of relative motion. The table position, $y(t)$, is the independent variable. The platform position, $x(t)$, is the dependent variable. Determine the transfer function for the platform position $X(s)$ in terms of the table position $Y(s)$. Consider only the translational motion in a vertical plane for the table and the platform.

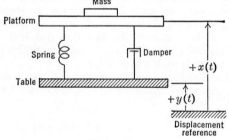

PROB. 7-1

**7.2** The accompanying figure shows a d-c generator supplied from three coupled

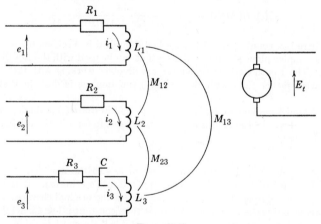

PROB. 7-2

fields. The self-inductance of these fields is $L_1$, $L_2$, and $L_3$, respectively. The mutual coupling between fields 1 and 2 is $M_{12}$, between fields 2 and 3 is $M_{23}$, and between fields 1 and 3 is $M_{13}$. The voltage constant between an ampere of field current and the generator voltage is $K_{1g}$, $K_{2g}$, and $K_{3g}$ for fields 1, 2, and 3, respectively. Field 3 is supplied through an $RC$ series combination.

Derive the expression for the generated voltage $E$ as a function of the applied controlled field voltages, $e_1$, $e_2$, and $e_3$.

**7.3** A bridge-type circuit sometimes used for obtaining a stabilizing voltage from a d-c motor is shown below. Consider $e_{in}(t)$, the input voltage to the motor, to be unaffected by the amount of current drawn from it. $L_{CF}$ and $R_{CF}$ are the inductance and resistance, respectively, of the motor commutating fields. $R_A$ is the resistance of the armature and commutator voltage drop. $K_e$, $K_T$, and $J$ have the same significance as they did in Section 7.5. $R_1$ and $R_2$ are high resistances, the magnitudes of which are so adjusted as to yield a satisfactory value for the stabilizing voltage $e_b(t)$. Neglect the effect of external load torques.

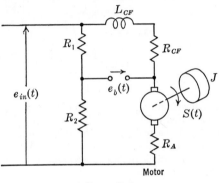

PROB. 7–3

Determine the transfer function $E_b(s)/E_{in}(s)$. Describe the factors that would influence the choice of values for the resistors $R_1$ and $R_2$.

**7.4** Frequently the design of a hydraulic control system involves a cascading of elements such as is illustrated here. The input position of this group of elements is $y(t)$ whereas $x(t)$, the displacement of piston 2, is the output position. The input, valve 1, and piston 1 are connected by the rigid member $A$–$A'$, at the $A'$ end of which is fastened valve 2. The ratio of the lengths along $A$–$A'$ between input, valves, and piston is as indicated. The cylinders of valve 1 and piston 1 are fixed; the cylinder of valve 2 is formed by a movable sleeve that is rigidly coupled to piston 2, with the pivoted linkage $B$–$B'$ having a 4:1 ratio of lengths as shown.

For the data given below, determine the transfer function $X(s)/Y(s)$ for this group of elements. Sketch on the complex plane approximately the nature of this transfer function as a function of frequency for sinusoidal motion of the input.

*Data*

$C_1$ = inches per second motion of piston 1 per inch displacement of valve 1
$C_2$ = inches per second motion of piston 2 per inch displacement of valve 2 relative to its sleeve

The output load reaction force may be neglected.

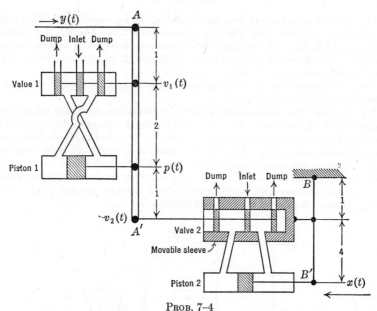

PROB. 7–4

**7.5** The accompanying diagram shows portion of a d-c generator control in which a pilot generator is connected in series with the self-excited shunt field of the main generator. An increase of the main generator voltage tends to increase its field current, which in turn increases the generator voltage still further. Such a type of feedback is said to be regenerative, and it has the property of increasing the effective gain of the generator.

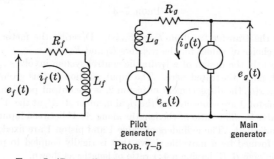

PROB. 7–5

$$T_f = L_f/R_f = \text{pilot field time constant, seconds}$$
$$T_g = L_g/R_g = \text{generator field time constant, seconds}$$
$$K_g = \text{volts of } e_g(t) \text{ per ampere in } L_g$$
$$K_f = \text{volts of } e_a(t) \text{ per ampere in } L_f$$

A positive $i_f(t)$ causes a positive $e_a(t)$ in the direction noted by the arrows. A positive $i_g(t)$ causes a positive $e_g(t)$ in the direction noted by the arrows.

Derive the expression for the transfer function $E_g(s)/E_f(s)$ for the elements shown. Discuss the effect on the generator field time constant that is obtained when the effective gain is increased by use of this type of connection.

**7.6** The transfer function of a hydraulic motor with a variable displacement pump was shown in Equation 7.6–23 to be

$$\frac{\theta(s)}{Y(s)} = \frac{S_p/d_m}{s\left[\dfrac{VJ}{Bd_m{}^2}s^2 + \dfrac{LJ}{d_m{}^2}s + 1\right]}$$

Determine the damping ratio $\zeta$, the undamped natural frequency $\omega_0$, and the actual resonant frequency of the motor for the following data:

$S_p = 6.290 \times 10^3$ cu in./min
$d_m = 2.02$ cu in./revolution
$V = 8.0$ cu in.
$J = 260$ lb-in.²
$B = 2.5 \times 10^5$ lb/sq in.
$L = 0.0022$ cu in./sec/lb/sq in.

What is the gain constant of this motor?

**7.7** For horizontal flight, the control characteristics of a missile frequently can be described more simply than was indicated in Section 7.7. As an approximation, the differential equation relating the control surface deflection, $\delta(t)$, and the angular heading of the missile, $\theta_m(t)$, can be written as

$$K_m\delta(t) = T_m\frac{d^2\theta_m(t)}{dt^2} + \frac{d\theta_m(t)}{dt}$$

where $K_m$ = radians per second of $\theta_m$ per radian of $\delta$, and
$T_m$ = missile time constant in seconds.

A rate gyro measuring the rate of change of the missile angle is used to obtain a voltage, $b(t)$, for control purposes,

$$b(t) = K_r\frac{d\theta_m}{dt}$$

where $K_r$ = volts of $b$ per radian per second of $\theta_m$.

The voltage $b(t)$ is subtracted from the input voltage $e_i(t)$; the resultant voltage is amplified and used to position the control surface deflection $\delta(t)$. Considering an ideal amplifier and power boost,

$$\delta(t) = K_a[e_i(t) - b(t)]$$

where $K_a$ = radians deflection of control surface per volt input to amplifier.

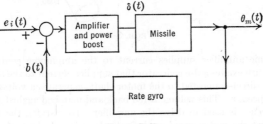

PROB. 7-7

The block diagram above indicates this simple system.

Determine the Laplace transform of the resultant transfer function, $\theta_m(s)/E_i(s)$. What is the effective time constant of this transfer function?

**7.8** Determine the numerical value for the $\theta_m/\delta$ transfer function of a missile in vertical flight for the values of the missile parameters listed below. Using these numerical values, factor the cubic term in the denominator. Does the transfer function have a damping ratio of greater than 0.5 for the quadratic factor?

$$d = 1.5 \text{ ft}$$
$$l = 16.0 \text{ ft}$$
$$K_f = 6500 \text{ lb-ft sec/radian}$$
$$K_{CL} = 15{,}200 \text{ lb/radian}$$
$$K_L = 210{,}000 \text{ lb/radian}$$
$$mg = 6000 \text{ lb}$$
$$F = 13{,}500 \text{ lb}$$
$$V = 2000 \text{ ft/sec}$$
$$J = 15{,}000 \text{ slug ft}^2$$
$$K_D = 4300 \text{ lb}$$

## Chapter 8

**8.1** Many applications in steel mill design require the speed of a large d-c motor to be held constant within very narrow limits regardless of load. A representative speed-control circuit is shown in schematic form below.

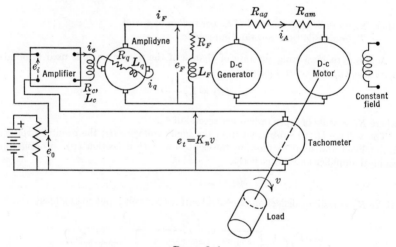

PROB. 8–1

The electronic amplifier supplies current to the amplidyne control field. The amplidyne in turn excites a d-c generator that supplies current to the main d-c motor. A tachometer, direct-connected to the motor shaft, generates a voltage proportional to the motor speed, $v$. This voltage is fed back and matched against a d-c reference, $e_0$. The difference is used to drive the amplifier. By varying the value of $e_0$, an operator can set the motor speed as desired. If $e_0$ is left alone, the motor should maintain very nearly this preset speed at all loads.

*Data*

(1) Amplidyne:
  (a) Control field: $R_c = 80$ ohms    $L_c = 8.0$ henries
  (b) Quadrature winding: $R_q = 1.06$ ohms    $L_q = 0.318$ henry
  (c) Gain—with 0.1 amp (dc) in the control field winding, the open-circuit output voltage is 270 volts

*Note.* The quadrature axis induced emf in the amplidyne is proportional to the control field current. The output voltage of the amplidyne is proportional to the quadrature axis current.

(2) Amplifier:
  (a) Gain = 12 volts/volt
  (b) Time constant and internal resistance—negligible
(3) D-c Generator:
  (a) Field circuit: $R_F = 7.75$ ohms    $L_F = 24.4$ henries

*Note.* These include the resistance and inductance of the amplidyne armature.

  (b) Gain: $K_g = 18.5$ volts/ampere of $i_F$
  (c) Armature resistance: $R_{ag} = 0.002$ ohm
(4) D-c Motor:
  (a) Emf constant: $K_e = 4.0$ volts/rpm
  (b) Torque constant: $K_T = 28.2$ ft-lb/amp
  (c) Armature resistance: $R_{am} = 0.010$ ohm
  (d) Full-load current: $i_A = 1250$ amp
(5) Tachometer constant: $K_n = 0.100$ volt/rpm of motor
(6) Load
  (a) Inertia = 4430 slug ft$^2$
  (b) Friction—negligible

For the condition of no external load other than the load inertia, determine the following:

1. The literal expression for the open-loop system transfer function from amplifier input voltage to tachometer voltage feedback, $E_t(s)/E_i(s)$.
2. The stability of the system from a plot of the open-loop transfer function on the complex plane.
3. The literal expression for the motor speed $V(s)$ in terms of the reference voltage $E_o(s)$.
4. The steady-state values of the reference voltage $e_0$ and the d-c generator field current $i_F$, with the motor having a speed of 150 rpm.

Assume now that the motor is loaded by some external means such that full-load current is drawn while the reference voltage $e_0$ is maintained at its value determined in part 4 above.

5. Find the change in the steady-state motor speed between operation at no load and full load. Compare this change in speed with that resulting when the d-c generator current is maintained at the value of $i_F$ determined in part 4 and the motor load current is increased from no load to full load.

**8.2**  Draw and label schematic and functional block diagrams of the closed-loop control system of Problem 8.1.  Use the nomenclature and symbols contained in Section 8.2 as well as the symbols given in Problem 8.1.  Indicate the numerical values of the transfer functions for each of the various blocks shown on the functional diagram.  Discuss your reason for representing the effect of motor load torques in the fashion you have selected.

**8.3**  One kind of d-c voltage regulator uses an amplifier consisting of a pentode tube followed by a three-phase grid-controlled thyratron rectifier to supply field current to the d-c generator.  Part of the output voltage of the generator is then fed back to the input, matched against a constant d-c voltage, and the difference is used to control the pentode grid voltage.  One phase of the circuit is shown schematically in the accompanying schematic diagram (*a*).  Each thyratron grid has a constant a-c voltage impressed that lags its particular plate voltage by 90°.  In

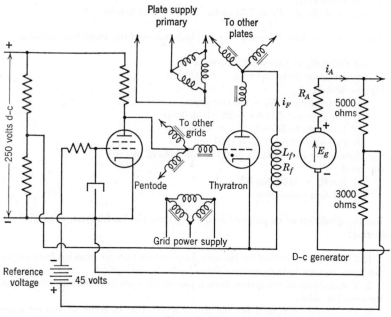

PROB. 8–3(*a*)

addition, the grids have a common d-c bias coming from the pentode plate, which will determine the thyratron firing point.  Thus the average generator field current can be determined by the pentode grid voltage.  Although this looks complicated, it may be represented in the schematic form shown in *b*.  Over the working range, at least, the pentode-thyratron combination may be considered a linear amplifier giving an average voltage across the generator field of *g* volts per volt applied to the pentode grid.  The resistors and condensers placed in the grid circuits to minimize response to "pickup" and commutator hash may be approximated by a simple *RC* circuit preceding the amplifier.

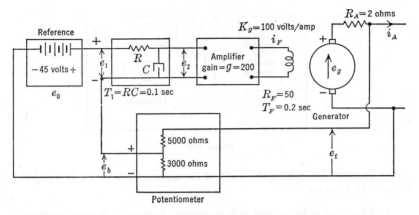

PROB. 8–3(b)

1. Set up the differential equation for $e_t$, the terminal voltage of the generator in terms of the reference voltage, $e_0$, the load current, $i_A$, and the other constants of the system. Neglect the current through the potentiometer in comparison with the current $i_A$.

2. Determine the open-loop transfer function from the actuating signal voltage $e_1$ to the feedback voltage $e_b$, with the load current zero. Plot this transfer function $E_b(s)/E_1(s)$ on the complex plane.

3. Determine the steady-state voltage $e_t$ when $i_A = 0$ and when $i_A = 20$ amp. Compare this performance with what would result if the generator, unregulated, were separately excited to the same no-load voltage and then loaded to 20 amp.

*Data*

$\quad g = 200$ volts/volt = amplifier gain

$\quad T_1 = 0.1$ sec = time constant of $RC$ phase lag circuit

$\quad R_F = 50$ ohms = generator field resistance

$\quad T_F = 0.2$ sec = generator field time constant

$\quad K_g = 100$ volts/amp = generated voltage/field current = $e_g/i_F$

$\quad R_A = 2.0$ ohms = generator armature resistance

$\quad e_0 = 45$ volts = reference voltage

$\quad K_h = \frac{3}{8}$ = part of $e_t$ fed back to input

Armature inductance is negligible.

**8.4** Draw and label a functional block diagram of the voltage regulator system described in Problem 8.3. Use the nomenclature and symbols in Section 8.2 as well as terms used in the problem description. Tabulate the numerical values of the transfer functions shown on the block diagram. What type system is this voltage regulator?

**8.5** A functional block diagram of a position control system is shown in the accompanying diagram. Stabilizing means are incorporated in the amplifier that supplies the power motor that is the controlled system element. It has been suggested that tachometer feedback may improve the operation of the control.

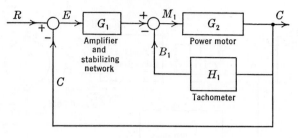

As a means of determining the worth of the tachometer feedback, it is desirable to know the following:

1. What type is the system with tachometer feedback? Without tachometer feedback?
2. What are the values of the first three error coefficients that describe the system with and without tachometer feedback?
3. Sketch on the complex plane in an approximate fashion the complex plane diagrams for the two methods of control.

Comment on the effectiveness of the tachometer feedback on improving the system performance. Would other values of $K_c$ than those suggested be more desirable?

*Data*

Amplifier and Stabilizing Network:

$$G_1 = K_a \frac{(T_1 s + 1)}{(T_2 s + 1)}$$

$$K_a = 1 \text{ volt/radian}$$

$$T_1 = 2.0 \text{ sec}$$

$$T_2 = 0.125 \text{ sec}$$

Power Motor:

$$G_2 = \frac{K_b}{s^2(T_3 s + 1)}$$

$$K_b = 1.6 \text{ radians/sec}^2/\text{volt}$$

$$T_3 = 0.02 \text{ sec}$$

Tachometer:

$$H_1 = K_c s \text{ (with tachometer, } K_c = 0.039 \text{ volt-sec/radian)}$$
$$\text{(without tachometer, } K_c = 0)$$

**8.6** A functional block diagram of a system for controlling torque is shown here. A high gain d-c generator serves as the control element and the controlled system element is an electric motor. The error signal is represented by the net mmf obtained from the difference between two generator control field windings, one supplied from a reference potentiometer, the other by a torque motor current signal proportional to load torque.

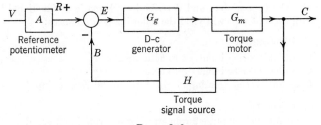

PROB. 8–6

For the system data listed below, answer the following questions.

What type control does this system represent? What is its characteristic error for a constant rate of change of reference input?

Sketch the approximate complex plane plot of the system. By how much could the forward gain be increased, with the same feedback gain, and stable system operation still be maintained? Explain your answer.

*Data*

Reference Element: $A$ = 0.01 amp/lb-ft

D-c Generator:

$$G_g = \frac{K_g}{T_g s + 1}$$

$$K_g = 30 \text{ amp/amp}$$

$$T_g = 0.05 \text{ sec}$$

Torque Motor:

$$G_m = \frac{K_m}{T_m s + 1}$$

$$K_m = 10 \text{ lb-ft/amp}$$

$$T_m = 0.5 \text{ sec}$$

Feedback Element: $H$ = 0.01 amp/lb-ft

**8.7** The open-loop transfer functions for two position control systems each having direct-feedback are:

*Type 1 System:*

$$\frac{C(s)}{E(s)} = \frac{16(4s + 1)}{s(16s + 1)\left(\dfrac{s}{16} + 1\right)}$$

*Type 2 System:*

$$\frac{C(s)}{E(s)} = \frac{0.25\left(\dfrac{s}{4} + 1\right)}{s^2(4s + 1)}$$

Compare the error coefficients for each of these systems.

Compare also the ratio of the maximum value of the controlled variable to the actuating signal $E(s)$ for a sinusoidal input signal of the following frequencies: $\omega$ = 0.01, 0.1, 1.0, and 10.0 radians per second.

**8.8** Specify the type system and describe by schematic or functional block diagrams control systems that will yield the following performances:

*System A:* Position control

         Constant position input—zero actuating error

         Constant velocity input—zero actuating error ·

         Constant acceleration input—$15°$ error for $90°/sec^2$ of input

*System B:* Speed control

         Constant speed input—2 rpm error for 500 rpm input speed

*System C:* Position control

         Constant position input—zero actuating error

         Constant velocity input—$\frac{1}{4}$ revolution error per 300 rpm

**8.9** For each of control systems described in Problems 3.7 and 3.8 perform the following:

1. Draw the system functional block diagram.
2. Determine the transfer function for each element indicated.
3. State the type for each system.
4. Draw the complex plane plot of the open-loop transfer function from actuating signal to feedback signal.

**8.10** A servomechanism has the open-loop transfer function given by the expression

$$G = \frac{G_1}{1 + G_1 H}$$

where $G_1 = \dfrac{100}{j\omega(1 + j0.25\omega)(1 + j0.0625\omega)}$

and $\quad H = \dfrac{0.167(j\omega)^2}{(1 + j0.8\omega)}$

Determine the error coefficients for this system.

What is the approximate error at $t = 2.0$ seconds for this system which is started at rest with a reference input that is described by the equation

$$R(t) = R_0 + R_1 t + R_2 t^2 + R_3 t^3$$

## Chapter 9

**9.1** A type 1 position control system with direct feedback has an open-loop transfer function,

$$\frac{C(s)}{E(s)} = G(s) = \frac{K}{s(1 + T_1 s)(1 + T_2 s)}$$

where $K = 10 \ sec^{-1}$,

     $T_1 = 0.100$ sec,

     $T_2 = 0.025$ sec.

Plot this transfer function on the complex plane as a function of frequency. What is the value of $M_m$? At what frequency does it occur?

**9.2** A regulator system, type 0, having direct feedback has a transfer function

$$\frac{C(s)}{E(s)} = G(s) = \frac{20}{(1 + 2.0s)(1 + 0.25s)(1 + 0.04s)}$$

Plot this transfer function on the complex plane for sinusoidal inputs. With the aid of the $M$ circles, determine the maximum value of $M$ and the frequency at which it occurs for closed-loop operation. What is the phase angle between the reference input and the controlled variable when $\omega = 2$ radians per second?

It has been suggested that by appropriate means the transfer function may be altered to

$$\frac{C(s)}{E(s)} = G'(s) = \frac{40}{(1 + 2.0s)(1 + 0.04s)(1 + 0.025s)}$$

What effect on the closed-loop system performance does this have?

**9.3** An autopilot system with a modified rate feedback is shown in the accompanying functional block diagram. The data for this system are tabulated below.

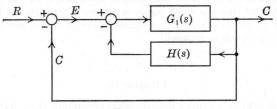

PROB. 9–3

Determine the maximum frequency response, $C/R\,(j\omega)$, for this system and the frequency at which it occurs. Compare the relative merits of the direct and the inverse complex plane methods of determining the solution to this problem.

$$G_1(s) = \frac{K_1}{s(s^2 + 2\zeta\omega_0 s + \omega_0^2)}$$

where $K_1 = 4800$ sec$^{-1}$
$\omega_0 = 14.1$ radians/sec
$\zeta = 0.6$
$H(s) = \dfrac{K_h s^2}{(T_c s + 1)}$
$K_h = 0.25$ sec$^2$
$T_c = 1.5$ sec

**9.4** What is the largest value of the velocity constant, $K_v$, for which the maximum value of the closed-loop frequency response of the system shown in the figure below will be 1.3? Make a plot of the error response for the system with this value of $K_v$.

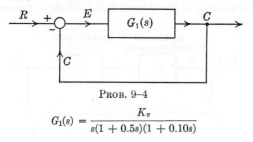

PROB. 9–4

$$G_1(s) = \frac{K_v}{s(1 + 0.5s)(1 + 0.10s)}$$

**9.5** In the control system described in Problem 9.3, it is desired to have the maximum value of $M$ be 1.3. With the system constants otherwise unchanged, what value of the rate feedback constant $K_h$ is required to obtain this condition? At what frequency will $M_m$ occur?

**9.6** For either the control system described in Problem 9.4 or 9.5, each system with the proper gain to cause it to have $M_m$ of 1.3, determine the response to a step function of the reference input. Consider the system to be initially at rest for either case. Compare the nature of the transient and the steady-state responses from the results obtained.

**9.7** Determine the value of $M_m = (E_t/E_0)$ for the voltage regulator described in Problem 8.3, with $i_A$ equal zero. What is the magnitude of the ratio of the peak value of the change in terminal voltage $e_t$ to the value of a step-function change in reference voltage $e_0$. For convenience in performing the transient analysis, it will be satisfactory to assume that the system is linear and that $e_0$ is initially zero. Compare the magnitude of $M_m$ and the maximum of the transient $e_t/e_0$ ratio.

**9.8** It is desired that the speed regulator system of Problem 3.8 have a maximum value of 1.4 for its steady-state frequency response. How much of a change in the amplifier gain will be required?

## Chapter 10

**10.1** It is desired to determine the network configuration, the values of resistance and capacitance, and the complex plane plot for each of the three $RC$ networks having the following characteristics.

*Network*

(a) 1. Phase lead of more than $45°$ at $\omega = 10$ radians per second.
    2. Minimum impedance of 10,000 ohms viewed from the voltage source.
    3. A ratio of maximum to minimum impedance of 20:1.

(b) 1. Phase lag having unity gain for direct current and an output to input ratio of approximately 1:15 at $\omega = 2.0$ radians per second.
    2. Maximum resistance of any element shall not exceed 2.0 megohms.
    3. Maximum capacitance shall not exceed 10 $\mu f$.

(c) 1. Lead-lag network having unity gain for direct current and for high frequencies and a minimum value of gain of about 0.05.
    2. An effective leading characteristic at $\omega = 30$ radians per second.
    3. Resistance and capacitance restrictions the same as those applying for network $b$.

Consider the impedance of the element that loads each of these networks to be infinite.

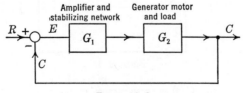

PROB. 10-2

**10.2** The diagram above shows a functional block diagram of a type 1 position control having two principal control elements $G_1$ and $G_2$. The transfer functions of these elements are

$$G_1 = 10\,\frac{(1+s)}{(1+8s)} \text{ volts/radian}$$

$$G_2 = \frac{4.8}{s\left(1+\dfrac{s}{20}\right)} \text{ radians/sec/volt}$$

Plot on the complex plane each transfer function as well as the combined open-loop transfer function.

Approximately what are the values of $M_m$ and $\omega_m$? What is the velocity gain constant of this system?

**10.3** A schematic diagram of a voltage regulator system similar to that described in Problem 3.7 is shown below. By means of the amplifier and appropriate stabilizing network indicated by the transfer function $G_a$, it is anticipated that a more accurate control can be obtained. The gain of the amplifier may be set at any value from 1:1 to 20:1, and any desired $RC$ stabilizing method may be used. However, to obtain a satisfactory degree of stability it is necessary that the value of $M_m$ should not exceed 1.4.

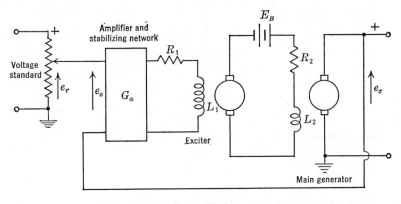

PROB. 10–3

What value of gain and what stabilizing network do you recommend for this regulator? What is the reason for selecting the stabilizing means you have chosen?

*Data*

$R_1 = 80$ ohms
$L_1 = 16$ henries
$K_1 = 320$ volts/amp
$R_2 = 5$ ohms
$L_2 = 5$ henries
$K_2 = 25$ volts/amp

**10.4** A portion of a d-c motor speed control is shown here. The exciter field, $F_1$, controlled by the voltage $e_s$, produces the signal mmf. The exciter in turn excites the generator field for the main generator that supplies the armature voltage to the d-c motor, the speed of which is being controlled. For stabilizing purposes, the exciter has a field $F_2$ that is degeneratively connected across the exciter through a series $RC$ network by means of the switch $S_1$.

Derive the transfer function from the exciter signal voltage to the generator voltage (for no load on the generator), with switch $S_1$ open and with $S_1$ closed.

Plot the two transfer functions on the complex plane for the accompanying data. What is the dominant effect of the feedback obtained with switch $S_1$ closed? Neglect the effect of the resistance and inductance of the exciter armature. To simplify the problem, the mutual coupling between fields $F_1$ and $F_2$ may be neglected.

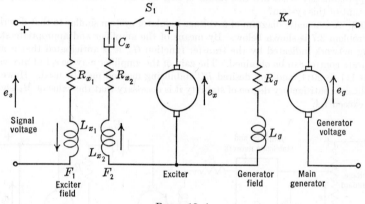

PROB. 10–4

*Data*

$R_{x_1}$ = 400 ohms
$L_{x_1}$ = 8.0 henries
$R_{x_2}$ = 1000 ohms
$C_x$ = 300 μf
$L_{x_2}$ = 8.0 henries
$K_{x_1} = K_{x_2}$ = 2400 exciter volts/field ampere in fields $x_1$ or $x_2$
$R_g$ = 6.6 ohms
$L_g$ = 3.3 henries
$K_g$ = 10 generator volts/field ampere

**10.5** A functional block diagram of a voltage regulator system employing rate feedback through an $RC$ network is shown below. To aid in the determination of the closed-loop frequency response of this system for the transfer functions given, plot on the complex plane the following functions:

(a) $G_1$    (c) $G_1H_1$

(b) $H_1$    (d) $C/E$

Compare the complex plane plot of $d$ with that obtained for $1/H_1$.

What is the maximum value of $M = (C/R)$ for the closed-loop system? Might this value of $M_m$ be improved by changing the value of the gain term of $H_1$ function? Explain.

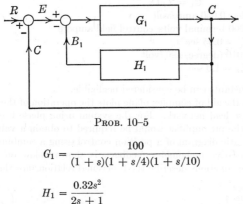

PROB. 10-5

$$G_1 = \frac{100}{(1 + s)(1 + s/4)(1 + s/10)}$$

$$H_1 = \frac{0.32s^2}{2s + 1}$$

**10.6** A schematic diagram of a position control is shown in the accompanying diagram. A selsyn generator and control transformer are used to obtain $E$, an electrical signal proportional to the error between reference input and load positions. This actuating error signal is amplified then rectified by the discriminator to obtain a d-c signal. A lead network is used on the preamplifier output to obtain phase lead

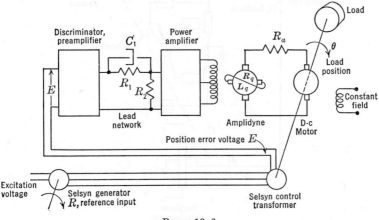

PROB. 10-6

action. The output of the lead network is supplied to the power amplifier that drives the amplidyne fields. The amplidyne drives the d-c motor positioning the load.

*Data*

Preamplifier and selsyn: 16 volts/degree

Phase Lead Network: $R_1 = 437,500$ ohms

$\qquad\qquad\qquad R_2 = 62,500$ ohms

$\qquad\qquad\qquad C_1 = 2\ \mu\text{f}$

Power Amplifier: 0.050 amp/volt

Amplidyne: 2000 terminal volts/control field ampere

$\qquad\quad T_q = 0.05$ sec

D-c Motor: 0.010 (degree/sec)/volt

$\qquad\quad T_m = 1.0$ sec

Other time constants can be considered negligible.

Compare with the aid of complex plane plots the operation of the system with and without the phase lead network. For the system using phase lead, what value of gain setting for the preamplifier would be required to obtain a value of $M_m$ of 1.4?

**10.7** A schematic diagram of a position control using a combination of degenerative and regenerative tachometer feedback is shown below on this page. The following transfer functions describe the functional relationships that exist:

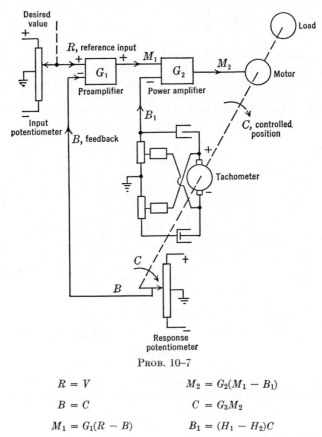

PROB. 10–7

$$R = V \qquad\qquad\qquad M_2 = G_2(M_1 - B_1)$$

$$B = C \qquad\qquad\qquad C = G_3 M_2$$

$$M_1 = G_1(R - B) \qquad\qquad B_1 = (H_1 - H_2)C$$

where $G_1 = 1$
$\quad G_2 = 10$
$\quad G_3 = \dfrac{5}{s(T_m s + 1)}$
$\quad H_1 = \dfrac{K_1 T_1 s^2}{1 + T_1 s}$
$\quad H_2 = K_2 s$

and
$\quad T_m = 0.5 \text{ sec}$
$\quad T_1 = 2.0 \text{ sec}$
$\quad K_1 = 0.5 \text{ sec}$

What value of $K_2$ will produce an infinite velocity gain constant for the system? Draw the complex plane diagram for the open-loop system with this value of $K_2$, and for $K_2$ greater and less than this value by 25 per cent.

**10.8** Suggest a means whereby the position control system of Problem 9.1 may be made to have a velocity gain constant of 60, and an $M_m$ of 1.3 or less. Indicate the necessary networks and/or gain changes to make this possible.

## Chapter 11

**11.1** A network frequently used in stabilizing servomechanisms is the integral-differential or lag-lead network shown in Figure 10.1–16. With proper choice of the time constants

$$T_1 = R_1 C_1 \qquad T_2 = R_2 C_2 \qquad T_{12} = R_1 C_2$$

the network has the approximate Bode attenuation diagram shown below.

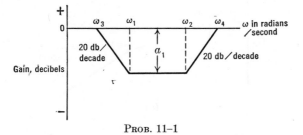

PROB. 11–1

The transfer function of such a network is of the form

$$G(j\omega) = \dfrac{\left(1 + j\dfrac{\omega}{\omega_1}\right)\left(1 + j\dfrac{\omega}{\omega_2}\right)}{\left(1 + j\dfrac{\omega}{\omega_3}\right)\left(1 + j\dfrac{\omega}{\omega_4}\right)}$$

(a) Knowing the values $\omega_1$, $\omega_2$, $\omega_3$, $\omega_4$ at which it is desired that the breaks occur, set up the necessary equations from which $R_1$, $R_2$, $C_1$, and $C_2$ can be determined.

(b) For $\omega_1 = 10$ radians per sec, $\omega_2 = 31.6$ radians per sec, $R_1 = 10{,}000$ ohms, and a maximum attenuation on the approximate diagram of $a_1 = 10$ decibels, find $R_2$, $C_1$, $C_2$.

(c) Plot phase of $G(j\omega)$ versus $\log_{10} \omega$ for the network of (b).

(d) Find the difference in decibels between the attenuation as shown on the approximate diagram ($a_1$) and the actual attenuation produced by this network at

$$\omega = \sqrt{\omega_1 \omega_2}$$

**11.2** Draw the straight-line attenuation diagrams showing the magnitude in decibels and phase angle in degrees as a function of frequency for the following transfer functions:

$$(a)\ G_a = \frac{200}{s(1 + 0.5s)(1 + 0.1s)}$$

$$(b)\ G_b = \frac{0.2s^2}{(1 + 0.4s)(1 + 0.04s)}$$

$$(c)\ G_c = \frac{5(0.6s + 1)}{s^2(4s + 1)}$$

$$(d)\ G_d = \frac{75(0.2s + 1)}{s(s^2 + 16s + 100)}$$

**11.3** Assuming the straight-line attenuation-frequency diagrams shown below to represent the approximate characteristics of physically realizable control system elements, express the transfer functions of these elements as functions of $s$. The frequency scale is logarithmic while the amplitude scale is in decibels. Consider the slopes of the straight lines shown to be maintained for frequencies higher and lower than those indicated.

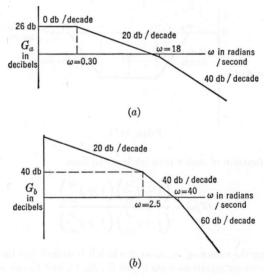

PROB. 11–3 (a and b)

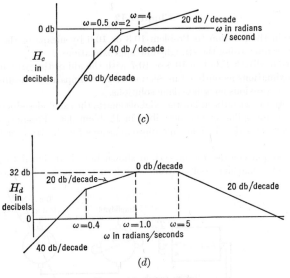

$(c)$

$(d)$

PROB. 11–3 ($c$ and $d$)

**11.4** Draw the straight-line approximation of the attenuation-frequency diagram and draw the phase shift as a function of frequency for the open-loop transfer function of Problem 10.2. Indicate the actual attenuation diagram for this control. From the contours of constant $M$ given on the Nichols charts (Figure 11.5–4), determine $M_m$ and $\omega_m$.

**11.5** For the values of transfer functions $G_1$ and $H_1$ given in Problem 10.5, draw the straight-line approximation of the attenuation diagram and draw the phase shift for the following transfer functions: $G_1$, $H_1$, $G_1H_1$, $1/H_1$.

**11.6** Show, with the aid of the straight-line approximations for the transfer functions, the values of the position, velocity, or acceleration gain constants of Problems 11.2$a$, $c$, and $d$ and Figures $a$ and $b$ of Problem 11.3. Compare the magnitudes of the actual value of these transfer functions at $\omega = 1$ with the values of the corresponding gain constants.

**11.7** For the control systems shown in Figures 11.4–1, 11.4–2, and 11.4–3 of the text, draw the actual attenuation diagrams corresponding to the straight-line diagrams shown. With the aid of the Nichols charts, plot on the same diagrams a series of significant contours of $M$. Sketch the closed-loop frequency response for Figure 11.4–3. If it is possible for each of these systems to have a $M_m$ of 1.3 by means of changing the gain alone, indicate the amount by which the gain should be changed for each system.

**11.8** Plot the actual attenuation and phase characteristics as a function of frequency for the hydraulic motor and the missile flight characteristics given below:

$(a)$ Hydraulic motor: $G_m = \dfrac{35,000}{s(s^2 + 16s + 1750)(0.1s + 1)}$

$(b)$ Missile flight: $G_f = \dfrac{14}{s(2.4s^2 + 1.5s + 1)}$

## Chapter 12

**12.1** Obtain the solution to Problem 10.3 or 10.6 by means of the attenuation and phase diagrams, using the straight-line approximations.

**12.2** Solve feedback Problem 10.5 or 10.7 with the aid of the straight-line attenuation approximations as outlined in Section 12.2. Compare the results with those obtained in the previous complex-plane solutions.

**12.3** Determine with the aid of the Nichols charts the exact closed-loop frequency response of the autopilot system described in Problem 9.3. For purposes of comparison indicate also the straight-line approximations for the transfer functions $G_1$ and $1/H$.

**12.4** The amplidyne d-c motor system shown here is designed to position the cutting head of a machine tool control. A selsyn transmitter is remotely located

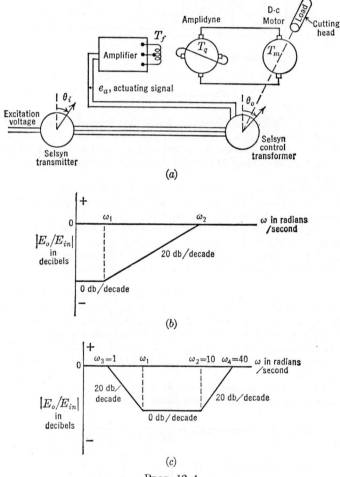

PROB. 12–4

and is positioned by a master template. The selsyn control transformer rotor is geared to the load and indicates cutting head position. The control transformer output voltage $e_a$ is the actuating signal, $e_a = \theta_i - \theta_o$.

The open-loop transfer function of the system is:

$$\frac{\theta_o(s)}{E_a(s)} = G(s) = \frac{K_1}{s(1 + T_f s)(1 + T_q s)(1 + T_m s)}$$

where $K_1$ = gain constant, seconds$^{-1}$,
$\quad T_f$ = control field time constant = 0.001 sec,
$\quad T_q$ = quadrature axis time constant = 0.025 sec, and
$\quad T_m$ = motor load time constant = 0.100 sec.

In order for the system to have an acceptable closed-loop response, it is necessary that there be at least a 45° positive phase margin at the 0 db gain point for the open-loop transfer function.

(a) What is the maximum permissible value of $K_1$? (Use the approximate Bode attenuation plot.)

(b) In an attempt to raise the permissible resultant gain, $K_1$, a simple phase lead network like that of Figure 10.1–8 and having the approximate characteristics shown in diagram b is built into the first stage of the amplifier. For $\omega_1 = 10$, $\omega_2 = 40$, what is the new permissible value of $K_1$? (Still with +45° phase margin at 0 db.) Draw the approximate Bode attenuation plot and write $G(j\omega)$ for the new system.

(c) As a second trial an integral-differential network like that of Figure 10.1–16 having the approximate characteristics shown in diagram c is used instead of the simple lead network. What value of $K_1$ can now be used and still give a +45° phase margin at the 0 db point of the open-loop transfer function?

(d) Compare the closed-loop frequency responses of systems a, b, and c. If you were the designer, what factors would influence you in selecting the most satisfactory system?

**12.5** With the data given for steel mill speed-regulating system of Problem 8.1, draw the open-loop attenuation and phase margin characteristics of the regulator $(E_t/E_i)$ as a function of frequency in radians per second. Compare the closed-loop response, that is, the motor speed to reference voltage ratio $V/E_o$, obtained using the exact and the straight-line approximation to the open-loop attenuation characteristics.

What means would you suggest to increase the value of $\omega_m$ of the closed-loop frequency response, without increasing the peak value $M_m$. Such means as decreasing the various field time constants by increasing their series resistance or by utilizing feedback should be discussed.

**12.6** It is desired to decrease the phase shift at zero db of the resultant transfer function $\theta/E_1$ that can be obtained using the amplifier, amplidyne, and motor indicated in the accompanying figure. Specifically it is suggested that tachometer feedback through a double $RC$ network be used as indicated by the dotted portion of the figure.

With the data given for the attenuation and phase angle plots, determine suitable values for $K_f$, $T_1$, and $T_2$. Indicate a set of suitable values for the required $RC$ network. Discuss the reasons for your selections.

Draw the phase angle and the exact attenuation characteristic as a function of fre-

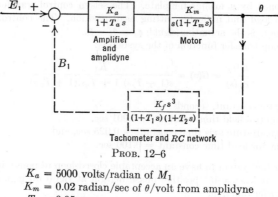

PROB. 12–6

$K_a = 5000$ volts/radian of $M_1$
$K_m = 0.02$ radian/sec of $\theta$/volt from amplidyne
$T_a = 0.05$ sec
$T_m = 0.40$ sec
$K_f = $ radians of $B_1$/radian/sec$^3$ of $\theta$
$T_1 = $ seconds
$T_2 = $ seconds

quency for the $\theta/E_1$ transfer function that results when the tachometer feedback and network you have chosen are used.

**12.7** The attenuation-phase shift concepts are useful in establishing the design parameters for hydraulic lead and lag elements as well as for electrical elements of this sort. For example, if the valve-piston speed displacement characteristic $C_1$ and the desired attenuation frequency are known, the proper linkage arrangement and linkage lengths may be selected readily.

Assume $C_1$ to be 25 in. per second motion of piston $P$ per inch of valve displacement. Also assume that a phase lead characteristic with an increase in gain of 16:1 from low to high frequencies is required. The frequency at which the straight-line approximation to the attenuation frequency characteristic again has a slope of 0 db per decade is 100 radians per second.

Determine a suitable valve-piston-linkage combination and indicate the ratio of the lengths of the links involved.

## Chapter 13

**13.1** Locate two different sets of poles and zeros each of which will produce the following performance

*A.* (1) Velocity error coefficient $> 0.0125$ sec
    (2) Damping ratio $> 0.5$
    (3) Decay rate $< 0.2$ sec
    (4) Natural frequency between 20 and 40 rad/sec

Determine two other different sets of poles and zeros, each of which will provide the specifications listed below

*B.* (1) Velocity error coefficient $> 0.002$ sec
    (2) Damping ratio $> 0.6$
    (3) Decay rate $< 0.05$ sec

**13.2** Verify the values of the root locus plots given in Figures 13.2–3 @ $s = 0$, $-\frac{1}{2}$ and $-1$. Also verify the value of gain for the closed-loop root at $s = -16.6$.

**13.3** For Figure 13.2–7 verify the values of the root locus plots at $s = 0$, $-\frac{1}{2}$, and $-1$. What is the value of gain for the closed loop pole @ $s = 2$?

**13.4** Plot the root locus for Problem 10.2. What are the closed-loop poles for the values of gain given.

**13.5** Plot the root locus for Problem 10.3 (or 10.6). For the gain and stabilizing networks chosen in the previous problem, what is the lowest value of decay rate? If an oscillatory solution has been obtained, what are the values of damping ratio and natural frequency obtained?

**13.6** For the voltage regulator with rate feedback shown in Problem 10.5 plot the root locus for the $G_1H_1$ function, i.e., the inner loop. With the values of gain given for $G_1$ and $H_1$, then plot the root locus for $C/E$. Do you recommend that the $C/E$ loop be operated at any other value of gain? Why?

**13.7** For the hydraulic motor and missile flight characteristics given in Problem 11.8, plot the root locus characteristics. Through the use of the root locus plot and by means of supplemental networks if necessary, what may be done to improve the control system performance.

**13.8** Problem 12.4 compares three different versions of the same basic control system from an attenuation-frequency point of view. Compare the root locus plots for these three different conditions. Based on the root locus plots, what system would you recommend? What are your reasons for this recommendation?

**13.9** On Figure 13.2–9 is shown the root locus plot for the resultant type 1 control system using lead-lag stabilization that was previously represented on Figures 10.1–18 and 12.1–7. Using the closed-loop poles obtained from Figure 13.2–9, determine the equations for the time response of this system to a step-input of position. Sketch the curve for this time response.

**13.10** A hydraulic power element having a sufficient power rating for a given application has the transfer function

$$G_1 = \frac{10}{s(0.5s + 1)(0.08s + 1)}$$

It is desired that position servomechanism be designed having a velocity error coefficient of 500 seconds$^{-1}$ and a minimum decay rate of 1 second. The decrement factor should be approximately 0.5.

Establish suitable transfer functions using this motor to meet the desired system requirements. Verify your results by means of suitable root locus plots.

### Chapter 14

**14.1** In the design of practical control systems, feedback terms are occasionally obtained from control quantities that can be easily and cheaply obtained and that produce a measure of the compensating effect sought. However, the action of such feedback terms on the resultant control performance may not be desirable under all conditions of operation.

The speed control system shown above indicates a form of control in which a measure of the controlled speed is obtained from the motor terminal voltage $V_t$. Only one gas tube of the three supplying 3-phase power to the motor is shown. Although the voltage $V_t$ is proportional to the sum of the voltage drop due to the current through the motor resistance $R_2$ and to the speed voltage of the motor, use

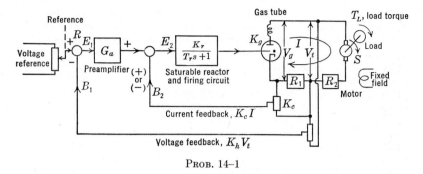

PROB. 14–1

of the $V_t$ feedback avoids the installation of a motor tachometer that may be expensive or troublesome to maintain. To reduce the error in motor speed caused by the $IR_2$ voltage drop, a current feedback term, $K_c I$, is sometimes fed back regeneratively and used as an auxiliary feedback quantity, $B_2$.

For the system shown with regenerative current feedback employed, express the equations for the operation of the system. From these equations, obtain a block diagram that shows the motor speed, the reference speed, and the load torque.

Can a degenerative current feedback be used advantageously to produce a control that has more desirable operation in the presence of load torques? Explain your answer.

For the system with regenerative current feedback and with the data given below, select suitable values for the feedback coefficient $K_c$ and the preamplifier transfer characteristic $G_a$. Draw the attenuation diagrams for $S/R$ and $S/T_L$ for this control, where $S$ is the actual speed of the motor. Comment on the effectiveness of the use of $V_t$ for a speed feedback signal.

*Data*

$R$ = reference input, 1 volt/radian/second of desired speed

$B_1$ = feedback volts obtained from motor terminal voltage

$G_a$ = preamplifier transfer function, volts from amplifier per volt of $E_1$
 ($= R - B_1$)

$B_2$ = current feedback voltage obtained from motor armature current

$E_2$ = net input voltage to saturable reactor

$K_r K_g$ = net d-c gain from input voltage $E_2$ to gas tube terminal voltage = 10 volts/volt

$T_r$ = time constant in seconds of saturable reactor = 1.0 sec

$V_g$ = equivalent generated voltage of gas tube $\left( V_g = \dfrac{K_r K_g}{T_r s + 1} E_2 \right)$

$R_1$ = effective resistance of gas-tube and associated reactors = 3 ohms

$R_2$ = effective resistance of motor = 1 ohm

$K_c$ = volts feedback per ampere of motor armature current

$K_h$ = 0.5 volt feedback/volt of motor terminal voltage

$J$ = inertia of motor and load in slug ft², = 0.12

$K_T$ = motor torque constant in pound-feet per ampere = 1.47

$K_e$ = motor emf constant in volts per radian per second = 2.0

$S$ = motor speed in radians per second

Neglect the current drawn by the potentiometers supplying the current and voltage feedback signals. Also neglect the inductance in the motor armature circuit.

**14.2** Shown on this page is a position control system having an amplidyne and a d-c armature controlled motor as its power element. In addition to the controlled variable position feedback, controlled variable velocity and acceleration signals are fed back through an appropriate double $RC$ feedback filter. For the system data given, determine the following features of system performance considered in the absence of load torques:

1. Is the system stable?
2. What is the straight-line approximation to the open-loop attenuation diagram, $C/E$?
3. What is the magnitude of the steady-state velocity error coefficient?
4. What is the magnitude of the maximum error for a sinusoidal reference input ($R$) of 25° amplitude and a 9-sec period?
5. What are the values of $M_m$ and $\omega_m$ for the closed-loop system?

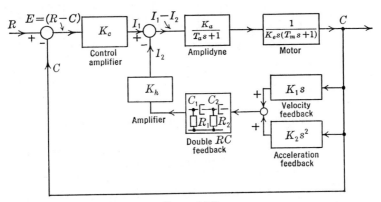

PROB. 14–2

*Data*

$K_c = 0.233$ = control field amperes per radian of error
$K_a = 12,000$ = amplidyne generated volts per control field ampere
$T_a = 0.078$ = amplidyne time constant, seconds
$K_e = 1.88$ = volts per radian per second of motor
$K_1 = 0.333$ = volts per motor radian per second
$K_2 = 0.0046$ = volts per motor radian per second$^2$
$K_h = 0.061$ = control field ampere per volt from filter
$R_1 = 250,000$ ohms
$R_2 = 100,000$ ohms
$C_1 = 1$ μf
$C_2 = 4$ μf
$T_m = 0.0402$ = motor time constant in seconds

**14.3** It is desired to compare a feedback stabilized control system with a similar series stabilized control system on the basis of their ability to operate accurately in the presence of variable loads on the output. The two systems are designed so that they have substantially identical response to a reference input signal, but they may or may not have the same response for applied load torques.

The two systems are shown below on this page. Assuming no gear backlash and linear operation throughout, is there any difference in the response of the two systems when a load torque is applied? What is the error for each system if a steady-load torque of 1000 lb-ft is applied? Assume that rated torque is developed in the stalled motor for 5 ma amplidyne field current and that rated torque is 5000 lb-ft at the load. The motor time constant is 0.1 sec, and the moment of inertia (referred to the motor shaft) of the motor armature, load, and gears is 0.71 lb-ft². Determine for each system the response of the controlled variable $C$ as a function of frequency for sinusoidal load torque inputs. Comment on the relative response of the two systems when subjected to a step-function input of torque, assuming linear operation throughout.

Assuming equal cost, weight, reliability, and serviceability, which system would you recommend?

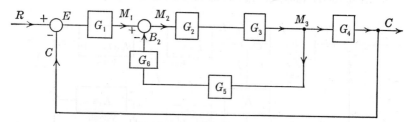

PROB. 14–3($a$).   Feedback stabilized control system.

$$G_1 = \frac{1}{2} \times \frac{250}{2\pi}$$

representing the error voltage developed out of the mixing resistors per radian of error between $C$ and $R$.

$$G_2 = \frac{1}{5} \times \frac{(1 + 0.1s)}{(1 + 0.02s)} \times 2000$$

representing the transfer function of a lead network which stabilizes the inner loop and of an amplifier. The amplifier is chosen so that $G_1G_2G_3G_4 = 100/s$ for $s$ very small.

$$G_3 = \frac{7.5}{s(1 + 0.5s)(1 + 0.1s)}$$

representing the transfer function of the motor and amplidyne.

$$G_4 = \frac{1}{600}$$

representing a gear train.

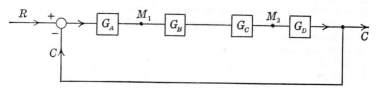

PROB. 14–3($b$).   Series stabilized control system.

$$G_5 = \frac{0.2s^2}{(s + 1)}$$

representing the transfer function of the tachometer and lead network.

$G_6 = 0.0276$   representing mixing resistors chosen so that $\dfrac{G_1G_4}{G_6G_5} =$ 1 for $\omega = 6$ thereby giving a crossover frequency of 6 radians/sec.

$G_A = \dfrac{1}{2} \times \dfrac{250}{2\pi}$   representing the error voltage developed out of the mixing resistors per radian of error between $C$ and $R$.

$G_B = \dfrac{2000(s+1)(1+0.5s)(1+0.1s)(\frac{1}{5})}{(\frac{100}{6}s+1)(0.03s+1)(1+0.02s+1)}$   representing an amplifier and network. The amplifier gain is chosen so that $G_AG_BG_CG_D = 100/s$ for low frequencies.

$G_C = \dfrac{7.5}{s(1+0.5s)(1+0.1s)}$   representing the motor amplidyne transfer function.

$G_D = \dfrac{1}{600}$   representing a gear train.

**14.4**  In the design of process controls we frequently find that the measurement of the controlled variable can be accomplished only if significant time delays can be tolerated. Such time delays may have the effect of markedly altering the control performance from that which would be obtained with direct feedback. To illustrate the operation of a system not having direct feedback, consider the speed-fuel control system shown in block diagram form below.

Prob. 14-4

$K_1 = 4.530$ lb/in.$^2$ per radian/sec   $T_1 = 0.0195$ sec
$K_2 = 0.694$ gal/min per lb/in.$^2$   $T_2 = 0.010$  sec
$K_3 = 4.320$ radians/sec per gal/min   $T_3 = 2.00$   sec
$K_4 = 0.533$ lb/in.$^2$ per gal/min   $T_4 = 0.025$  sec
$K_5 = 1.00$ radian/sec per radian/sec   $T_5 = 0.013$  sec
$T_6 = 0.050$  sec
$T_7 = 0.0065$ sec

In this system the primary controlled variable is the speed, $C_1$, which is measured by means of a speed indicator and compared to the reference speed input, $R_1$. The error in speed actuates the governor control amplifier to establish the reference pressure input. This pressure reference has added to it an indicated pressure that is derived from the quantity of fuel flow. The fuel control error signal actuates the fuel control amplifier. For a given set of operating conditions, the fuel flow establishes the value of the controlled speed.

*A.* By means of approximate straight-line attenuation diagrams for various portions of this system, draw the frequency response showing the ratio of controlled speed ($C$) to reference speed input ($R_1$) as a function of frequency. Also draw the exact attenuation and phase shift characteristics corresponding to the straight-line attenuation characteristics drawn above.

*B.* Obtain the attenuation characteristics, straight-line and exact, as well as the phase shift for the ratio of fuel flow ($M_2$) to reference speed input ($R_1$). Discuss the significance of the units of amplitude as well as the shape of the $M_2/R_1$ curves that are obtained. Comment on the effect of the feedback being other than direct feedback.

**14.5** Regulator control systems using a hydraulic pump and motor frequently have the pump driven by a prime mover that does not maintain constant speed.

As a result, the amount of oil pumped to the motor for a given piston stroke is affected by the prime mover speed; the speed of the motor and its attached load is a direct function of the change in the prime mover speed from its nominal value. For small changes in prime mover speed, the change in prime mover speed can be considered as an unwanted disturbance $U$ which acts as a supplemental input to the regulator system.

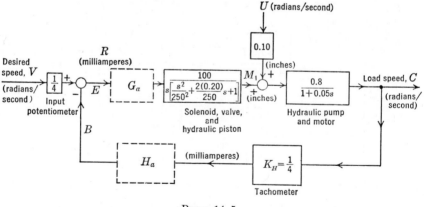

PROB. 14–5

Shown above in block diagram form is a speed control system using a hydraulic drive. The solid blocks indicate transfer functions that form the basic system. The dotted blocks indicate locations in the system where additional components may be conveniently added. An electric solenoid positions a pilot valve proportional to the difference between the reference input $R$ and the feedback signal $B$. Oil flowing through the pilot valve causes the hydraulic stroking piston to move at a rate proportional to the pilot valve opening. The solenoid valve combination has a high resonance frequency and relatively low damping.

The speed of the hydraulic motor and its connected load is approximately proportional to the stroking piston position $M_1$. The feedback signal is obtained from a tachometer and can be considered to be directly proportional to load speed. The effect of changes in the prime mover speed is represented by the disturbance input $U$, which has a similar effect on the load speed to that produced by a change in the stroking piston position for a constant prime mover speed.

For the system constants given determine the following:

    $A$. The frequency response from desired value to load speed, $C/V$.

    $B$. The frequency response for prime mover speed change, $C/U$.

    $C$. The value of $E$ for:

$$1.\ u(t) = U_0$$

$$2.\ u(t) = U_1 t$$

What additional series or feedback stabilizing means, $G_a$ or $H_a$, would you recommend to improve the performance of the control?

**14.6** A simplified form of roll control for an airplane is shown below. The input to the autopilot is obtained from the difference between the signal from the preamplifier and the roll rate gyro feedback signal $B_2$. The combined autopilot and airplane characteristic is given by the transfer function $G_2$. The actuating signal $E$ is the input to the preamplifier and is the difference between the reference input $R$ and the principal feedback $B_1$.

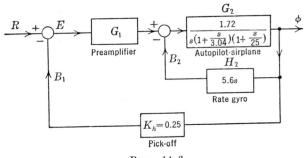

PROB. 14-6

What transfer characteristic should the preamplifier $G_1$ have so that the maximum value of the closed-loop frequency response $\phi/R$ does not exceed 1.3?

**14.7** The pitch steering control of an airplane is complicated by the oscillatory response of the airplane itself and by the additional delay caused by the path time constant. In addition to the rate gyro and the path feedbacks, an accelerometer feedback has been suggested as a means of improving the performance of the system. The block diagram below shows the proposed steering control system, with recommended values for the various transfer functions.

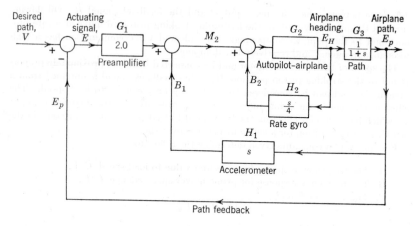

PROB. 14-7

$$G_2 = \frac{8(1 + s)}{s\left(1 + \dfrac{s}{15}\right)\left(1 + \dfrac{s}{30}\right)\left[\dfrac{s^2}{4^2} + \dfrac{2(0.6)}{4}s + 1\right]}$$

Is the proposed system stable? What is its velocity error coefficient? Draw the straight-line attenuation diagrams necessary to establish the closed-loop frequency response of the system. What is the actual value of $M_{\max}$, and at what frequency does it occur? What comments do you have regarding the proposed system design?

**14.8** Starting with the block diagrams indicated below, rearrange and simplify the blocks to obtain, in terms of the transfer functions of the individual elements, the literal expression for the desired transfer functions listed below each figure.

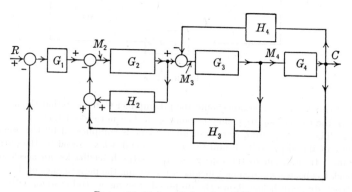

PROB. 14-8(a).  Determine $C/R$.

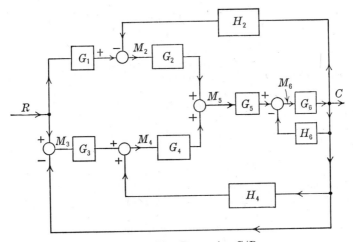

PROB. 14–8(b). Determine $C/R$.

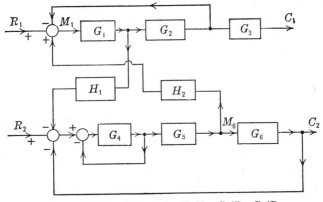

PROB. 14–8(c). Determine $C_1/R_1$; $C_2/R_2$; $C_1/R_2$.

**14.9** A. The series of equations listed below describe the performance of various portions of a speed controller in which the effect of load disturbances is neglected. Draw a block diagram that represents this system of equations. Indicate the various transfer functions associated with each of the blocks shown.

$$(1) \quad K_1(R - C) = (L_1 s + R_1)I_1$$

where $R$ = reference input, radians per second,
$\quad C$ = controlled variable, radians per second,
$\quad K_1$ = volts per radian per second,
$\quad I_1$ = control signal current, amperes,
$\quad L_1$ = inductance of control circuit, henries,
$\quad R_1$ = resistance of control circuit, ohms, and
$\quad T_1$ = $L_1/R_1$, seconds.

$$(2)\ E_e = A_1 I_1 - A_2 I_2 - A_6 I_6$$

where $E_e$ = pilot exciter voltage,
$I_2$ = pilot exciter feedback current, amperes,
$I_6$ = main generator feedback current, amperes, and
$A_1, A_2, A_6$ = pilot exciter volts per ampere.

$$(3)\ \frac{(T_2 s + 1)}{(T_b s + 1)} I_2 R_2 = E_e$$

where $T_2, T_b$ = time constants, seconds, and
$R_2$ = resistance of pilot exciter feedback circuit, ohms.

$$(4)\ (L_e s + R_e) I_e = E_e$$

where $L_e$ = inductance of main exciter control field, henries,
$R_e$ = resistance of main exciter control field circuit, ohms,
$T_e = L_e/R_e$, seconds, and
$I_e$ = current in main exciter control field, amperes.

$$(5)\ E_x = A_e I_e - A_4 I_4 - A_5 I_5$$

where $E_x$ = main exciter voltage,
$I_4$ = main exciter feedback current, amperes,
$I_5$ = generator feedback current, amperes, and
$A_e, A_4, A_5$ = main exciter volts per ampere.

$$(6)\ E_x = \frac{(T_4 s + 1)}{(T_c s + 1)} I_4 R_4$$

where $T_4, T_c$ = time constants, seconds, and
$R_4$ = main exciter feedback circuit resistance, ohms.

$$(7)\ E_x = (L_F s + R_F) I_F$$

where $L_F$ = inductance of generator field, henries,
$R_F$ = resistance of generator field, ohms,
$T_F = L_F/R_F$ = generator field time constant, seconds, and
$I_F$ = generator field current, amperes.

$$(8)\ E_g = A_g I_F$$

where $E_g$ = generator voltage, and
$A_g$ = generator volts per ampere.

$$(9)\ T_7 s E_g = (L_6 s + R_6) I_6$$

where $T_7$ = time constant, seconds,
$L_6$ = inductance of generator feedback field, henries,
$R_6$ = resistance of generator feedback field, ohms, and
$T_6 = L_6/R_6$ = time constant, seconds.

$$(10)\ I_5 = \frac{K_5 s E_g}{T_5 s + 1}$$

where $T_5$ = time constant for generator feedback current, seconds, and
$K_5$ = amperes per volt per second.

$$(11) \quad E_g = K_e(T_m s + 1)C$$

where $K_e$ = motor speed voltage constant, volts per radian per second,
$T_m$ = motor time constant, seconds.

B. The lateral equations of motion of an airplane involve three simultaneous equations containing as dependent variables: $\psi$, the angle of yaw; $\phi$, the angle of roll; and $\beta$, the angle of side slip. The independent variables are the control surface deflection angles: $\delta_r$, the rudder angle, and $\delta_a$, the aileron angle. These three equations of lateral motion are given below, with the linearized aerodynamic coefficients grouped together in the form of time constants and gains.

*Yaw Moment Equation*

$$K_1(T_1 s + 1)s\psi + K_2(T_2 s + 1)s\phi - K_3\beta = -K_4\delta_a + K_5(T_5 s + 1)\delta_r$$

*Roll Moment Equation*

$$K_6(T_6 s + 1)s\psi + K_7(T_7 s + 1)s\phi + K_8\beta = K_9(T_9 s + 1)\delta_a + K_{10}\delta_r$$

*Side Force Equation*

$$K_{11}s\psi - K_{12}\phi + K_{13}(T_{13} s + 1)\beta = K_{14}(T_{14} s + 1)\delta_r$$

The rudder angle $\delta_r$ provides the primary control of the side slip angle $\beta$ and the yaw angle $\psi$. The aileron angle $\delta_a$ provides the primary control of the roll angle $\phi$.

Draw a block diagram that satisfies the relationships set forth by the above equations. Comment on the conditions necessary for the three equations to be considered independently.

## Chapter 15

**15.1** For the position control system of Problem 9.1 calculate the magnitude of the ratio of peak overshoot to reference input for a step input of reference position. Compare this value to the value of $M_m$ previously obtained. Compare also the value of the transient oscillation frequency with the value of $\omega_m$ determined previously.

**15.2** Determine the transient response to a step-function input for the control system of Problem 10.2 initially at rest. The values of $M_m$ and $\omega_m$ for this system have previously been determined in Problem 11.4. Compare the transient and steady-state performance figures thus obtained with the corresponding values determined by using the appropriate performance charts, Figures 15.4–7 through 15.4–23.

**15.3** The requirements of a position control system have been set forth in the following set of specifications:

    (1) $M_m = 1.3$ or less

    (2) $\omega_m = 2.0$ cycles/sec or more

    (3) Velocity gain constant = 200 sec$^{-1}$

The attenuation rate of the open loop control will be 60 db per decade for frequencies in excess of $\omega = 120$ radians per second.

Determine the open-loop transfer function of a suitable control for this application. Indicate the reason for your selection of this transfer function.

**15.4** The transfer function of a servomechanism has the following form:

$$\frac{C}{E} = \frac{A(1 + T_2s)^2}{s(1 + T_1s)^2(1 + T_3s)}$$

The following specifications are to be met by the servomechanism:

(a) The decibel gain at $\omega = \omega_1$ must equal 48 db and $\omega_1 = 0.4$ radian/sec.
(b) The ratio of $\omega_3/\omega_c$ is equal to 4.
(c) The maximum steady-state response, $|C/R|_m$, must not exceed 1.4.
(d) The maximum overshoot in the transient response to a step function must not exceed 1.35.

For a control meeting these requirements, determine:

(1) The required d-c gain $A$.
(2) $T_1$, $T_2$, and $T_3$.
(3) The frequency, $\omega_m$, at which $C/R|_m$ occurs.
(4) The natural frequency of the system, $\omega_t$.
(5) The response time, $t_p$, from the start of the step function until $C/R|_p$ occurs, and the settling time, $t_s$, from the start of the step function until the output continues to differ from the input by less than 5 per cent.

Draw the straight-line attenuation diagram of the system.

**15.5** In Figure 12.4–2 of the text are the closed-loop response as well as the actual and approximate open-loop attenuation characteristics of the control system described in Figures 12.2–2 and 12.2–5. Compare the values of $M_m$ and $\omega_m$ obtained from Figure 12.4–2 with the corresponding values obtained from the appropriate curves on the performance charts of Figures 15.4–7 through 15.4–23.

Determine the transient response of this control to a step position of reference input for the system initially at rest. Compare the results with the approximate values obtained from the performance charts of this chapter.

**15.6** To further illustrate the degree of similarity between the transient response of regulator (type 0) and servomechanism (type 1) systems, having comparable attenuation characteristics in the vicinity of 0 db and for higher frequencies, consider the following two-system transfer functions:

*Regulator System:*

$$\frac{C}{E} = \frac{100(0.625s + 1)}{(5s + 1)(2.5s + 1)(0.0625s + 1)}$$

*Servomechanism System:*

$$\frac{C}{E} = \frac{20(0.625s + 1)}{s(2.5s + 1)(0.0625s + 1)}$$

These transfer functions represent relatively low-gain systems characteristic of some industrial applications.

Calculate the steady-state and transient response to a step input of position for these two systems. Compare these results with the approximate values obtained from the performance charts of this chapter.

**15.7** In Problem 14.5 the steady-state response to reference input and disturbance functions for a hydraulically controlled speed regulator was determined. Determine now the corresponding transient response in the controlled speed for a step input of the desired speed ($V$) or of the disturbance function ($U$). Compare the steady-state and transient performances to these two different types of forcing functions.

**15.8** Determine the open-loop attenuation frequency characteristics of a servo-mechanism meeting the following specifications:

$$M_m = 1.35$$

$$\omega_m = 1.0 \text{ cps or higher}$$

Error less than 1 per cent for a sinusoidal input with a 9-sec period

Choose a design that also obtains low values for peak overshoot and settling time to transient position inputs. Indicate the values of these performance figures for the design you have chosen. Give your reasons for selecting this design.

**15.9** *A*. On Figures 12.1–2 and 13.2–3, Figures 12.1–7 and 13.2–9, and Figures 12.2–5 and 13.3–6 are shown attenuation-frequency and root locus plots, respectively, for three different control systems. Using the methods of estimating closed-loop poles from open-loop attenuation characteristics suggested in Section 15.1, compare the closed-loop poles obtained by the approximate and the root locus methods.

*B*. For Problem 13.4 where root locus plots were obtained for same systems as those for which the straight line attenuation-frequency plots were drawn in Problem 12.1, compare the estimated closed-loop poles obtained by the methods in Section 15.1 with those determined from the root locus plots. What conclusions can be drawn or suggestion be made for using the approximate method of estimating transient performance of control systems?

### Chapter 16

**16.1** Draw the computer circuit setup which performs the summation

$$x = 10y + 2z + 4w + r$$

where $y$, $z$, $w$, and $r$ are inputs and $x$ is the output.

**16.2** Draw the computer diagram with parameter values which can be used to solve the differential equation

$$\frac{d^3x}{dt^3} + 2\frac{d^2x}{dt^2} + 3\frac{dx}{dt} + x = y$$

where $y$ is the input and $x$ is the output.

**16.3** Use the differential equation method to set up the following equations:

$$a\frac{d^3y}{dt^3} + b\frac{d^2y}{dt^2} + cy = \frac{dx}{dt} + x + e$$

$$f\frac{d^2x}{dt^2} + g\frac{dx}{dt} + h = f(t) + \frac{dy}{dt}$$

where $f(t)$ is the input function and $x$ and $y$ are dependent variables.

**16.4** A temperature control problem in the field of chemical engineering involves the components shown in the following block diagram:

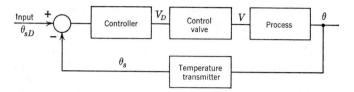

*Process*

$$121 \frac{d^2\theta}{dt^2} + 33 \frac{d\theta}{dt} + \theta = K_1 V$$

*Temperature Transmitter*

$$2.7 \frac{d\theta_s}{dt} + \theta_s = K_2\theta$$

*Controller*

$$0.04 \frac{d^3 V_D}{dt^3} + 0.4 \frac{d^2 V_D}{dt^2} + \frac{dV_D}{dt} = K_3(\theta_{sD} - \theta_s)$$

*Control Valve*

$$2.4 \frac{dV}{dt} + V = K_4 V_D$$

Generate a computer setup which can be used to study the transient behavior of the system.

**16.5** Set up the computer circuit which can be used to solve the following sets of algebraic equations:

(a)
$$x + 2y = 3$$
$$3x + y = 4$$

(b)
$$x + y + z = 1$$
$$2x + 3y + z = 2$$
$$3x + y + 2z = 1$$

(c)
$$30x + 6y + 15z + 10w + 6v = 450$$
$$3x + 6y + 2z + 1.2w + 1.2v = 90$$
$$2x + 4y + 8z + 8w + 4v = 120$$
$$5x + 4y + 10z + 10w + 4v = 150$$
$$12x + 6y + 3z + 4w + 12v = 180$$

(d)
$$x^2 + 20y = 120$$
$$y = 10 - x$$

**16.6** There are alternate computer circuits that can be used to generate a given transfer function. Derive the transfer function for each of the following setups and describe why one circuit is preferable over the other:

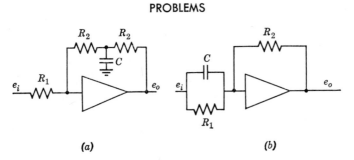

PROB. 16-6

**16.7** Calculate the transfer impedance for the following general complex computer circuit:

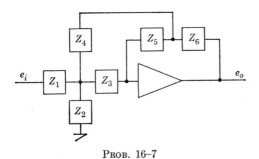

PROB. 16-7

**16.8** Determine the computer setups, with values of resistors and capacitors for the following transfer functions:

$$(a) \quad \frac{e_o(s)}{e_i(s)} = \frac{5(0.1s + 1)(s + 1)}{(0.2s + 1)(10s + 1)(35s + 1)}$$

$$(b) \quad \frac{e_o(s)}{e_i(s)} = \frac{(s + 3)(s + 4)(s^2 + 8s + 100)}{s(s + 1)(s + 2)(s^2 + 16s + 100)}$$

**16.9** Set up computer circuit using only one amplifier which will solve the equations of Problem 16.2.

**16.10** Given the system

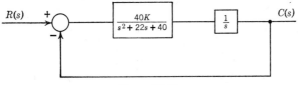

PROB. 16-10

$$r(t) = 25 \text{ units applied at } t = 0$$

(a) From an attenuation-phase diagram analysis, determine $K$ for about a 30 per cent overshoot (45° phase margin).

(b) Using the value of $K$ found in part (a), set up the computer diagram complete with component values and scale factors. Assume the maximum amplifier voltage is 100 volts.

**16.11**  Given the mechanical system

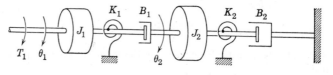

PROB. 16–11

(a) Write the equations describing the system dynamic behavior.

(b) For:

$$J_1 = 2 \text{ lb-ft-sec}^2 \qquad K_2 = 2 \text{ lb-ft/radian}$$
$$J_2 = 3 \text{ lb-ft-sec}^2 \qquad B_1 = 1 \text{ lb-ft/radian/sec}$$
$$K_1 = 1 \text{ lb-ft/radian} \qquad B_2 = 1 \text{ lb-ft/radian/sec}$$

Set up the computer diagram for an investigation of the transient behavior of the system for a step input of

$$T_1 = 0.5 \text{ lb-ft}$$

It is desirable to record

$$T_1, \theta_1, \theta_2.$$

**16.12**  Given the turbine speed control system defined by the equations:

(1) Turbine acceleration, $\dfrac{d\omega_T}{dt}$, radian/sec²

$$\frac{d\omega_T}{dt} = \frac{1}{J_T}[T_D - T_L - B\omega_T]$$

(2) Pilot valve displacement $x$, milli-inches

$$x = K_x(\omega_R - \omega_T)$$

(3) Control valve angle, $\theta$, degrees

$$\theta = \frac{K_\theta x}{\tau s + 1}$$

(4) Turbine inertia, $J_T = 0.1$ lb-in. sec²
(5) Load torque, $T_L = 750$ lb-in.
(6) Reference speed $\omega_R = 6000$ rpm
(7) Pilot valve gain, $K_x = 0.15$ milli-inches/radian/sec

(8) Control valve gain, $K_\theta = 1°/\text{milli-inch}$
(9) Control valve time constant, $\tau = 0.02$ sec
(10) Turbine speed $\omega_T$, radian/sec
(11) Turbine developed torque, $T_D = f(\theta)$ lb-in. as given by

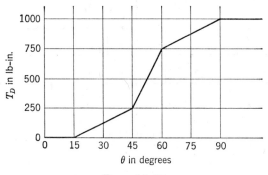

PROB. 16–12

(a) Draw the block diagram defined by these equations.
(b) Set up a computer diagram to study the system on an analog computer whose maximum amplifier voltage is 50 volts. It is desirable to record $T_D$, $T_L$, $\omega_R$, $\omega_T$, $x$, and $\theta$. $\omega_R$ and $T_L$ will be applied as step inputs.

**16.13** Generate the function

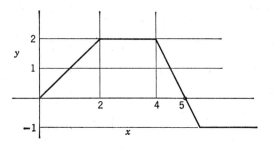

PROB. 16–13

**16.14** In a hydraulic orifice the fluid velocity through the orifice and the pressure drop across it are given by

$$P = Kv|v| \qquad \begin{aligned} P &= \text{pressure in psi} \\ v &= \text{fluid velocity in ft/sec} \\ |v| &= \text{magnitude of } v \end{aligned}$$

For $K = 2$ psi/ft/sec
$|v|$ max $= 10$ ft/sec

Plot $P$ as a function of $v$, assign scale factors, approximate the curve with straight line segments, and set up a computer diagram which can be used in a computer study.

**16.15** Determine a computer setup which will generate the following hysteresis function:

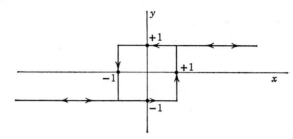

PROB. 16-15

# INDEX

(Italicized numbers following author's name are bibliographic reference numbers.)